MW00353025

Study Guide and Solutions Manual

to accompany

Invitation to Organic Chemistry

A. William Johnson

JONES AND BARTLETT PUBLISHERS
Sudbury, Massachusetts
BOSTON TORONTO LONDON SINGAPORE

World Headquarters
40 Tall Pine Drive
Sudbury, MA 01776
978-443-5000
info@jbpub.com
www.jbpub.com

Jones and Bartlett Publishers Canada
2100 Bloor Street West, Suite 6-272
Toronto, ON M6S 5A5
CANADA

Jones and Bartlett Publishers International
Barb House, Barb Mews
London W6 7PA
UK

Copyright © 1999 by Jones and Bartlett Publishers, Inc.

All rights reserved. No part of this material protected by this copyright notice may be reproduced or utilized in any form, electronic or mechanical, including photocopying, recording, or by any information storage and retrieval system, without written permission from the copyright owner.

ISBN 0-7637-0744-9

Printed in the United States of America
04 03 02 01 00 99 10 9 8 7 6 5 4 3 2 1

Table of Contents

Introduction to the Student

Use of this *Study Guide* will significantly help you in your study and learning of organic chemistry. It contains a number of special features that supplement the textbook and organize the content in new ways to facilitate study, review, and self-testing. This *Study Guide* is especially focused on assisting you in learning how to solve problems involving the synthesis of simple organic compounds. If you learn to manipulate families of organic compounds for purposes of elementary syntheses (that is, to devise sequences of transformations) you will have an excellent command of the essentials of organic chemistry!

Your initial attention in your study of organic chemistry should be on each chapter in sequence in the textbook. When you have completed initial study of the chapter and you get into serious follow-up study, use this Study Guide. Each chapter herein opens with a section entitled Learning Objectives to make clear what knowledge and skills you should have acquired as a result of studying that chapter.

Each chapter of the *Study Guide* also includes a GLOSSARY of terms that were introduced in the chapter. Definitions are included. These terms are drawn from the text content and the chapter summaries. Review and understanding of the precise meaning of these terms is essential for communicating about organic chemistry.

Chapters in this *Study Guide* also present in chart form a succinct SUMMARY OF REACTIONS studied for the particular family of compounds. If appropriate, a SUMMARY OF PREPARATION of this family of compounds also is included. These charts make effective summaries for study and reference in preparation for quizzes and examinations.

This *Study Guide* contains two additional helpful summaries. First, the chart entitled *Key to Transformations* is reproduced from the textbook. This chart, in a simplistic overview way, summarizes most of the chemistry encountered in chapters 3 to 15—those chapters dealing with the major families of organic compounds considered in the text. It is an ideal reference chart to keep visible as you are studying individual reactions and chapters. It places reactions in context and helps you to see the "big picture." Second, at the end of the *Study Guide* is a *Summary of Preparations of Families of Compounds* which brings into one location all of the different means of synthesizing a member of any family of compounds. This *Summary* should be especially helpful in your term-end review.

Finally, the major portion of this *Study Guide* is taken up with the SOLUTIONS TO PROBLEMS that are included in the text, both those within each chapter as well as the Additional Problems at the end of each chapter. Keep in mind that there is an organization to the problems in the text. Those within the chapter are related directly to the material discussed immediately preceding the problem. Those in the Additional Problems are grouped by major topics encountered in the chapter—the groupings themselves will help you in deciding upon your initial approach to the problem. The final grouping in each chapter is called MIXED PROBLEMS and includes a broad variety of problems which require you to call upon all of your knowledge and experience acquired to that point. Finally, a few problems in each chapter are marked as being more challenging synthesis problems for those who wish to test themselves further—they generally require more than three transformations for their solution. They are marked with an asterisk in this *Study Guide.*

The tackling of problems is the only effective way to determine whether you really understand the organic chemistry you have studied—can you apply it to solve problems? Many students have not previously encountered problems that require a logical and conceptual analysis prior to devising solutions. Such deductive reasoning is critical in most career fields, and organic chemistry is one of the best means of learning such analytical thinking. The textbook and this *Study Guide* include features to help you develop the ability to solve such problems. First, the textbook contains many *"How to Solve a Problem"* sections, which lead you through the reasoning behind solving individual problems related to that chapter's content. Practice the approaches described therein. Second, immediately following this Introduction to the Study Guide is a section entitled *"How to Solve Synthesis Problems"* which is a generalized step-by-step approach to problem solving. Refer to this approach often.

I hope you find this *Study Guide* useful as you learn organic chemistry. It will assist you in learning a disciplined, careful, and analytic approach to problem solving, a skill that will stand you in good stead in your chosen career. Finally, I remind you that to make your learning of organic chemistry effective it is essential to keep up. Don't wait until just before exams to cram and test yourself with problems—it doesn't work for most students studying organic chemistry. Instead, keep up with the content and tackle problems regularly.

Much effort has been expended to ensure that the solutions provided in this *Study Guide* are correct. However, it is easy for errors to creep in to 2490 answers and I will appreciate anyone calling such to my attention. Also, if you have suggestions for improvement of the *Study Guide* to make it even more useful, please communicate them to me through the publisher.

I extend my sincere thanks to those members of Jones and Bartlett Publishers who have contributed to the final outcome of the *Study Guide* preparation. I particularly want to thank Ivee Wong for overseeing production of the *Study Guide.* Special thanks goes to Anne Moody (Truman State University) for checking the accuracy of solutions.

A. William Johnson

How to Solve Synthesis Problems

By this stage of your education you probably have become accustomed to problems of the type associated with general chemistry or physics. Such problems are often mathematical and involve the application of formulas which have been memorized. Problems in organic chemistry are very different, and, at this level, are non-mathematical. Instead, they call for analysis, reasoning, and deduction. What makes the process even more interesting is that there may be more than one appropriate solution!

Starting in Chapter 3 of the textbook you are introduced to reactions that involve converting one organic compound into another. The accumulation of such reactions and their appropriate sequential use permits **organic synthesis**—the conversion of one compound into another by a single or several separate transformations. Recall from the introductory essay in the textbook that organic synthesis is one of the three major activities undertaken by organic chemists.

Having a ready command of how one compound can be converted into another is the key to being able to solve synthesis problems. This *Study Guide* contains a number of sections designed to help you develop such a skill. The chart entitled *Key to Transformations,* which follows this section, summarizes much of the synthesis content of the textbook on a single page. As you are learning to solve synthesis problems, refer to this chart for assistance. Most chapters of this *Study Guide* contain one or more charts summarizing the individual reactions described in the textbook chapter. These reactions are what enable the transformations outlined in the *Key* to occur. Finally, the section at the end of this *Study Guide* entitled *Summary of Preparation of Families of Compounds* brings together in one place all of the different methods of synthesizing various families of compounds.

When you are faced with synthesis problems I suggest you try the following several steps in sequence:

1. Analyze the problem before searching for solutions. Do this so that you clearly understand what is at the heart of the problem. Identify in each chemical structure just what portions change as one compound is converted to another, and what remains unchanged. Most chapters in the text include one or more examples of problem analysis in features called "*How to Solve a Problem.*" Work with them to help develop your own approach.

2. Once you have identified specifically what changes in the chemical reaction in question, determine what overall transformation must occur. Do this initially without worrying about the particular reagent(s) required. In other words, ask yourself specifically *what* group or groups in the structure must be replaced by what other group, not *how* it must happen. Use the *Key to Transformations* for help if needed.

3. Look for similarities to other transformations with which you already have become familiar.

4. Identify what kind of a chemical process is needed to accomplish the identified transformation. We will encounter only about five basic kinds of reactions (processes) in the entire text—substitutions (nucleophilic and electrophilic), additions (nucleophilic and electrophilic), eliminations, oxidations, and reductions.

5. Now try to visualize a hypothetical reagent that can bring about the change identified in steps 1, 2, and 4.

6. Write the reaction as you now envisage it. Then ask yourself if what you know about the chosen reagent and its usual behavior verifies that it really would be expected to produce the desired product? Would you really expect that reagent to react with the starting material? Why and how?

7. If stuck, don't just look up the answer in this *Study Guide.* Instead, first struggle with the problem a while. For instance, jot down the kinds of reactions the starting compound typically undergoes. Alternatively, jot down the known preparations of the kind of compound you are trying to prepare. Finally, consider the kind of reaction your proposed reagent usually accomplishes. Look at the *Key to Transformations* and at the *Summary of Preparations* in this *Study Guide.* You will learn more from struggling with a problem for a while and trying different approaches than from simply looking up the answer.

When doing multi-step syntheses (that is a problem that asks you to prepare compound **C** starting with compound **A**, think backwards from the product **C** (a process called *retrosynthesis*). Think of the different means of preparation you have studied for **C** and the kinds of compounds that can be used as starting materials — do you recognize compound **A** as a starting material? If not, then you may have more than one step to consider (**A** to **B** to **C**). Apply the same thinking going from your desired product **C** to compound **B**, then from **B** to starting material **A**. Use the *Key to Transformations* in working backwards.

8. Finally, look up the answer to the problem in this *Study Guide.* If you still do not understand how the answer was developed, refer again to the *Key to Transformations*, the *Summary of Preparations*, and to the appropriate location in the text for discussion of the reactions.

9. Re-read this problem-solving section as often as necessary during your study in order to develop your own analytical approach to problems. You will see many concrete examples of the steps just described in the example problems called "*How to Solve a Problem.*"

This text provides many opportunities for you to test yourself by working on problems—there are over 2490 individual problems! Only by tackling problems as practice can you really learn how to solve problems, and only then can you determine for yourself whether you have a command of the material. Don't come out of an exam saying "I thought I knew that stuff" when you really had not tested yourself before-hand. Use the many "*How to Solve a Problem*" examples provided in this textbook to guide you—they include not just answers, but will teach you how to develop the thinking skills that go into finding the answers. Use them, understand them, and then try that approach yourself. The "Additional Problems" section at the end of each text chapter contain problems of varying degrees of difficulty for practice. As you become more able to solve problems tackle some of those labeled as being somewhat more challenging, and more interesting, problems (marked with an asterisk). You will acquire a feeling of pride as your problem solving skills improve.

Symbols and Abbreviations

Below are listed the common symbols and abbreviations that are used in this Study Guide and in the textbook, *Invitation to Organic Chemistry*. Do not expect to encounter or understand all of them now—you will be introduced to them gradually throughout your study.

Bonds

—	a single bond
=	a double bond
≡	a triple bond
	a single bond in a three-dimensional drawing coming out of the plane of the paper
	a single bond in a three-dimensional drawing going behind the plane of the paper
	a single bond closer to you than are other bonds in a structure
- - - - -	a hydrogen bond
....	a bond partially broken or partially formed
$^{+}\delta$	a partial positive charge is located on an atom
$^{-}\delta$	a partial negative charge is located on an atom

Arrows

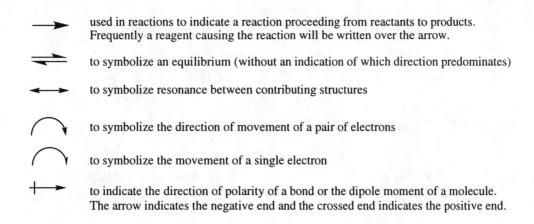

$\longrightarrow$	used in reactions to indicate a reaction proceeding from reactants to products. Frequently a reagent causing the reaction will be written over the arrow.
$\rightleftharpoons$	to symbolize an equilibrium (without an indication of which direction predominates)
$\longleftrightarrow$	to symbolize resonance between contributing structures
	to symbolize the direction of movement of a pair of electrons
	to symbolize the movement of a single electron
$+\!\!\!\longrightarrow$	to indicate the direction of polarity of a bond or the dipole moment of a molecule. The arrow indicates the negative end and the crossed end indicates the positive end.

DMSO	dimethylsulfoxide	$(CH_3)_2S{=}O$
Ether	ethyl ether	$CH_3CH_2OCH_2CH_3$
THF	tetrahydrofuran	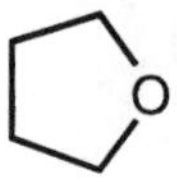
EtOH	ethanol	CH_3CH_2OH
NBS	N-bromosuccinimide	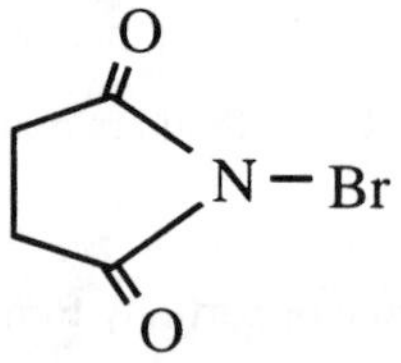
PCC	pyridinium chlorochromate	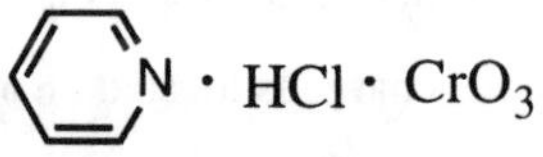
DCC	dicylohexylcarbodiimide	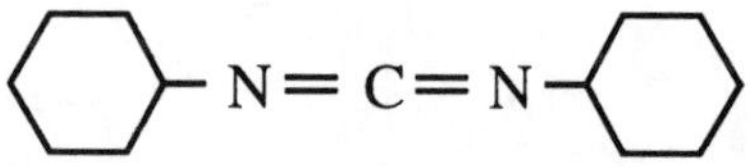
Boc	t-butyloxycarbonyl group	$(CH_3)_3C-O-C(=O)-$
TMS	tetramethylsilane	$(CH_3)_4Si$
2,4-DNPH	2,4-dinitrophenylhydrazine	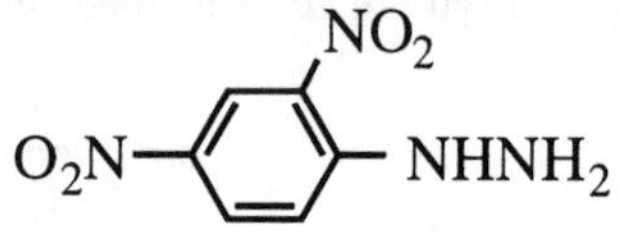
RaNi	Raney nickel	a unique nickel catalyst often used for hydrogenolysis

Key to Transformations

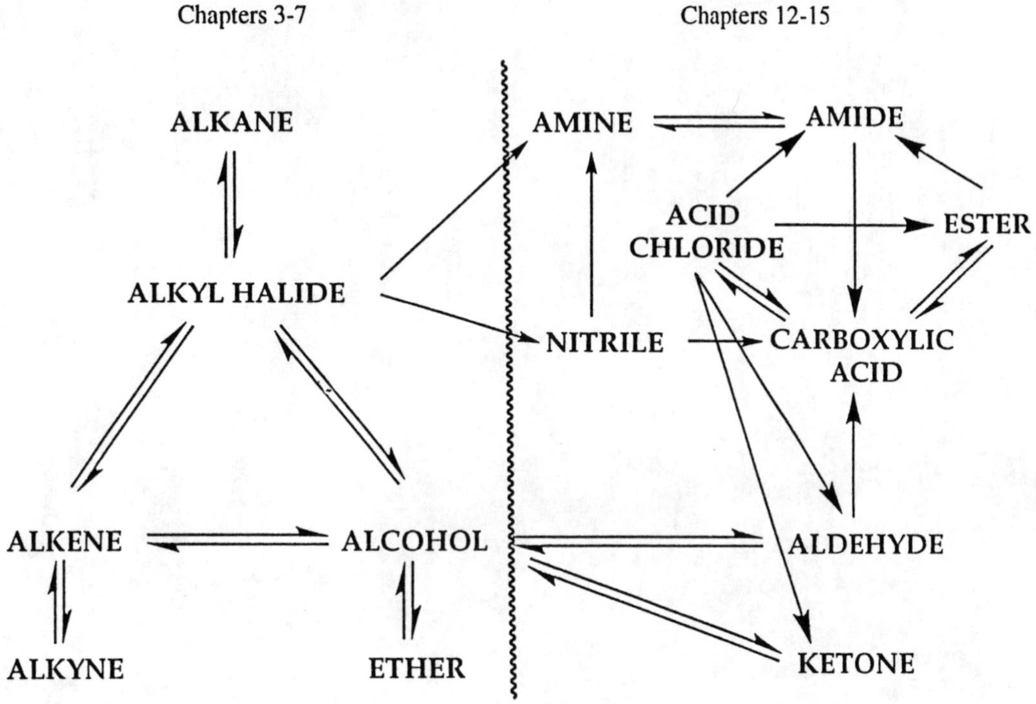
Chapters 3-7
Chapters 12-15
ALKANE
ALKYL HALIDE
ALKENE
ALCOHOL
ALKYNE
ETHER
AMINE
AMIDE
ACID CHLORIDE
ESTER
NITRILE
CARBOXYLIC ACID
ALDEHYDE
KETONE

CHAPTER 1

Carbon Compounds: Bonding and Structure

I. Textbook Chapter Contents

This introductory chapter reviews the basics of atomic and molecular structure preparatory to their application to organic chemistry. The emphasis is on the chemical bond of organic compounds and its effect on the structure of compounds and their various physical and chemical properties.

II. Learning Objectives

- Refresh your understanding of atomic structure, including the writing of the electron configuration for elements of the first three rows of the periodic table.

- Know the concept of electronegativity and be able to determine the relative electronegative and electropositive character of two elements.

- Know the octet rule and its role in ionic bonding.

- Explain how a covalent bond is formed.

- Describe the sp^3 hybridization of carbon, its involvement in the formation of single covalent bonds in alkanes, and the tetrahedral shape of resulting organic compounds. Draw three dimensional representations of tetrahedral carbon.

- Be able to calculate the formal charge on atoms involved in covalent bonding.

- Be able to relate empirical formula, molecular formula, and molecular weight.

- Draw the structural formula of simple organic compounds using dot, dash, condensed, combination, and bond-line drawings. From a molecular formula be able to draw a chemical structure using the different drawings. From a structural formula determine a molecular formula.

- Know that there are classifications of organic compounds, especially by families, each of which contains a functional group.

- Understand how physical properties, such as polarity, solubility, and boiling point arise from the molecular structure of organic compounds.

- Refresh your understanding of Brønsted acids, acid-base reactions, and pK_as. Determine the direction of an equilibrium from a consideration of the relative acidity or the relative basicity of the compounds/ions on both sides of the equilibrium.

- Know the meaning of electrophile, nucleophile, Lewis acid, Lewis base, Brønsted acid, and Brønsted base.

- Realize that a covalent bond can be broken and that the electrons of the bond can distribute themselves in three different patterns to product three different reactive intermediates.

- Begin to become familiar with the use of arrows to indicate the breaking or formation of bonds and the necessary electron shifts, initially in acid-base reactions.

III. Glossary

acid dissociation constant a number (K_a) which reflects the strength of an acid in water

acyclic compound a compound in which the atoms may be connected in many ways, but which does not involve a closed ring of atoms

aliphatic compound a compound which is not aromatic. A compound which is derived from a saturated hydrocarbon

anion an ion with a negative charge

aromatic compound a compound having the property of aromaticity, usually derived from benzene and related carbocyclic or heterocyclic compounds

atomic number describes the position of an element in the periodic table, and also is indicative of the number of protons in the nucleus of the neutral atom

atomic orbitals a region of space, with an associated energy level, surrounding the nucleus of an atom. Each orbital may contain a maximum of two paired electrons

atomic weight the average of the mass number of all of the isotopes of an element

Aufbau principle orbitals of lower energy are filled with electrons before those of higher energy

bond moment the polarity of a covalent bond. It cannot be measured but can be inferred from the dipole moment of a compound and from calculations based on molecular structure

Brønsted acid a proton donor

Brønsted base a proton acceptor

carbanion a carbon atom that is surrounded by eight electrons, is negatively charged, has three substituents, and has an unshared pair of electrons

carbocation a carbon atom that is surrounded by six electrons, is positively charged, has three substituents, and has a vacant p-orbital

carbocyclic compound a compound in which some of the carbon atoms are connected to form a ring

carbon radical a carbon atom that is surrounded by seven electrons, is neutral, has three substituents, and has a single unshared electron

cation an ion with a positive charge

connectivities an indication of which atoms are bonded (connected) to which other atoms in a molecule

covalent bond a bond between two atoms in which a pair of valence electrons is shared

dipole moment a measure of the polarity of a molecule which has magnitude and direction (that is, it is a vector quantity)

electron configuration the arrangement of electrons into orbitals about the nucleus of an atom including an indication of the principal quantum number, the orbital type, and the number of electrons in each orbital

electronegativity the tendency of an atom or group to attract electrons

electrons a particle carrying a negative charge and usually located in shells about the nucleus of an atom or ion

electrophile an electron pair acceptor involved in a reaction

electropositivity the tendency of an atom or group to give up electrons

empirical formula a formula indicating which elements are present in a compound and the ratio of the number of each to the other

family of compounds a group of compounds which contain the same functional group

formal charge the net charge on each atom in a molecule determined by accounting for all of the electrons in the molecule and their source

functional group that portion of a compound which is particularly reactive and subject to change through chemical reactions

ground state the lowest energy state that any atom or molecule may have

heterocyclic a compound in which some of the atoms are connected to form a ring which contains at least one atom other than carbon (that is, a heteroatom—usually O, N, or S)

Hund's rule when more than one orbital of the same energy level is available to be filled with electrons, each orbital will first acquire one electron before any orbital acquires a second electron

hybridization a mixing of the characteristics of atomic orbitals, including energy level and shape

hydrophilic a compound or portion thereof which is attracted to and soluble in water

hydrophobic a compound or portion thereof which is repelled by and insoluble in water

ionic bond an electrostatic bond between atoms of opposite formal charge

K_a acid dissociation constant

Lewis acid an electron acceptor

Lewis base an electron donor

Lewis structures structural formulas in which all of the valence electrons of each atom are shown as dots about the element symbol

mass number the number of protons plus the number of neutrons in an atom of an element

molecular orbital an orbital formed by the overlap of two atomic orbitals and which normally contains two paired electrons

molecular formula the absolute number of atoms of each element present in a compound

molecular weight the sum of the atomic weights of the elements present in a compound

nucleophile an electron pair donor involved in a reaction

nucleus the core of an atom that contains the protons and neutrons, and is responsible for most of the mass of the atom

octet rule in forming bonds atoms will tend to acquire the electron configuration of the inert gas nearest to them in the periodic table

orbital a region of space, with an associated energy level, surrounding the nucleus of an atom or ion. Each orbital may contain a maximum of two paired electrons

Pauli exclusion principle a maximum of two electrons, and of opposing spin, may occupy an orbital

pK_a a measure of the strength of an acid. It is the negative log of the acid dissociation constant (K_a)

polarized bond a covalent bond in which the electron density is not equally shared between the two atoms

principal quantum number whole numbers assigned to the electron shells, starting with that closest to the nucleus having a value of 1

reaction mechanism the detailed steps by which a reaction occurs

reactive intermediate a highly reactive, short-lived chemical species involved in many chemical reactions (carbanion, carbocation, carbon radical)

shells a region of space about an atom or ion where electrons are located. Shells are designated by principal quantum number and can contain a maximum number of electrons (such as 2, 8, etc.) distributed in orbitals

sigma bond a bond formed by the end-on overlap of an orbital from each atom and which contains two paired electrons. The highest electron density is along the axis between the two atomic nuclei - the bond is therefore cylindrically symmetrical

single bond a covalent bond containing two electrons, normally a sigma bond

structural formula a drawing indicating the connectivities of each atom present in a molecule

tetrahedral hybridization the hybridization of a single s orbital and three p orbitals to form four sp3 hybrid orbitals directed to the corners of an imaginary tetrahedron

transition state a mid-point in a reaction at which the structure of the reactant is partially changed and is at its highest energy level

valence electrons electrons in the outer shell of an atom and available for use in bonding

van der Waals forces weak attractive forces between non-polar molecules

IV. Solutions to Problems

Chapters in the text "Invitation to Organic Chemistry" contain a feature entitled "**How to Solve a Problem**," designed to help students reason through problems (rather than just memorize). Review those in chapter one (pages 12, 19, 24, and 33) and the explained answers in this section of the Study Guide to develop your own approach to arriving at the answers included herein.

1.1 The atomic number of each element indicates the number of electrons which need to be placed in orbitals. Recall that the orbital sequence for the first three principal quantum numbers is 1s, 2s, 2p, 3s, 3p, and 3d. Application of the Aufbau Principle, the Pauli Exclusion Principle, and Hund's rule in sequence leads to the following electron configurations.

Silicon (Z = 14)	$1s^2 2s^2 2p^6 3s^2 3p^2$
Phosphorus (Z = 15)	$1s^2 2s^2 2p^6 3s^2 3p^3$
Sulfur (Z = 16)	$1s^2 2s^2 2p^6 3s^2 3p^4$
Chlorine (Z = 17)	$1s^2 2s^2 2p^6 3s^2 3p^5$
Argon (Z = 18)	$1s^2 2s^2 2p^6 3s^2 3p^6$

1.2 The ground state electronic configurations for sodium and chlorine are developed as described for Problem 1.1. Conversion of elemental sodium to cationic sodium requires the loss of the $3s^1$ electron, leaving behind a noble gas (Neon) configuration for Na^+. Conversion of elemental chlorine to anionic chloride requires the gain of an outer shell electron, that is into the 3p orbital, resulting in a noble gas (Argon) configuration for the chloride anion.

Sodium (Z = 11)	$1s^2 2s^2 2p^6 3s^1$
Chlorine (Z = 17)	$1s^2 2s^2 2p^6 3s^2 3p^5$
Sodium cation	$1s^2 2s^2 2p^6$
Chloride anion	$1s^2 2s^2 2p^6 3s^2 3p^6$

1.3 Three carbons can only be connected in a single continuous chain which is propane. A total of 8 hydrogens are required to fill all of the remaining valences.

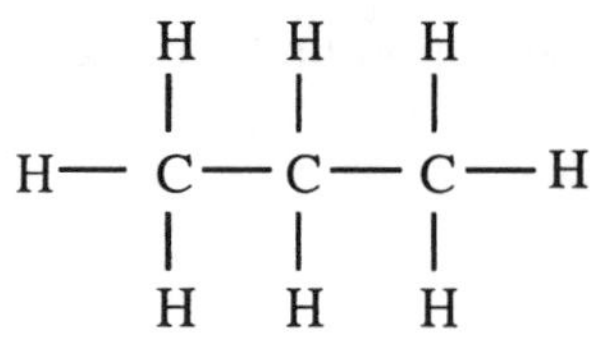

propane

1.4 Five carbons can be connected in three different patterns as shown for these structures which all have the molecular formula C_5H_{12}.

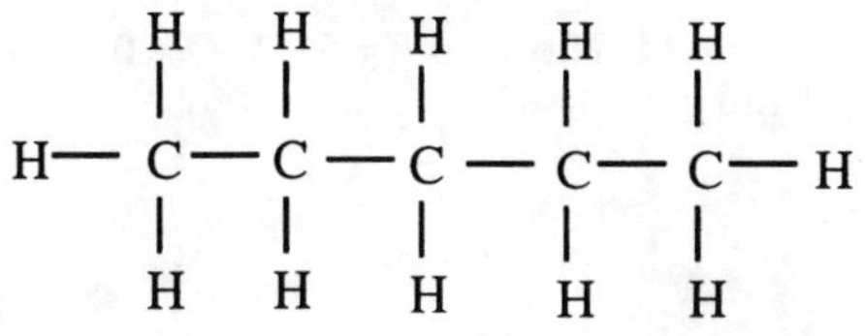

n-pentane

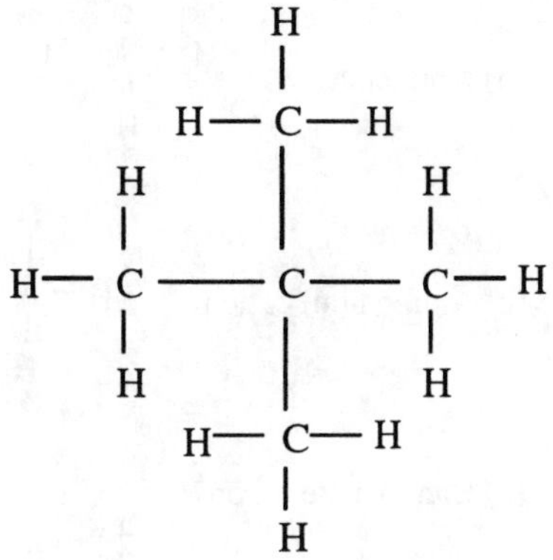

neopentane

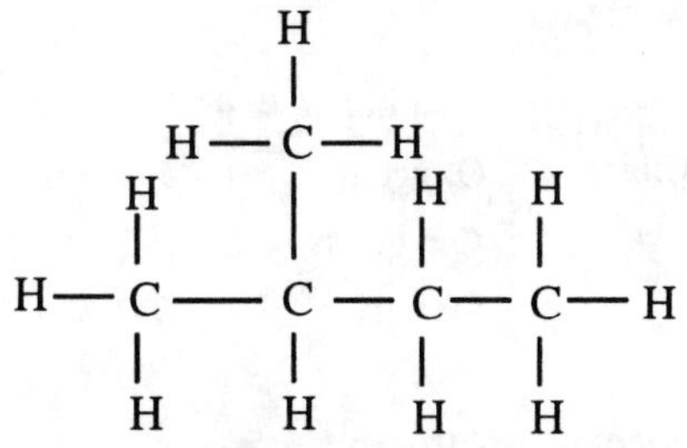

isopentane

1.5 First of all, the carbon skeleton of three carbons can only be connected in one pattern, a continuous chain. There are four possible patterns in which the two chlorine atoms can be located on a three-carbon chain.

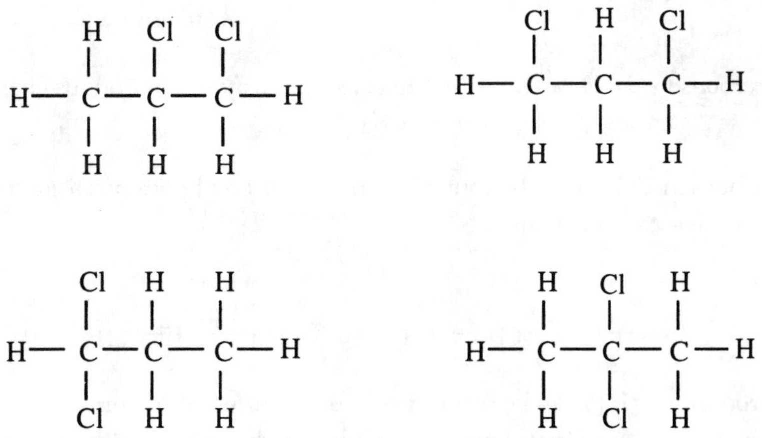

1.6

(a) Hydroxide anion 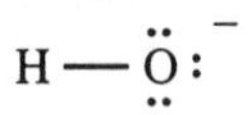

Formal Charge Oxygen = 6 - 6 - 1 = -1

(b) Ammonia 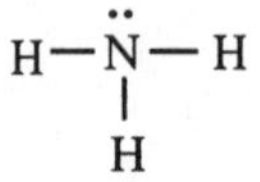

Formal Charge Nitrogen = 5 - 2 - 3 = 0

(c) Ammonium cation 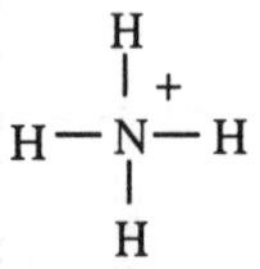

Formal Charge Nitrogen = 5 - 0 - 4 = +1

(d) Bicarbonate anion 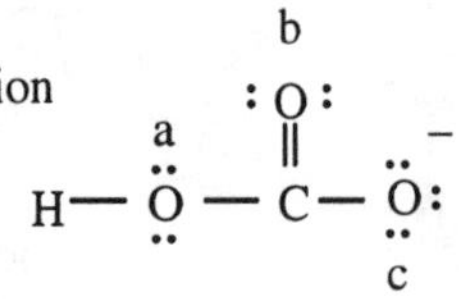

Formal Charge
Carbon = 4 - 0 - 4 = 0
Oxygen a = 6 - 4 -2 = 0
Oxygen b = 6 - 4 -2 = 0
Oxygen c = 6 - 6 -1 = -1

(e) Amide anion 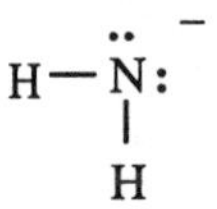

Formal Charge Nitrogen = 5 - 4 - 2 = -1

(f) Nitric Acid 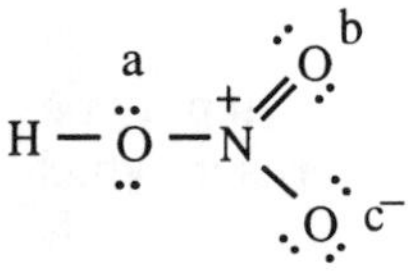

Formal Charge
Oxygen a = 6 - 4 - 2 = 0
Oxygen b = 6 - 4 - 2 = 0
Oxygen c = 6 - 6 - 1 = -1
Nitrogen = 5 - 0 - 4 = +1

1.7 (a) Three carbons in C_3H_8 can only be connected one way - a continuous chain.

$$CH_3—CH_2—CH_3$$

(b) Four carbons in C_4H_{10} can be connected in two different patterns, a continuous chain or a branch off a three carbon chain.

$CH_3—CH_2—CH_2—CH_3$ or 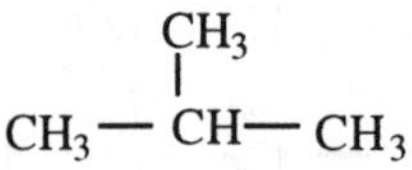

(c) Five carbons in C_5H_{12} can be connected in three different patterns - a continuous chain, a four carbon chain with a single branch, or a three carbon chain with two branches.

$CH_3—CH_2—CH_2—CH_2—CH_3$ 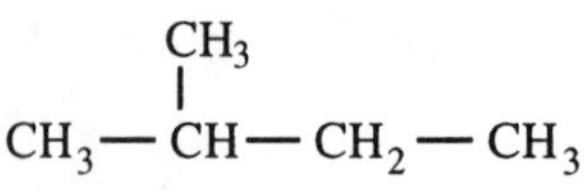 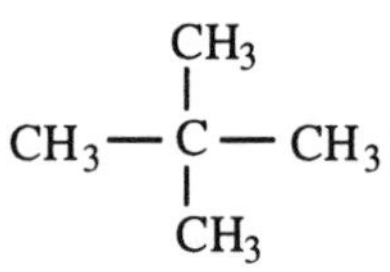

1.8 (a) C_4H_8 (b) C_6H_{14} (c) C_6H_{14}

1.9 (a) The formula weight for an empirical formula C_2H_5 is 29. Since the molecular weight is twice 29, or 58, the molecular formula must be two times the empirical formula, or C_4H_{10}.
(b) The formula weight for C_4H_8O is 72. Since the molecular weight is twice the formula weight, the molecular formula must be twice the empirical formula, or $C_8H_{16}O_2$.

1.10 Since chlorine is more electronegative than hydrogen it is the negative end of the bond moment. Since there is only one bond in HCl, the dipole moment is the same as the bond moment.

Bond moment: 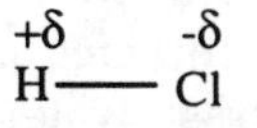
+δ
-δ
H
Cl

Dipole moment: 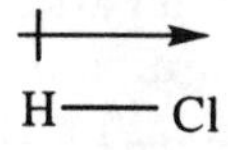
H
Cl

1.11 From Table 1.2 it can be determined that carbon is slightly more electronegative than hydrogen, and that fluorine and oxygen are both more electronegative than carbon.

(a) 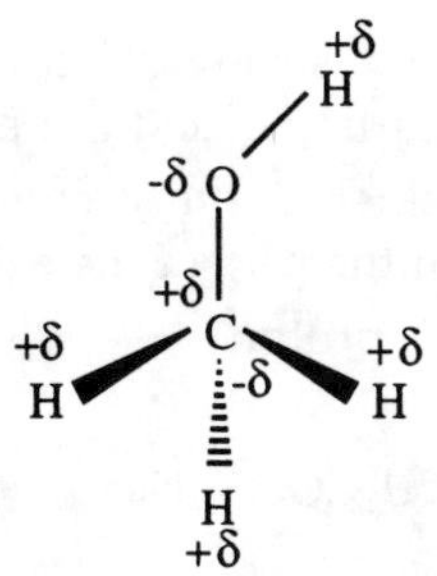
+δ
H
-δ O
+δ
C
-δ
+δ
H
+δ
H
H
+δ

(b) 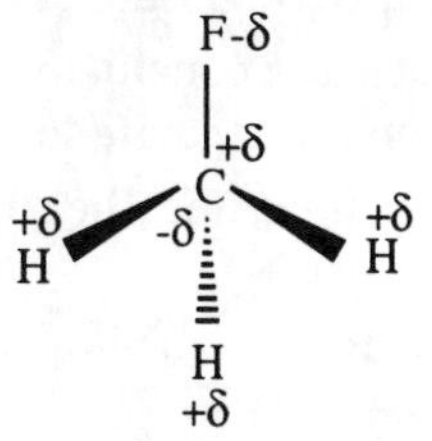
F-δ
+δ
C
-δ
+δ
H
+δ
H
H
+δ

1.12 In H_2O, the oxygen atom is more electronegative than the hydrogen atoms. The molecule cannot be linear or the dipole moment would be zero. Therefore it must be non-linear with the dipole moment in the direction of the oxygen atom. Similarly, in NH_3 the nitrogen atom is more electronegative than the hydrogen atoms. The molecule cannot be planar and trigonal or the dipole moment would be zero. One feasible structure is that of a pyramid with the nitrogen atom at one apex resulting in a dipole moment toward the nitrogen apex.

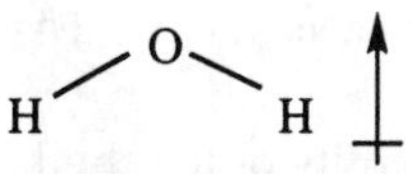
O
H
H

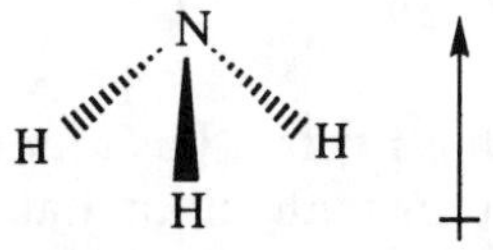
N
H
H
H

1.13 Chlorine is more electronegative than carbon. The dipole moment for chloroform should be larger than that for methyl chloride because the vector directions of three chlorine atoms are additive.

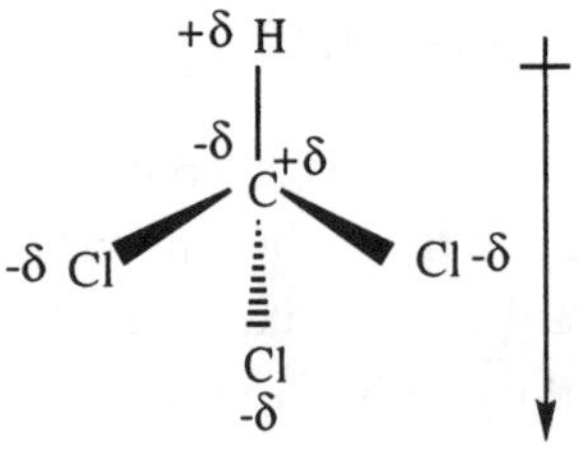
+δ H
-δ
+δ
C
-δ Cl
Cl -δ
Cl
-δ

chloroform

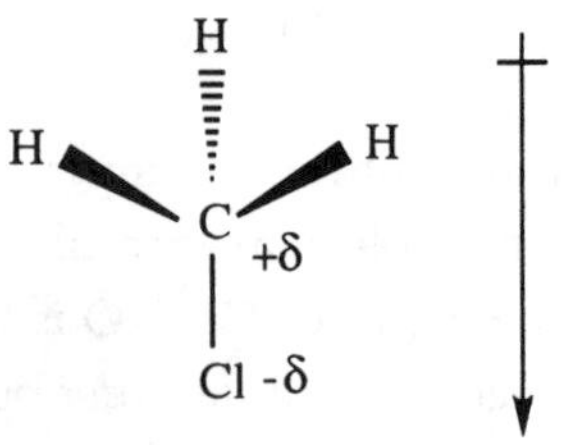
H
H
H
C
+δ
Cl -δ

methyl chloride
(chloromethane)

1.14 The boiling points of compounds generally are reflective of the strength of the intermolecular attractive forces between molecules. Methane molecules are non-polar, each with a zero dipole moment and therefore they interact only with relatively weak intermolecular forces (van der Waal's). In contrast, water molecules are polar (dipole moment 1.8) and the dipole-dipole association between molecules is much stronger. Therefore, since it requires more energy to dissociate water molecules than methane molecules, water has a higher boiling point.

1.15 The equilibrium will lie in the direction in which the strongest acid loses a proton. Since acetic acid is a stronger acid (smaller pK_a) than carbonic acid the equilibrium will lie to the right. The same conclusion is reached by considering the strength of the two bases, bicarbonate ion and acetate ion. As deduced from the pK_a of the acids, the bicarbonate ion is the strongest base and therefore will acquire the proton.

$$CH_3COOH \; + \; Na^+ \; HCO_3^- \rightleftharpoons CH_3COO^- \; Na^+ \; + \; H_2CO_3$$

$pK_a = 4.7$ (CH₃COOH); $pK_a = 6.4$ (H_2CO_3)

equilibrium $\longrightarrow$ direction

1.16 Phenol (pK_a 10) is a stronger acid than water (pK_a 15.7). Thus, in an equilibrium of phenol and hydroxide ion (whose conjugate acid is water) phenol will lose a proton, producing phenoxide anion.

$$C_6H_5OH \; + \; NaOH \rightleftharpoons C_6H_5ONa \; + \; H_2O$$

phenol (pK_a 10) — sodium phenoxide — pK_a 15.7

1.17 Atomic carbon, which is neutral, has four electrons in its outer shell. When a carbon atom shares a pair of electrons with another atom (i.e., when each atom contributes a share of its own electrons to form the shared pair), neutrality is retained as in the four bonds in methane (CH_4).

In a carbanion the carbon shares three of its electrons with three other atoms but has full control of a fourth pair of electrons. Thus carbon has acquired an additional electron from another atom (not sharing it) thereby changing it from neutral to negatively charged. It has a formal charge of -1.

In a carbocation the carbon shares three of its electrons with three other atoms but has lost one of its original electrons. This loss of an electron changes it from neutral to positively charged. It has a formal charge of +1.

In a radical the carbon shares three of its electrons with three other atoms and retains a single unshared electron. Since it started out neutral, and has suffered no net acquisition or loss of an electron, the radical carbon must remain neutral. It has a formal charge of 0.

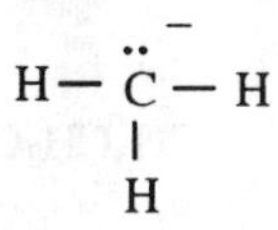
Carbanion

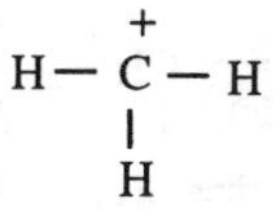
Carbocation

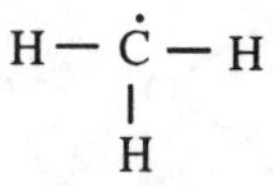
Carbon radical

1.18 Carbon (Z = 6) $1s^22s^22p^2$
Nitrogen (Z = 7) $1s^22s^22p^3$
Oxygen (Z = 8) $1s^22s^22p^4$

1.19 Potassium (Z = 19) $1s^22s^22p^63s^23p^64s^1$
Fluorine (Z = 9) $1s^22s^22p^5$
Potassium cation $1s^22s^22p^63s^23p^6$
Fluoride anion $1s^22s^22p^6$

1.20 (a) magnesium is electropositive; (b) sulfur is electronegative; (c) calcium is electropositive; (d) selenium is electronegative.

1.21 Electronegativity decreases down a group in the periodic table. Therefore the decreasing electronegativity order is oxygen > sulfur > selenium > tellurium.

1.22

Element	**Electron Configuration**	**Valence electrons**	**Valence**
oxygen	$1s^22s^22p^4$	six	two
carbon	$1s^22s^22p^2$	four	four
nitrogen	$1s^22s^22p^3$	five	three
hydrogen	$1s^1$	one	one
fluorine	$1s^22s^22p^5$	seven	one
sulfur	$1s^22s^22p^63s^23p^4$	six	two
phosphorus	$1s^22s^22p^63s^23p^3$	five	three

1.23 $CH_3CH_2CH_2CH_2F$, $CH_3CH_2CHFCH_3$, $(CH_3)_2CHCH_2F$, $(CH_3)_3CF$

1.24

(a) 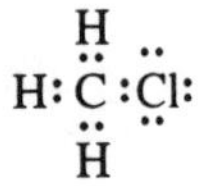 (b) 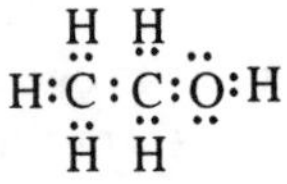 (c) 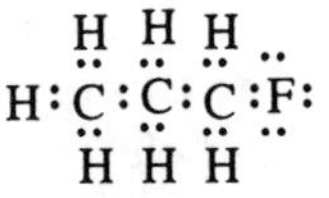

1.25

(a) 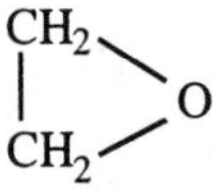 (b) 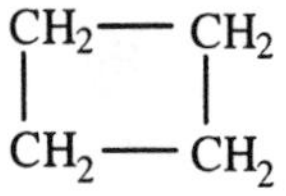 (c) $CH_3CH_2CH_2CH_2CH_3$

heterocyclic carbocyclic acyclic

1.26 (a) $C_6H_{13}Cl$; (b) C_6H_{12}; (c) C_3H_7N; (d) C_7H_{16}

1.27 (a) $(CH_2)_4CHCH_2CH_3$; (b) $(CH_3)_2CHCH_2CH_2CH(CH_3)_2$; (c) $(CH_3)_2CHOCH(CH_3)_2$

1.28

(a) 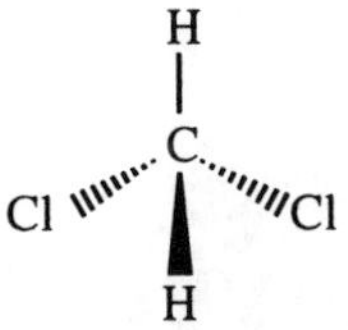 (b) 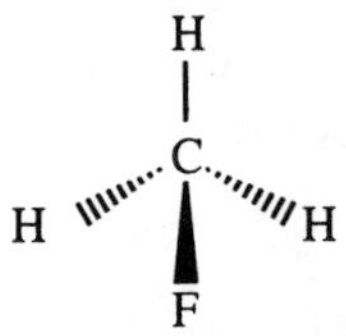 (c) 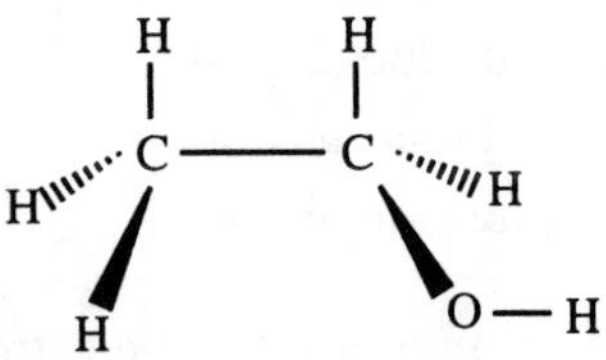

1.29 The bond polarity is determined by deducing the relative electronegativities of the two atoms involved (refer to Table 1.2). The bond polarities decrease in the following orders:

(a) O-H > N-H > C-H
(b) O-H > S-H > Se-H
(c) C-F > C-Cl > C-Br > C-I
(d) C-Li > C-Na > C-K

1.30

(a) 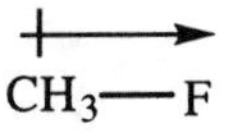

(b) $Cl_3C—CCl_3$
has no dipole moment

(c) 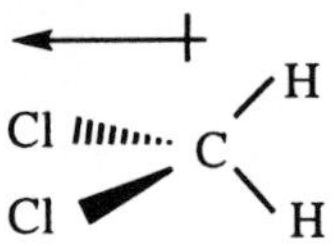

(d) 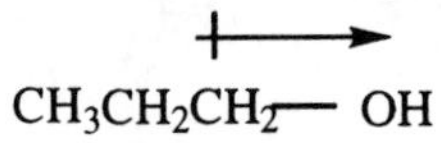

1.31 The equilibrium lies in the direction in which the strongest acid, in this case methanol, has lost its proton.

$$\underset{pK_a = 16}{CH_3OH} + NH_2^- \rightleftharpoons CH_3O^- + \underset{pK_a = 33}{NH_3}$$

$\xrightarrow[\text{direction}]{\text{equilibrium}}$

1.32 The compound with the largest acid dissociation constant, compound B, is the most acidic. The pK_a of compound A is 7 and that of B is 4.

1.33 The reaction will lie to the right since methanol (pK_a = 16) is a stronger acid than hydrogen (pK_a = 35, the conjugate acid of sodium hydride). Alternatively, the hydride anion may be viewed as a stronger base than methoxide anion.

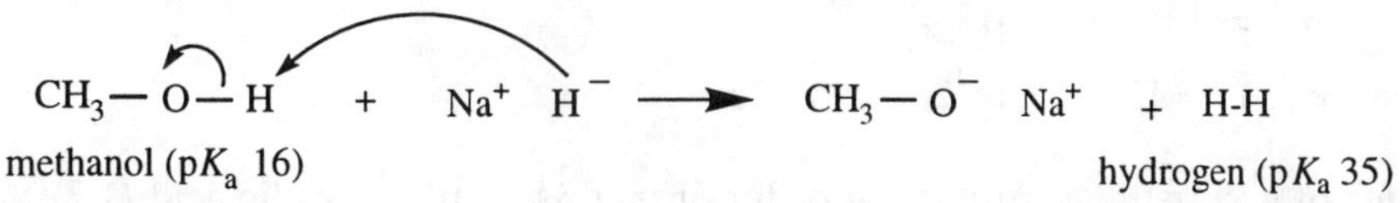

CH_3— O — H + Na^+ H^- ⟶ CH_3— O^- Na^+ + H-H
methanol (pK_a 16)
hydrogen (pK_a 35)

1.34 The methyl carbanion has a single negative charge on carbon because it carries an extra electron compared to neutral carbon. The carbanion is a Lewis base because it can donate electrons to form a new covalent bond. It also can be called a nucleophile. The methyl carbocation has a single positive charge on carbon because it is short one electron compared to neutral carbon. The carbocation is a Lewis acid because it can serve as an electron acceptor to form a new covalent bond. It also can be called an electrophile.

Carbanion 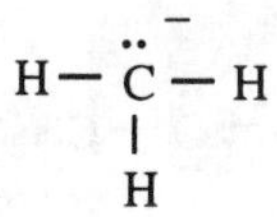 Carbocation 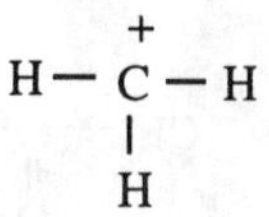

	Carbanion		Carbocation
Formal Charge Hydrogen	= 1 - 0 - 1 = 0	**Formal Charge** Hydrogen	= 1 - 0 - 1 = 0
Carbon	= 4 - 2 - 3 = -1	Carbon	= 4 - 0 - 3 = +1

1.35 The formula weight of a compound with empirical formula C_2H_5O is

$$(2 \times 12) + (5 \times 1) + (1 \times 16) = 45$$

Division of this formula weight into the given molecular weight of 90 equals 2. Thus, the molecular formula is two times the empirical formula, or $C_4H_{10}O_2$. As a cross-check the molecular weight of such a formula is

$$(4 \times 12) + (10 \times 1) + (2 \times 16) = 90$$

1.36 The structures of the ethers can be derived by considering the structures of all of the C_4H_{10} compounds, and then deriving all possible structures in which an oxygen is inserted between two carbons.

C_4H_{10}		$C_4H_{10}O$
$CH_3CH_2CH_2CH_3$	-------→	CH_3CH_2-O-CH_2CH_3 and CH_3-O-$CH_2CH_2CH_3$
$CH_3CH(CH_3)CH_3$	-------→	$(CH_3)_2CH$-O-CH_3

Therefore, there are three ethers of formula $C_4H_{10}O$.

1.37 Boron (Z = 5) $1s^22s^22p^1$

Aluminum (Z = 13) $1s^22s^22p^63s^23p^1$

1.38 Order of *decreasing* acidity is the order of *increasing* pK_a: oxalic acid (1.3) > formic acid (3.8) > ascorbic acid (4.2) > acetic acid (4.8)

1.39

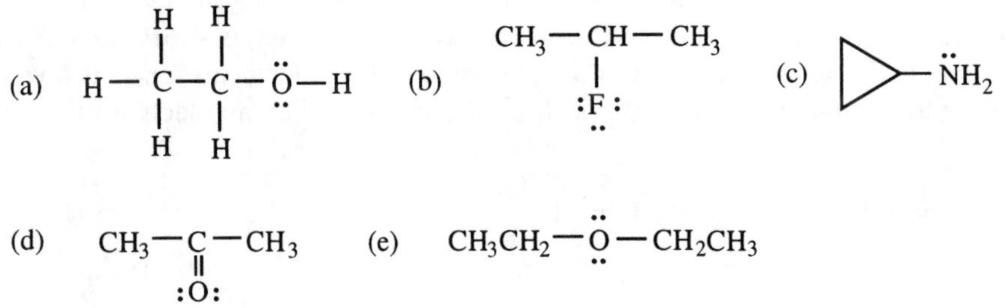
(a)
H H
H—C—C—Ö—H
H H
(b)
CH3—CH—CH3
:F:
(c)
NH2
(d)
CH3—C—CH3
:O:
(e)
CH3CH2—Ö—CH2CH3

1.40 The hydrogen atoms in silane (SiH_4) will have a higher electron density than the hydrogen atoms in methane (CH_4) because carbon is more electronegative than the silicon (atoms higher in the periodic table are more electronegative than those below). The more electronegative carbon withdraws electron density from hydrogen in the covalent bond, leaving it relatively electron deficient.

1.41 The electron configuration of silicon (Z = 14) is $1s^22s^22p^63s^23p^2$. The electron configuration in the outer shell is exactly analogous to that in carbon (which is directly above silicon in the periodic table). With four hydrogens to surround silicon, the most stable spatial arrangement is for them to be oriented to the corners of an imaginary tetrahedron. The outer shell atomic orbitals of silicon (principal quantum number 3) can hybridize to form four sp^3 hybrid orbitals. Overlap of each of these orbitals with a hydrogen atom *1s* orbital would produce four sigma bonds oriented tetrahedrally about silicon and each carrying a pair of electrons. Thus, silane is a tetrahedral molecule.

1.42

(a) Carbocyclic 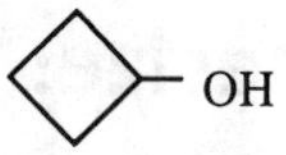 or 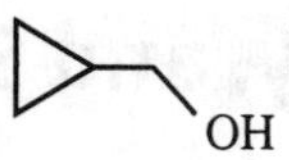 or 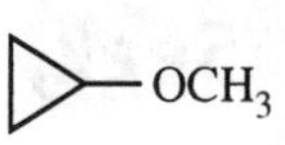

Heterocyclic 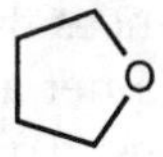 or 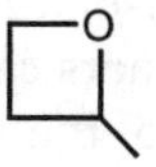 or 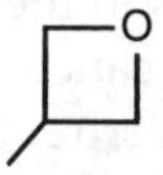

or 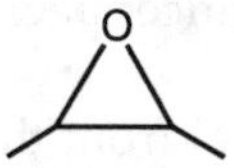 or  or 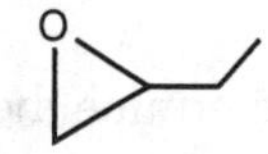

(b) Carbocyclic 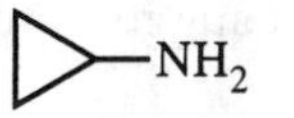 Heterocyclic 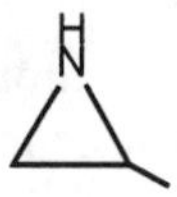 or 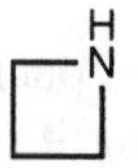

1.43 The electron configuration of nitrogen (Z = 7) is $1s^22s^22p^3$. If the four orbitals of the outer shell (a 2s orbital and three 2p orbitals) are hybridized four sp^3 hybrid orbitals will be produced. The five outer shell electrons will occupy these orbitals, two in one orbital and one in each of the remaining three orbitals. This produces a nitrogen whose configuration can be shown as follows:

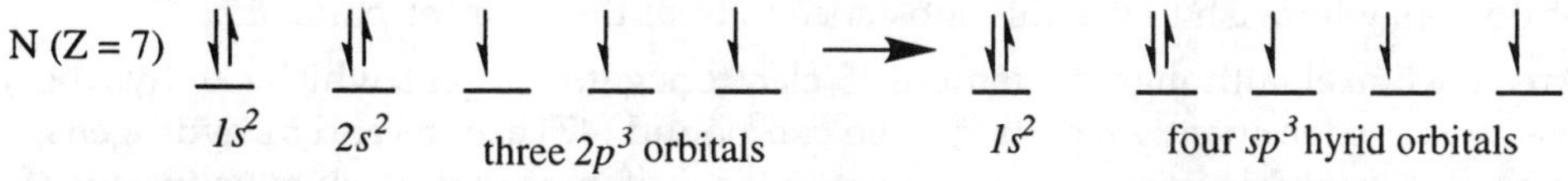

N (Z = 7)
1s2
2s2
three 2p3 orbitals
1s2
four sp3 hyrid orbitals

Covalent bonds are formed by sharing one electron with a single electron from three hydrogen atoms, the 1s orbital overlapping with the three half-filled sp^3 hybrid orbitals to form molecular orbitals, three sigma bonds. These three molecular orbitals are oriented to three of the corners of a tetrahedron, with the fourth "corner" containing the filled sp^3 hybrid orbital. This means the nitrogen and three hydrogens outline the shape of a pyramid. The two electrons in the filled sp^3 hybrid orbital are the "unshared pair" which endow ammonia with its basic/nucleophilic character. Thus the shape of ammonia is as follows:

V. Conceptual Problem
Seek, Identify, and Synthesize: Paclitaxel

In the early 1960s, the National Cancer Institute asked researchers to collect and analyze samples of indigenous plants in the hope of isolating substances that might some day prove effective in the fight against cancer. Researchers cast a wide net and among their catches was a chemical compound isolated from the bark of the Pacific yew. To test its medicinal properties, they placed the compound into some artificially preserved cancer cells—it killed the cells. They quickly set about to analyze this cancer-fighting substance: paclitaxel.

■ Can you determine the molecular formula of paclitaxel from the structure (shown in the text)?

- Ans: The molecular formula of paclitaxel is $C_{47}H_{51}NO_{14}$

■ A molecule of paclitaxel has 113 atoms in it. Does that suggest anything to you about how difficult it might be to synthesize in the laboratory?

- Ans: The total synthesis of paclitaxel is a very complicated and extensive process, requiring not only the assemblage of the correct atoms in the correct sequence (i.e., the connectivities) but also the correct stereochemistry (orientation in space) at twelve different carbon atoms. It was achieved in 1994 almost simultaneously by two different research groups.

■ Knowing what you do about organic compounds in general (as described near the end of this chapter), would you expect paclitaxel to be water-soluble? If not, what difficulties might that pose for doctors who wish to use this substance to treat their cancer patients?

- Ans: Paclitaxel, although containing 15 electronegative atoms which can hydrogen bond with water, is predominantly a hydrocarbon compound (47 carbons and 51 hydrogens). Therefore, it is insoluble in water. Since the human system is mainly an aqueous one (for example, blood is mainly water) paclitaxel is insoluble in the major human transport system. Therefore, to be effective against tumors a unique delivery system is required to get the agent to the tumor site.

■ One of the biggest difficulties facing the research community working with paclitaxel was how little of it could be extracted from the bark of one yew tree—barely a gram. Not only that, but the tree was killed in the process of stripping the bark. It was clear that chemists would have to find a way to synthesize this compound in the lab. Researchers in France, working with the European yew, discovered in the needles of that kind of tree a compound that was closely related to paclitaxel. This substance could be used as the starting point of a "semisynthesis" that required just a few steps.

■ In addition to providing a relatively easy way to synthesize paclitaxel, what other advantage does use of the compound from the European yew have?

- Ans: A significant advantage of using semisynthesis, starting with a product of the European yew needles, is that the tree is not sacrificed when the needles are harvested. In contrast the Pacific yew tree dies when its bark is removed to harvest paclitaxel.

CHAPTER 2

AlKanes

I. Textbook Chapter Contents

This chapter introduces the family of alkanes (and cycloalkanes) which serves as the "parent" family of all organic compounds. The IUPAC nomenclature system is introduced. The concept of isomerism is developed and both constitutional and stereochemical isomers are described.

II. Learning Objectives

- Know the structure of alkanes, the relationship of molecular formulas to structural formulas, and the general formula for alkanes (C_nH_{2n+2}).

- Derive the IUPAC names for alkanes and substituted alkanes with chains of up to twenty carbons.

- Derive structural formulas from IUPAC names.

- Know the historic names for alkanes up to C4.

- Know the names for common alkyl groups.

- Be able to describe and categorize conformational (rotational) isomers and draw them using Newman projection drawings and wedge-and-dash drawings.

- Understand the non-polar nature of alkanes, the implication for physical properties, and the paucity of chemical reactions.

- Know the nomenclature and structure of cycloalkanes and cycloalkyl groups.

- Understand that *cis* and *trans* isomers of cycloalkanes represent a kind of configurational isomerism. Differentiate between *cis*- and *trans*- isomers of cycloalkanes.

- Use the chair conformation of cyclohexane to describe its conformational conversion.

- Identify axial and equatorial substituents in cyclohexanes and determine the relative stability of the two possible conformations of a mono-substituted cyclohexane.

- Recognize *cis*– and *trans*– di-substituted cyclohexanes and their conversion of conformation. Be able to identify the most stable configurational isomer and the most stable conformation.

- Write a balanced equation for the combustion of any alkane or cycloalkane.

III. Glossary

acyclic hydrocarbon a hydrocarbon that does not contain any rings

aliphatic hydrocarbon a saturated hydrocarbon comprised mainly of chains or rings of carbons and the requisite number of hydrogens

alkanes a family of saturated hydrocarbons. Acyclic members have the general formula $C_nH_{2n+2.}$ while cyclic members (cycloalkanes) have the general formula C_nH_{2n}

alkyl group the structural unit remaining when a hydrogen is removed from an alkane

angular strain an increase in the energy level of a compound (that is, destabilization) resulting from carbon-carbon bonds forced to have bond angles significantly different from tetrahedral (109.5°)

axial bond a bond on a cyclohexane ring which extends approximately parallel to an axis and perpendicular to the average plane of the ring

branched alkane an alkane in which not all of the carbons are in a continuous chain

chair conformation a conformation of cyclohexane in which the carbon skeleton approximates the shape of a chair and all bond angles are 109.5°. There are six axial and six equatorial carbon-hydrogen bonds, one of each on each carbon

***cis/trans* isomers** stereoisomers that have their substituents attached to opposite sides of a fixed plane of reference such as a ring.

combustion the complete oxidation of an organic compound, usually an alkane, to form carbon dioxide and water, producing energy in the process

configurational isomers stereoisomers that cannot be interconverted other than by breaking of bonds

conformational isomers stereoisomers that can be interconverted by rotation about one or more sigma bonds

conformers conformational isomers

constitutional isomers compounds that share the same molecular formula but have different bond connectivities

conversion of conformation the simultaneous rotation of six carbon-carbon bonds that converts a chair conformation of cyclohexane into a different chair conformation. All original axial bonds are converted into equatorial bonds and vice-versa

cyclic hydrocarbon a hydrocarbon which includes at least one ring of carbon atoms

cycloalkane an alkane in which two ends of a chain are joined to form a ring

1,3-diaxial interactions the steric interaction between an axial substituent on carbon 1 of cyclohexane with axial hydrogens or axial substituents on carbons 3 and 5

eclipsed conformation substituents on adjacent carbons are aligned parallel to each other

equatorial bond a bond on a cyclohexane ring which extends approximately 109.5° to an axis perpendicular to the average plane of the ring

halogenation a chemical reaction in which a hydrogen atom of an alkane is replaced by a halogen atom, producing an alkyl halide

heat of combustion the net energy evolved when a compound is combusted (oxidized) to carbon dioxide and water

homologous series a series of compounds of the same family differing from each other by a common structural unit, usually by a methylene (CH_2) group

hydrocarbon a compound containing only carbon and hydrogen

isomers compounds that share the same molecular formula but have different structural formulas

Newman projection a means of representing the three dimensional structure of a compound emphasizing the view along a carbon-carbon bond and the orientation of substituents on the two carbons

nomenclature a system for assigning names to compounds

octane rating a numeric comparison of the combustion characteristics of gasolines. 2,2,4-Trimethylpentane is assigned an octane rating of 100 and heptane is assigned a rating of 0

parent name the stem name plus suffix for a compound. Names of other compounds may be derived from the parent name

saturated hydrocarbon a hydrocarbon containing only single bonds

staggered conformation substituents on adjacent carbons are oriented in a direction 60° off parallel to each other

stem name the part of an alkane name that indicates the number of carbon atoms involved in the chain

stereoisomers compounds that share the same molecular formula and the same bond connectivities but have different spatial arrangements of atoms or groups

steric effect (strain) an increase in the energy level of a compound (that is, destabilization) resulting from repulsion between two groups that are too close together

straight chain alkene an alkane in which all of the carbons are in a continuous chain (that is, there are no branches)

substituent a group or atom that can be attached to a parent compound in place of a hydrogen atom

suffix the ending of a name that indicates the family to which the compound belongs (e.g., -ane designates alkane)

tetrahedral hybridization the hybridization of a single s orbital and three p orbitals to form four sp^3 hybrid orbitals which are directed to the corners of an imaginary tetrahedron

torsional strain an increase in the energy level of a compound (that is, destabilization) resulting from carbon-carbon bonds carrying eclipsed substituents

waxes long chain alkanes, such as $C_{27}H_{56}$ found on apples, are waxes

IV. Solutions to Problems

For "**How to Solve a Problem,**" review pages 42, 43, 52, 55, 60, and 67 in the text.

2.1

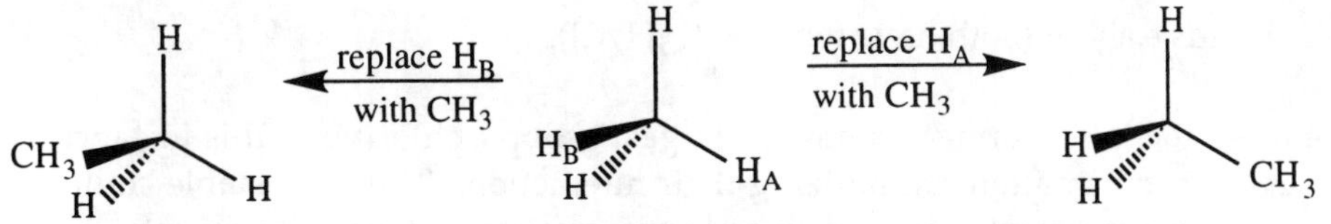
replace H_B with CH_3
replace H_A with CH_3
H
CH_3
H_B
H_A

I (ethane) methane II (ethane)

I and II are identical as can be seen by rotating II about its vertical axis 120° after which I and II appear superimposable on one another. It follows that H_A and H_B are equivalent.

2.2 Using the general formula for alkanes, C_nH_{2n+2}, the formulas are (a) C_7H_{16}, (b) $C_{16}H_{34}$, (c) $C_{30}H_{62}$, and (d) $C_{100}H_{202}$.

2.3 The pentanes have the molecular formula C_5H_{12}. There are only three different patterns by which five carbon atoms can be connected and from them can be derived the condensed formulas.

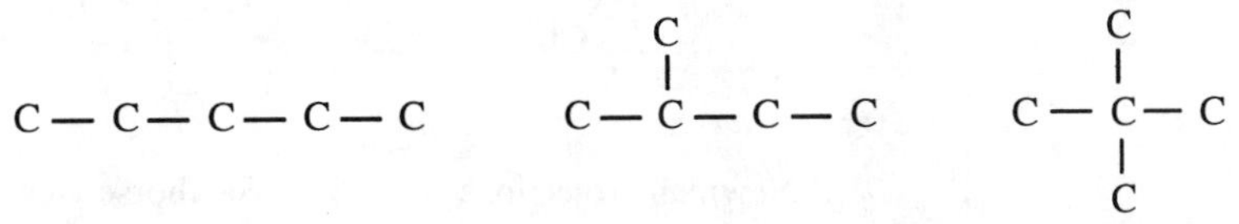

$CH_3CH_2CH_2CH_2CH_3$ $(CH_3)_2CHCH_2CH_3$ $(CH_3)_4C$

2.4

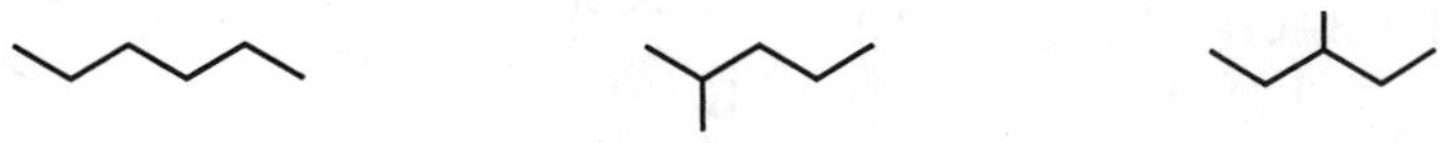

$CH_3(CH_2)_4CH_3$ $(CH_3)_2CH(CH_2)_2CH_3$ $(CH_3CH_2)_2CHCH_3$

$(CH_3)_2CHCH(CH_3)_2$ $(CH_3)_3CCH_2CH_3$

2.5 Constitutional isomers must have the same molecular formulas, differing only in the connectivities. The pairs of constitutional isomers are as follows:

compounds a and h (both have formula C_5H_{12});
compounds b and c (both have formula C_6H_{14});
compounds d and f (both have formula C_4H_{10});
compounds e and g (both have formula C_3H_7Cl).

2.6 The most stable conformation has the largest groups, chlorine in this instance, oriented in a staggered conformation, minimizing their interaction. The least stable conformation has the same groups oriented in an eclipsed conformation with maximum interaction.

Most stable

Least stable

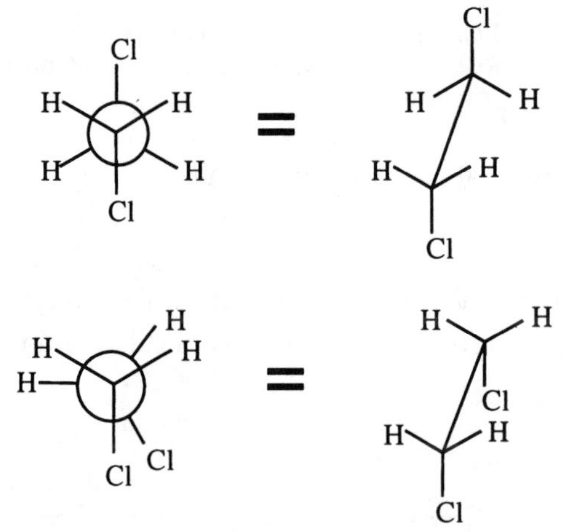

Newman projections Sawhorse view

2.7

(a) CH_3-CH_2-CH_2-CH_2-CH_3

(b) 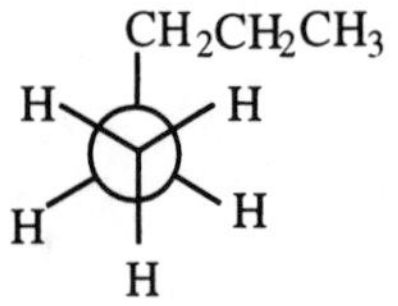

(c) 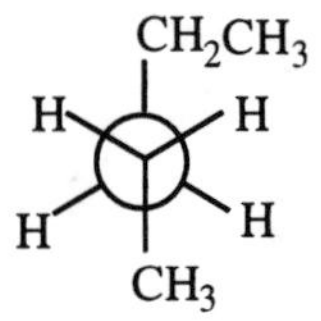

2.8 (a) 2,2-dimethylbutane; (b) 2-methylpentane; (c) 2-methylpropane

2.9

(a) 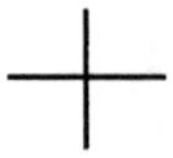

(b) 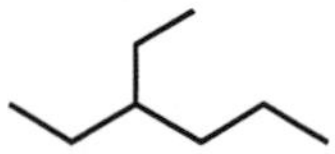

(c) 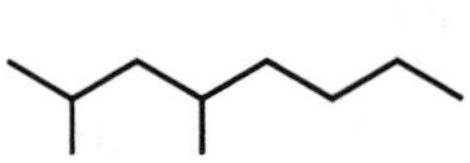

2.10 (a) $CH_3CH_2CH(CH_3)CH_2CH_3$; (b) $(CH_3)_3CCH_2CH_2CH_3$

2.11

2-methylpentane $(CH_3)_2CHCH_2CH_2CH_3$

$(CH_3)_2CHCH_2CH_2CH_2-$ primary

$(CH_3)_2CH-\underset{|}{CH}-CH_2CH_3$ secondary

$CH_3-\overset{CH_3}{\overset{|}{\underset{|}{C}}}-CH_2CH_2CH_3$ tertiary

2.12 The least compact structure (hexane) should be the highest boiling compound and the most compact structure (2,2-dimethylbutane) should be the lowest boiling compound. The boiling points decrease in the order

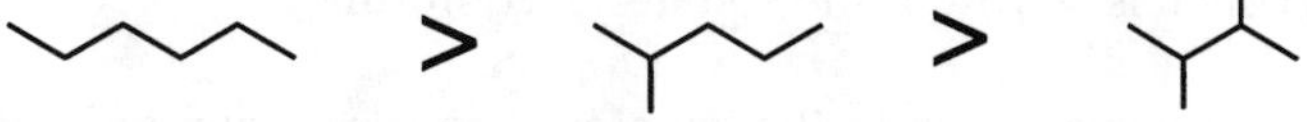

hexane 2-methylpentane 2,3-dimethylbutane

2.13 (a) methylcyclopropane; (b) 1,2-dimethylcyclopentane; (c) 1,1-dimethylcyclohexane; (d) 3-cyclopropylpentane

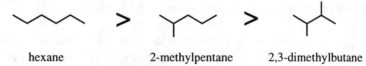

2.14

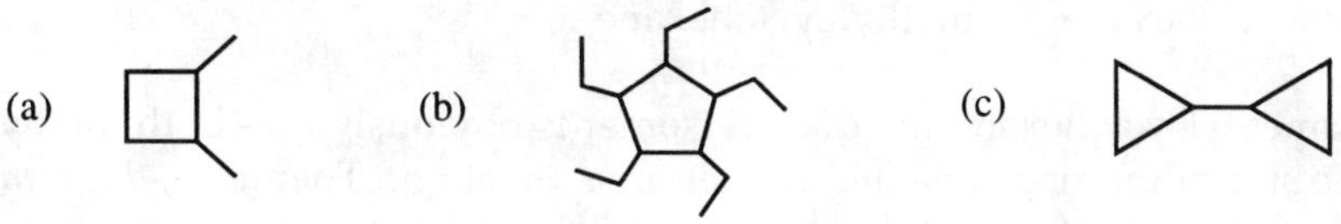
(a)
(b)
(c)

2.15

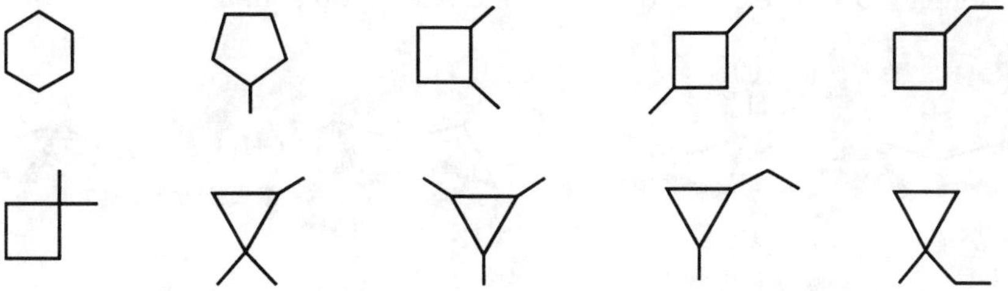

2.16

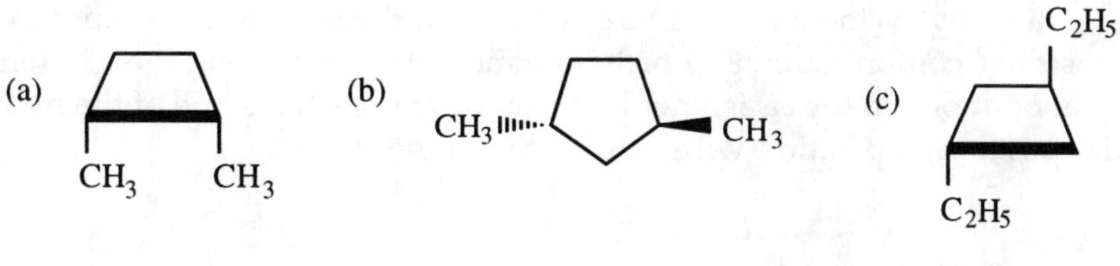
(a)
CH3
CH3
(b)
CH3
CH3
(c)
C2H5
C2H5

2.17

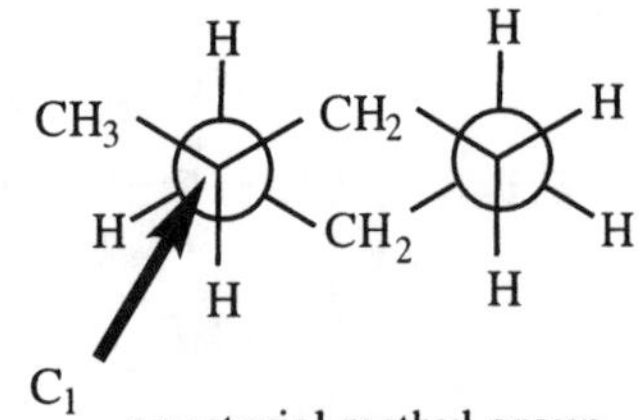
H
H
CH3
CH2
H
H
CH2
H
H
H
C1

equatorial methyl group
(more stable)

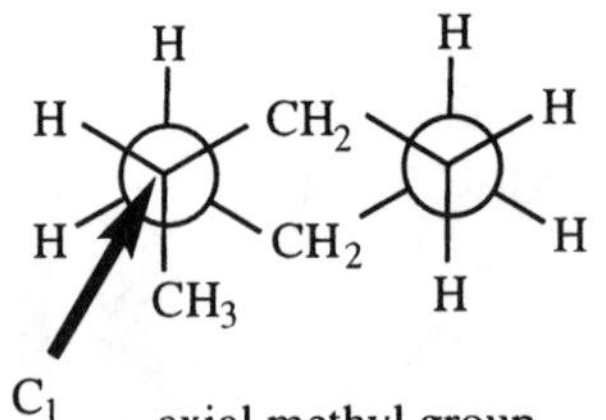
H
H
H
CH2
H
H
CH2
H
CH3
H
C1

axial methyl group
(less stable)

There is a 1,3-diaxial interaction between the axial methyl group and hydrogen atoms on carbons 3 and 5 which is absent in the equatorial conformer.

2.18 The relative proportions existing in the equatorial conformation will be a function of the size of the substituents, the bulkier substituent being less hindered when attached in an equatorial position. Therefore, the proportion of each compound existing in the equatorial conformation should be in the following order:

isopropylcyclohexane > *n*-propylcyclohexane
t-butylcyclohexane > isopropylcyclohexane
isopropylcyclohexane > methylcyclohexane

2.19 In 1,3-dimethylcyclohexane the diaxial isomer is obviously *cis* - both methyl groups are on the same side of the ring, oriented in the same direction. Therefore, the *trans* isomer must have one group equatorial and one group axial. In 1,4-dimethylcyclohexane the diaxial isomer is obviously *trans* - the methyl groups are oriented in opposite directions. Therefore, the *cis* isomer must have one group axial and one group equatorial.

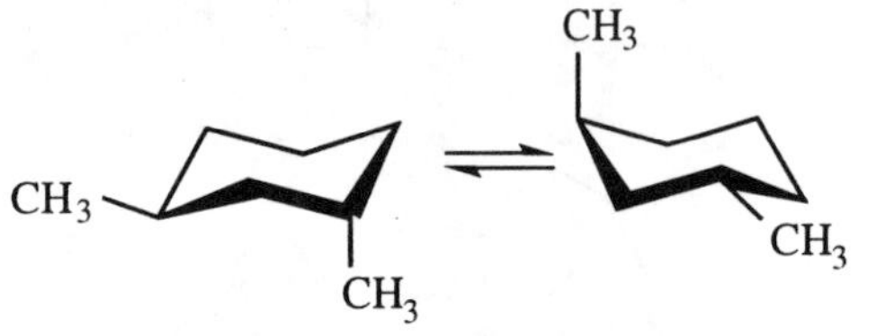
CH3
CH3
CH3
CH3

(a) *trans*-1,3-dimethylcyclohexane

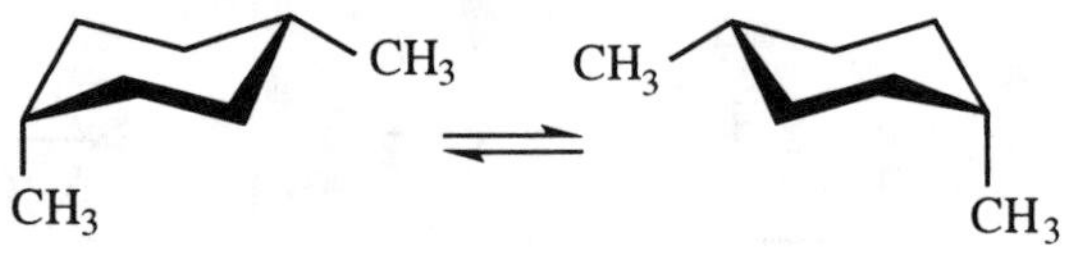
CH3
CH3
CH3
CH3

(b) *cis*-1,4-dimethylcyclohexane

2.20 *Trans*-1,4-dimethylcyclohexane is more stable than the *cis* isomer because in the former there exists one conformation in which both methyl groups are in the less hindered equatorial position. In the *cis* isomer both conformations have one of the methyl groups in the axial position, a position with larger steric hindrance.

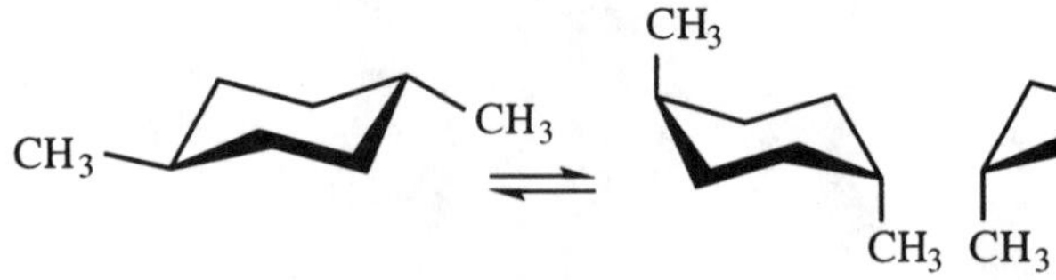
CH3
CH3
CH3
CH3

trans-1,4-dimethylcyclohexane

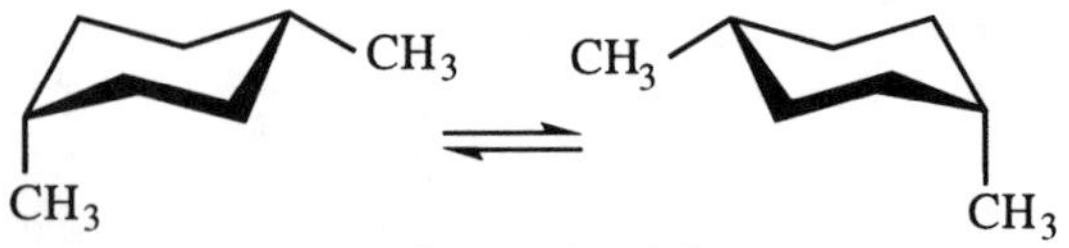
CH3
CH3
CH3
CH3

cis-1,4-dimethylcyclohexane

2.21 The technique for balancing an oxidation equation is to determine the number of carbons in the substrate (5 in the case of 2-methylbutane, C_5H_{12}) and use that same number for the number of molecules of CO_2 to be produced (since each carbon will appear in the form of CO_2). Then determine the number of molecules of water produced by deducing the multiplier needed (6) to account for all of the hydrogens in the substrate (12). Finally, total up the number of oxygens in the products (16) and assign the necessary multiplier (8) to the oxygen molecules required.

$$(CH_3)_2CHCH_2CH_3\ (= C_5H_{12}) \quad + \quad 8O_2 \longrightarrow 5CO_2 \quad + \quad 6H_2O$$

2.22 (a) $C_{30}H_{62}$; (b) C_8H_{18}; (c) $C_{22}H_{46}$

2.23

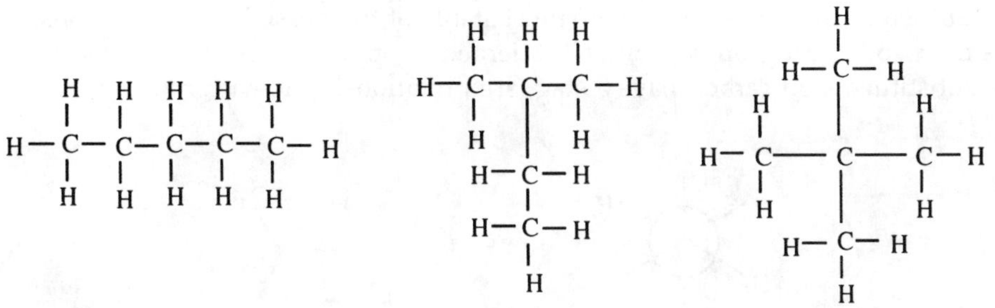

$CH_3CH_2CH_2CH_2CH_3$ $(CH_3)_2CHCH_2CH_3$ $(CH_3)_4C$

2.24 (a) C_6H_{14}; (b) C_5H_{12}; (c) C_7H_{16}

2.25 The two bromines can be oriented anti, gauche, or eclipsed.

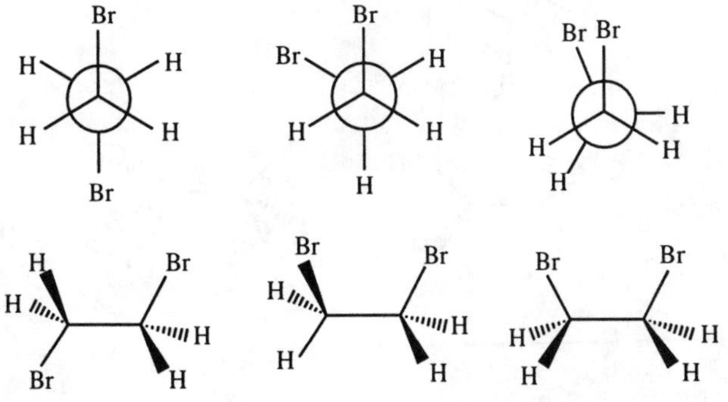

2.26 For each of the two conformations shown, the first two drawings are the usual representations when interactions between hydrogens are of relatively minor concern compared to the interactions involving methyl groups. The third structure in each case is used when hydrogen-hydrogen interaction is a concern.

Most stable conformation

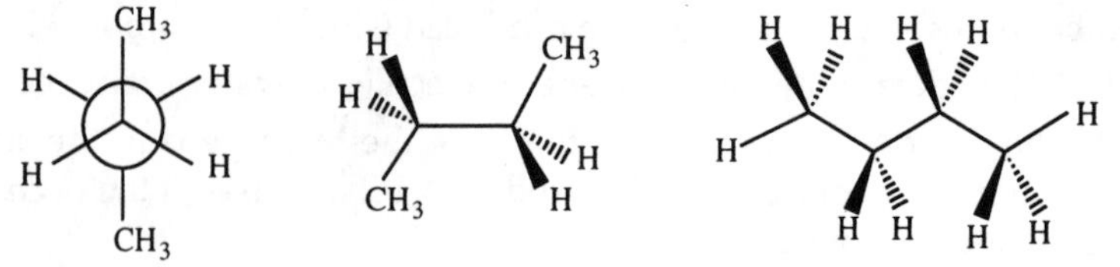

Least stable conformation

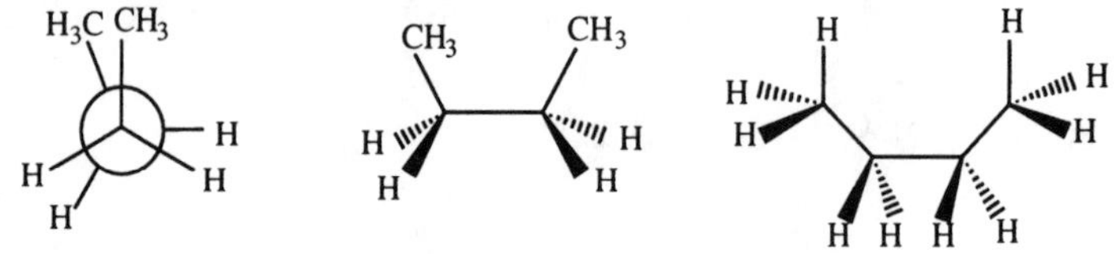

2.27 The *anti*-conformation shown is the most stable of the possible conformations because (a) it has the two largest groups (F and Cl) oriented in opposite directions, and (b) because all of the substituents on carbon have a staggered relationship to each other.

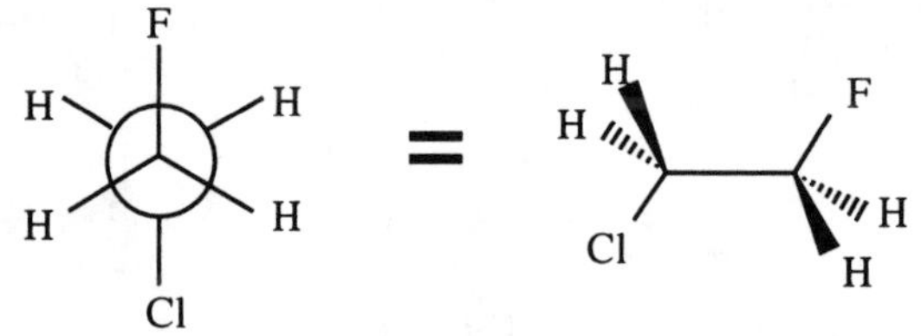

2.28 Compounds (a) and (c) are identical. Compounds (b) and (d) are two different constitutional isomers of (a).

2.29

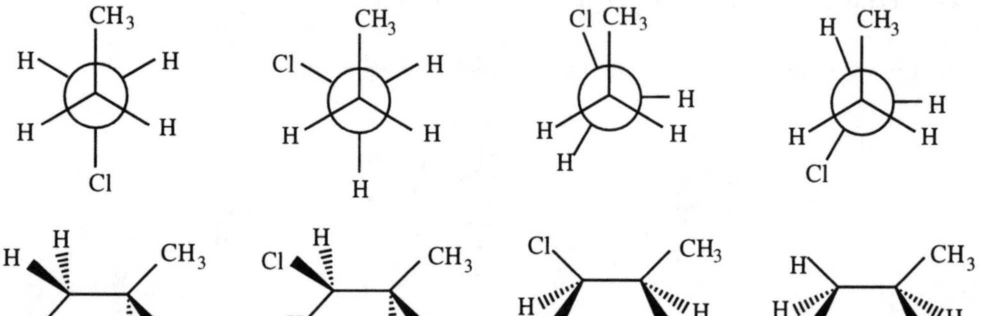

2.30

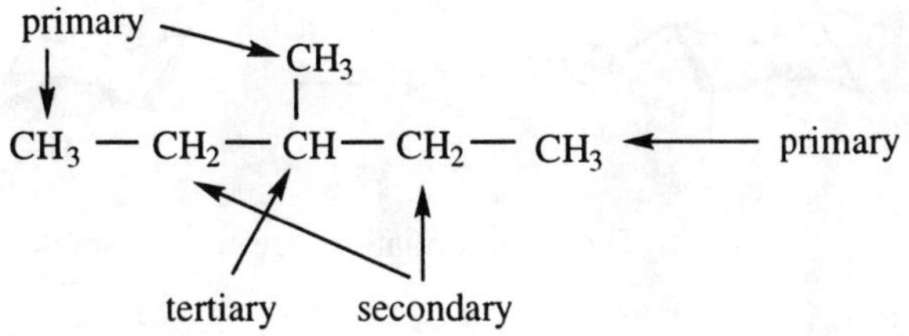
primary
CH3
CH3 — CH2 — CH — CH2 — CH3
primary
tertiary
secondary

2.31

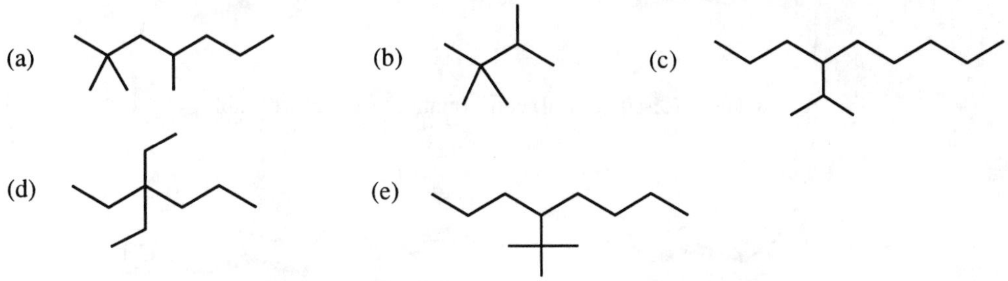
(a)
(b)
(c)
(d)
(e)

2.32 (a) $(CH_3)_3CCH_2CH(CH_3)CH_2CH_2CH_3$ (b) $(CH_3)_3CCH(CH_3)_2$
(c) $CH_3CH_2CH_2CH(CH(CH_3)_2)(CH_2)_4CH_3$ (d) $(CH_3CH_2)_3CCH_2CH_2CH_3$
(e) $CH_3(CH_2)_2CH(C(CH_3)_3)(CH_2)_3CH_3$

2.33 (a) 1-isopropyl-1-methylcyclohexane; (b) *cis*-1,3-dimethylcyclohexane;
(c) 1-ethyl-3-methylcycloheptane; (d) *cis*-1-*t*-butyl-4-methylcyclohexane;
(e) cyclopropylcyclopropane; (f) *trans*-1,2-dimethylcyclobutane

2.34 (a) 2,6-dimethylheptane (C_9H_{20}); (b) 2,3-dimethylhexane (C_8H_{18});
(c) 2,2-dimethylbutane (C_6H_{14}); (d) 3-ethylpentane (C_7H_{16});
(e) 2,3-dimethylpentane (C_7H_{16}); (f) 4-ethyl-2-methylhexane (C_9H_{20})

2.35

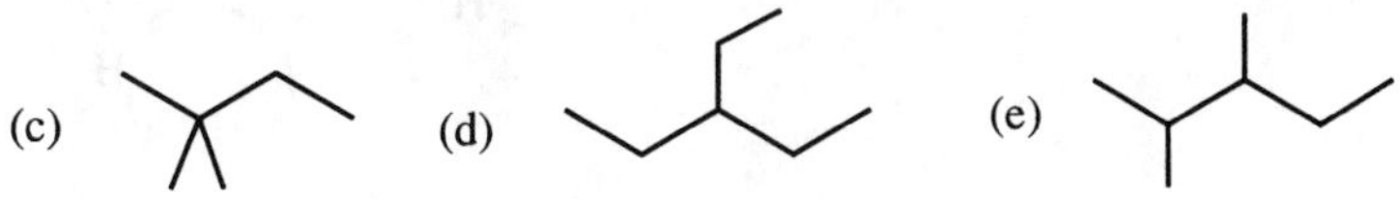
(c)
(d)
(e)

2.36

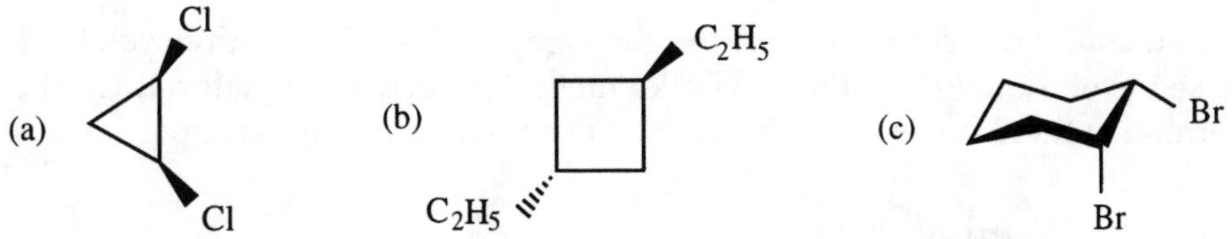
(a)
Cl
Cl
(b)
C2H5
C2H5
(c)
Br
Br

2.37

(a) 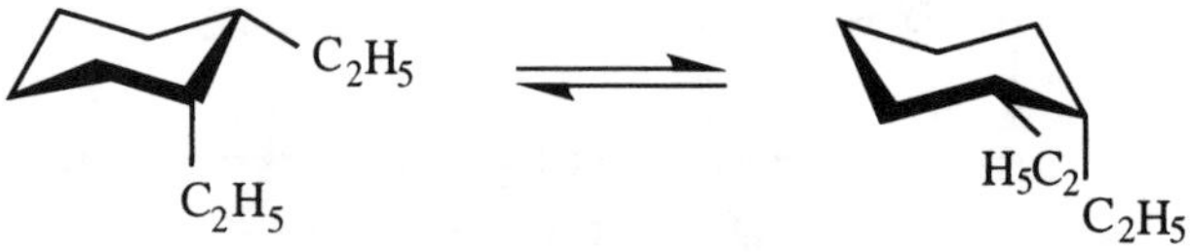
C2H5
C2H5
H5C2
C2H5

These conformations are equally stable

b) 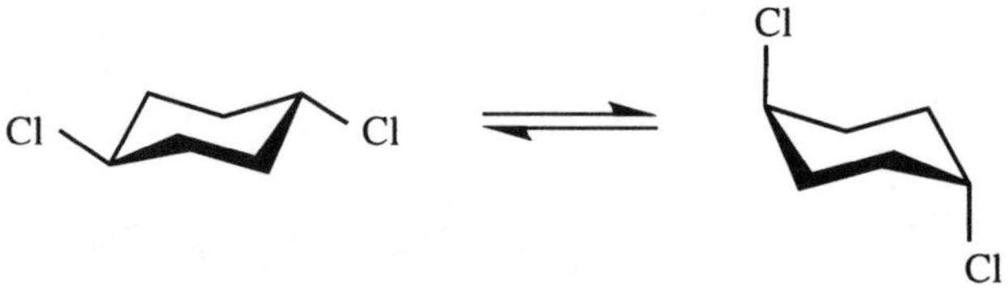
Cl
Cl
Cl
Cl

The left (di-equatorial) conformation is the more stable

(c) 
CH3
(CH3)3C
(CH3)3C
CH3

The left conformation, with the largest group in the equatorial position, is the more stable

2.38 The chair form is the more stable (i.e., of lower energy). In the chair form the hydrogens all are in staggered positions with respect to adjacent hydrogens whereas in a planar conformation the hydrogens are eclipsed, creating torsional strain. The chair form has ideal carbon-carbon bond angles of 109.5°, whereas the planar form has bond angles of 120°, larger than the ideal angle for tetrahedral carbon, thereby inducing angular strain.

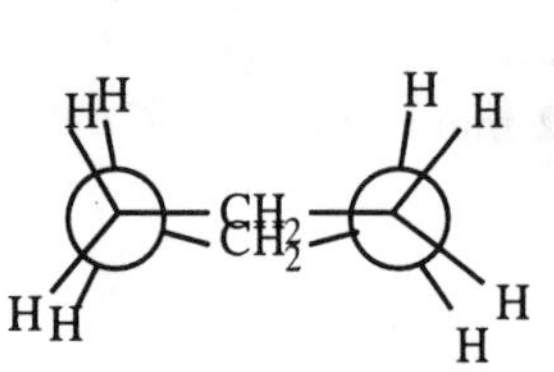
CH2
CH2

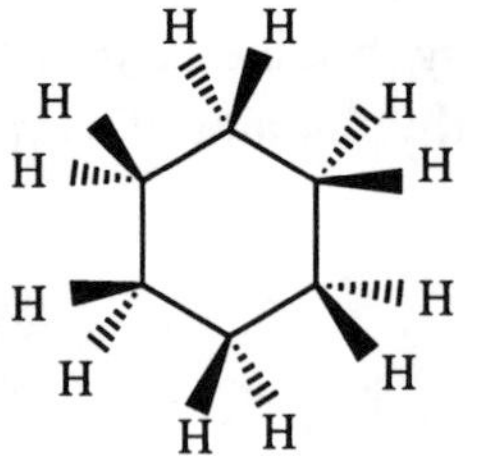

Planar cyclohexane with eclipsed hydrogens and 120° C-C-C bond angles

2.39 The 1,3-diequatorial conformation (on the right) of *cis*-1,3-dimethylcyclohexane is the more stable of the two because the bulky methyl groups are equatorial. In the diaxial conformation there is steric hindrance between the two methyl groups.

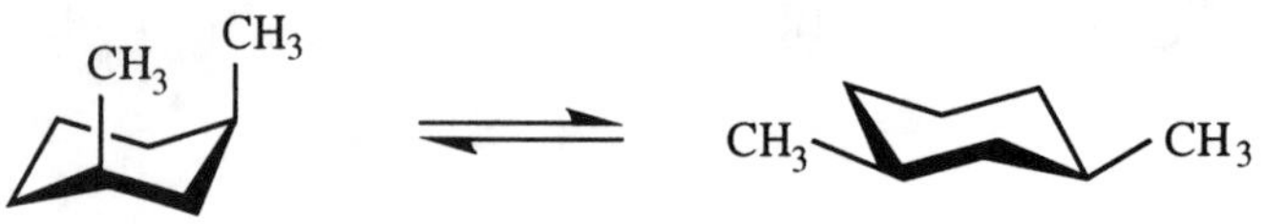
CH3
CH3
CH3
CH3

2.40 The more stable stereoisomers are (a) *trans*-1-isopropyl-2-methylcyclohexane, (b) *cis*-1-isopropyl-3-methylcyclohexane, and (c) *trans*-1-isopropyl-4-methylcyclohexane.

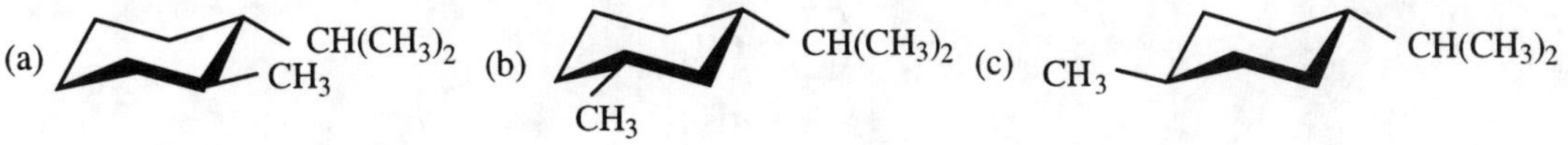
(a)
CH(CH3)2
CH3
(b)
CH(CH3)2
CH3
(c)
CH3
CH(CH3)2

2.41 The molecular formula cannot have more than six carbons (if it had seven the formula weight of the carbons is already 84 without even counting the hydrogens!). Thus, the molecular formula must be C_6H_{14} [MW = (6 x 12) + (14 x 1) = 86]. The structural formula is one of the following five isomers:

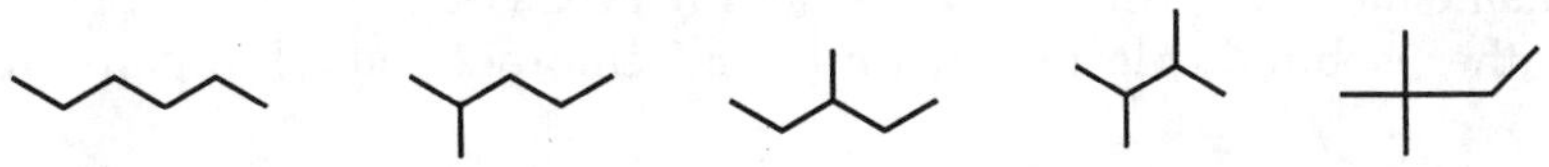

The first isomer (hexane) has the least compact structure and therefore the highest boiling point (69°) while the last isomer has the most compact structure and therefore the lowest boiling point (50°).

2.42 The nonane will be found floating on top of the water. The reasons are that the hydrocarbon is insoluble in water (it is non-polar), and that hydrocarbons are less dense than water, and therefore are the top layer.

2.43 Straight run gasoline has an octane rating of about 70 which is well below that (85-95) required for a modern internal combustion engine. The lower octane rating means the gasoline undergoes combustion too early in the cylinder, exerting a pressure back on the cylinder head before it has reached the top of its stroke. This causes "knocking" and lowers the power output of the engine.

2.44 The members of the homologous series, each differing by a CH_2 group from the next closest member of the series, are hexane ($CH_3(CH_2)_4CH_3$), heptane ($CH_3(CH_2)_5CH_3$), and octane ($CH_3(CH_2)_6CH_3$).

2.45

β-D-Glucose

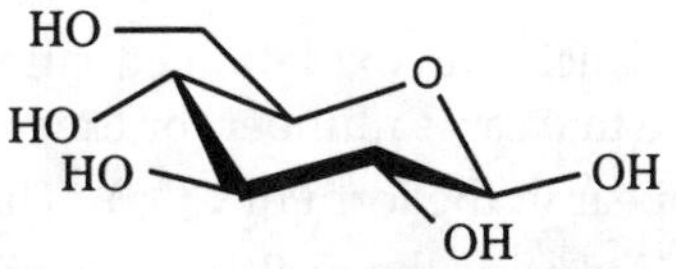
HO
O
HO
HO
OH
OH

2.46 In the case of the dimethylcyclohexanes the most stable stereoisomer in each case will be that with both methyl groups in equatorial positions. For the 1,2-disubstituted isomer such is the case for the *trans* isomer, for the 1,3-disubstituted isomer such is the case for the *cis* isomer, and for the 1,4-disubstituted isomer such is the case for the *trans* isomer.

2.47 (a) The substituent order is not alphabetic. The correct name is 1-ethyl-2-methylcyclohexane.

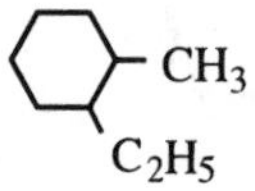
CH3
C2H5

(b) The longest straight chain is not a butane unit. The correct name is 2-methylpentane.

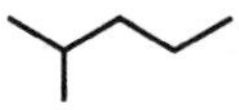

(c) This name mixes historic (isobutane) and IUPAC (1-chloro-) nomenclature. It should be named either isobutyl chloride (historic) or 1-chloro-2-methylpropane (IUPAC).

Cl

(d) The numbers assigned to substituents are not the lowest possible. The correct name is 1,2-difluoropropane.

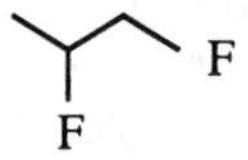
F
F

(e) The lowest possible numbers are not used. The correct name is 1,2-dimethylcyclopentane.

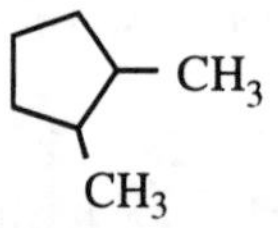
CH3
CH3

(f) The longest chain is not a pentane. The correct name is 3-ethyl-3,5-dimethylheptane.

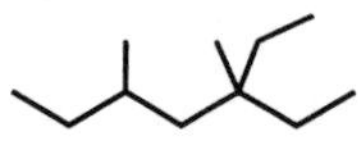

2.48 The technique for balancing an oxidation equation is to determine the number of carbons in the substrate and use that same number for the number of molecules of CO_2 produced (since each carbon will appear in the form of CO_2). Then determine the number of molecules of water produced by deducing the multiplier needed to account for all of the hydrogens in the starting compound. Finally, total up the number of oxygens in the products and assign the necessary multiplier to the oxygen molecules required.

(a) $C_5H_{10} + 7.5\,O_2 \longrightarrow 5\,CO_2 + 5\,H_2O$

(b) $C_8H_{18} + 12.5\,O_2 \longrightarrow 8\,CO_2 + 9\,H_2O$

2.49 There are only three constitutional isomers of molecular formula C_5H_{12}. Draw each and match them to the description of hydrogens.

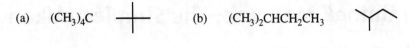

(a) $(CH_3)_4C$  (b) $(CH_3)_2CHCH_2CH_3$ 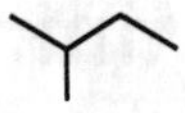

(c) $CH_3CH_2CH_2CH_2CH_3$ 

2.50 Two kinds of representations may be employed, with the second being the more common.

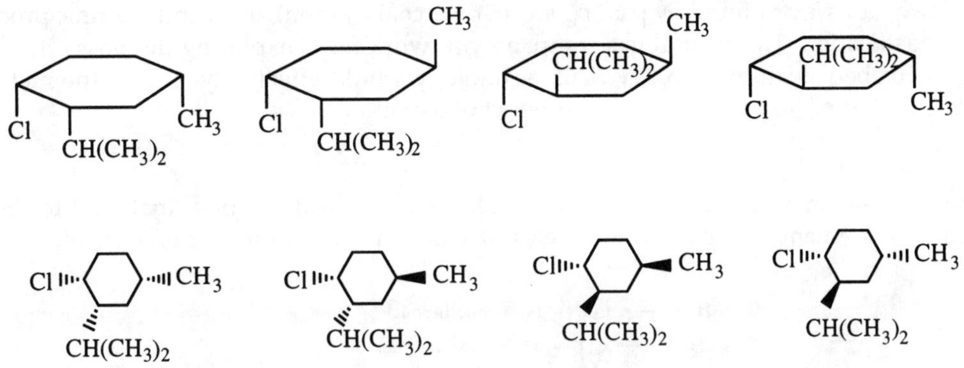
CH3
Cl
CH(CH3)2
Cl
CH(CH3)2
CH3
CH(CH3)2
Cl
CH3
CH(CH3)2
Cl
CH3
Cl
CH3
CH(CH3)2
Cl
CH3
CH(CH3)2
Cl
CH3
CH(CH3)2
Cl
CH3
CH(CH3)2

2.51 (a) constitutional isomers; (b) configurational isomers; (c) conformational isomers; (d) configurational isomers; (e) constitutional isomers; (f) conformational isomers.

2.52 There are four constitutional isomers (in this instance positional isomers) of chlorobutane as shown below:

$CH_3CH_2CH_2CH_2Cl$ $CH_3CH_2CHClCH_3$ $(CH_3)_2CHCH_2Cl$ $(CH_3)_3CCl$

2.53

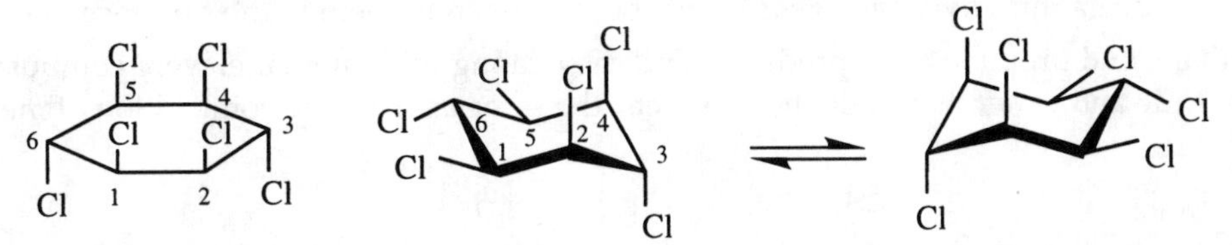
Cl
Cl
5
4
Cl
Cl
3
6
Cl
1
2
Cl
Cl
Cl
Cl
Cl
6
5
2
4
Cl
1
3
Cl
Cl
Cl
Cl
Cl
Cl
Cl
Cl

γ-Gammexane

These are the two possible conformations. However, note that they are identical. Therefore, there exists only a single conformation of γ-gammexane.

V. Conceptual Problem

"Mining" Methane: The Simplest Alkane

The combustion of methane gas in the presence of oxygen gas produces carbon dioxide gas and water—this is the reaction that occurs in a gas furnace. The reaction is exothermic and is a clean and efficient source of energy. Methane is most readily obtained as part of the natural gas from gas or oil wells, but it can also be produced, along with steam, from the exothermic reactions of a mixture of carbon monoxide gas and hydrogen gas (synthesis gas). This mixture of two gases is produced by passing steam over coal (carbon), in an endothermic process called coal gasification. The natural gas company you work for is exploring the possibility of investing in coalbed steam technology. This technology would effectively "mine" the methane that is currently considered just a dangerous by-product of coal mines.

■ Starting with steam and coal, write the two balanced chemical reaction, that lead to the production of methane. Indicate whether each reaction is endothermic or exothermic.

$$C + H_2O \longrightarrow CO + H_2 \quad \text{(endothermic)}$$
$$CO + 3H_2O \longrightarrow CH_4 + H_2O \quad \text{(exothermic)}$$

■ What factors would you need to consider to determine the practicality of producing methane in this way?

- Ans: The practicality of producing methane by this process would be determined, in part, by the cost for the coal, whether the exothermicity of the second reaction exceeds the endothermicity of the first reaction, whether the exothermicity of the second reaction could "fuel" the endothermicity of the first reaction, and the ability to engineer the combined processes.

■ What if, in addition to methane, ethane and propane were also produced by the reaction of carbon monoxide gas and hydrogen gas? What could happen to them in the presence of oxygen?

- Ans: If ethane and propane were produced and they, along with methane, were combusted, carbon dioxide and water would be the products, the same as from the combustion of methane.

$$CH_4 + 2O_2 \longrightarrow CO_2 + 2H_2O$$
$$C_2H_6 + 3.5O_2 \longrightarrow 2CO_2 + 3H_2O$$
$$C_3H_8 + 5O_2 \longrightarrow 3CO_2 + 4H_2O$$

■ What happens if the coal used in coal gasification contains an impurity, such as sulfur?

- Ans: If the coal contained sulfur as an impurity there would be no reaction with the water (steam). If any oxygen were present the sulfur would be oxidized to sulfur dioxide which would be converted to sulfurous acid through reaction with water. If oxygen were absent, the hydrogen present in the synthesis gas would convert sulfur to hydrogen sulfide.

CHAPTER 3

Alkyl Halides (Haloalkanes)

I. Textbook Chapter Contents

This chapter introduces alkyl halides (haloalkanes), compounds in which one or more halogen atoms have replaced hydrogen atoms in a parent alkane structure. The halide is the functional group of the family. The concepts of chirality, reaction mechanisms, and organic synthesis are introduced. The first type of chemical reaction, a substitution reaction, is introduced. The first type of reactive intermediate—the carbocation—is introduced.

II. Learning Objectives

- Know the IUPAC nomenclature of haloalkanes and the common nomenclature for simple alkyl halides.
- Be able to distinguish chiral and achiral compounds, and identify a stereocenter, an enantiomer, and a plane of symmetry.
- Determine and designate the absolute configuration about a stereocenter.
- Know the nucleophilic substitution reactions of alkyl halides.
- Know the S_N1 and S_N2 mechanisms for nucleophilic substitution reactions, including the meaning of transition state, reactive intermediate, leaving group, rate-determining step, reaction energy profile, backside attack, racemization, and inversion of configuration.
- Be able to describe the structure of a carbocation, its hyperconjugative stabilization, and the relative stability of different alkyl carbocations.
- Be able to differentiate between a primary, secondary, and tertiary halide using the silver nitrate and sodium iodide tests.
- Know the structure and preparation of the three organometallic compounds — organolithium compounds, Grignard reagents (organomagnesium compounds), and organocuprate compounds (lithium dialkyl cuprates).
- Write equations for the synthesis of alkanes using an organocuprate reagent and an alkyl halide.

- Write equations for the conversion of alkyl halides into alcohols.
- Become comfortable with the use of arrows to indicate bonds being broken or formed and the accompanying electron shifts when writing reactions and their mechanisms.
- Begin to learn how to analyze synthesis problems and deduce appropriate solutions.

III. Glossary

absolute configuration the actual arrangement of four substituents about a stereocenter represented by the symbols *R* or *S*

achiral compound a compound not having the characteristic of handedness—its structure is superimposable on its mirror image and usually has a plane of symmetry

alkyl halide a compound derived by replacing a hydrogen of an alkane by a halogen

aprotic solvent a solvent lacking a polar X-H bond and which therefore cannot form hydrogen bonds

backside attack the approach of a nucleophile to a carbon from the side opposite that from which the leaving group departs

carbanion a carbon atom that is negatively charged, has three substituents, and an unshared pair of electrons

carbocation a carbon atom that is positively charged, has three substituents, and a vacant p-orbital

chiral compound a compound having the property of handedness. Îts structure is non-superimposable on its mirror image

chirality the property of handedness. The object is not superimposable on its mirror image

concerted reaction a reaction in which two changes occur at approximately the same time rather than in sequence

E1 reaction a unimolecular reaction in which X leaves an alkyl group to form a carbocation; H is then abstracted from the carbocation to form a double bond

E2 reaction a bimolecular concerted reaction in which H and X leave to form a double bond

elimination reaction a reaction in which two substituents on adjacent carbons leave and a double bond is formed in their place

enantiomers two stereoisomers that are chiral and that have an object-mirror image relationship; they each have the property of rotating a beam of plane polarized light

energy of activation the energy required to bring a ground state reactant to the transition state

Grignard reagent an organomagnesium bromide reagent whose complex structure is simplified to be represented as RMgBr

haloalkane a compound in which a halogen has replaced a hydrogen in an alkane

hyperconjugation the sharing of electron density from carbon-hydrogen sigma bonds with an adjacent site of electron deficiency, typically a carbocation

inversion of configuration a stereocenter changing from one absolute configuration to the opposite absolute configuration during the course of a reaction

leaving group an atom or group which departs or is displaced during a substitution reaction

lithium dialkyl cuprate an organometallic reagent represented as R_2CuLi

nucleophilic substitution a reaction in which a nucleophile has replaced a leaving group

organolithium compound a reagent in which lithium is bonded to a carbon (R-Li)

organometallic compound a compound in which a metal is bonded to a carbon (R-metal)

plane of symmetry an imaginary plane through a compound in which one half is the mirror image of the other half. Such compounds are not enantiomers (that is, they are superimposable on their mirror images)

polarizability the ease with which a pair of bonding electrons are shifted or moved

protic solvent a solvent with a polar X-H bond, which therefore can form hydrogen bonds

R a symbol used to represent alkyl groups in general

***R* enantiomer** a description of the absolute configuration of one enantiomer; substituents, which can be assigned priority labels, are arranged about the stereocenter such that their priority sequence decreases in a clockwise direction.

racemate a 50:50 mixture of two enantiomers

racemic mixture a 50:50 mixture of two enantiomers

racemization the conversion of an enantiomer into a racemic mixture

rate of reaction the speed with which a reaction occurs; is represented by a rate equation

rate-determining step the slowest step in a multi-step reaction; the overall reaction cannot occur faster than this slowest step

***S* enantiomer** a description of the absolute configuration of one enantiomer; the substituents, which can be assigned priority labels, are arranged about the stereocenter such their priority sequence decreases in a counter-clockwise direction

S_N1 reaction a unimolecular reaction in which a leaving group departs, leaving behind a carbocation as a reactive intermediate, that reacts with a nucleophile to form a substitution product with racemization of configuration

S_N2 reaction a bimolecular concerted reaction in which a nucleophile displaces a leaving group in a backside attack to form a substitution product with inversion of configuration

side reaction a reaction, other than the desired reaction, occurring side-by-side the desired reaction and under the same experimental conditions, producing a by-product

solvolysis a substitution reaction, most often S_N1, in which the solvent also serves as the nucleophile

steric effect the effect on a reaction exerted by the spatial requirements of substituents, usually to decrease or increase the reaction rate

stereocenter a carbon atom with four different groups attached

stereospecific reaction a reaction that occurs with predictable stereochemistry and/or during which the stereocenter does not racemize

substrate a compound undergoing a reaction

substitution reaction a reaction in which one atom or group, called the leaving group, is replaced by another group

transition state a mid-point in a reaction at which the structure of the reactant is at its highest energy level

trigonal hybridization the hybridization of a single s orbital and two p orbitals to form three sp^2 hybrid orbitals directed to the corners of an imaginary equilateral triangle, with an unhybridized p orbital oriented perpendicular to the plane of the triangle

IV. Summary of Reactions of Alkyl Halides

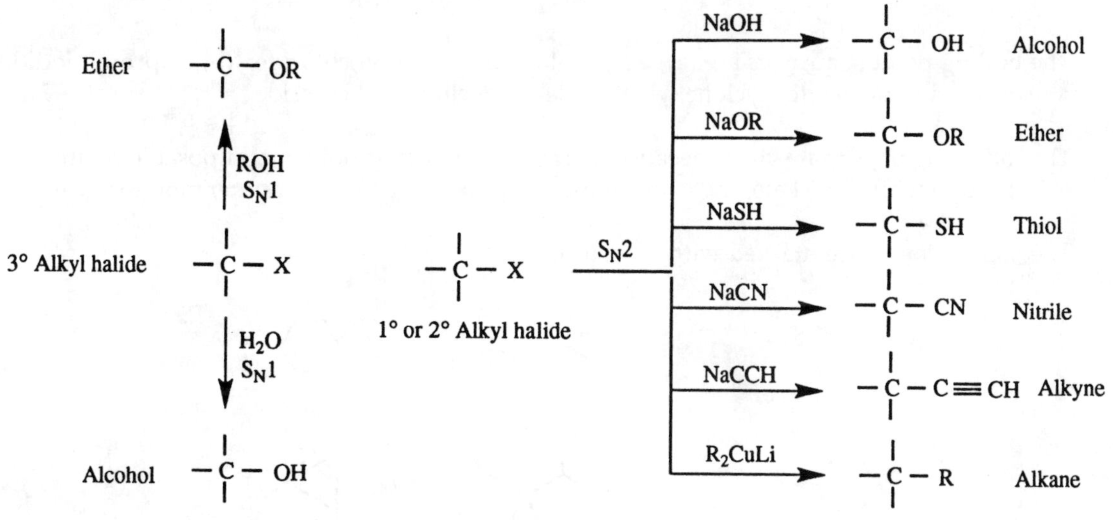
Ether
ROH
SN1
3° Alkyl halide
H2O
SN1
Alcohol
1° or 2° Alkyl halide
SN2
NaOH
Alcohol
NaOR
Ether
NaSH
Thiol
NaCN
Nitrile
NaCCH
Alkyne
R2CuLi
Alkane

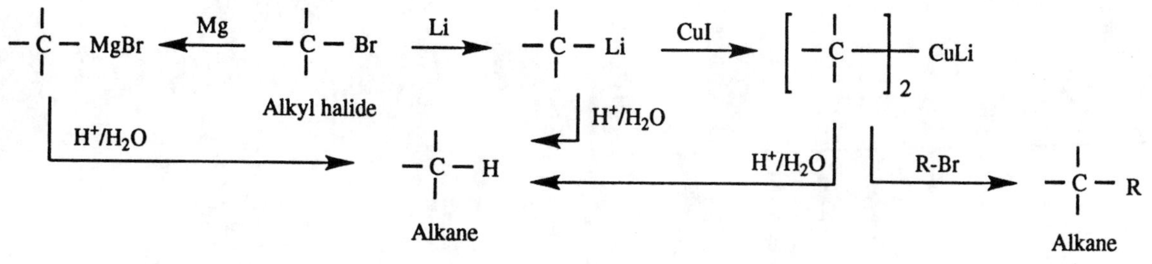
Mg
Li
CuI
CuLi
Alkyl halide
H+/H2O
H+/H2O
H+/H2O
R-Br
Alkane
Alkane

V. Solutions to Problems

For "**How to Solve a Problem**", review pages 77, 81, 83, 88, 89, 94, 96, 102, and 108.

3.1

(a) 

(b) $CH_3CF_2CH_2CH_3$

(c) 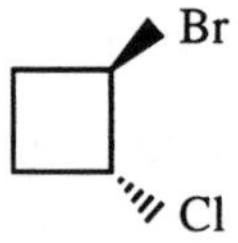

3.2 (a) 1,1-difluorocyclopropane; (b) 1-iodo-2,2-dimethylpropane; (c) triiodomethane; (d) 2-bromo-4-chloro-6-methylheptane

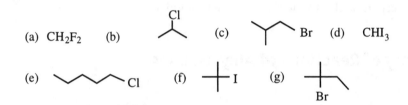

3.3

(a) CH_2F_2

(b) 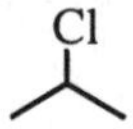

(c) 

(d) CHI_3

(e) 

(f) 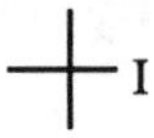

(g) 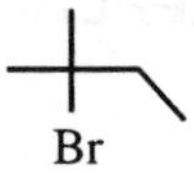

3.4 The boiling point sequences are (a) ethyl chloride > methyl chloride; (b) isopropyl iodide > isopropyl fluoride; (c) cyclohexyl chloride > cyclopropyl chloride

3.5 The following objects are chiral because their mirror image is not superimposable on the object: automobile, ice skate, shoe, boombox, computer keyboard, computer monitor case.

3.6 The stereocenters are marked with an asterisk.

(a) 

(none)

(b) 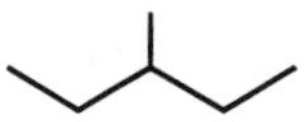

(none)

(c) 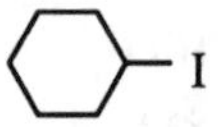

(none)

(d) 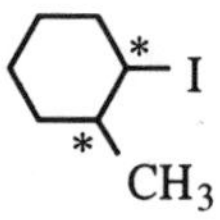

(e) 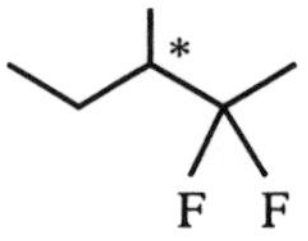

(f) 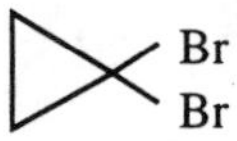

(none)

3.7 The following compounds, the only ones with a stereocenter, will exist as a racemic mixture: 1-iodo-2-methylpentane and 1-bromo-3-fluorocyclohexane. The remainder do not have a stereocenter and are therefore not chiral.

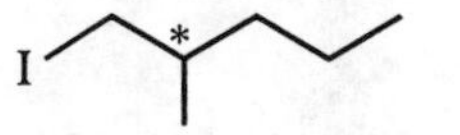
I
*

1-Iodo-2-methylpentane

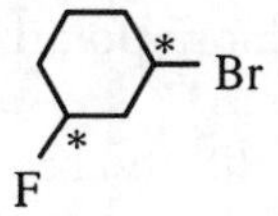
*
Br
*
F

1-Bromo-3-fluorocyclohexane

3.8 (a) The priority assignments for the groups attached to the stereocenter in 3-bromohexane are as follows: **a** = bromine, **b** = propyl, **c** = ethyl, **d** = hydrogen. Viewing the molecule along the C-H axis (that is, from below the drawing) indicates the **a** to **b** to **c** direction is clockwise. Therefore, the structure is (*R*)-3-bromohexane.

(a)

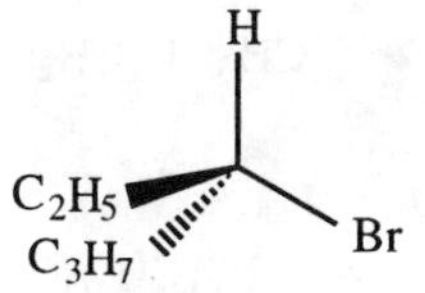
H
C2H5
C3H7
Br

(*R*)-3-bromohexane

(b)

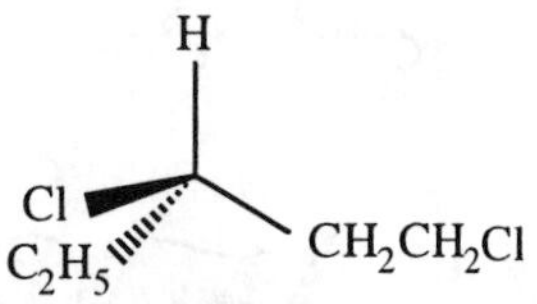
H
Cl
C2H5
CH2CH2Cl

(*R*)-1,3-dichloropentane

(b) The priority assignments for the groups attached to the stereocenter in 1,3-dichloropentane are as follows: **a** = chlorine, **b** = chloroethyl, **c** = ethyl, **d** = hydrogen. Viewing the molecule along the C-H axis (that is, from below the drawing) indicates the **a** to **b** to **c** direction is clockwise. Therefore, the structure is (*R*)-1,3-dichloropentane.

3.9

(a)

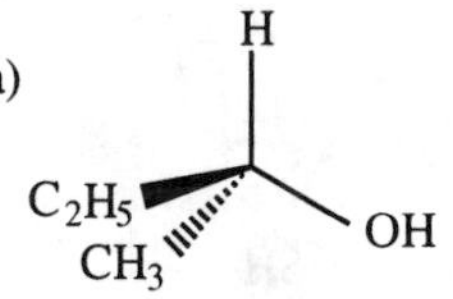
H
C2H5
CH3
OH

(b)

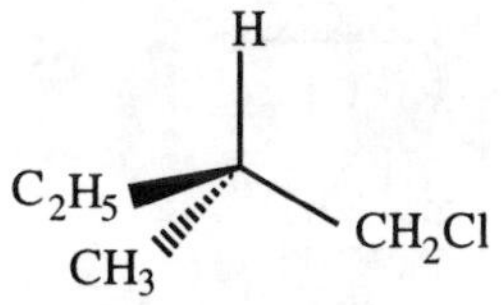
H
C2H5
CH3
CH2Cl

(c)

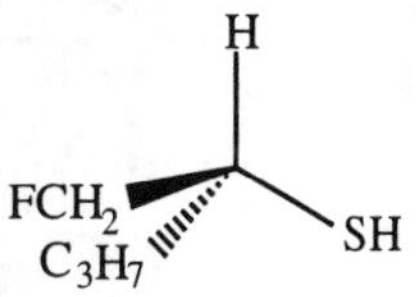
H
FCH2
C3H7
SH

3.10 (a) sodium iodide; (b) sodium hydroxide; (c) sodium acetylide ($HC\equiv C:^{-}\ Na^{+}$)

3.11

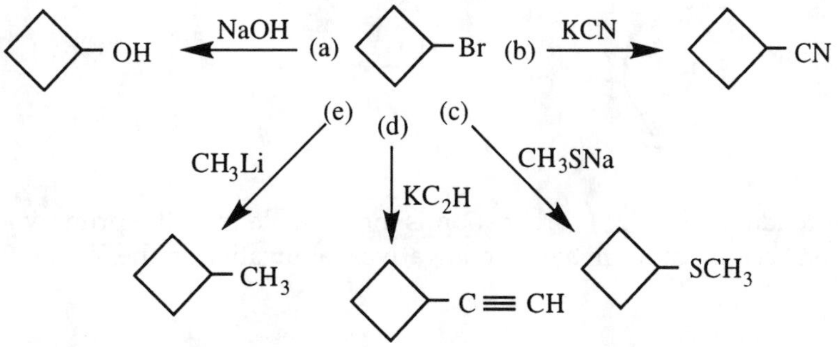
OH
NaOH
(a)
Br
(b)
KCN
CN
(e)
(d)
(c)
CH3Li
KC2H
CH3SNa
CH3
C≡CH
SCH3

3.12 S_N2 reactivity sequences are:

(a) cyclohexyl bromide > cyclohexyl fluoride; the bromide is a better leaving group than fluoride because it is more polarizable.

(b) *n*-butyl bromide > *t*-butyl bromide; the *n*-butyl group is more easily substituted because, being primary, there is less steric hindrance to backside attack than in *t*-butyl bromide.

(c) 1-iodopentane > 2-iodopentane; 1-iodopentane is a primary halide whereas 2-iodopentane is secondary. The primary halide has less steric hindrance to backside attack by a nucleophile.

3.13

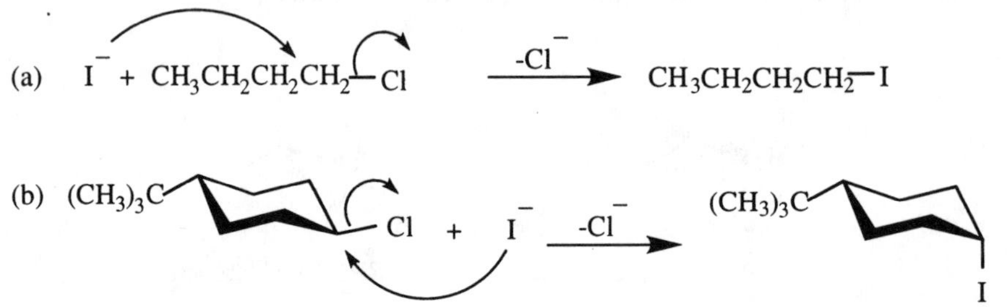
(a)
I⁻ + CH3CH2CH2CH2–Cl
-Cl⁻
CH3CH2CH2CH2–I
(b) (CH3)3C
Cl + I⁻
-Cl⁻
(CH3)3C
I

3.14

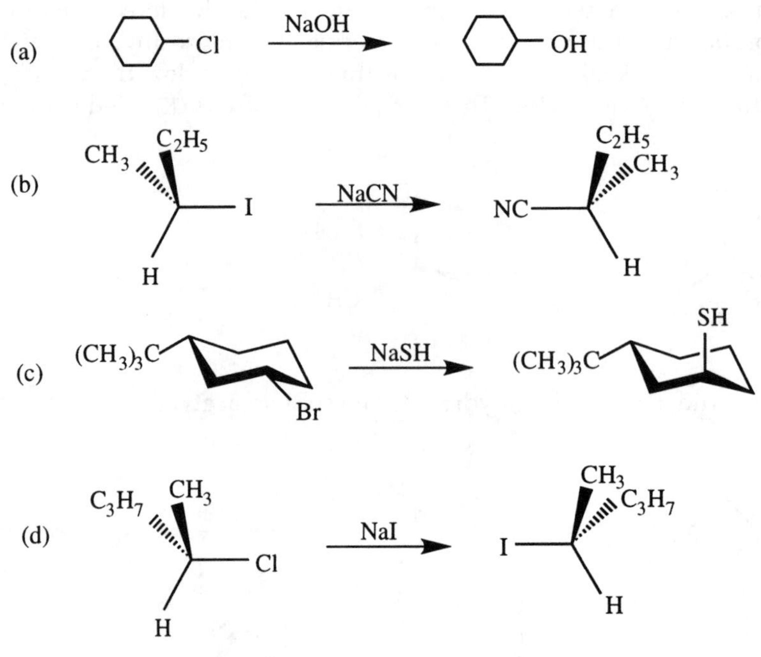
(a)
Cl
NaOH
OH
(b)
CH3
C2H5
I
H
NaCN
C2H5
CH3
NC
H
(c)
(CH3)3C
Br
NaSH
(CH3)3C
SH
(d)
C3H7
CH3
Cl
H
NaI
CH3
C3H7
I
H

3.15 (a) The secondary isopropyl carbocation is more stable than the primary *n*-butyl carbocation because of more hyperconjugative stabilization in the former (6 hydrogens vs 2);

(b) the *t*-pentyl carbocation is more stable than the secondary cyclopentyl carbocation because of more hyperconjugative stabilization in the former (9 hydrogens vs 4);

(c) The tertiary carbocation from 2-chloro-2-methylpentane is more stable than the secondary carbocation from 2-chloropentane because of more hyperconjugative stabilization in the former (8 hydrogens vs 5);

(d) the secondary carbocation from 2-bromobutane is more stable than the primary carbocation from 1-bromobutane because of more hyperconjugative stabilization in the former (5 hydrogens vs 2).

3.16 (a) The *t*-butyl carbocation forms faster from *t*-butyl bromide than from *t*-butyl chloride because of the higher polarizability of bromine than chlorine and the lower bond strength of bromides than chlorides, both factors resulting in bromide being a better leaving group than chloride;

(b) The carbocation forms faster from 1-iodo-1-methylcyclopentane than from iodocyclopentane because the former produces a tertiary carbocation and the latter produces a secondary carbocation. The tertiary carbocation is more stable due to increased hyperconjugation (7 vs 4 hydrogens).

3.17

(a) $CH_3\text{-}CHBr\text{-}CH_2\text{-}CH_2\text{-}CH_3 \xrightarrow{NaOH} CH_3\text{-}CHOH\text{-}CH_2\text{-}CH_2\text{-}CH_3$

(b)

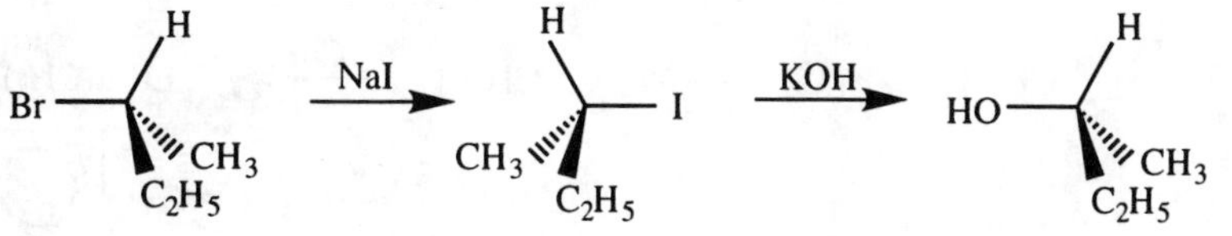
H
Br
CH3
C2H5
NaI
H
CH3
I
C2H5
KOH
H
HO
CH3
C2H5

(R) (S) (R)

(c)

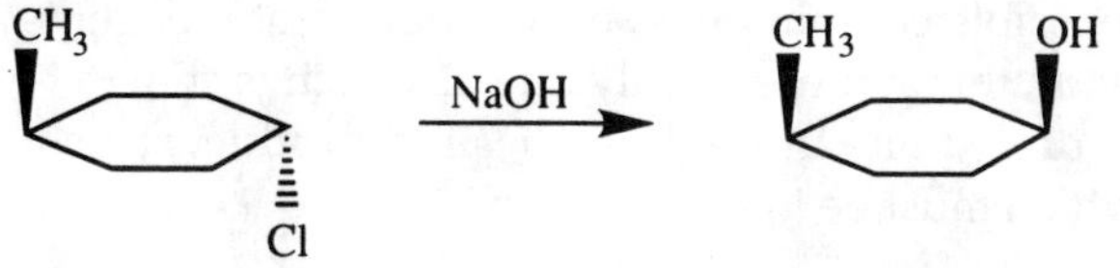
CH3
Cl
NaOH
CH3
OH

(d) $(CH_3)_2CBrCH_2CH_2CH_3 \xrightarrow{NaCN} (CH_3)_2C(CN)CH_2CH_2CH_3$ minor

+

$(CH_3)_2C{=}CHCH_2CH_3$ major

3.18

(a) $CH_3CH_2CH_2CH_2Br \xrightarrow[\text{ether}]{\text{Mg}} CH_3CH_2CH_2CH_2MgBr$

(b) 
Br
Li
ether
Li
+ LiBr

(c) 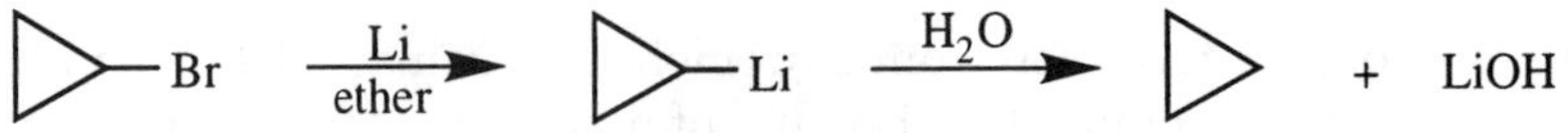
Br
Li
ether
Li
H_2O
+ LiOH

3.19

(a) 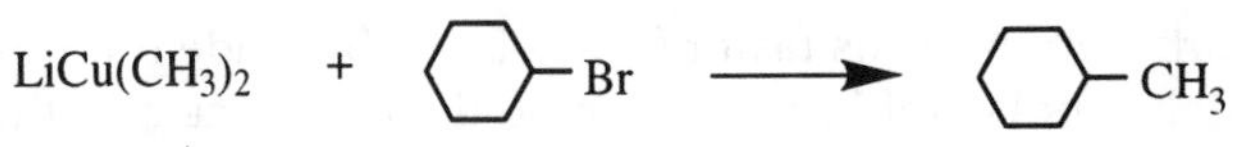
$LiCu(CH_3)_2$ +
Br
CH_3

(b) $LiCu(C_2H_5)_2 + (CH_3)_3C\text{-}Br \longrightarrow (CH_3)_2C{=}CH_2$

(c) 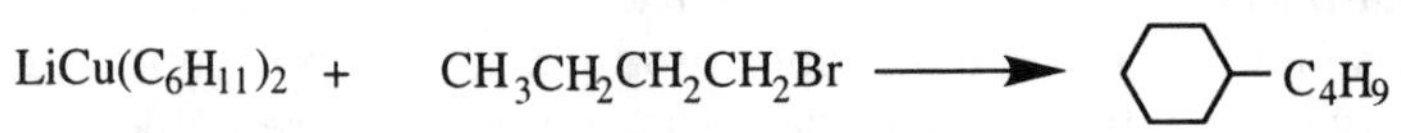
$LiCu(C_6H_{11})_2$ + $CH_3CH_2CH_2CH_2Br$
C_4H_9

3.20 All of these syntheses are of alkanes. Therefore, a synthesis must involve the joining together of two alkyl groups. One alkyl group can arise from an alkyl bromide. The other can arise in the form of an organometallic reagent, effectively supplying a carbanion which can carry out an S_N2 reaction on the alkyl bromide.

(a) 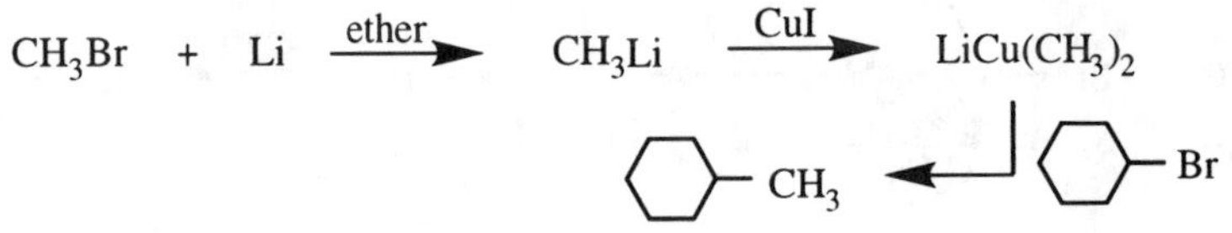
CH_3Br + Li
ether
CH_3Li
CuI
$LiCu(CH_3)_2$
CH_3
Br

(b) There are several possible combinations of organocuprate reagents and alkyl halides that could be employed in this synthesis, only one of which is shown below. In choosing your synthesis, draw a dotted line through the desired product structure to identify the two necessary fragments which must be joined together.

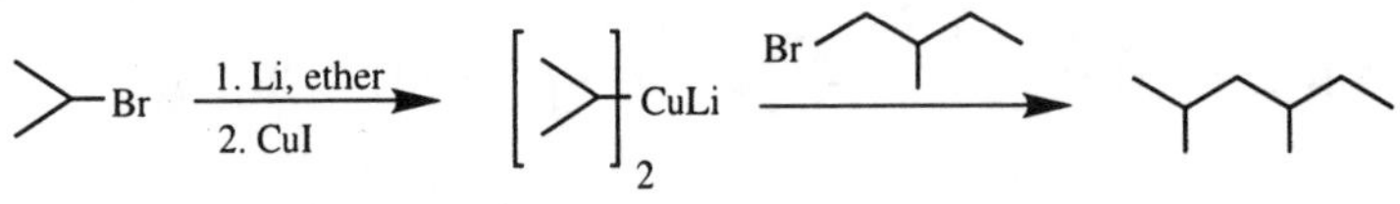
Br
1. Li, ether
2. CuI
CuLi
2
Br

(c) 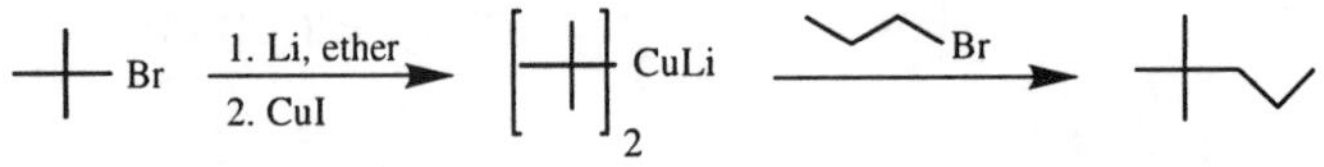
Br
1. Li, ether
2. CuI
CuLi
2
Br

3.21 (a) *cis*-1-fluoro-2-iodocyclopropane; (b) *trans*-1,4-dibromocyclohexane; (c) 2,4-dichlorohexane; (d) 2,2-dichloro-3-methylbutane

3.22

(a) $Cl_2FC\text{-}CH_2CH_2\text{-}Br$ (b) 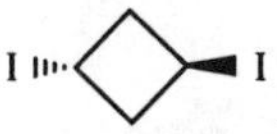 (c) 

(d) 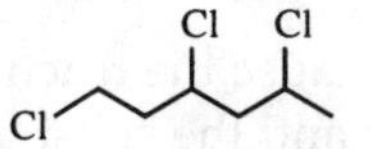 (e) $CH_3CHClCH_3$ (f) $(CH_3)_3C\text{-}F$

3.23 The following compounds have a stereocenter with its position as indicated: 2-iodohexane (C_2); 1,2-dichlorocyclohexane (C_1 and C_2); 3-fluoro-2-methylpentane (C_3); 3,4-dimethylheptane (C_3 and C_4).

3.24 The only chiral bromobutane is $CH_3CHBrCH_2CH_3$.

3.25 (a) Br- > CH_3O- > CH_3- > H-
(b) -NH_2 > $ClCH_2$- > CH_3CH_2- > CH_3-
(c) HO- > -CHO > $HOCH_2$- > CH_3CH_2-

3.26 (a) $CH_3CH_2CH_2CH_2I$; (b) $CH_3CH_2CH_2CH_2OH$; (c) $CH_3CH_2CH_2CH_2CN$; (d) $CH_3CH_2CH_2CH_2OCH_3$.

3.27

(a) 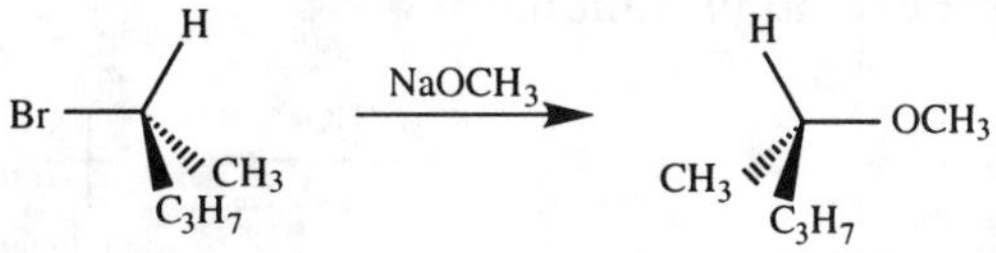
Br
H
CH3
C3H7
NaOCH3
H
OCH3
CH3
C3H7

(b) 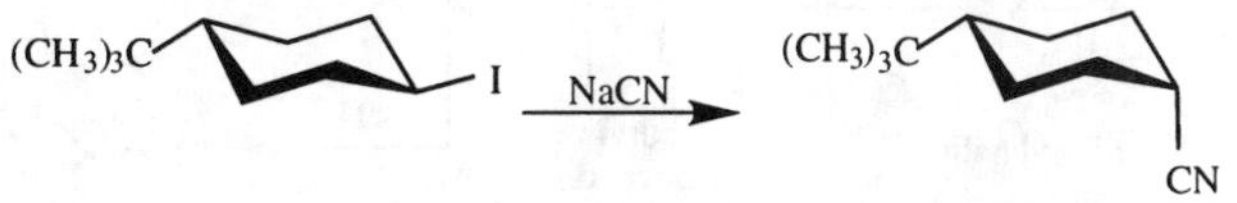
(CH3)3C
I
NaCN
(CH3)3C
CN

3.28 In each of the structures given envision what portion can be obtained readily as a nucleophile. Reaction of this nucleophile with an alkyl halide will produce the desired product by substitution.

(a) $CH_3CH_2CH_2$-Br and NaOH produces $CH_3CH_2CH_2OH$
(b) $(CH_3)_2CHCH_2CH_2$-I and $NaSCH_3$ produces $(CH_3)_2CHCH_2CH_2SCH_3$
(c) CH_3CH_2-Br and $NaOCH_3$ produces $CH_3CH_2OCH_3$

3.29 (a) The sodium hydroxide reaction would proceed faster because it is the stronger nucleophile.

(b) The sodium iodide reaction would proceed faster because it is the stronger nucleophile.

(c) Using two molar equivalents would be faster because the reaction is second order, depending on the concentration of the nucleophile and the substrate.

(d) The faster reaction would be with *n*-butyl bromide because primary halides react faster than tertiary halides in an S_N2 reaction due to lower steric effects.

(e) 1-Bromobutane would react faster (in the S_N2 reaction) because of lower steric effects.

(f) 1-Iodobutane would react faster because the iodide ion is a better leaving group than the chloride ion.

(g) Sodium methoxide would react faster because it is the strongest nucleophile.

3.30 Solvolysis of a tertiary alkyl halide involves a S_N1 reaction and a carbocation intermediate. The ratio of the products (isobutylene and *t*-butyl alcohol) is determined by the rate of their formation from the *t*-butyl cation. Since the *t*-butyl bromide, chloride, and iodide all form the same *t*-butyl carbocation intermediate, the product ratio should be identical from each tertiary alkyl halide.

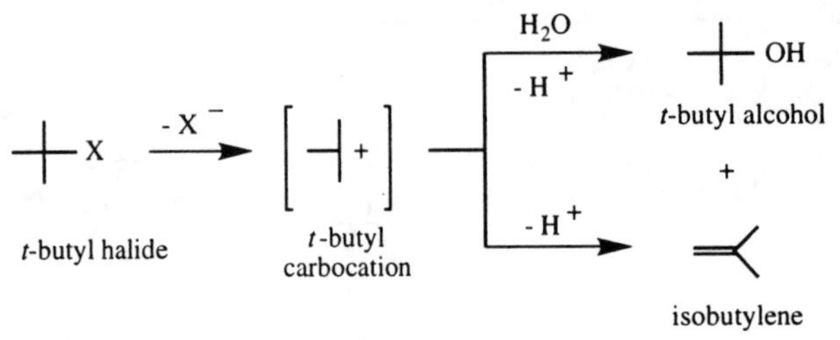
X
- X⁻
+
H_2O
- H⁺
OH
t-butyl alcohol
+
- H⁺
t-butyl halide
t-butyl
carbocation
isobutylene

3.31

(a) 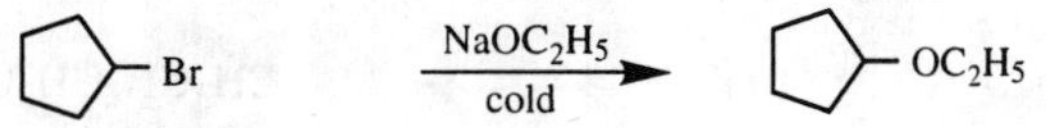
Br
NaOC2H5
cold
OC2H5

cyclopentyl bromide

(b) 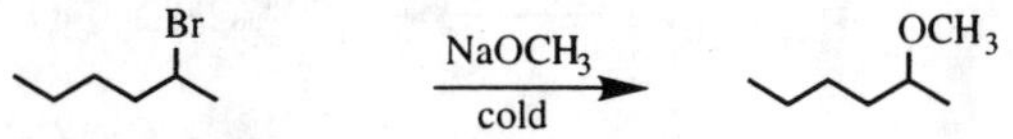
Br
NaOCH3
cold
OCH3

2-bromohexane

(c) $CH_3CH_2CH(CH_3)CH_2Br \xrightarrow{NaCN} CH_3CH_2CH(CH_3)CH_2CN$

1-bromo-2-methylbutane

(d) 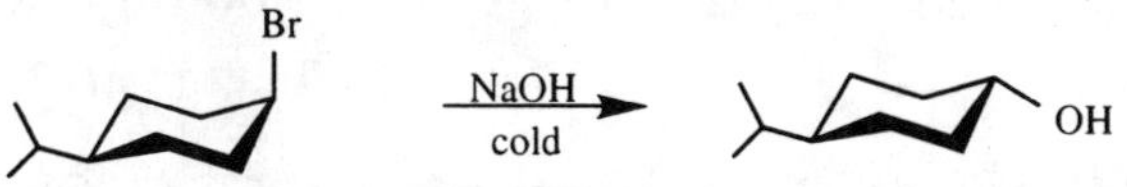
Br
NaOH
cold
OH

cis-1-bromo-4-isopropylcyclohexane

3.32

(a) 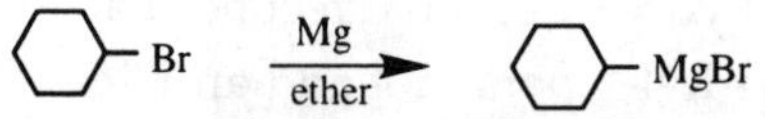
Br
Mg
ether
MgBr

(b) 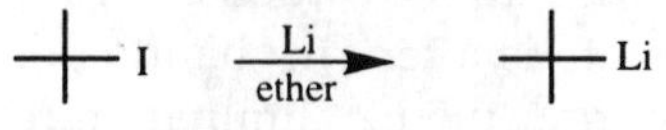
I
Li
ether
Li

(c) 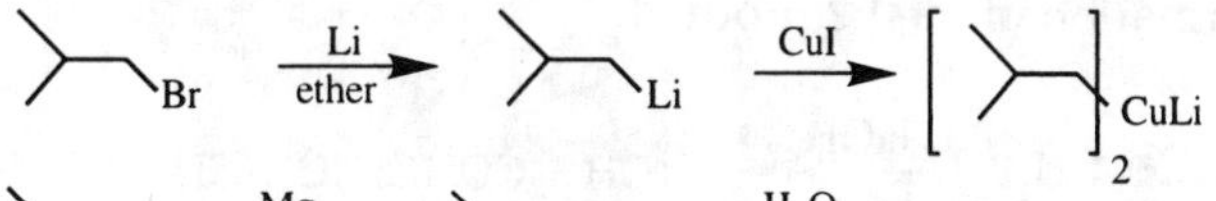
Br
Li
ether
Li
CuI
CuLi
2

(d) 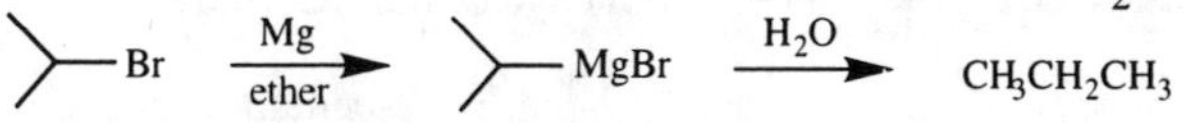
Br
Mg
ether
MgBr
H2O
CH3CH2CH3

(e) 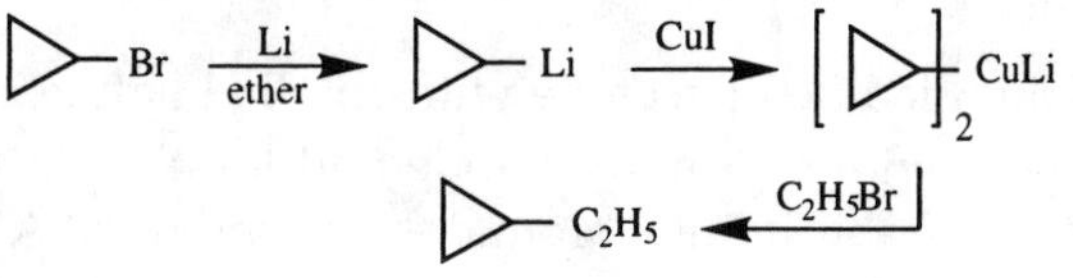
Br
Li
ether
Li
CuI
CuLi
2
C2H5Br
C2H5

3.33 (a) identical compounds; (b) enantiomers; (c) enantiomers; (d) enantiomers; (e) enantiomers.

3.34

(c) 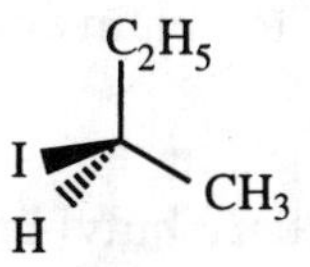
C2H5
I
H
CH3

(d) 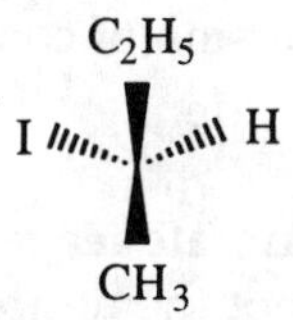
C2H5
I
H
CH3

(e) 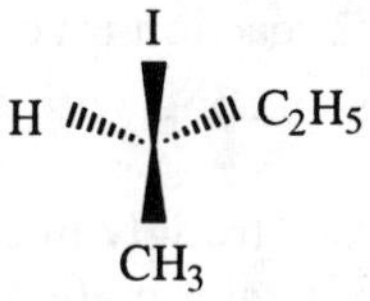
I
H
C2H5
CH3

3.35

(a) $CH_3CH_2CH_2I$ + CH_3O^- ⟶ $CH_3CH_2CH_2OCH_3$

(b) $(CH_3)_3CO^-$ + CH_3CH_2Br ⟶ $(CH_3)_3C\text{-}O\text{-}CH_2CH_3$

(c) 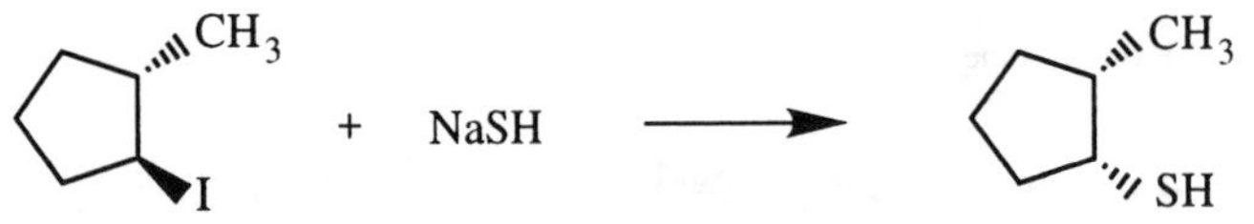

(d) *S*-2-iodopentane + NaOH ⟶ (*R*) $CH_3CHOHCH_2CH_2CH_3$
R-2-pentanol

(e) $(CH_3)_3C\text{-}I$ + NaOH ⟶ $(CH_3)_3C\text{-}OH$ + $(CH_3)_2C{=}CH_2$
Minor major

3.36 The strong nucleophile, sodium hydroxide, can effect both an S_N2 reaction (by attacking the tertiary carbon) to form 2-methyl-2-pentanol and an E2 reaction (by attacking a β-hydrogen - a hydrogen on a carbon next to the carbon carrying the bromine) to form 2-methyl-2-pentene. Since the substrate is a tertiary halide both reactions will occur but the major product will be the alkene from the E2 elimination reaction. The use of heat will maximize formation of the E2 product.

$$(CH_3)_2CBrCH_2CH_2CH_3 \xrightarrow[\text{heat}]{\text{NaOH}} (CH_3)_2COHCH_2CH_2CH_3 + (CH_3)_2C{=}CHCH_2CH_3$$

2-methyl-2-pentanol 2-methyl-2-pentene

3.37 The reaction of sodium iodide in acetone with an alkyl halide is a S_N2 reaction which proceeds most rapidly with a primary halide and least rapidly with a tertiary halide. Thus, compound B is probably *n*-butyl bromide and compound A is probably t-butyl bromide.

3.38 (a) Use of ethoxide anion, a strong nucleophile, with *t*-butyl bromide would effect mainly an E2 elimination reaction, producing isobutylene as the major product, rather than the desired S_N2 product.

(b) Since the S_N2 reaction involves an inversion of configuration, to obtain an equatorial alcohol requires starting with an axial iodide.

(c) Reaction of the strongly nucleophilic cuprate reagent with tertiary butyl bromide would effect mainly an E2 elimination reaction, not the desired substitution reaction.

3.39 (a) (*R*)-2-iodobutane; (b) (*S*)-2-chloro-2-iodobutane; (c) (*R*)-2-aminopentane; (d) (*S*)-2-fluoropentane.

3.40 (a) This transformation requires a substitution of hydroxide for bromide. Since the starting material is a primary alkyl bromide the S_N2 reaction should be used. Conditions should be warm sodium hydroxide in DMSO solvent.

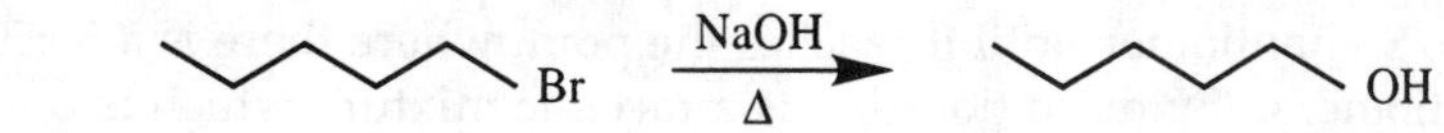

Br
NaOH
Δ
OH

(b) This transformation also calls for replacing a bromide with a hydroxide. However, since the starting material is a tertiary halide, there is risk of a competing elimination reaction. Therefore, it is necessary to use a mild nucleophile (water) under moderate temperature conditions. Water also could be the solvent (that is, carry out a solvolysis reaction). In spite of these preferred conditions, some by-product (isobutylene) will be formed.

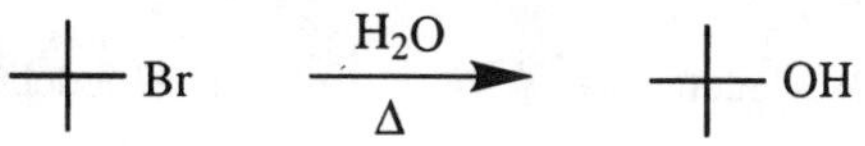

Br
H₂O
Δ
OH

(c) This transformation involves replacing a bromide with a methoxy group. However, since the substrate is a tertiary halide, use of the strong nucleophile sodium methoxide would lead to almost exclusively elimination, not substitution. Therefore, a very mild nucleophile (methanol) should be used and it could be employed in a methanol solution (that is, a solvolysis reaction).

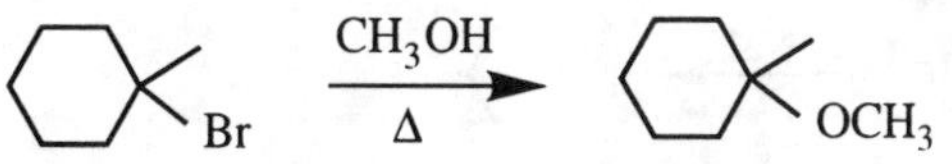

Br
CH₃OH
Δ
OCH₃

3.41 Sodium methoxide is a much stronger nucleophile than is methanol. Since cyclohexyl bromide is a secondary halide it can be substituted or eliminated readily, depending on the choice of reaction conditions. The elimination reaction to form cyclohexene is favored by stronger reaction conditions (high temperatures and strong nucleophiles). Therefore, use of heat and the stronger nucleophile sodium methoxide will afford mainly cyclohexene via E2 elimination.

3.42 The substituent priorities are **a** = COOH (with its C=O structure), **b** = $(CH_3)_2CHCH_2C_6H_4$ (with its C=C structure), **c** = CH_3, and **d** = H.

(*R*)-Ibuprofen

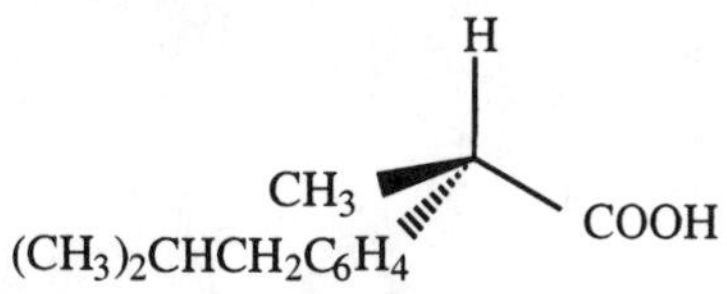

H
CH₃
COOH
(CH₃)₂CHCH₂C₆H₄

3.43 The reaction is an S_N2 reaction with iodide serving both as a good nucleophile and as a good leaving group. Every time an iodide anion carries out an S_N2 reaction on the optically active R-enantiomer the constitution of the substrate is unchanged (iodide replacing iodide) but an *S* enantiomer is formed. As this process proceeds *R* enantiomer gradually is converted into S-enantiomer until it reaches the point where there is a 50:50 mixture of the *R* and *S* enantiomers. By definition that is a racemic mixture which is optically inactive. Any further S_N2 reactions are equally likely to involve the *R* and the *S* enantiomer, so the 50:50 mixture persists.

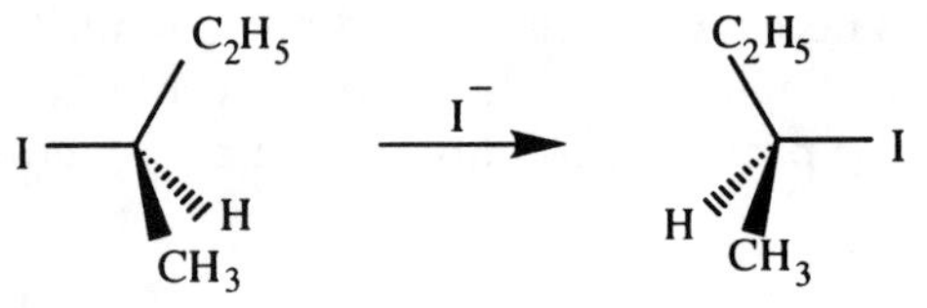
C2H5
I
H
CH3
I−
C2H5
I
H
CH3

(*R*)-2-iodobutane (*S*)-2-iodobutane

3.44 To solve these problems draw the desired product, and then draw a dotted line through the bond to be formed. Then identify a reaction to form that bond from an alkyl bromide.

(a) 
Br
1. Li, ether
2. CuI
CuLi
2
Br

(b) 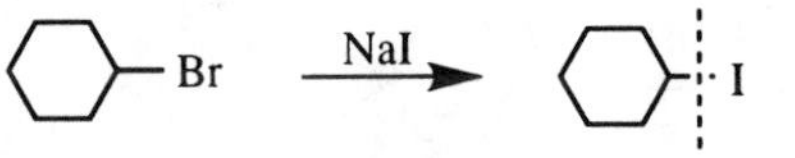
Br
NaI
I

(c) 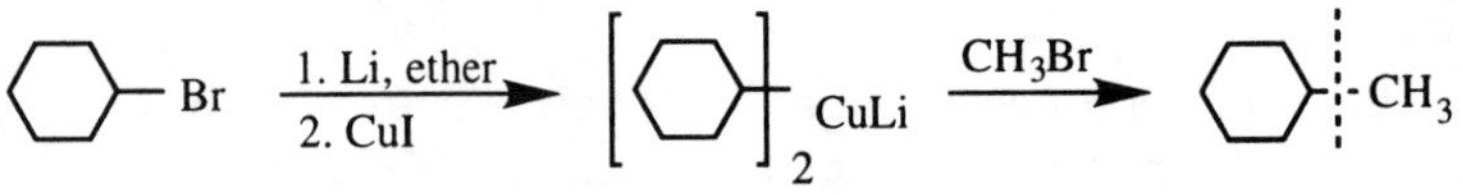
Br
1. Li, ether
2. CuI
CuLi
2
CH3Br
CH3

(d) 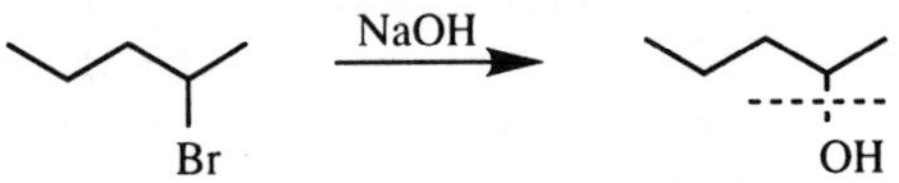
Br
NaOH
OH

(e) 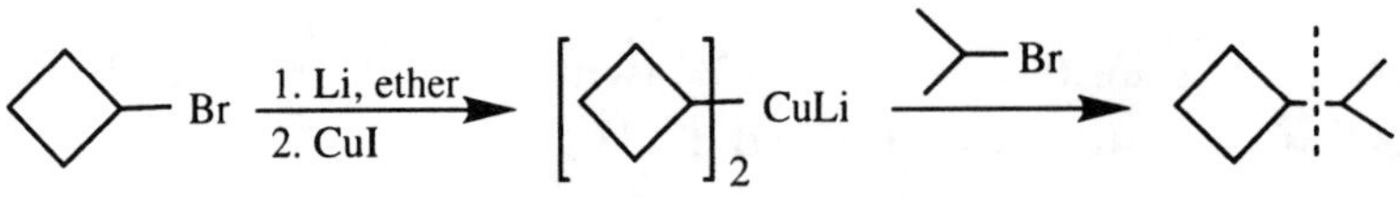
Br
1. Li, ether
2. CuI
CuLi
2
Br

3.45 Isomer D is a constitutional isomer of A, B, and C. The latter three are configurational isomers. B and C are a pair of enantiomers (they are called optical isomers - see Chapter 17).

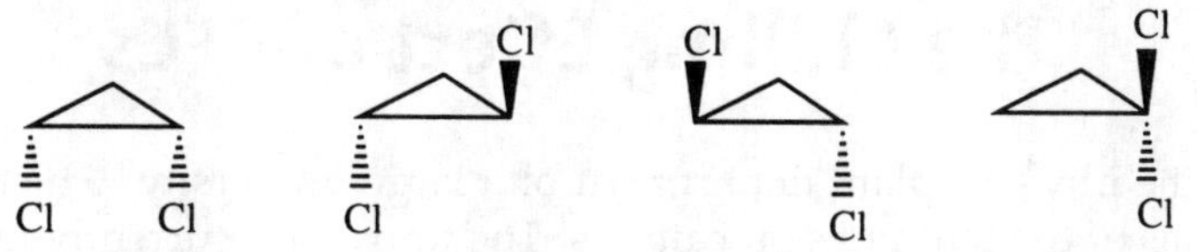

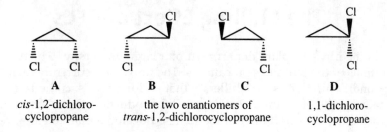

A *cis*-1,2-dichloro-cyclopropane

B **C** the two enantiomers of *trans*-1,2-dichlorocyclopropane

D 1,1-dichloro-cyclopropane

3.46

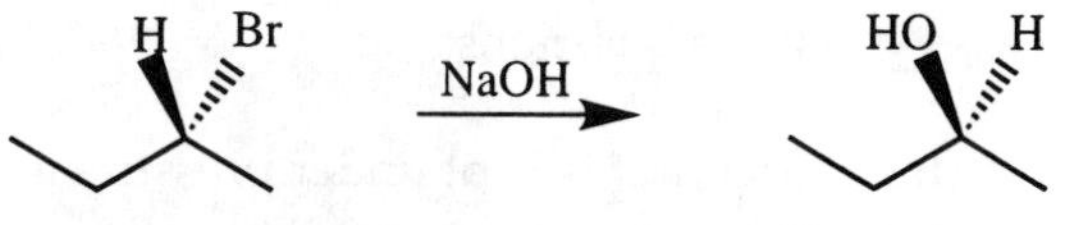
H
Br
NaOH
HO
H

(*R*)-2-bromobutane (*S*)-2-butanol

3.47 The initial solution would appear to be simply substitution of the alkyl bromide with sodium hydroxide. However, an S_N2 reaction would produce (*S*)-2-butanol by inversion of configuration as indicated in problem 3.46. Since the task is to carry out a substitution process with overall retention of configuration, the only alternative is to carry out *two* inversion reactions (*R* to *S* to *R*). Iodide ion is an excellent nucleophile and will replace bromide, resulting in inversion. Then, substitution of the alkyl iodide with hydroxide will accomplish a second inversion, resulting in overall retention of configuration in the alkyl group.

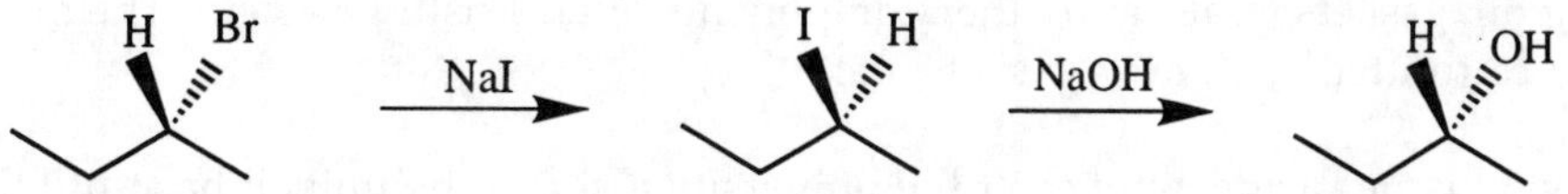
H
Br
NaI
I
H
NaOH
H
OH

(*R*)-2-bromobutane (*S*)-2-iodobutane (*R*)-2-butanol

VI. Conceptual Problem

The Chilling Effect of CFCs

You work in the physical plant department of a large university, which oversees the day-to-day operations of the buildings on campus. The university currently maintains 14 large-scale air-conditioning units (or"chillers") that still use CFCs as the refrigerant. These units were installed well before the 1996 ban on CFC production. Some are as little as 10 years old, others are much older. It is part of your job to help develop a plan to either retrofit or replace all the CFC units, as well as establish guidelines for future purchases of refrigeration equipment. A member of the budget committee comes to you because she is concerned about the potential costs of replacing so many units. She asks you these questions:

- Since a cooling unit is sealed (the refrigerant is kept under pressure in a sealed system), why does the continued use of CFCs pose any risk to the environment?
  - Ans: The problem is that it is hard to maintain a system at zero emission when it is under pressure. The pressure causes the seals to wear out allowing CFCs to slowly escape into the atmosphere. That's why periodically refrigerant has to be added to such systems.

- Can't the university simply buy a different refrigerant to replace the CFCs and use it in the existing units? What would be the concern associated with such refrigerant replacement?
  - Ans: There are several new refrigerants available and others being developed but none have exactly the same properties as CFCs. First, you have to consider the pressure of the system. For example HFC-134a is designed for medium pressure systems and HCFC-123 is designed for low pressure systems. Second, consider whether the new refrigerant will be compatible with the lubricating oil, gaskets, seals, and other components of an existing system. The existing units will have to be retrofitted with new gaskets, etc.

- Environmental issues aside, why can't the university just run the units it has until they are no longer operational and replace them on an as-needed basis? Wouldn't this be the most cost-efficient plan?
  - Ans: Not really. First there will be gradual leakage no matter how well the units are maintained and so more CFC will have to be purchased as a replacement. Given the fact that there are dwindling stocks means that it will become increasingly expensive. Also, older units generally are more expensive to service and they tend to be less energy efficient, so there is money to be saved in the cost of running new units once they have been purchased.

- After answering the questions above, you describe a broad outline of your plan to replace the oldest units first, maintaining some of the younger CFC units for a longer time. What can you do to keep these CFC units as environmentally safe as possible?
  - Ans: You can develop a schedule for leak testing, making sure that the service contractor keeps the systems running efficiently. You can also have a system for capturing emissions when the system is"purged" and then cleaned. Finally, as older units are replaced the university can salvage the remaining CFCs for use in retained units.

CHAPTER 4

Alcohols

I. Textbook Chapter Contents

This chapter introduces the family of compounds known as alcohols (alkanols by the IUPAC system), which contain the -OH (hydroxyl) functional group. The reactions and preparation of alcohols are described. This chapter also introduces compounds known as carbohydrates (also known as sugars or saccharides) as a biologically important example of alcohols.

II. Learning Objectives

- Know the IUPAC nomenclature of alkanols and the common names of simple alcohols. Be able to recognize a thiol.
- Distinguish between primary, secondary, and tertiary alcohols.
- Understand the nature and effects of hydrogen bonding in alcohols.
- Recognize the fact that alcohols are weak Brønsted acids and can be converted into alkoxides.
- Know how to convert an alcohol into an alkyl halide using mineral acid and understand the mechanism and limitations of this conversion. Recognize an oxonium ion.
- Know how to convert an alcohol into an alkyl halide using thionyl chloride and pyridine, and understand the mechanism of the reaction which occurs with inversion of configuration.
- Know how to convert an alcohol to an alkyl halide with overall retention of configuration, utilizing the conversion of an alcohol to a tosylate ester.
- Write equations for the oxidation of primary and secondary alcohols to aldehydes and ketones, respectively.
- Write equations for the preparation of alcohols from alkyl halides.
- Become familiar with carbohydrate terminology, including pyranose and furanose, aldo- and keto- sugars, monosaccharides, disaccharides, and polysaccharides.
- Recognize the open-chain and two anomeric forms of glucose.
- Recognize the difference between starch and cellulose and the hydrolysis of both into glucose.
- Grasp the concept of retrosynthesis and its application to the conversion of one compound into another and for devising schemes for multi-step syntheses.

III. Glossary

alcohol a family of compounds containing the hydroxyl (-OH) functional group

aldehyde a family of compounds containing a carbonyl group (C=O) whose carbon is attached to at least one hydrogen

aldose a monosaccharide containing an aldehyde group

alkanol the IUPAC family name for an alcohol

alkoxide the oxyanion resulting from the removal of a proton from an alcohol

amylose a linear polymer of α-glucose in which the glucose units are connected via glycoside linkages from carbon 1 of one glucose to carbon 4 of another

amylopectin a polymer of α-glucose which contains an amylose backbone with additional glucose units branched from carbon 6 to carbon 1

anomeric carbon the hemiacetal carbon in a carbohydrate, about which two configurations may exist in equilibrium

blood sugar an alternate name for glucose

carbohydrate a polyhydroxy aldehyde or ketone which generally is naturally occurring

carboxylic acids a family of compounds with the general formula RCOOH

cellulose a polymer of β-glucose containing glycoside linkages from carbon 1 of one glucose to carbon 4 of another

2-deoxyribose an aldopentose without a hydroxyl group on carbon 2

disaccharide a carbohydrate which can be hydrolyzed to two monosaccharide molecules

Fischer projection a line drawing of the structure of a compound in two dimensions implying the three-dimensional structure of the compound; horizontal lines represent bonds projecting above the paper and vertical lines represent bonds projecting below the paper

fructose a ketohexose of formula $C_6H_{12}O_6$, specifically 1,3,4,5,6-pentahydroxy-2-hexanone

furanose a five-membered hemiacetal form of a monosaccharide

glucose an aldohexose of formula $C_6H_{12}O_6$, specifically 2,3,4,5,6-pentahydroxyhexanal; it is also called blood sugar

glycogen a polymer of α-glucose involving glycoside linkages between carbon 1 of one glucose and carbon 4 of another, plus additional glucose units linked to carbon 6

glycoside an acetal of a carbohydrate

hydrogen bond a weak association between a hydrogen, which is attached to an electronegative atom, and an electronegative atom with unshared electrons

hydrophilic a species which is attracted to or dissolves in water

hydrophobic a species which is repelled by and does not dissolve in water

hydroxyl group the -O–H group

inductive effect the relative electron-attracting or electron-donating effect exerted by a substituent as the result of electronegativity differences

ketone a family of compounds containing a carbonyl group (C=O) whose carbon is attached to two other carbon atoms

ketose a monosaccharide containing a ketone group

lactose a disaccharide comprised of a glucose unit joined to a galactose unit through a glycoside linkage; 4-O-(α-D-galactopyranosyl)-α-D-glucopyranose

maltose a disaccharide comprised of one glucose unit joined to a second glucose unit through a glycoside linkage; 4-O-(α-D-glucopyranosyl)-α-D-glucopyranose

monosaccharide a simple carbohydrate which cannot be hydrolyzed further

oxidation an increase in the oxygen content of an organic species, or a decrease in its hydrogen content

oxonium ion an oxygen atom with three groups covalently attached, making the oxygen atom positively charged

polymer a macromolecule containing many units of a simple compound (monomer) joined together

polysaccharide a carbohydrate which can be hydrolyzed to produce a large number of molecules of a monosaccharide; a polymer of a saccharide

pyranose a six-membered hemiacetal form of a monosaccharide

reduction a decrease in the oxygen content of an organic species or an increase in its hydrogen content

retrosynthesis a mental process for analyzing and solving synthesis problems. It involves working backwards from product to possible precursors in a stepwise manner

ribose an aldopentose

saccharide an alternate term for a carbohydrate arising from their sweet taste

starch a mixture of amylase and amylopectin, both of which are polymers of α-glucose

sucrose a disaccharide comprised of a glucose unit joined to a fructose unit through a glycoside linkage; α-D-glucopyranosyl-α-D-fructofuranoside

sugar an alternate term for a saccharide

thiol sulfur analog of an alcohol

tosylate an ester (TsOR) formed by reaction between p-toluenesulfonyl chloride, abbreviated TsCl, and an alcohol (ROH)

IV. Summary of Reactions of Alcohols

V. Summary of Preparation of Alcohols

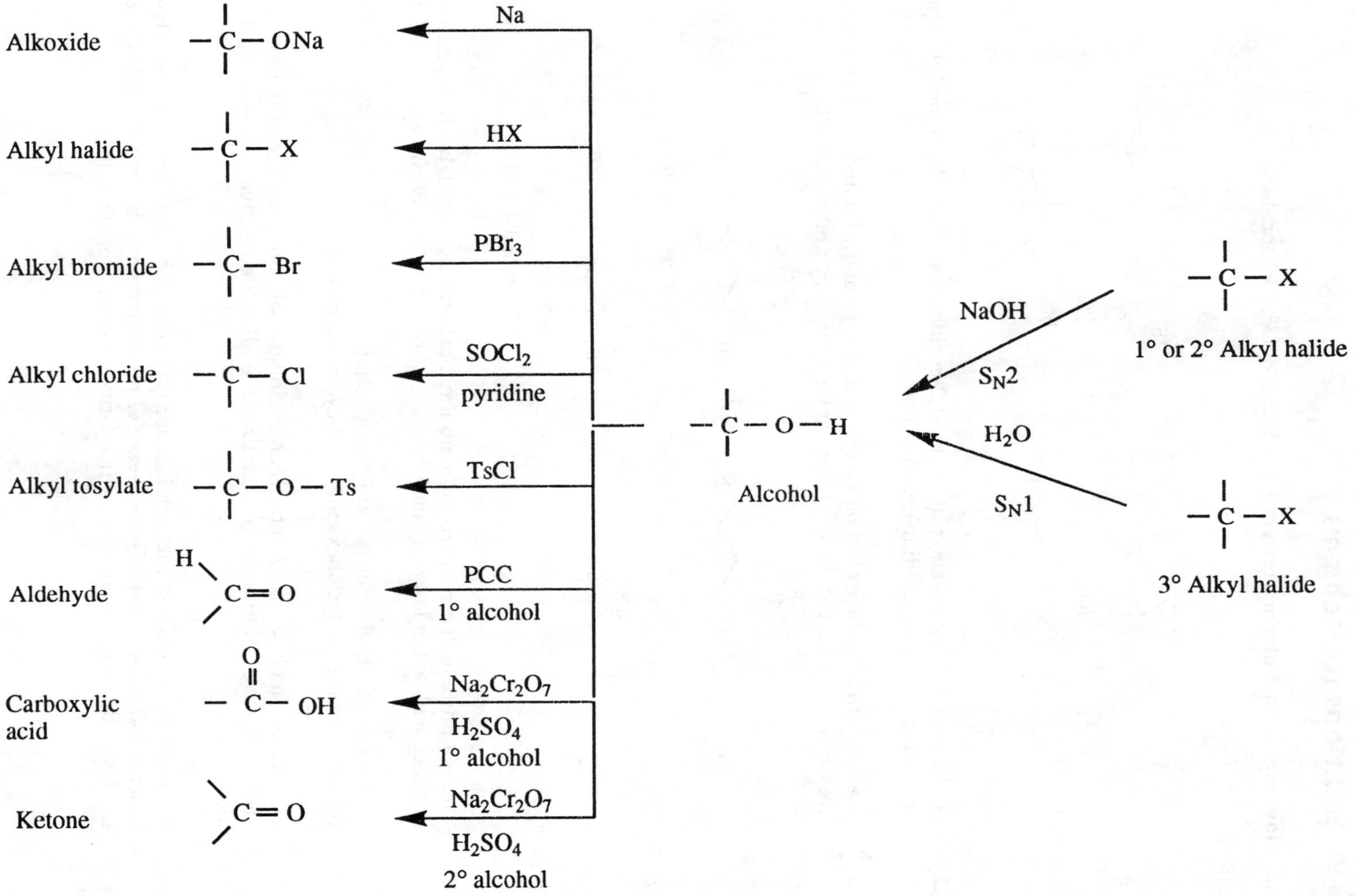
Alkoxide
Alkyl halide
Alkyl bromide
Alkyl chloride
Alkyl tosylate
Aldehyde
Carboxylic acid
Ketone
Na
HX
PBr_3
$SOCl_2$ pyridine
TsCl
PCC 1° alcohol
$Na_2Cr_2O_7$ H_2SO_4 1° alcohol
$Na_2Cr_2O_7$ H_2SO_4 2° alcohol
Alcohol
NaOH S_N2
H_2O S_N1
1° or 2° Alkyl halide
3° Alkyl halide

VI. Solutions to Problems

For "**How to Solve a Problem,**" review pages 122, 128, 133, 136, and 143)

4.1

(a) 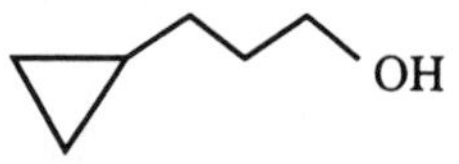
(b) 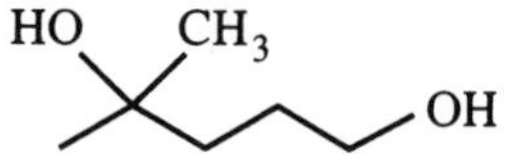

(c) 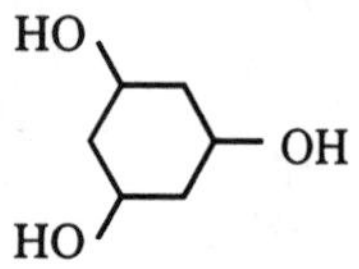
(d) 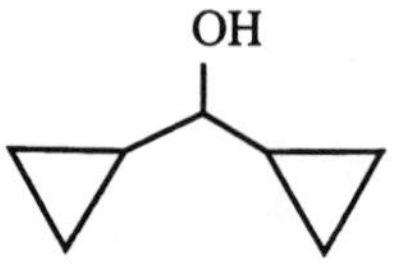

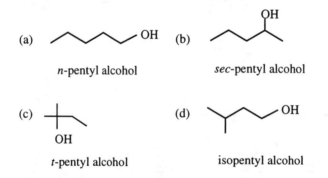

4.2 (a) 2,2-dimethyl-1-propanol; (b) *trans*-1,2-cyclobutane-diol; (c) 3-methyl-3-pentanol; (d) 2-propanol; (e) 2,6-dimethyl-4-heptanol

4.3 The structures for these alcohols can be deduced from the limited number of possibilities for five carbons, and using the specific meaning of the key prefix symbols.

(a) 

n-pentyl alcohol

(b) 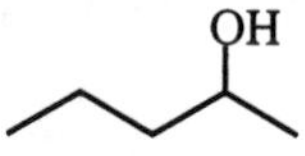

sec-pentyl alcohol

(c) 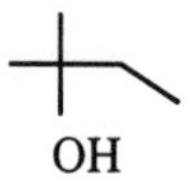

t-pentyl alcohol

(d) 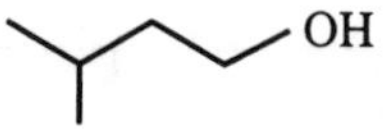

isopentyl alcohol

4.4 Compounds which can hydrogen bond the most effectively will be the highest boiling. Alkanes will be the lowest boiling because of only van der Waal's attractive forces.

(a) ethane < ethyl chloride < ethyl alcohol
(b) cyclohexane < cyclohexanol < 1,2-cyclohexanediol

4.5 (a) cyclohexanol < 2,2,6,6-tetrachlorocyclohexanol: the presence of the four highly electronegative chlorine atoms stabilizes the alkoxide relative to the unsubstituted alkoxide.

(b) isopropyl alcohol < methanol: isopropyl alcohol can be viewed as a methanol carrying two methyl substituents. The presence of the two methyl substituents helps to destabilize the alkoxide anion because of their relative electron donating ability.

4.6

(a) $(CH_3)_2CHOH + K \longrightarrow (CH_3)_2CHO^- K^+ + 1/2\ H_2$

(b) $CH_3CH_2CH_2OH + K \longrightarrow CH_3CH_2CH_2O^- K^+ + 1/2\ H_2$

(c)

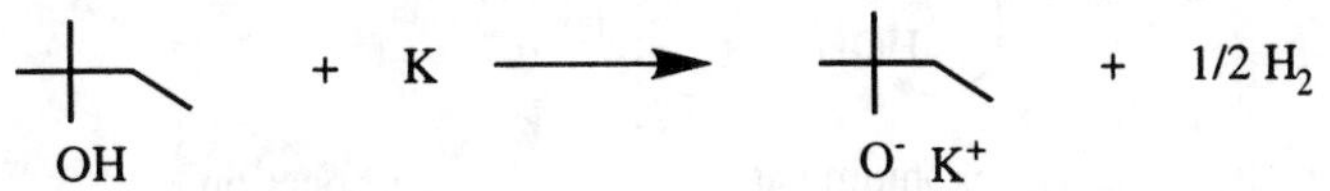

4.7 The most acidic alcohol is ethanol, the one carrying the fewest electron donating alkyl groups on the carbon which also carries the alkoxide group.

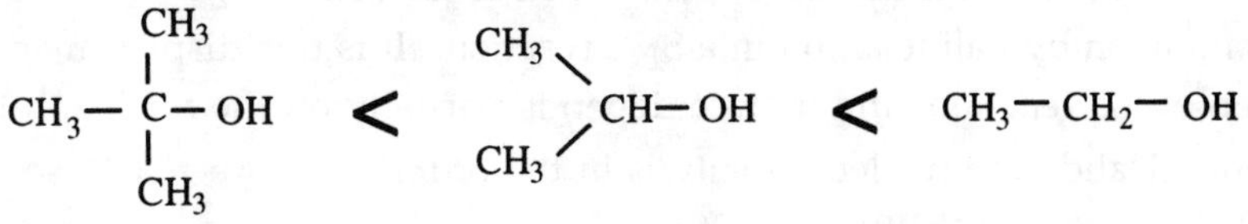

2-methyl-2-propanol (*t*-butyl alcohol) < 2-propanol (isopropyl alcohol) < ethanol (ethyl alcohol)

4.8 The order of basicity of the alkoxides is the opposite of the order of acidity of the corresponding alcohols. The strongest base is derived from the weakest acid.

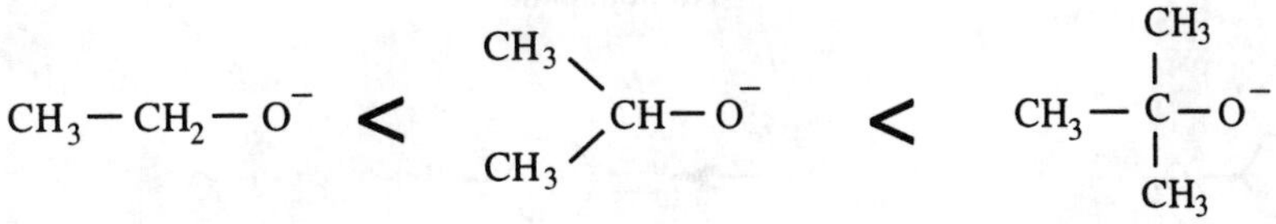

ethoxide < 2-propoxide (isopropoxide) < 2-methyl-2-propoxide (*t*-butoxide)

4.9 The reactants are sodium ethoxide, a strong nucleophile/base, and methyl bromide, a compound containing a good leaving group (bromide). The nucleophile would be expected to attack the carbon carrying the leaving group, thereby effecting an S_N2 substitution reaction. Ethoxide therefore replaces bromide. The product is ethyl methyl ether and the by-product is sodium bromide.

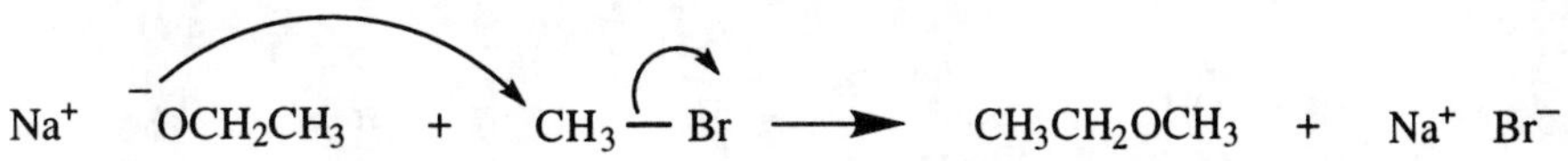

ethyl methyl ether

4.10 2-Methyl-2-butanol is a tertiary alcohol, and in the presence of a hydrogen halide acid (HX) forms a tertiary carbocation. The cation then reacts with halide anion in the solution to form the tertiary alkyl halide. The slow step (i.e., the rate-controlling step) in the reaction is the oxonium ion dissociating to the carbocation and this step is exactly the same regardless of which acid was used. Thus the overall rates of the reaction (which cannot be faster than the slowest step) are identical for the three acids, HCl, HBr, and HI.

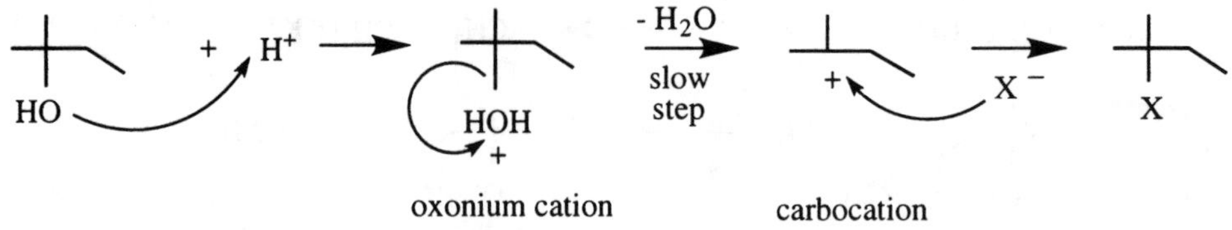
HO
H+
HOH
- H2O
slow
step
X
X
oxonium cation
carbocation

4.11 2-Methyl-1-butanol is a primary alcohol and conversion to the alkyl halide using HX does not involve formation of a carbocation (because of the relative instability of a primary carbocation). Instead, the alcohol is protonated as usual but H_2O must be displaced from the oxonium ion by halide anion in a S_N2 reaction. It is this displacement which is the slow step of the reaction, and its rate depends partially on the nucleophilicity of the halide ion. Halide ion nucleophilicity is in the order $I^- > Br^- > Cl^-$, so the overall reaction rates are in the same sequence.

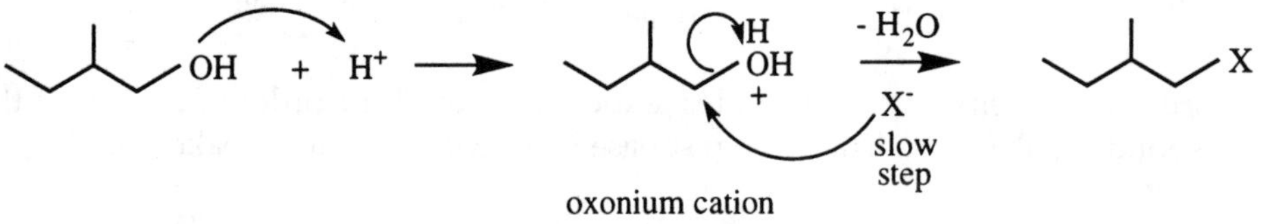
OH
H+
H
OH
- H2O
X-
slow
step
X
oxonium cation

4.12

(a) 
OH
HBr
Br
H2O

(b) 
OH
HBr
Br
H2O

(c) 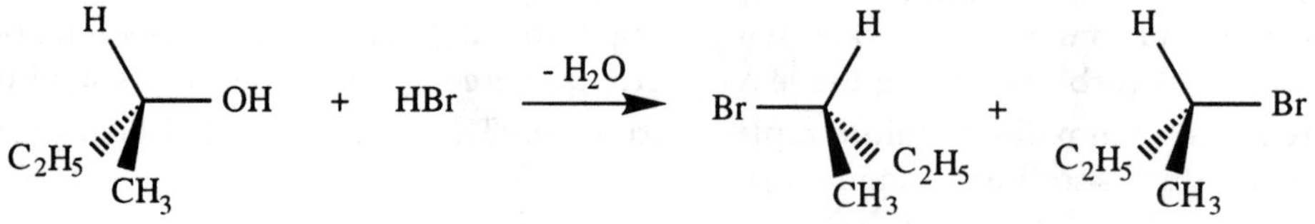
H
OH
C2H5
CH3
HBr
- H2O
Br
H
C2H5
CH3
H
Br
C2H5
CH3

4.13

(a) 
OH
HBr
Br
H2O

(b) 
OH
HCl
Cl
H2O

(c) 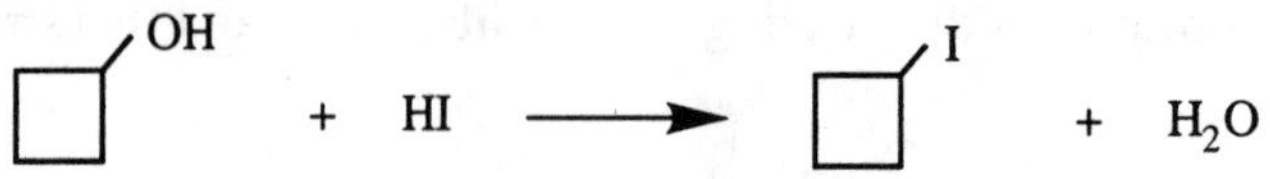
OH
HI
I
H2O

4.14

(a) 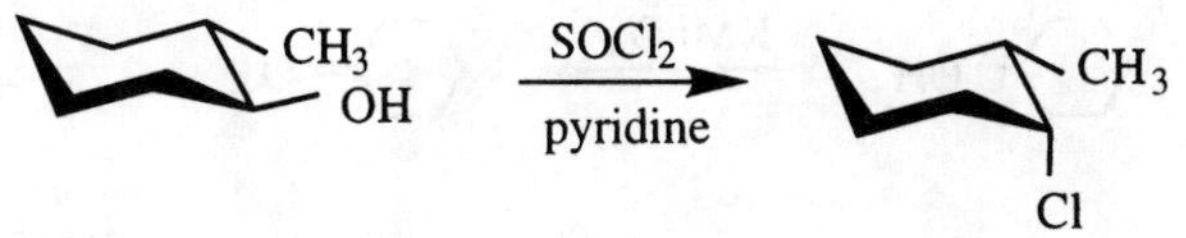
CH3
OH
SOCl2
pyridine
CH3
Cl

(b) 
OH
HBr
Br

(c) 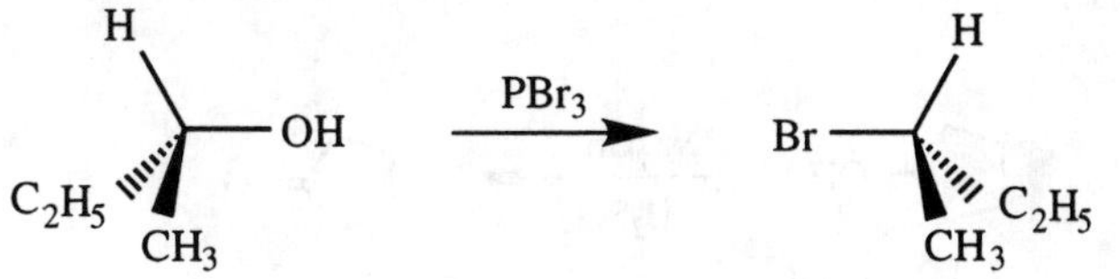
H
OH
C2H5
CH3
PBr3
H
Br
C2H5
CH3

4.15 (*S*)-2-butanol can be converted in a single step into (*R*)-2-chlorobutane using the stereospecific reagent thionyl chloride, a reaction which proceeds with inversion of configuration. No single-step reagent accomplishes retention of configuration in such a conversion and therefore the *R* alcohol cannot be converted into the *R* chloride in a single step. Thus, the *R* alcohol must be first converted into the *S* alcohol by a two step process involving tosylation (with no change in configuration) followed by a S_N2 reaction with hydroxide (with inversion of configuration). Then the same $SOCl_2$ reaction can be employed. Overall two inversions will be accomplished, leading to overall retention of configuration.

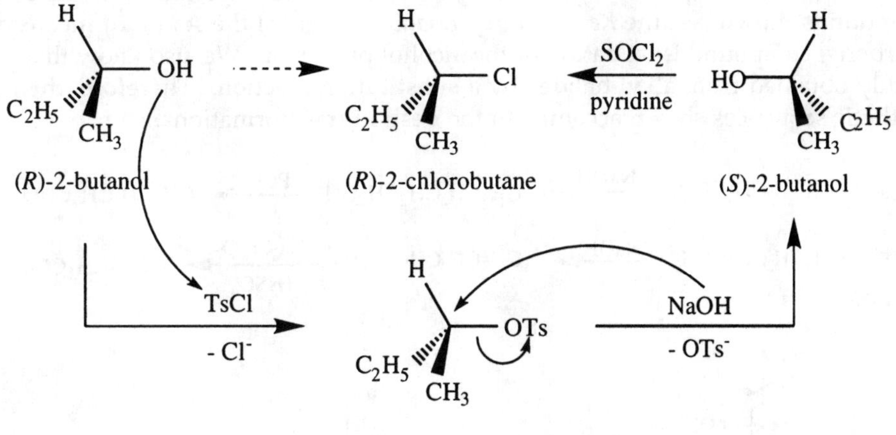
(R)-2-butanol
(R)-2-chlorobutane
(S)-2-butanol
SOCl2
pyridine
TsCl
- Cl-
NaOH
- OTs-
OTs

4.16

(a) 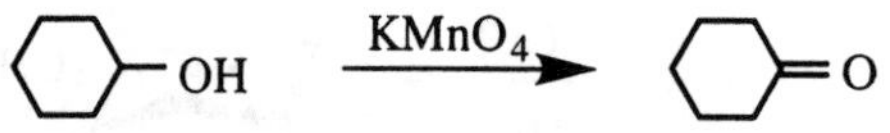
OH
KMnO4
O

(b) $CH_3CH_2CH_2CH_2OH \xrightarrow{PCC} CH_3CH_2CH_2CHO$

(c) 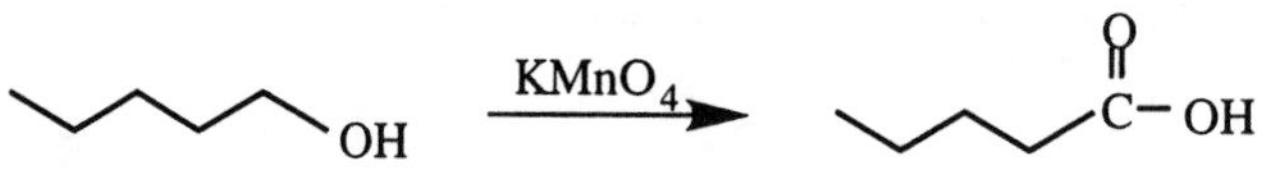
OH
KMnO4
C−OH
O

4.17

(a) 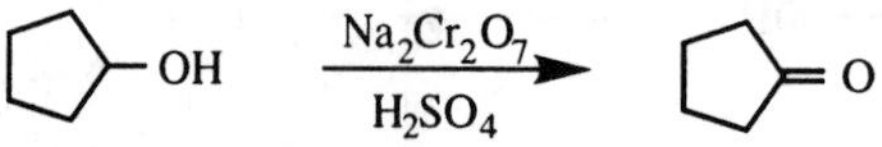
OH
Na2Cr2O7
H2SO4
O

cyclopentanol

(b) $(CH_3)_2CHCHOHCH_2CH_3 \xrightarrow{KMnO_4} (CH_3)_2CHCOCH_2CH_3$

2-methyl-3-pentanol

(c) 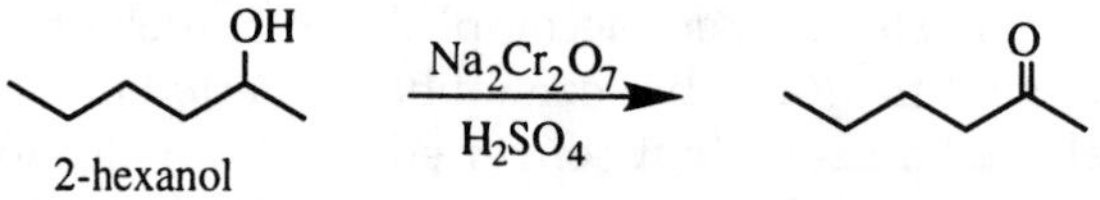
OH
Na2Cr2O7
H2SO4
O

2-hexanol

(d) 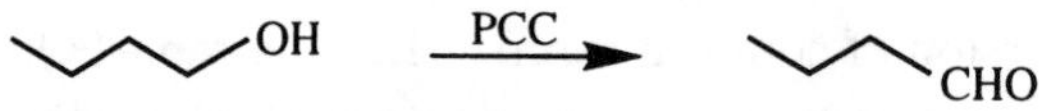
OH
PCC
CHO

1-butanol

4.18 There is no means of proceeding in a single step from the alkyl halides to the carbonyl compounds shown (see the *Key to Transformations*). One of the standard means of preparing a carbonyl compound is oxidation of the alcohol precursor. We also know that alcohols are readily obtained from alkyl halides by a substitution reaction. Therefore, the two step synthetic sequences shown accomplish the desired transformations.

(a) $CH_3CH_2CH_2CH_2Br \xrightarrow{NaOH} CH_3CH_2CH_2CH_2OH \xrightarrow{PCC} CH_3CH_2CH_2CHO$

(b) $CH_3CH_2CHBrCH_3 \xrightarrow{NaOH} CH_3CH_2CHOHCH_3 \xrightarrow[H_2SO_4]{Na_2Cr_2O_7} CH_3CH_2COCH_3$

4.19

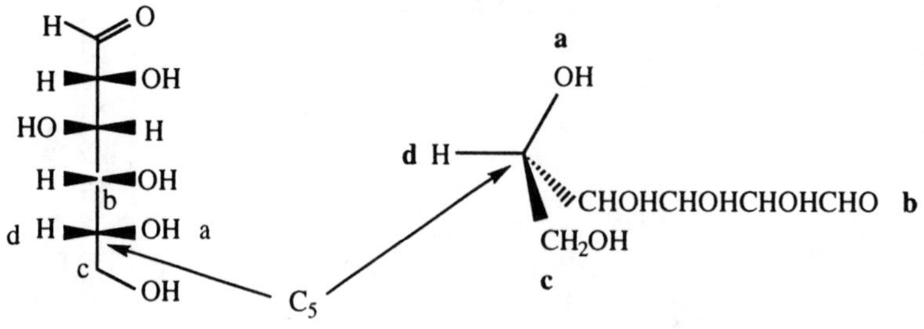
H
O
H
OH
HO
H
H
OH
b
d H
OH a
c
OH
C5
a
OH
d H
CHOHCHOHCHOHCHO b
CH2OH
c

D-glucose

R-configuration at C_5

4.20

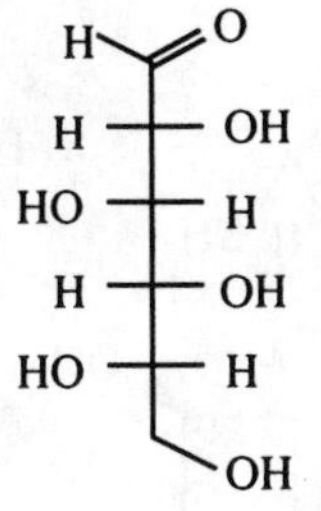

L-epimer of Glucose

4.21

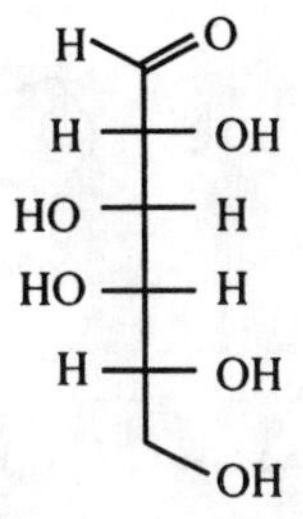

D-Galactose

4.22 The name implies that the structure is β-D-glucose without hydroxyl groups at C_2 and C_3.

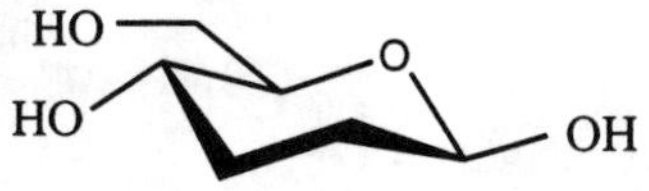

β-2,3-dideoxyglucose

4.23 In maltose the potential aldehyde group (C_1) of one glucose unit is masked by being involved in a glycoside (acetal) linkage with the C_4 hydroxyl group of a second unit of glucose. However, C_1 of the second glucose is not involved in an acetal linkage. Instead, it is in a hemiacetal linkage which can equilibrate with the open chain form which contains an aldehyde group. It is this group which can be oxidized, making maltose a "reducing sugar."

In sucrose the potential aldehyde group (C_1) of the glucose unit is tied up in a glycoside (acetal) linkage with C_2 of fructose. Fructose, being a ketose, does not have a potential aldehyde group. Therefore, in sucrose there is no group capable of being readily oxidized, making it a "non-reducing sugar."

4.24 (a) *trans*-1,4-cyclohexanediol
(b) 2-methyl-3-pentanol
(c) 2,3,4,5- hexanetetrol
(d) (S)-2-hexanol
(e) 2-methyl-1,4-butanediol
(f) 1-butanethiol
(g) *cis*-1,2-cyclobutanediol
(h) 5-ethyl-2,6-dimethyl-3-heptanol
(i) *cis*-3-methylcyclohexanol

4.25

(a) 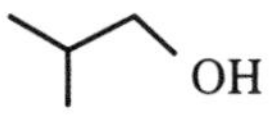
OH

(b) 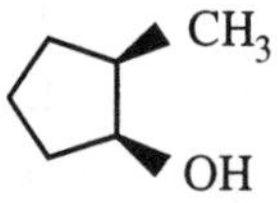
CH3
OH

(c) 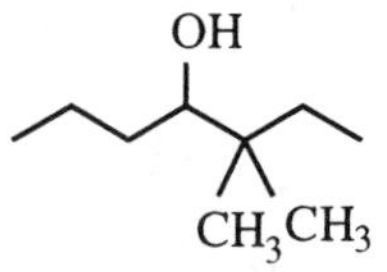
OH
CH3CH3

(d) 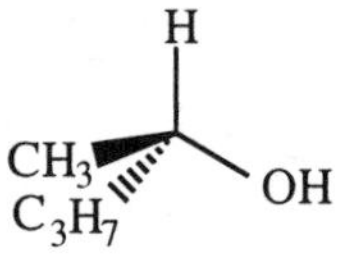
H
CH3
C3H7
OH

(e) 
Cl
OH

(f) CH_3CH_2OK

(g) 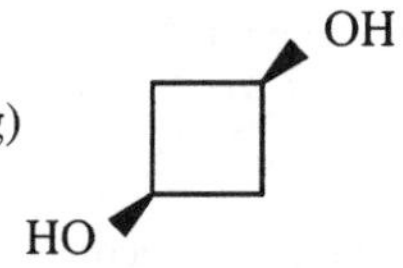
OH
HO

(h) 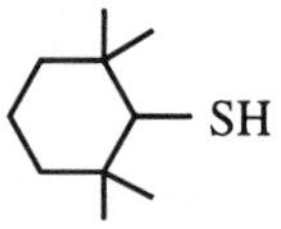
SH

(i) $(CH_3)_3COH$

(j) $(CH_3)_2CHONa$

(k) 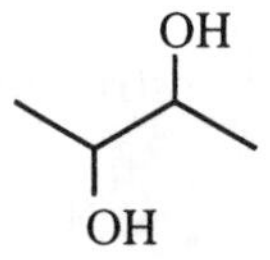
OH
OH

4.26

(a) 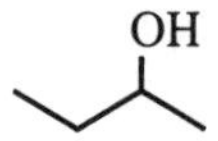
OH

2-butanol
(secondary)

(b) 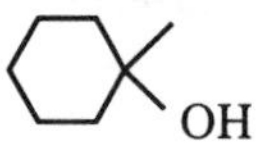
OH

1-methylcyclohexanol
(tertiary)

(c) 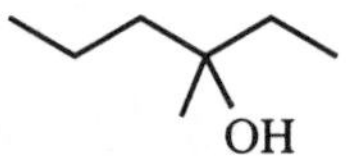
OH

3-methyl-3-hexanol
(tertiary)

(d) 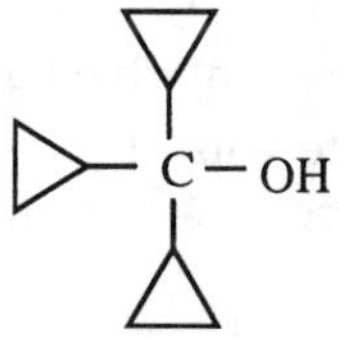
C—OH

tricyclopropylmethyl alcohol
(tertiary)

(e) 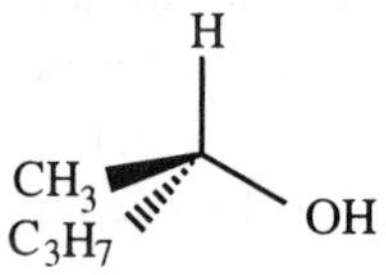
H
CH3
C3H7
OH

(*R*)-2-pentanol
(secondary)

4.27 (a) The water solubility order is 1,3,5- hexanetriol > 1-hexanol > hexane. The more hydroxyl groups that are present the more hydrogen bonding can occur with water, leading to increased solubility of the C_6 compounds.

(b) The water solubility order is ethanol > 1-hexanol > 1-decanol. The larger is the hydrophobic portion of a molecule the less soluble it is in water to the point where in 1-decanol the hydrogen bonding ability of the hydroxyl group (the hydrophilic group) is outweighed by the ten-carbon hydrophobic alkane chain.

4.28 Hydrogen bonding can occur when hydrogen is attached to a strongly electronegative element, such as oxygen. In that instance the H-O bond is polarized. The positive end of the dipole (hydrogen) serves as an electron acceptor and the negative end of the dipole (oxygen) serves as an electron donor. The electrostatic attraction between these dipoles in two different molecules is the "hydrogen bond" ($H^{+\delta}$-----$^{-\delta}O$). In an alkane the electronegativity differences between carbon and hydrogen are minute so there is no significant polarization and, therefore, no significant electrostatic attraction.

4.29

(a) $CH_3OH + Na \longrightarrow CH_3ONa + 1/2\ H_2$

sodium methoxide

(b) $(CH_3)_2CHOH + Na \longrightarrow (CH_3)_2CHONa + 1/2\ H_2$

sodium isopropoxide

(c) $CH_3(CH_2)_4CH_2OH + Na \longrightarrow CH_3(CH_2)_4CH_2ONa + 1/2\ H_2$

sodium hexoxide

4.30 Relative to ethanol (CH_3CH_2OH), *t*-butyl alcohol ($(CH_3)_3COH$) has two methyl groups on the α-carbon, with the methyl groups being electron-donating relative to hydrogen. Thus, the oxygen of *t*-butyl alcohol has a higher electron density than that in ethanol, making it hold on to the hydrogen more strongly. 2,2,2-Trichloroethanol (Cl_3CCH_2OH) has the strong electron-withdrawing chlorines so the oxygen has a lower electron density making it hold its hydrogen less strongly. Thus, the order of increasing acidity is:

t-butyl alcohol < ethanol < 2,2,2-trichloroethanol

4.31 The boiling point of compounds of the same family is related to the compactness of the structure (i.e., the total surface area), the more compact structure having fewer intermolecular attractive forces which need to be broken before vaporization. t-Butyl alcohol is almost spherical and is more compact than the linear n-butyl alcohol, and therefore lower boiling (bp 82° vs bp 117° for n-butyl alcohol). Solubility of alcohols in water has to do with the relative size of the hydrophobic hydrocarbon portion of the molecules. The long linear chain of n-butyl alcohol presents a larger hydrophobic presence than does the more compact t-butyl group. Therefore, n-butyl alcohol is less soluble than t-butyl alcohol.

4.32

Methanol as hydrogen donor molecule
(i.e., water as electron donor)

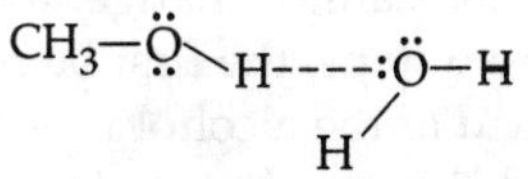
CH3—Ö
H----:Ö—H
H

Methanol as hydrogen acceptor molecule
(i.e., methanol as electron donor)

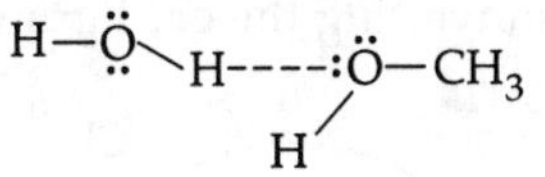
H—Ö
H----:Ö—CH3
H

4.33

(a) 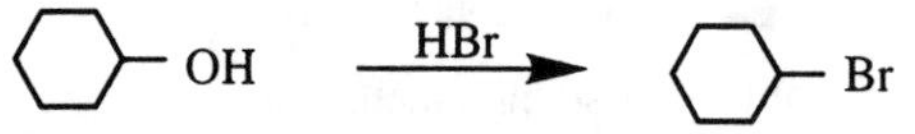
OH
HBr
Br

(b) 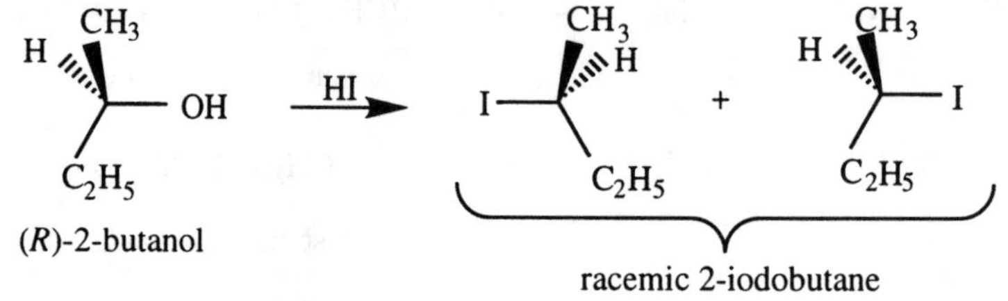
CH3
H
OH
C2H5
(R)-2-butanol
HI
I
+
racemic 2-iodobutane

(c) 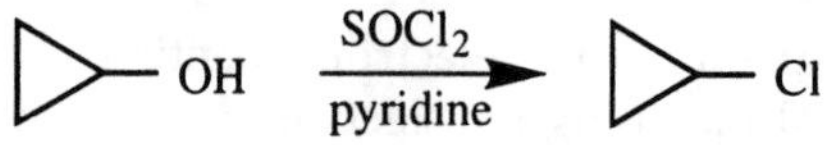
OH
SOCl2
pyridine
Cl

(d) $CH_3CH_2CHOHCH_2CH_3 \xrightarrow[H_2SO_4]{Na_2Cr_2O_7} CH_3CH_2COCH_2CH_3$

(e) 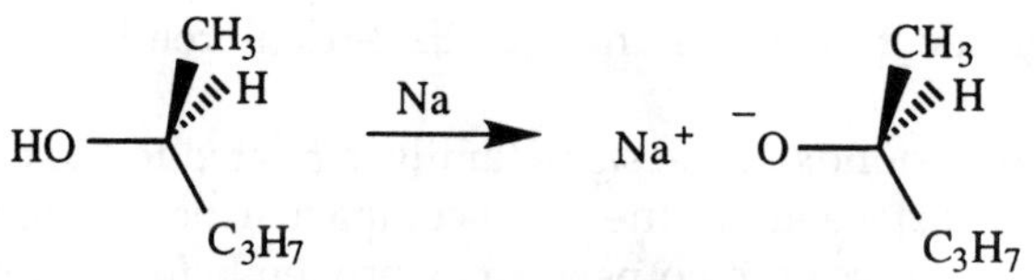
CH3
H
HO
C3H7
Na
Na+
O

(*S*)-2-pentanol

4.34 The reaction between an alcohol and tosyl chloride involves attack of the nucleophilic oxygen of the alcohol on the TsCl, displacing chloride to form a tosylate (R-O-Ts). The carbon-oxygen bond of the alcohol is never broken so its

R-O-H + Ts-Cl
R-O-Ts + HCl

configuration cannot change. By contrast, the reaction of an alcohol with thionyl chloride involves two steps, the first being analogous to the above reaction in which the oxygen-carbon bond of the alcohol is not broken and a sulfite ester is formed (R-O-SOCl). However, the second step involves an S_N2 displacement of OSOCl from carbon by chloride anion, thereby inverting the configuration of the carbon atom.

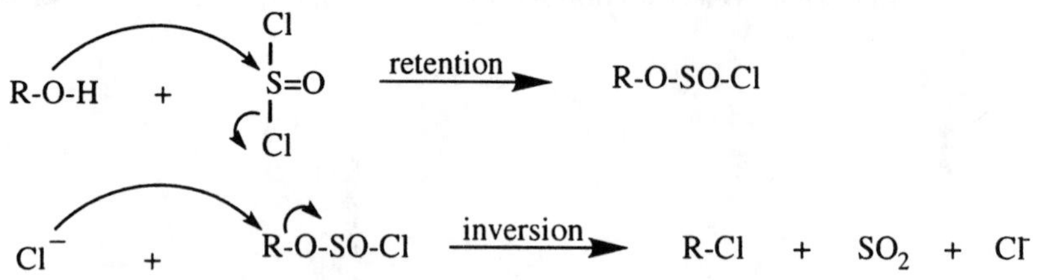
R-O-H +
Cl
S=O
Cl
retention
R-O-SO-Cl
Cl⁻ +
R-O-SO-Cl
inversion
R-Cl + SO2 + Cl⁻

4.35 In order to achieve overall retention of configuration it is necessary either to use a single reagent which accomplishes that conversion (there is no such reagent for this conversion) or to effect two inversions. In order to achieve overall inversion it is necessary to use a single reagent which accomplishes that task, and thionyl chloride is such a reagent.

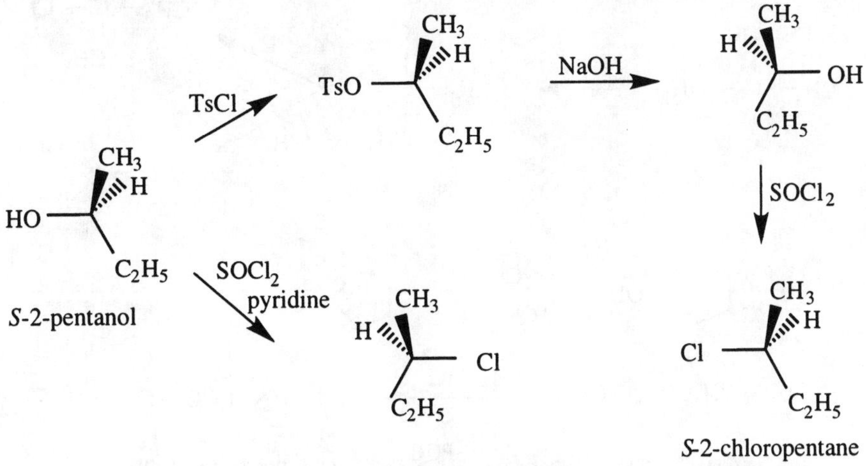
TsCl
TsO
NaOH
OH
$SOCl_2$
$SOCl_2$ pyridine
HO
Cl
S-2-pentanol
S-2-chloropentane

4.36

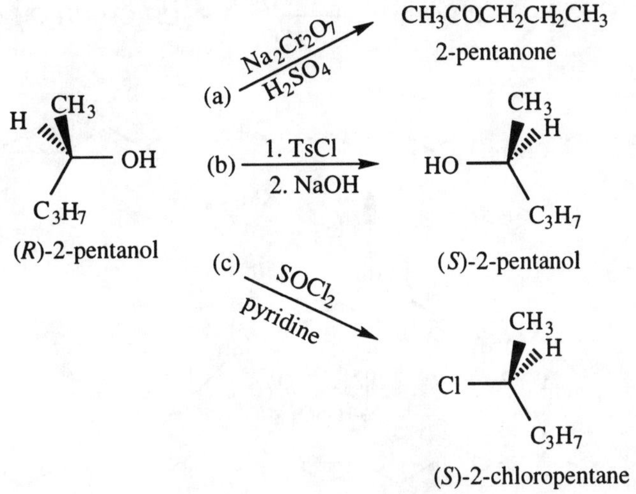
(a) $Na_2Cr_2O_7$ H_2SO_4
$CH_3COCH_2CH_2CH_3$
2-pentanone
(b) 1. TsCl 2. NaOH
(c) $SOCl_2$ pyridine
(R)-2-pentanol
(S)-2-pentanol
(S)-2-chloropentane

4.37 The formation of 1-chlorobutane from the reaction of 1-butanol with hydrochloric acid involves initial protonation of the alcohol to an oxonium ion. Water is then displaced from the primary oxonium ion in a S_N2 reaction by chloride ion, the only significant reaction for that oxonium ion. However, the oxonium ion from *t*-butyl alcohol will dissociate slowly but spontaneously to the stabilized *t*-butyl carbocation. The carbocation will react in an S_N1 reaction with chloride to form *t*-butyl chloride but it also will lose a proton in an elimination reaction to form an alkene, isobutylene. The latter accounts for about 20% of the starting material.

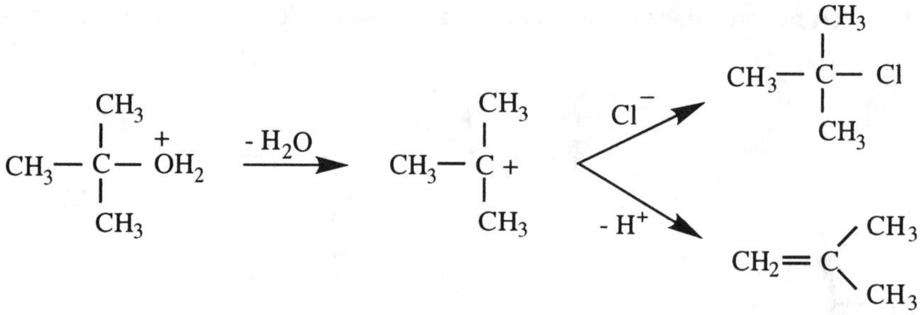

4.38

(a) 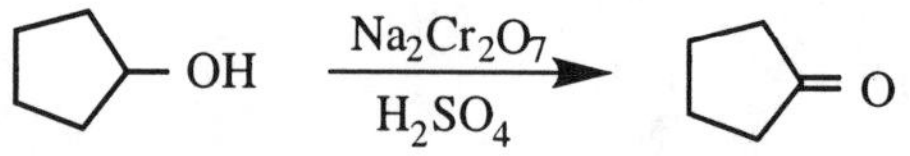

(b) $CH_3CH_2CH_2CH_2OH \xrightarrow{KMnO_4} CH_3CH_2CH_2COOH$

(c) $CH_3CH_2CH_2CH_2CH_2OH \xrightarrow{PCC} CH_3CH_2CH_2CH_2CHO$

(d) $CH_3CH_2CH_2CH_2CH_2OH \xrightarrow[H_2SO_4]{Na_2Cr_2O_7} CH_3CH_2CH_2CH_2COOH$

4.39

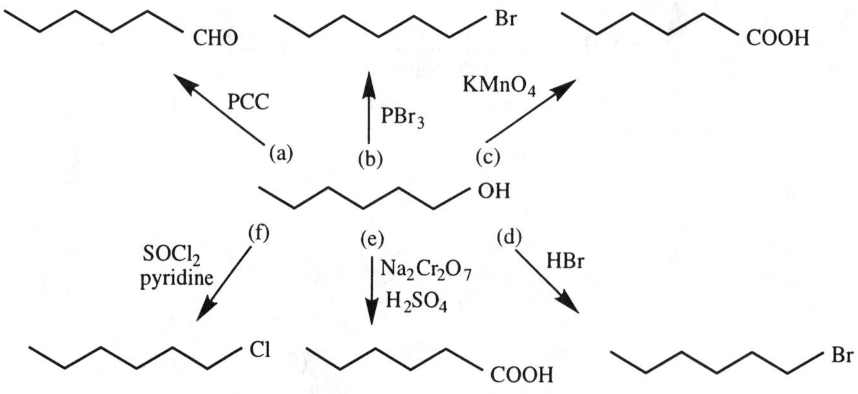

4.40 For D-glyceraldehyde, which has the R-configuration, the group priorities are **a** = hydroxyl, **b** = aldehyde group (-CHO), **c** = hydroxymethyl group ($-CH_2OH$), and **d** = hydrogen. Therefore, the Fischer projection for D-glyceraldehyde is as shown:

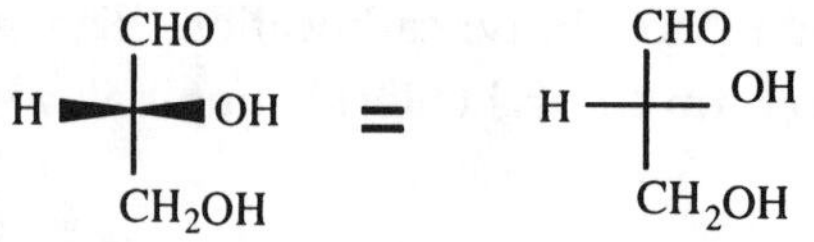

D(*R*)-Glyceraldehyde

The identification of each of the remaining structures is made by simply determining whether they are D- (*R*) or L- (*S*) using the same group priorities.

(a) L (b) D (c) D (d) L (e) D

4.41 Substituents on carbon 1 of cyclohexane-shaped rings are more stable in the equatorial position than in the axial position because they are then removed from steric hindrance with the axial hydrogen on C3 and C5.

4.42 (a) The use of the term deoxy means that a structure which normally has a hydroxyl group is missing the oxygen (i.e., the -OH has been replaced by -H).

(b) The term "epimer" implies the opposite configuration at a particular specified carbon atom.

(c) The anomeric carbon is a carbonyl carbon which can be converted to an intramolecular hemiacetal with the resulting hydroxyl group capable of assuming two possible stereochemical orientations.

4.43 Starch is a polymer of the α- form of glucose (the hydroxyl group on the anomeric carbon is axial) whereas cellulose is a polymer of the β- form of glucose (the hydroxyl group on the anomeric carbon is equatorial).

4.44 An aldotetrose is a four carbon carbohydrate with an aldehyde group as C1. The D-configuration means the stereocenter at C3 has the hydroxyl to the right. A 2-ketopentose is a C5 carbohydrate with a ketone group on C2. The L- configuration means the stereocenter at C4 has the hydroxyl group on the left.

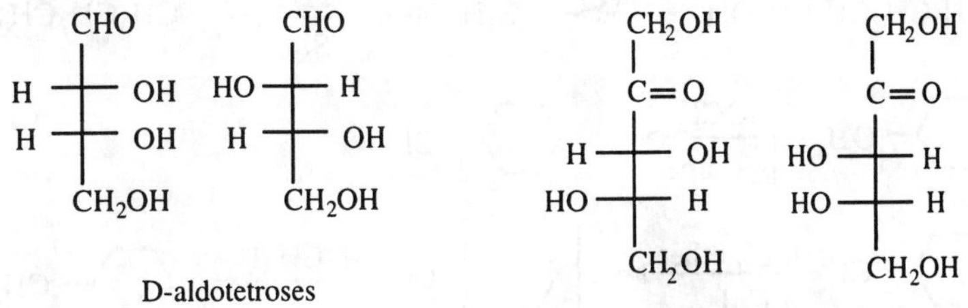
CHO
H
OH
H
OH
CH2OH
CHO
HO
H
H
OH
CH2OH
CH2OH
C=O
H
OH
HO
H
CH2OH
CH2OH
C=O
HO
H
HO
H
CH2OH

D-aldotetroses

L-2-ketopentoses

4.45 We have seen D-galactose before and its structure is shown below. L-Galactose, also drawn below, is the mirror image of D-galactose. Since L-fucose is related to L-galactose by its alternate name of L-6-deoxygalactose, the 6-deoxy term indicates the -OH of galactose on C6 has been replaced by -H. Therefore, the structure of L-fucose is as shown:

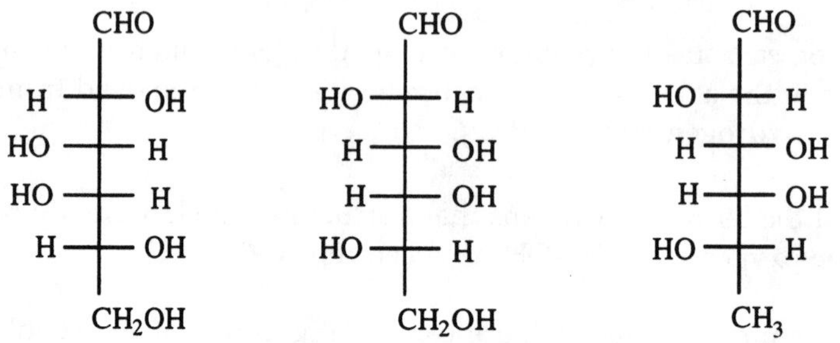
CHO
H OH
HO H
HO H
H OH
CH_2OH
CHO
HO H
H OH
H OH
HO H
CH_2OH
CHO
HO H
H OH
H OH
HO H
CH_3

D-Galactose L-Galactose L-fucose

4.46 Alcohols are Lewis bases (electron donors) because the oxygen atom contains unshared electrons which, in the course of a reaction, can be shared with (that is, form a bond with) another atom. An example is the protonation of an alcohol to form an oxonium ion. Oxonium ions are intermediates in many organic reactions.

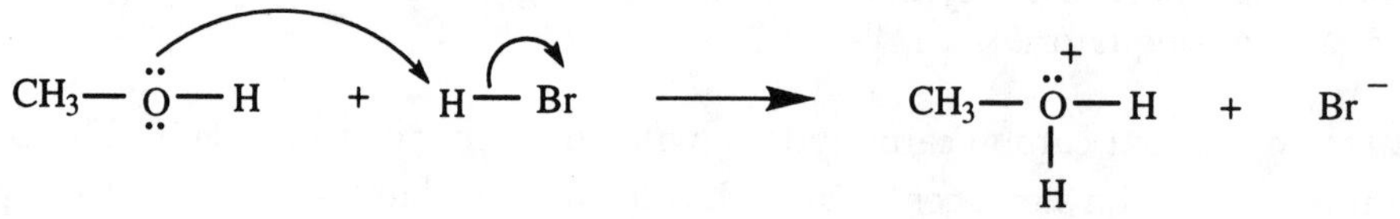
CH_3—O—H + H—Br → CH_3—O—H + Br^-
H

oxonium ion

4.47

(a) $CH_3CH_2CH_2CH_2OH \xrightarrow{Na} C_4H_9ONa \xrightarrow[S_N2]{CH_3I} CH_3CH_2CH_2CH_2OCH_3$

(b)

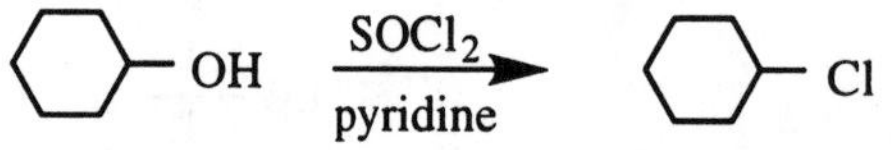
OH
$SOCl_2$
pyridine
Cl

(c)

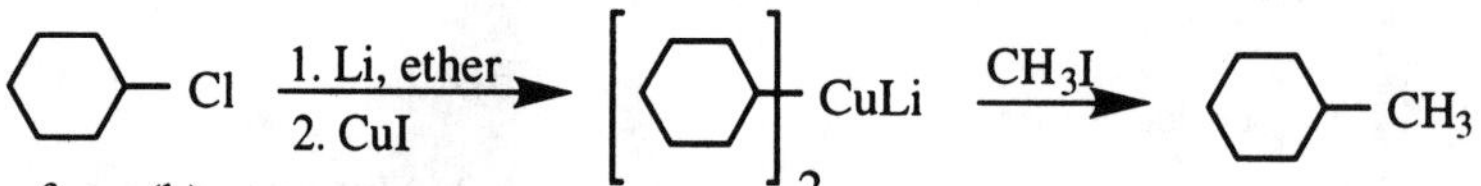
Cl
1. Li, ether
2. CuI
CuLi
2
CH_3I
CH_3

from (b)

(d)

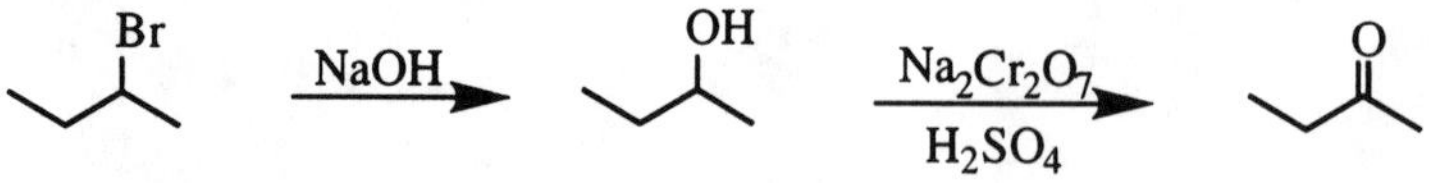
Br
NaOH
OH
$Na_2Cr_2O_7$
H_2SO_4
O

(e) $CH_3CH_2CH_2CH_2OH \xrightarrow{PCC} CH_3CH_2CH_2CHO$

(f) $CH_3CH_2OH \xrightarrow{TsCl} CH_3CH_2OTs$

4.48 (a) The longest straight chain for this compound is not C_4 (butane) but C_5 (pentane). Thus, the correct name is 3-methyl-3-pentanol.

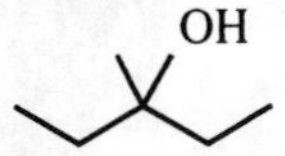
OH

(b) The lowest possible position number for a hydroxyl group in this compound is on C_1, not C_2. The correct name is 1,4-pentanediol.

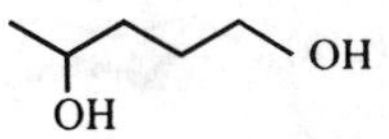
OH
OH

(c) Isobutanol is incorrect because it mixes a common name prefix (iso) with a IUPAC parent name (butanol). The correct name is isobutyl alcohol (common name) or 2-methyl-1-propanol (IUPAC name).

OH

(d) Any hydroxyalkane should be named as an alcohol, not as an alkane. The correct name is 3-chlorocyclohexanol.

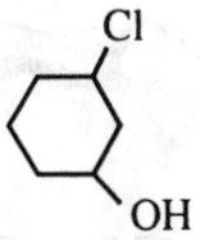
Cl
OH

4.49 The strong oxidant $Na_2Cr_2O_7$ with H_2SO_4 will oxidize a primary alcohol and an aldehyde to a carboxylic acid. It will oxidize a secondary alcohol to a ketone. Therefore, the oxidation of glucose will produce a tetraketo dicarboxylic acid:

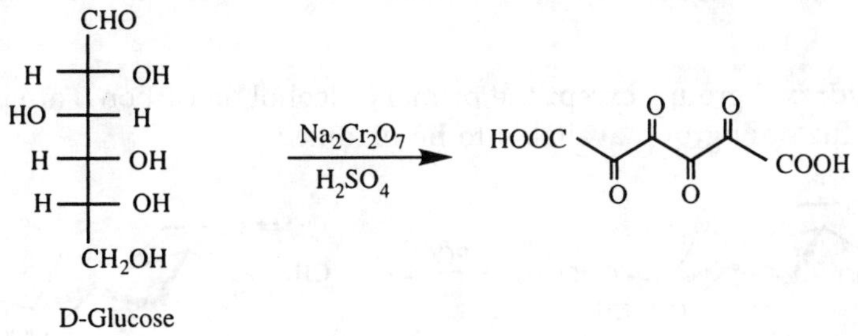
CHO
H OH
HO H
H OH
H OH
CH2OH
D-Glucose
Na2Cr2O7
H2SO4
HOOC
O O
O O
COOH

4.50

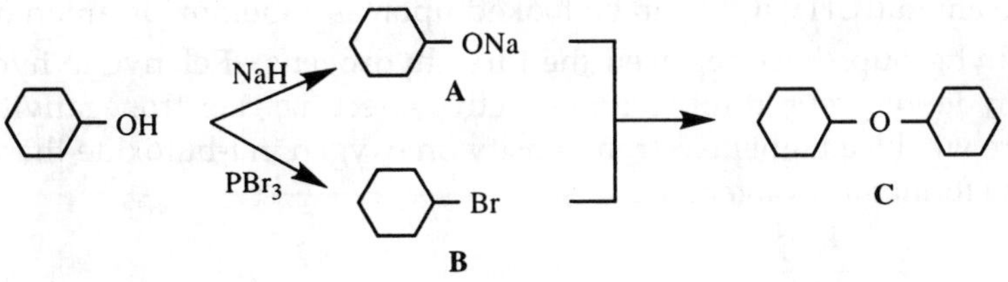
OH
NaH
PBr3
ONa
A
Br
B
O
C

4.51 It must be a tertiary alcohol since they are converted very rapidly to alkyl halides with the Lucas reagent. The compound is *t*-butyl alcohol - $(CH_3)_3COH$.

4.52

(a) 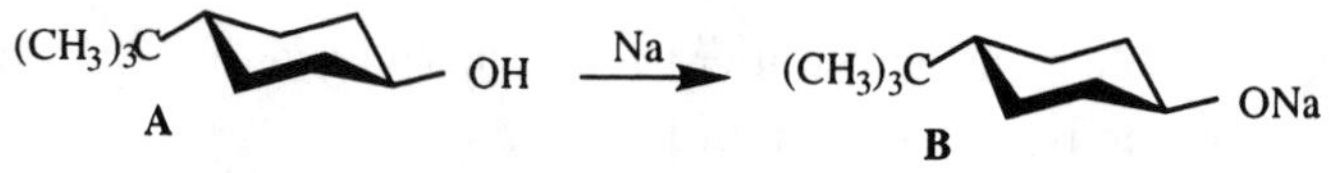

(b) 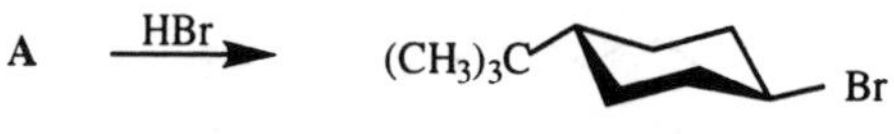 (plus some cis-isomer)

(c) 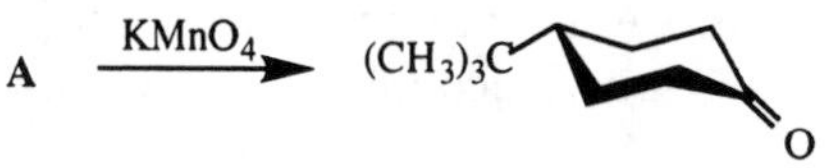

(d) 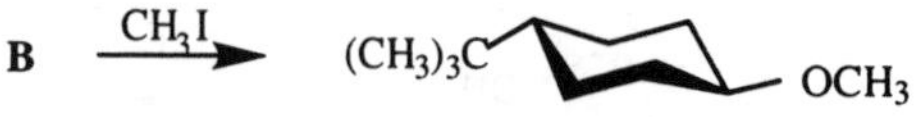

(e) 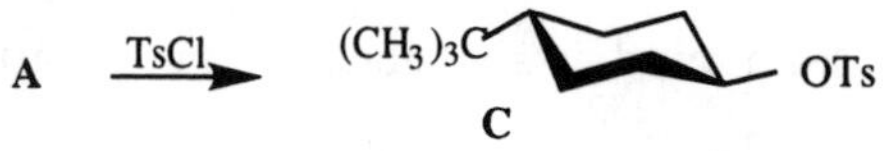

(f) 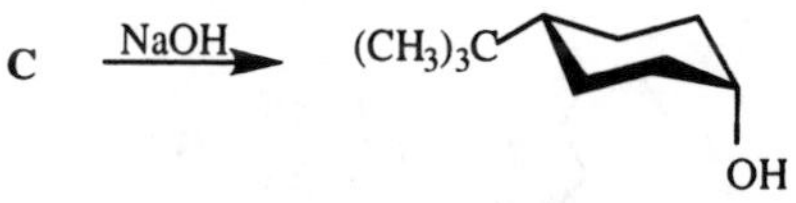

(g) 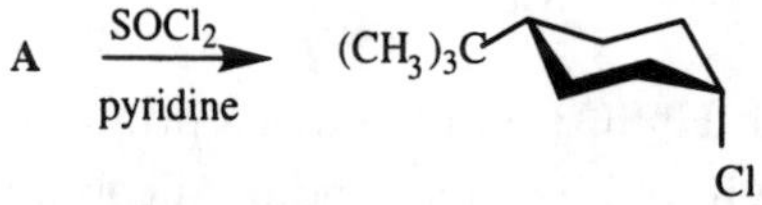

(h) 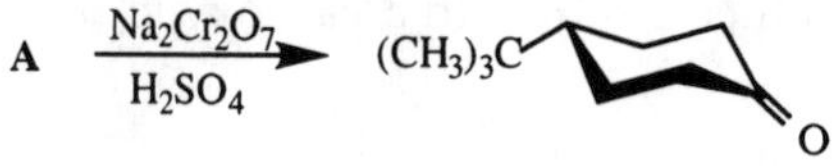

4.53 All of the hydroxyl groups except the primary alcohol on carbon 6 are protected. Therefore, the latter is the only group available to be oxidized.

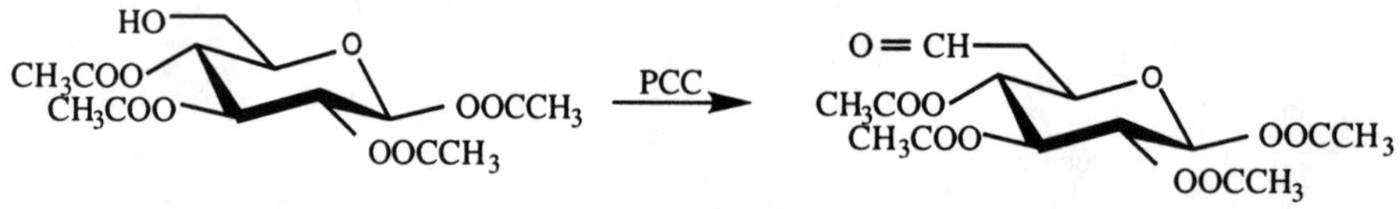

4.54 *t*-Butoxide anion ($(CH_3)_3CO^-$)can be looked upon as a methoxide anion (CH_3O^-) in which three methyl groups have replaced the three hydrogens. Relative to hydrogen, methyl is an electron donor group through an inductive effect (i.e., electronegativity differences). Thus, there will be a higher electron density on oxygen in *t*-butoxide than in methoxide, making the former a stronger base.

4.55

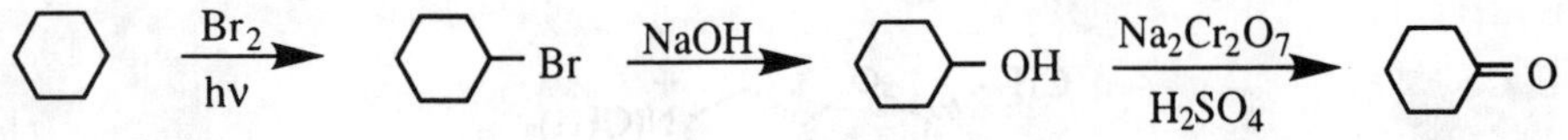

4.56 There are only four C_4 alkanols. In order to produce a ketone, the alcohol must be secondary. There is only one secondary C_4 alcohol, 2-butanol ($CH_3CH_2CHOHCH_3$).

4.57 Table sugar is sucrose, a disaccharide whose glycoside linkage between glucose and fructose can be hydrolyzed by dilute acid. Thus, one molecule of sweetener (sucrose) is converted into two molecules of sweetener (glucose and fructose). Furthermore, fructose is sweeter than is sucrose. Therefore, the overall sweetness of the solution will be increased.

$$\text{Sucrose} \xrightarrow[H_2O]{H^+} \text{Glucose} + \text{Fructose}$$

VII. Concept Problem

A Case of Mistaken Identity or Murder?

A famous mycologist, Sir Eugene Francisco, was found dead in his kitchen one Sunday, ostensibly from eating an omelette freshly prepared with mushrooms he had collected just that morning. The police initially classified it as an accidental death, due to mushroom poisoning. Then a close friend of Sir Eugene's notifies them that Sir Eugene was an expert on mushroom identification and therefore highly unlikely to mistakenly pick and eat the wrong species. And not only that, but Sir Eugene had been embroiled in a highly political battle for the presidential seat of an international mycology society. At this point, you, as the county forensic expert, are contacted by the police to help in the investigation. It is also part of your job to explain the scientific evidence to the police and a jury.

The mushroom presumed to be the culprit is Amanita muscaria, a mushroom that grows locally and is known to contain the deadly poisonous compound muscarine.
Muscarine is a bifunctional compound containing a secondary alcohol and a quaternary ammonium salt (you'll learn more about this in Chapter 12). A sample of muscarine chloride isolated from the mushroom has a melting point of 180-181 oC and is optically active (you may want to review Section 3.3). A sample obtained from Sir Eugene's body has the same melting point, but shows absolutely no optical activity. During the course of the trial, you are asked a series of questions, some over basic chemistry, and some that require you to provide your professional opinion. Based on the facts you've collected and your knowledge of organic chemistry, answer the following questions.

■ How would you characterize the structure of muscarine? (Do this by identifying the number of stereocenters and assigning them a configuration.)

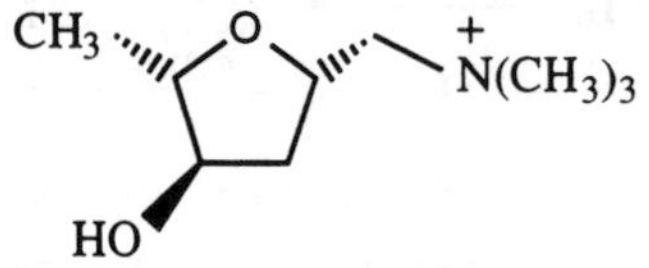
CH3
O
+
N(CH3)3
HO

muscarine

• Ans: There are three stereocenters in muscarine. Assigning the ring oxygen as position 1 and numbering to the left the configurations are 2S, 3R, 5S.

■ Given that the naturally ocurring muscarine has the configuration shown, draw the other enantiomer. What would be the properties of this enantiomer? What would be the optical properties of a 50/50 mixture of the two enantiomers?

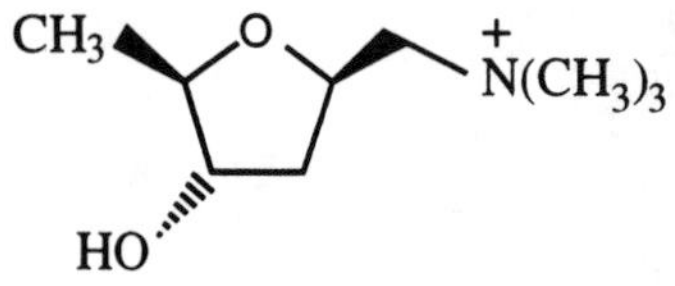
CH3
O
+
N(CH3)3
HO

enantiomer of muscarine

• Ans: This enantiomer would have identical physical properties except for the direction of rotation of light which would be opposite to that of natural muscarine. A 50/50 mixture of the two enantiomers, called a racemate or racemic mixture, would not be optically active.

■ What explanation can you give the jury as to why the muscarine found in the victim's body does not have an optical rotation like that from the actual mushrooms?

• Ans: It must be a racemic mixture of the two enantiomers of muscarine. It could be that somehow it racemized in the body—although it seems highly unlikely that a series of chemical reactions would convert all three stereocenters to the opposite configuration, and accomplish this on exactly half of the ingested material.

■ Can you give a professional opinion explaining the presence of the racemic muscarine in Sir Eugene's body?

• Ans: It is likely that the muscarine found in Sir Eugene's body did not come from a "natural" source, since the natural source of muscarine is optically active. Hence, Sir Eugene did not eat any muscarine-containing mushrooms, but rather was given a form of muscarine synthesized in a lab which most likely would be the racemic, non-optically active, form.

■ What is your conclusion? Is it murder, or a case of mistaken identity (of the mushroom, that is)?

• Ans: Sir Eugene Francisco was murdered by the intentional administration of racemic muscarine.

CHAPTER 5

Ethers

I. Textbook Chapter Contents

This chapter introduces ethers, a family of compounds which contain an oxygen atom between two carbon atoms. They are a relatively inert group of compounds but the functional group is found in a large number of naturally occurring compounds.

II. Learning Objectives

- Be able to name dialkyl ethers using common names or by using the name of an alkoxy group.
- Write equations for the preparation of ethers using the Williamson synthesis.
- Write an equation for the cleavage of an ether to an alcohol and an alkyl iodide using hydroiodic acid.
- Recognize cyclic ethers. Know the structure and nomenclature of epoxides, also known as oxiranes.
- Know the preparation of an epoxide/oxirane by epoxidation of alkenes using peracids.

- Write equations for the acid-catalyzed ring opening of epoxides/oxiranes to form 1,2-diols. Know the mechanism and the stereochemistry for this reaction.

- Write equations for the ring-opening of epoxides/oxiranes with nucleophiles, including hydroxide anion and alkoxide anions. Know the mechanisms and stereochemistry for this reaction.

- Write equations for the reaction of a Grignard reagent or an organolithium compound with an epoxide/oxirane to form a homologated alcohol.

- Be able to accomplish a two-carbon homologation of an alcohol by its initial conversion to an alkyl bromide, conversion of the latter to a Grignard reagent, and then reaction with an epoxide/oxirane.

III. Glossary

alkoxy group an alkyl group attached to oxygen (RO-)

crown ether a large cyclic polyether

cyclic ether an ether in which the oxygen atom is part of a heterocyclic ring

epoxidation the conversion of an alkene into an epoxide/oxirane using a peracid

epoxide a three-membered cyclic ether, also called an oxirane

ether a family of compounds in which an oxygen atom is attached to two carbon atoms

ether cleavage the cleaving of an ether into an alcohol and an alkyl halide (usually iodide) using hydrogen iodide

oxirane a three-membered cyclic ether, also called an epoxide

peracid a compound of general formula RCO_3H formed from a carboxylic acid by reaction with hydrogen peroxide

polyether a compound containing many ether groups

thioether a sulfur analog of an ether

Williamson synthesis a synthesis of ethers involving an S_N2 nucleophilic attack by an alkoxy group on an alkyl halide

IV. Summary of Reactions of Ethers

V. Summary of Preparation of Ethers

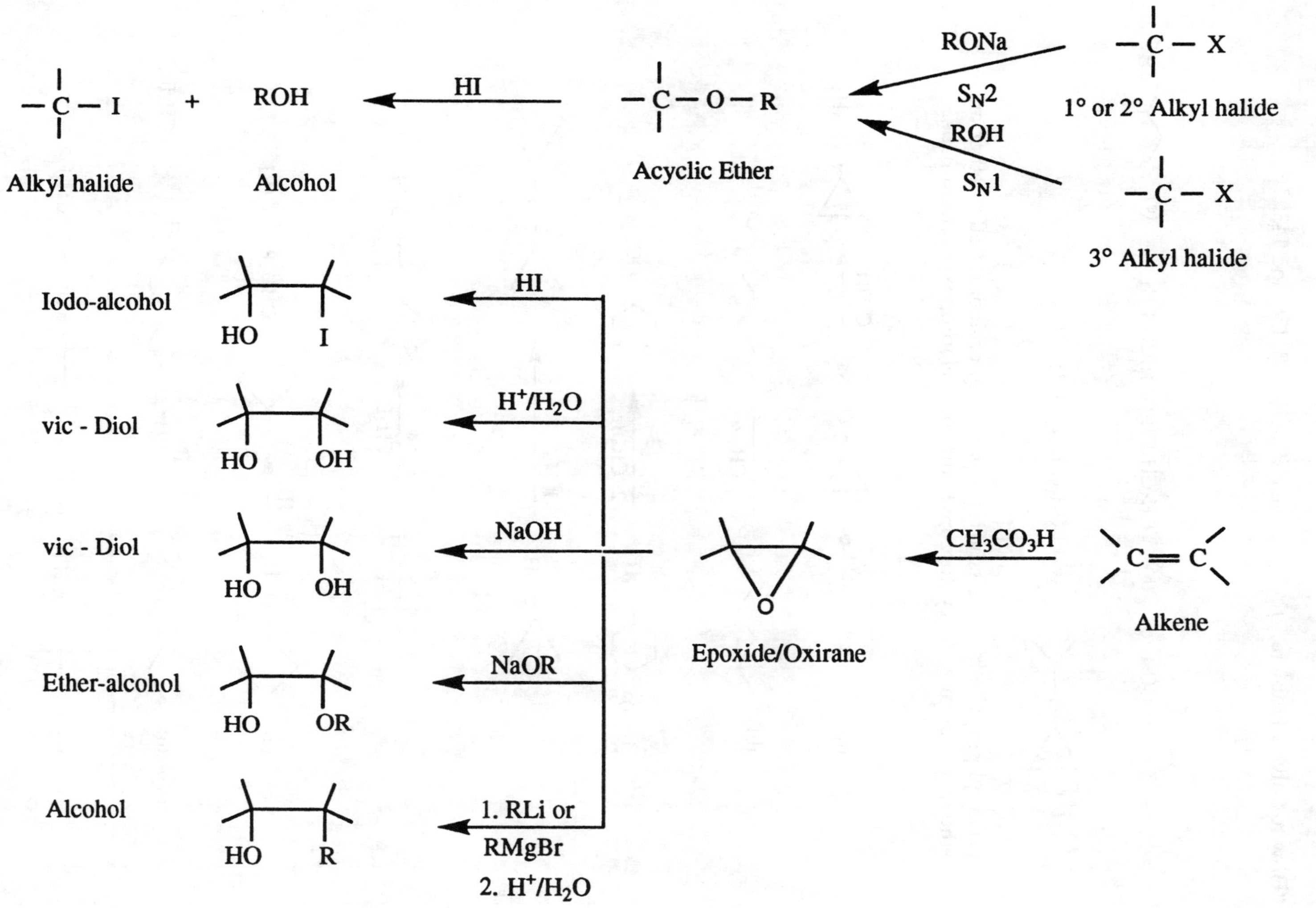
Alkyl halide
Alcohol
HI
Acyclic Ether
RONa
S_N2
ROH
S_N1
1° or 2° Alkyl halide
3° Alkyl halide
Iodo-alcohol
vic - Diol
vic - Diol
Ether-alcohol
Alcohol
HI
H^+/H_2O
NaOH
NaOR
1. RLi or RMgBr
2. H^+/H_2O
Epoxide/Oxirane
CH_3CO_3H
Alkene

VI. Solutions to Problems

For "**How to Solve a Problem,**" review pages 122, 128, 133, 136, and 143.

5.1

(a) 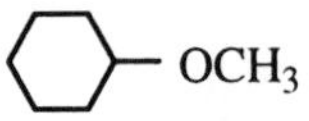
OCH3

(b) $CH_3CH_2CH_2OCH_2CH_2CH_3$

(c) 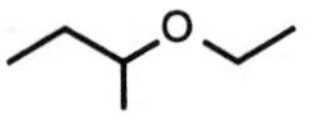
O

(d) 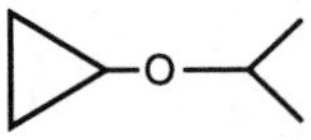
O

(e) $CH_3CH_2CH_2OCH_2CH_3$

5.2 (a) ethyl propyl ether or 1-ethoxypropane; (b) cyclobutyl ethyl ether or ethoxycyclobutane; (c) cyclopropyl ether or cyclopropoxycyclopropane.

5.3

(a) 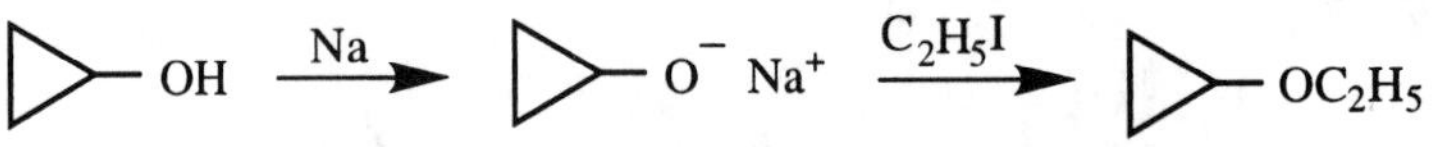
OH
Na
O⁻ Na⁺
C2H5I
OC2H5

(b) 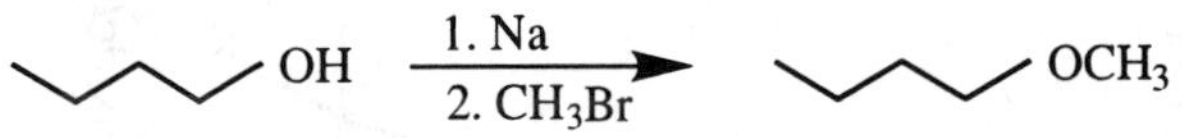
OH
1. Na
2. CH3Br
OCH3

5.4

(a) 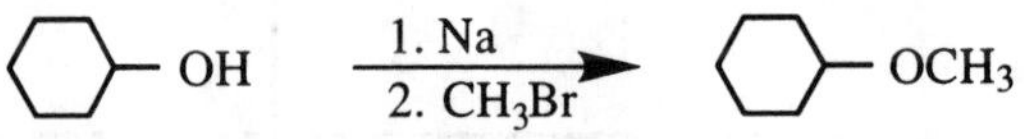
OH
1. Na
2. CH3Br
OCH3

(b) 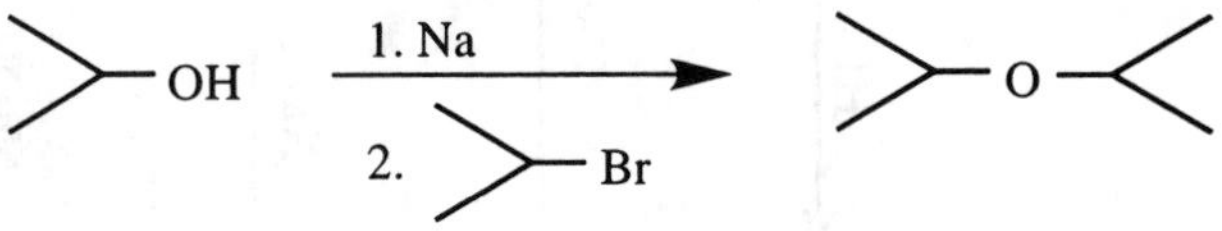
OH
1. Na
2.
Br
O

(c) 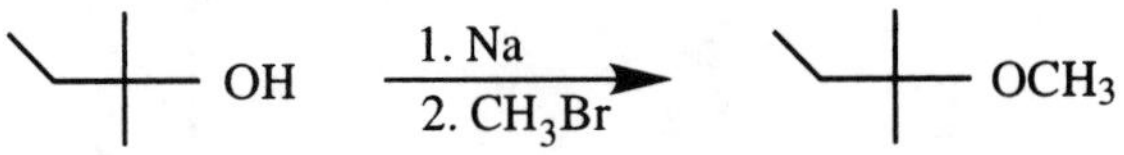
OH
1. Na
2. CH3Br
OCH3

5.5

(a) 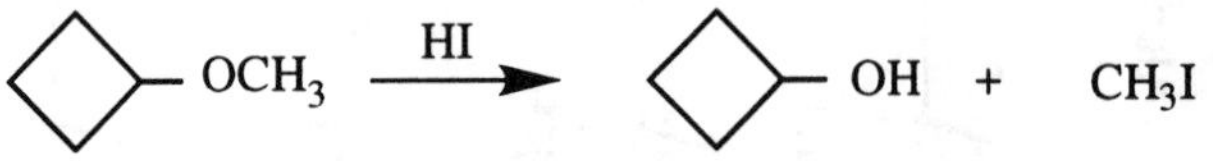
OCH3
HI
OH
+
CH3I

(b) 
OCH3
HI
OH
+
CH3I

(c) 
OCH3
HI
OH
+
CH3I

5.6 In order for such a conversion to occur the chlorine must be displaced as an anion - it is an adequate leaving group. Such a displacement normally occurs only by using a nucleophile. The hydroxyl group on the next carbon can be converted into the strongly nucleophilic alkoxide anion by reaction with sodium metal and it is perfectly positioned to carry out a backside S_N2 displacement, which is an *internal* Williamson ether synthesis.

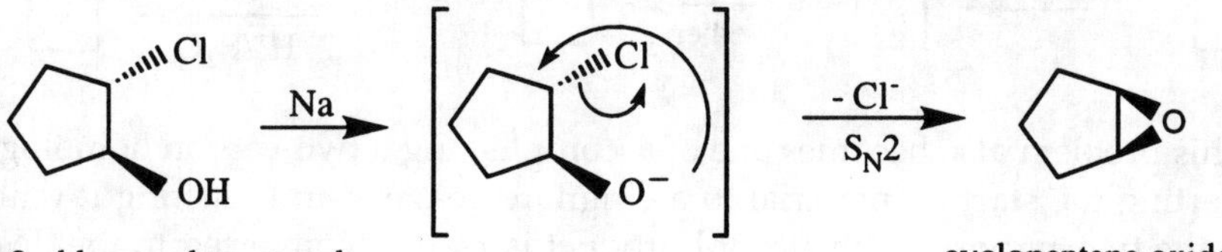
Cl
OH
Na
Cl
O⁻
- Cl⁻
SN2
O

trans-2-chlorocyclopentanol

cyclopentene oxide

5.7

(a)

CH3COOOH
O

(b)

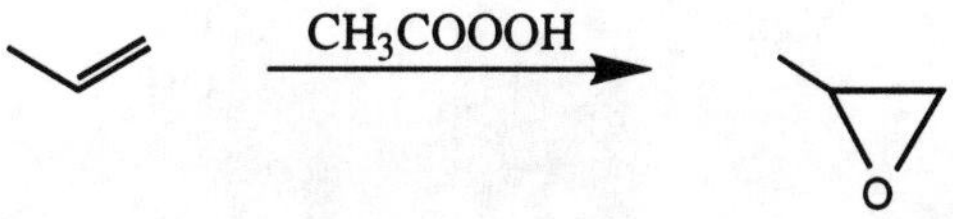
CH3COOOH
O

5.8 The diol product is *trans* because the oxirane ring opens by nucleophilic attack of water on a carbon attached to the oxonium ion, which serves as a leaving group. The water makes a backside attack from above the cyclohexane ring while the epoxide oxygen becomes a hydroxyl group below that ring.

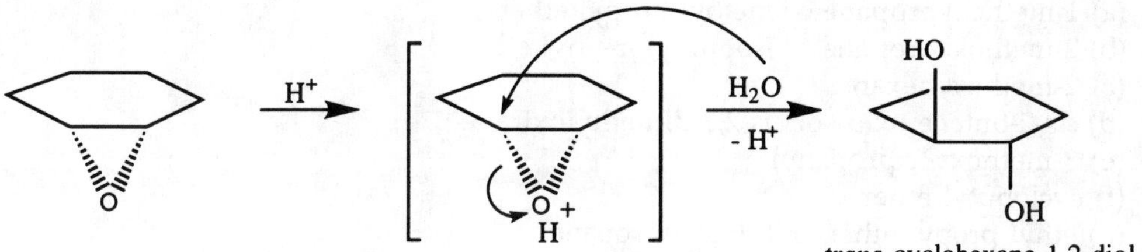
O
H+
O+
H
H2O
- H+
HO
OH

trans-cyclohexane-1,2-diol

5.9

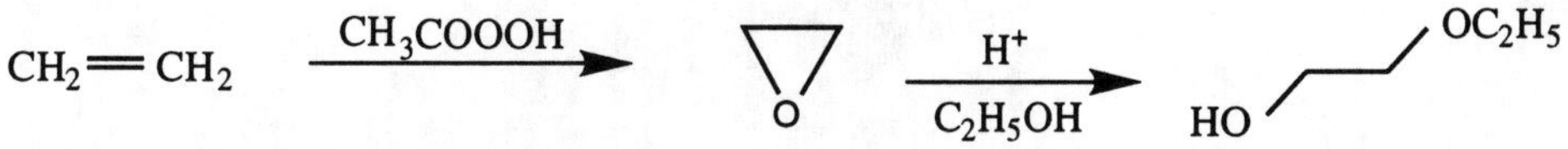
CH2=CH2
CH3COOOH
O
H+
C2H5OH
OC2H5
HO

5.10

(a)

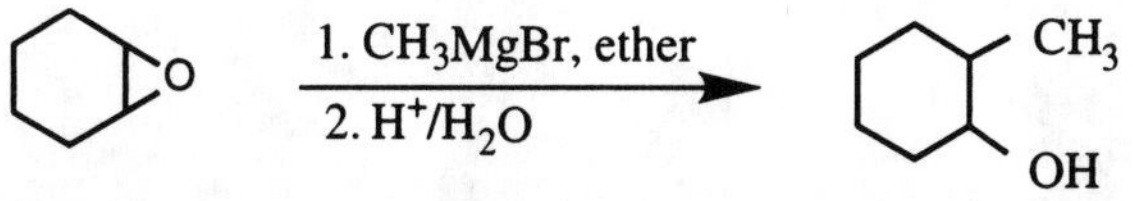
O
1. CH3MgBr, ether
2. H+/H2O
CH3
OH

(b)

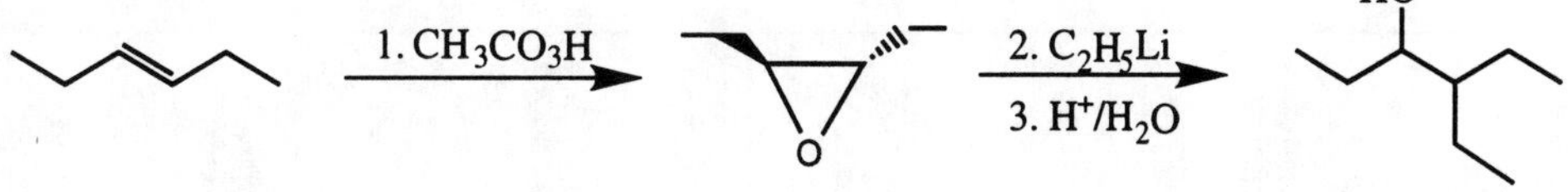
1. CH3CO3H
O
2. C2H5Li
3. H+/H2O
HO

5.11 (a) The problem becomes one of effecting a two-carbon homologation and the only route described so far is use of ethylene oxide in reaction with a Grignard reagent. First the starting alcohol must be converted to the necessary alkyl bromide using PBr_3 or HBr.

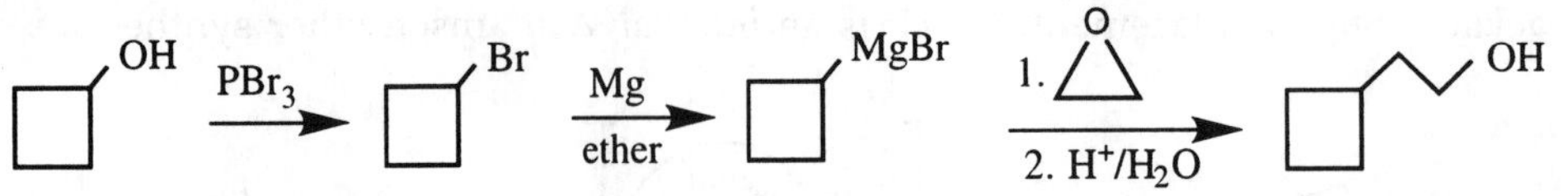
OH
PBr3
Br
Mg
ether
MgBr
1.
O
2. H+/H2O
OH

(b) This problem also becomes one of accomplishing a two-carbon homologation. Therefore, converting the starting material to a Grignard reagent and reacting it with ethylene oxide adds the two carbons. The alcohol product is readily converted to the desired alkyl bromide using HBr or PBr_3.

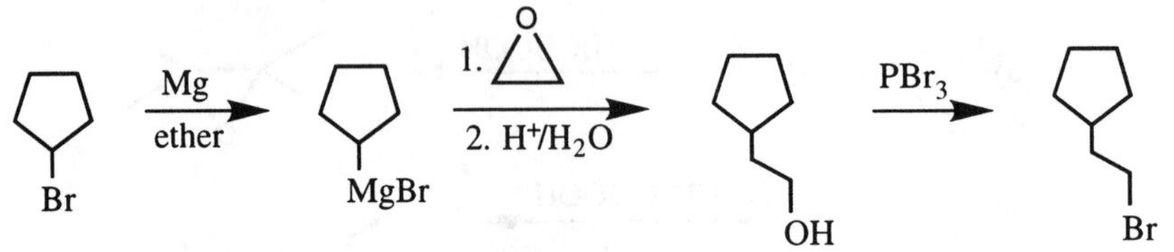
Br
Mg
ether
MgBr
1.
O
2. H+/H2O
OH
PBr3
Br

5.12

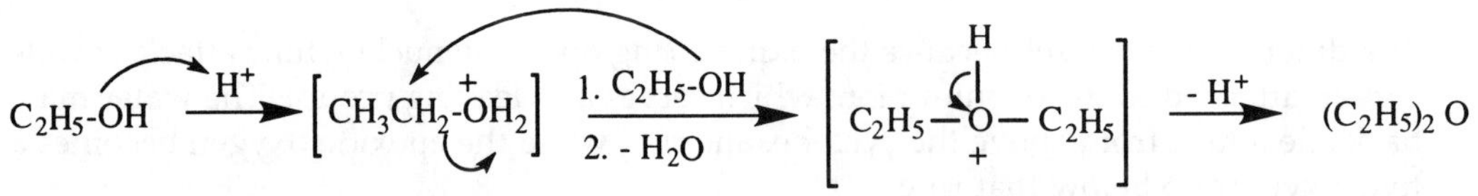
C2H5-OH
H+
CH3CH2-OH2
1. C2H5-OH
2. - H2O
H
C2H5—O—C2H5
- H+
(C2H5)2 O

5.13 (a) 1-methoxypropane or methyl propyl ether
(b) 2-methoxypropane or isopropyl methyl ether
(c) 2-methoxyhexane
(d) *cis*-2-butene oxide or *cis*-2,3-dimethyloxirane
(e) 3-methoxy-1-propanol
(f) cyclobutyl ether
(g) ethyl propyl ether or 1-ethoxypropane

5.14

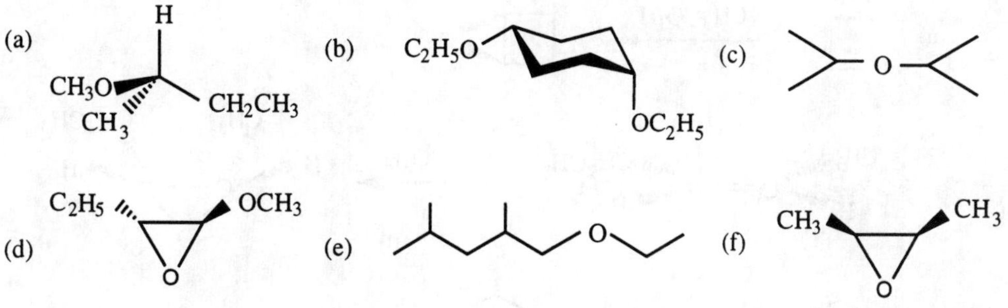
(a)
H
CH_3O
CH_3
CH_2CH_3
(b)
C_2H_5O
OC_2H_5
(c)
O
C_2H_5
OCH_3
(d)
O
(e)
O
(f)
CH_3
CH_3
O

5.15 The compound $C_4H_{10}O$ could be an alcohol or an ether derived from a butane. Two alcohols are derived from butane and two from isobutane. Two ethers can be derived from butane, and only one ether can be derived from isobutane. Therefore, there are four alcohols and three ethers with the formula $C_4H_{10}O$.

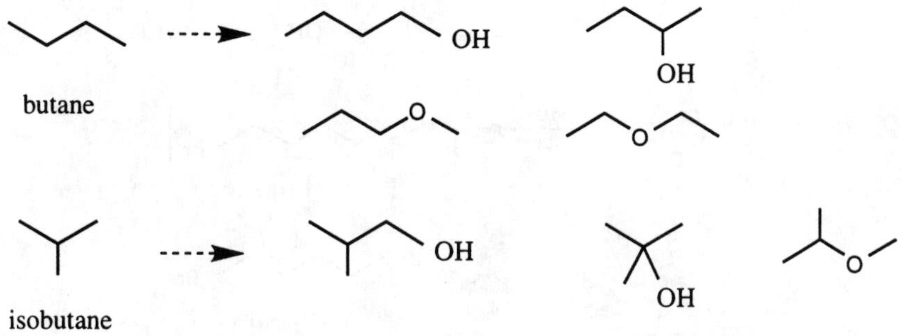
OH
OH
butane
O
O
OH
OH
O
isobutane

5.16 $(CH_3)_3C\text{-}O\text{-}CH_2CH_3$

5.17

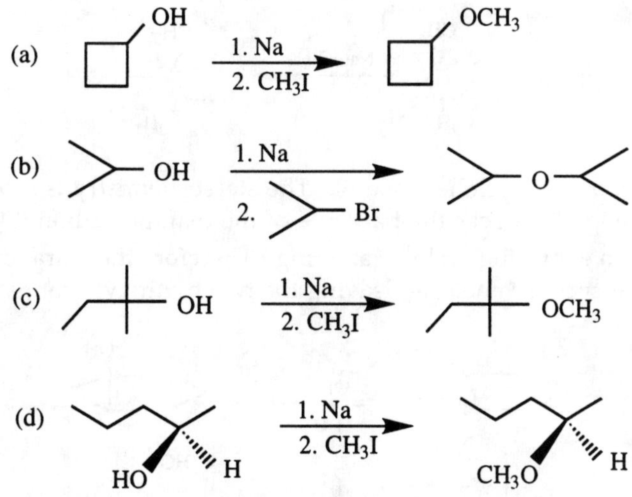
(a)
OH
1. Na
2. CH_3I
OCH_3
(b)
OH
1. Na
2.
Br
O
(c)
OH
1. Na
2. CH_3I
OCH_3
(d)
HO
H
1. Na
2. CH_3I
CH_3O
H

5.18

(a) 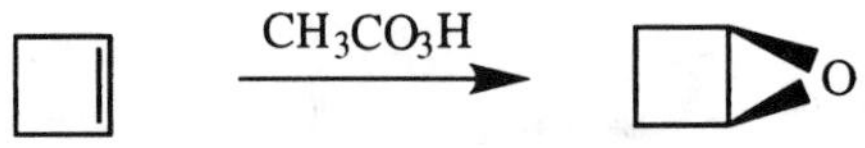
CH3CO3H
O

(b) 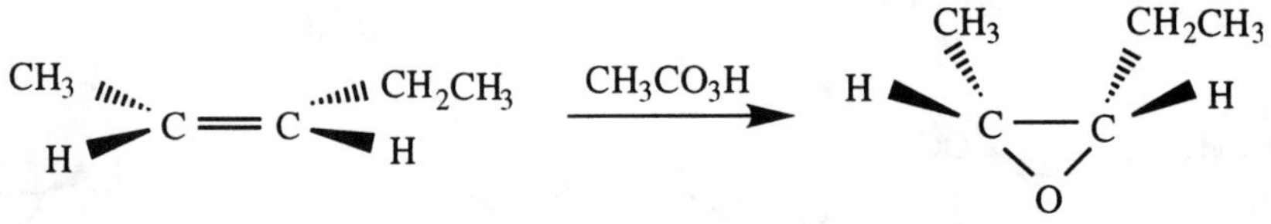
CH3
H
C=C
CH2CH3
H
CH3CO3H
H
CH3
CH2CH3
H
O

(c) 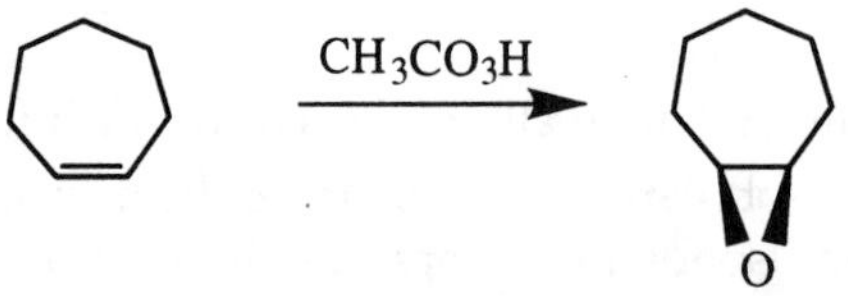
CH3CO3H
O

5.19

(a) 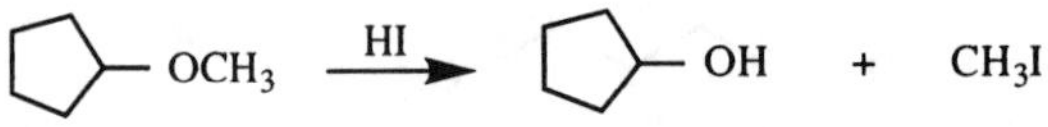
OCH3
HI
OH
+
CH3I

(b) 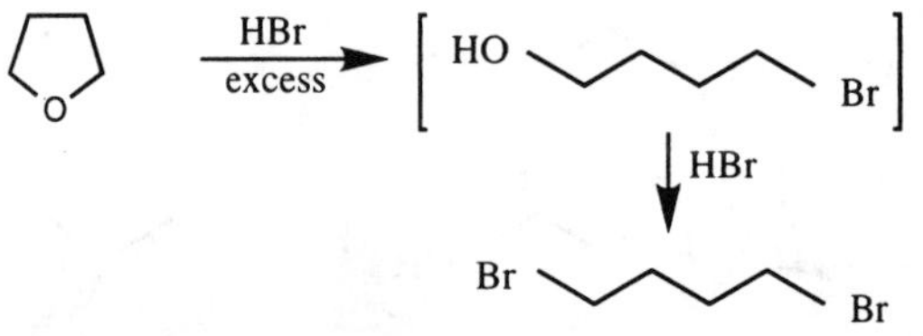
O
HBr
excess
HO
Br
HBr
Br
Br

(c) 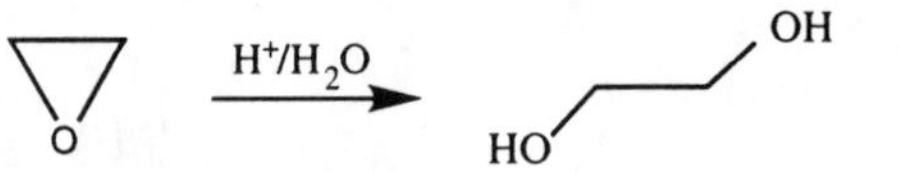
O
H+/H2O
OH
HO

(d) 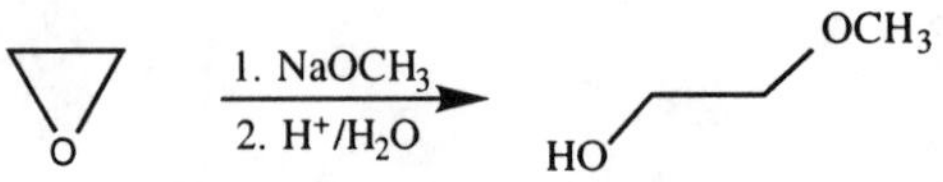
O
1. NaOCH3
2. H+/H2O
OCH3
HO

(e) 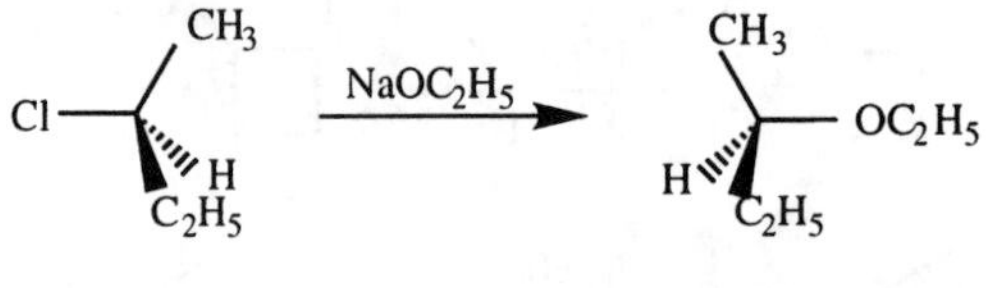
CH3
Cl
H
C2H5
NaOC2H5
CH3
H
OC2H5
C2H5

5.20 The product is *trans*-1,2-cyclohexanediol. The stereochemistry is *trans* because the hydroxide nucleophile attacks the backside of the oxirane carbon (S$_N$2 reaction), approaching from above the cyclohexane ring. Therefore the oxirane ring opens to the lower side of the cyclohexane ring, leaving the two hydroxyl groups *trans* to each other.

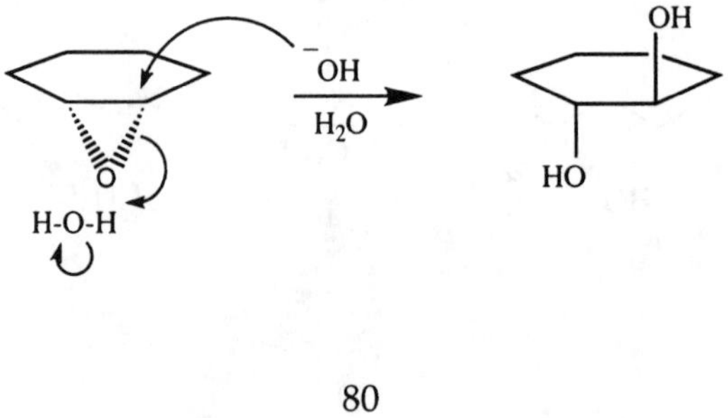
O
H-O-H
−OH
H2O
OH
HO

5.21

(a) $CH_3CH_2CH_2OCH_2CH_2CH_3 \xrightarrow{HI} CH_3CH_2CH_2OH + CH_3CH_2CH_2I$

(b)

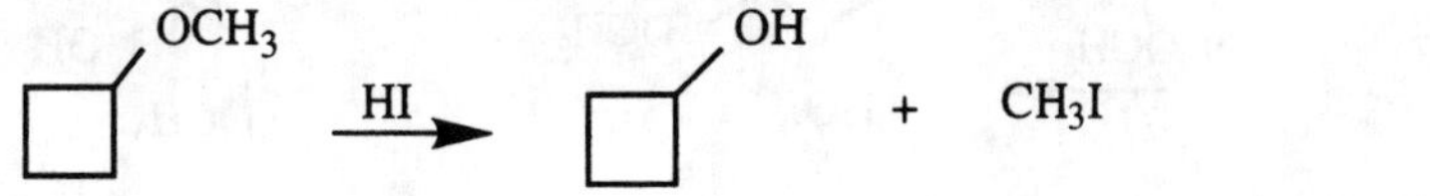

(c)

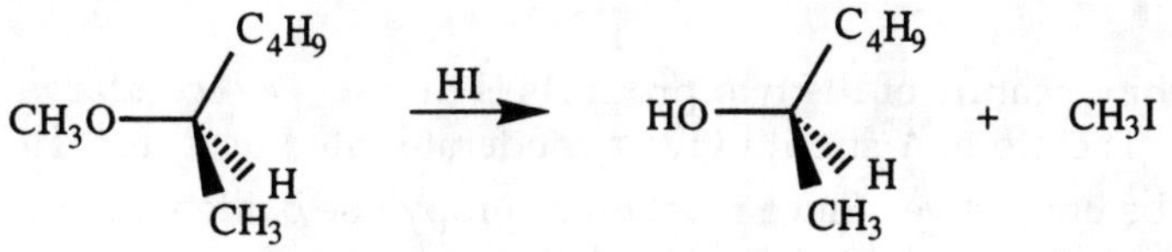

5.22

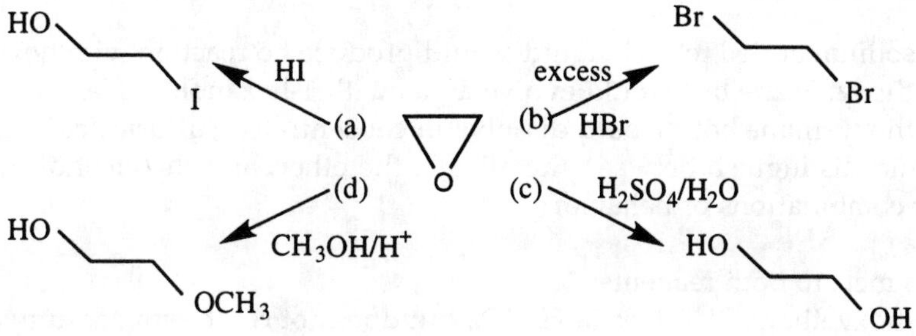

5.23

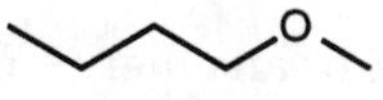

1-methoxybutane

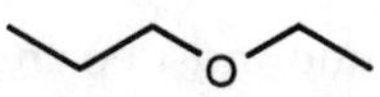

1-ethoxypropane

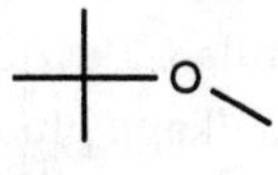

2-methoxy-2-methylpropane
(*t*-butyl methyl ether)

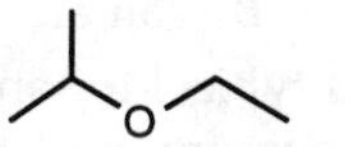

2-ethoxypropane

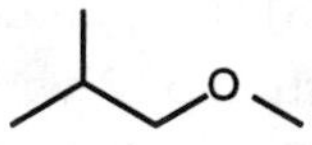

1-methoxy-2-methylpropane

5.24

hexane

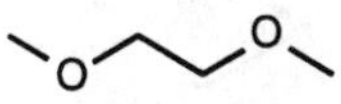

1,2-dimethoxyethane

1-hexanol

The boiling point and water solubility sequences are determined mainly by the ability of each compound to hydrogen bond.

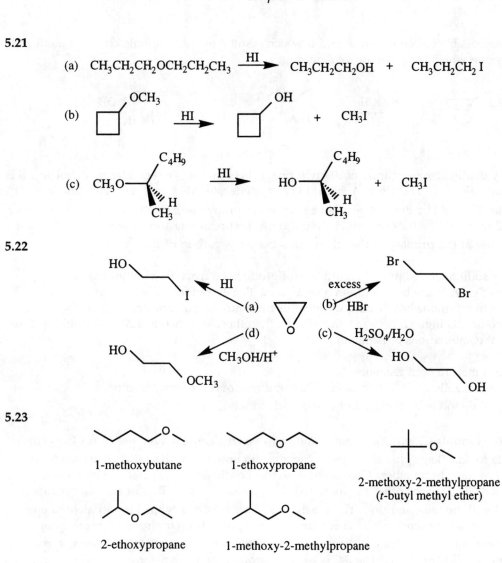

Boiling point sequence:
hexane < 1,2-dimethoxypropane < 1-hexanol
Solubility in water sequence:
hexane < 1,2-dimethoxypropane < 1-hexanol

5.25 The two possible structures are **A** and **B** which result from nucleophilic attack of methoxide on a carbon which is part of the oxirane ring.

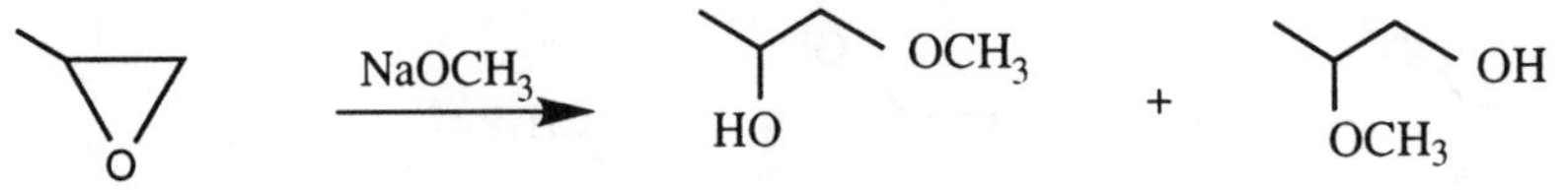
NaOCH3
OCH3
HO
+
OH
OCH3

A **B**

The key distinguishing feature of the two products is that **A** is a secondary alcohol and **B** is a primary alcohol. Therefore, **A** should give a moderate-rate Lucas test (HCl and $ZnCl_2$) whereas **B** should be unreactive. Since reaction of propylene oxide with methoxide will be an S_N2 reaction, the major product should be **A**, that resulting from preferential attack of methoxide at the primary, rather than the secondary, carbon of the oxirane.

5.26 Metallic sodium added to each liquid would produce no reaction with hexane or 1,2-dimethoxyhexane but would evolve a gas with 1-hexanol. 1-Hexanol and 1,2-dimethoxyethane both would dissolve in concentrated sulfuric acid. Thus, these two tests would distinguish between the alkane, the ether, and the alcohol by exhibiting three different combinations of behavior:

hexane is inert to both reagents;
1,2-dimethoxyethane dissolves in H_2SO_4 but does not react with sodium;
1-hexanol dissolves in H_2SO_4 and reacts with sodium.

5.27 From the formula $C_4H_{10}O$ the compound must be an alcohol or an ether (it fits the general formula for an alkane plus an oxygen). Since **A** did not react with sodium it cannot be an alcohol so must be an ether. Consistent with this conclusion it was cleaved by HI and produced CH_3I, so the other fragment (**B**) is a C_3 unit. Further, **B** is an alcohol because it reacted with metallic sodium. The reaction of **B** with HBr is typical for an alcohol and produces an alkyl bromide (**C**). There are only two possible C_3 bromides, 1-bromopropane and 2-bromopropane. Since **C** reacted slowly with both reagents the behavior is typical of a secondary alkyl bromide. Thus, **C** is 2-bromopropane and this means **B** must be 2-propanol and **A** must be 2-methoxypropane.

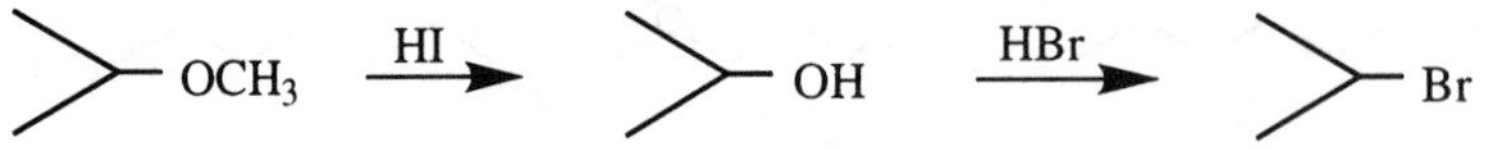
OCH3
HI
OH
HBr
Br

A **B** **C**

5.28

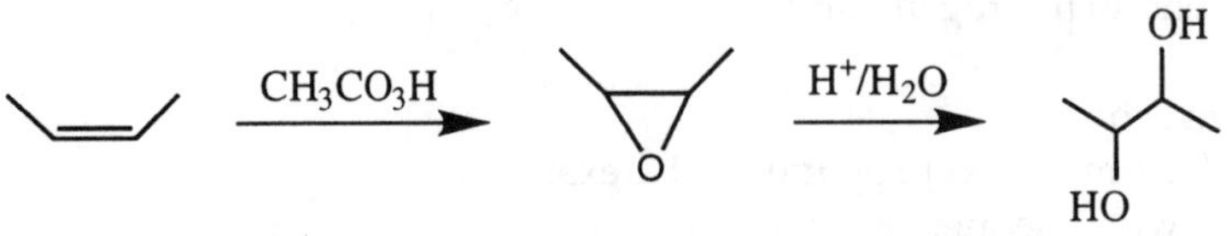
CH3CO3H
H+/H2O
OH
HO

5.29

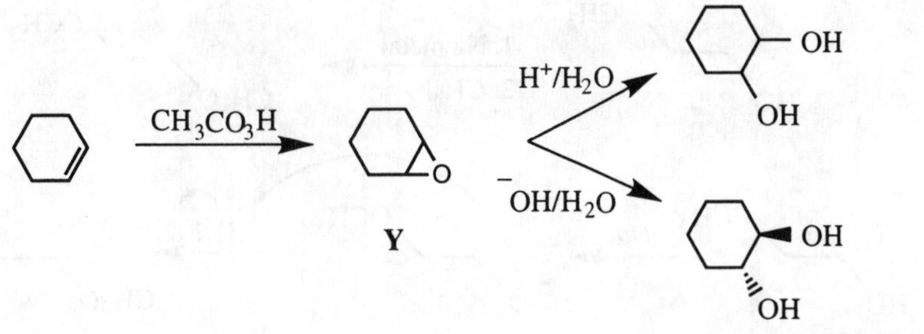

CH_3CO_3H
Y
H^+/H_2O
$^-OH/H_2O$
OH
OH
OH
OH

trans-1,2-cyclohexanediol

5.30

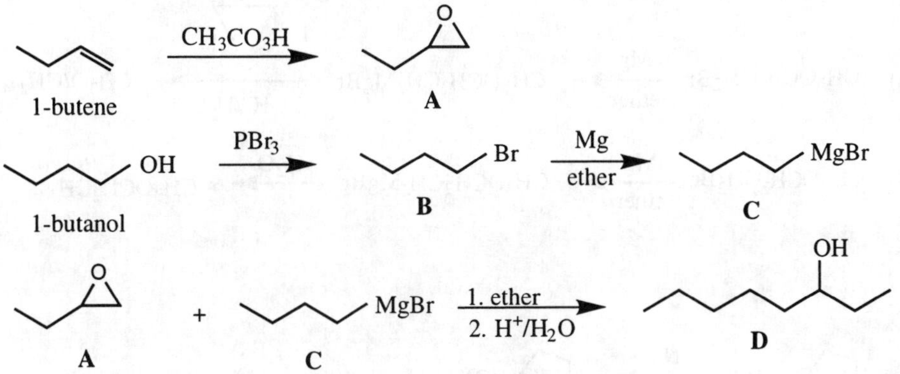

CH_3CO_3H
1-butene
A
OH
PBr_3
Br
Mg
ether
MgBr
1-butanol
B
C
+
MgBr
1. ether
2. H^+/H_2O
OH
A
C
D

5.31

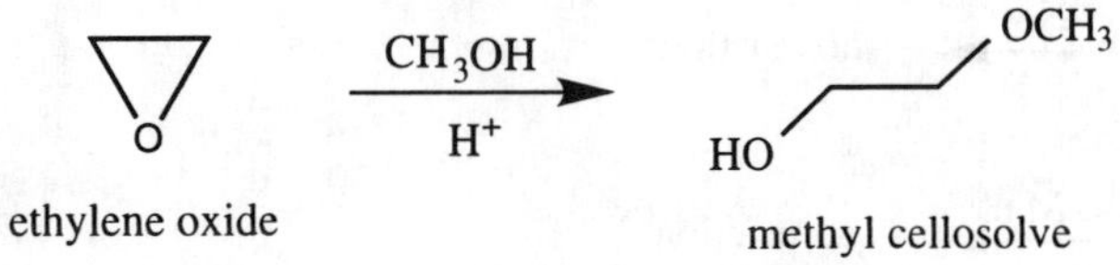

CH_3OH
H^+
OCH_3
HO
ethylene oxide
methyl cellosolve

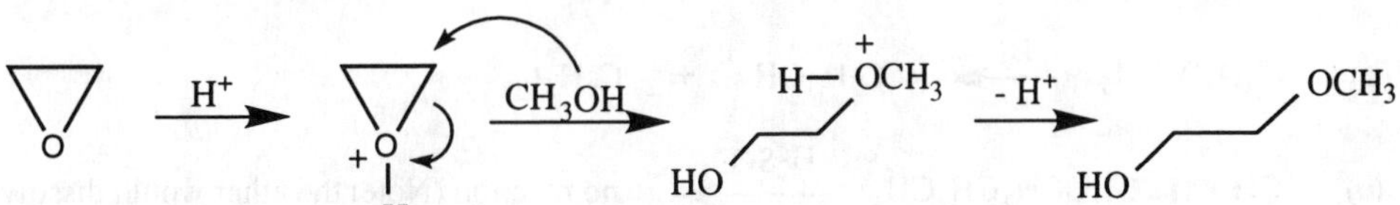

H^+
CH_3OH
H
$H-\overset{+}{O}CH_3$
HO
$-H^+$
OCH_3
HO

5.32

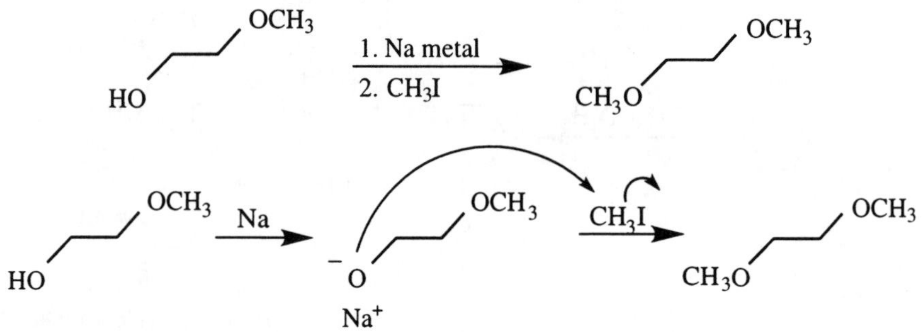

5.33

(a) 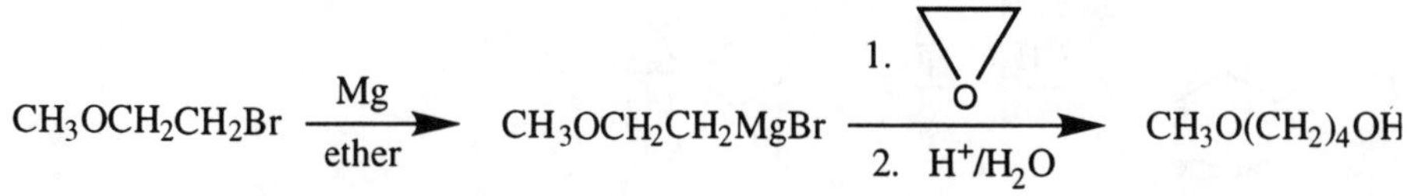

(b) $CH_3OCH_2CH_2Br \xrightarrow[\text{ether}]{\text{Mg}} CH_3OCH_2CH_2MgBr \xrightarrow{H_2O} CH_3OCH_2CH_3$

5.34

(a) 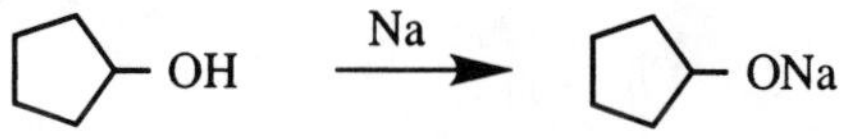

(b) 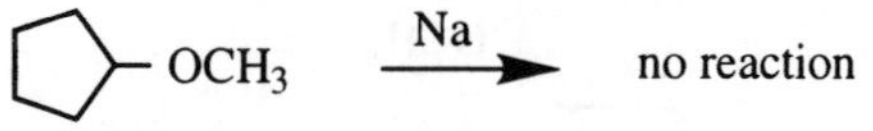

(c) 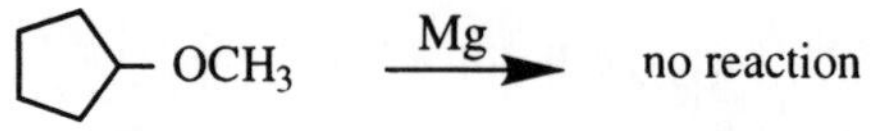

(d) $C_2H_5OC_2H_5 \xrightarrow{\text{HI}} C_2H_5OH + C_2H_5I$

(e) $CH_3CH_2CH_2OCH_2CH_2CH_3 \xrightarrow{H_2SO_4}$ no reaction (Note: the ether would dissolve by virtue of forming an oxonium ion but there would be no conversion; addition of water would lead to recovery of the ether)

(f) 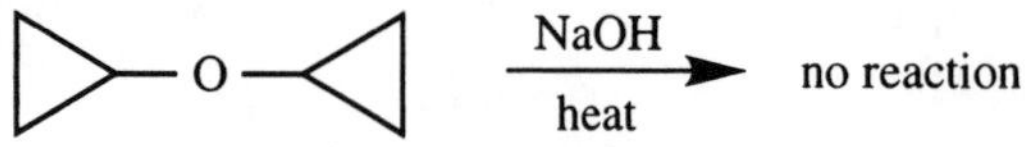

5.35

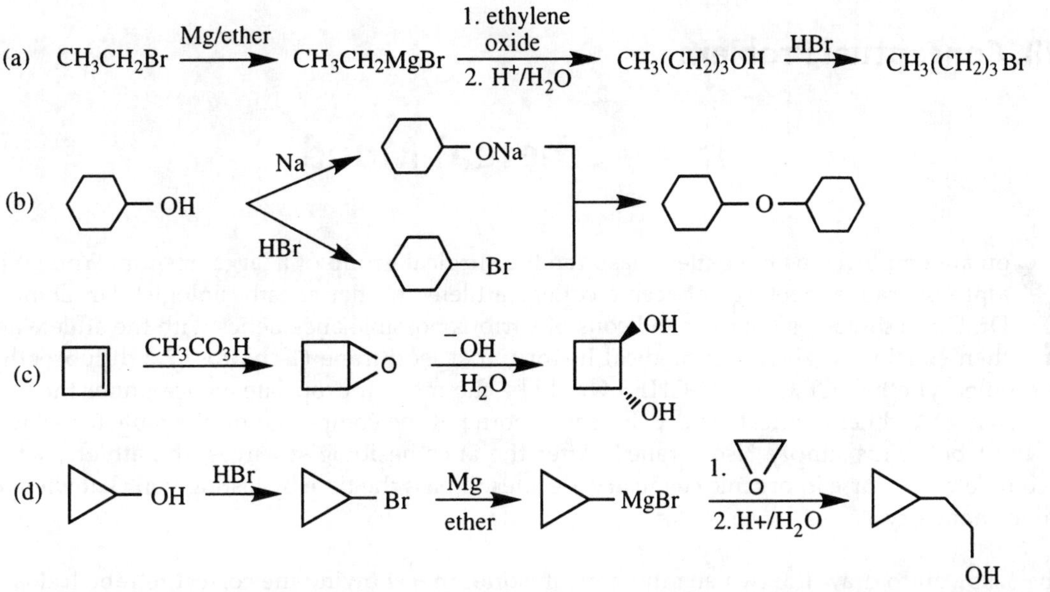
(a)
CH3CH2Br
Mg/ether
CH3CH2MgBr
1. ethylene oxide
2. H+/H2O
CH3(CH2)3OH
HBr
CH3(CH2)3 Br
(b)
OH
Na
HBr
ONa
Br
O
(c)
CH3CO3H
O
OH
H2O
OH
OH
(d)
OH
HBr
Br
Mg
ether
MgBr
1.
O
2. H+/H2O
OH

5.36 (a) Concentrated sulfuric acid. The acid would dissolve diethyl ether by protonating the ethereal oxygen and forming an oxonium ion but pentane would not be protonated and would not dissolve.

(b) Metallic sodium. Hydrogen gas would be evolved with ethanol as the sodium reacted with the hydroxyl group to form sodium ethoxide. There would be no reaction with methyl ethyl ether.

(c) Metallic sodium. Hydrogen gas would be evolved with pentanol as the sodium reacted with the hydroxyl group to form sodium pentoxide. There would be no reaction with pentane.

5.37 Since the compound is an alcohol and an ether there must be at least one -OH functional group and one C-O-C functional group. Since there are three oxygens in the compound there must be two of one group and one of the other. There cannot be an -OH group on a carbon which also carries an alkoxy group (that would be a hemiacetal group - see Section 13.4.2). Finally, recall that excess HI will convert any -OH group to an iodo group and any ether group to two iodo groups. Since only 1,2-diiodoethane (ICH_2CH_2I) was obtained upon HI cleavage, and since there are four carbons in the unknown compound, two C_2 units must be joined and this only can occur via an ether linkage. Therefore, the structure for $C_4H_{10}O_3$ is $HOCH_2CH_2OCH_2CH_2OH$.

VII. Conceptual Problem

In an Ethereal Mood

You are employed as the patient liason in the surgical group of a large hospital. You sit in on a pre-operative meeting between a college athlete and her anesthesiologist, Dr. Dunn. Dr. Dunn discusses the pros and cons of various possible anesthetics with the athlete and then concludes, given her medical history, that isoflurane (1-chloro-2,2,2-difluoroethyl difluoromethyl ether, $CF_3CHCl\text{-}O\text{-}CHF_2$) would be the most appropriate choice under the circumstances and her medical history. He sets a bottle of the compound on the table for all to see—the label reads simply "isoflurane." After the anesthesiologist leaves, the athlete, who has just completed a course in organic chemistry, decides to pass the time by testing your knowledge of organic chemistry.

- She asks you to draw the two enantiomers of isoflurane, showing the correct tetrahedral geometry and configurations about the stereocenter. She wonders whether the anesthetic is used as an enantiomer or as a racemate?
  - Ans: Since the bottle does not indicate configuration before the name, you surmise that it is the racemic form.

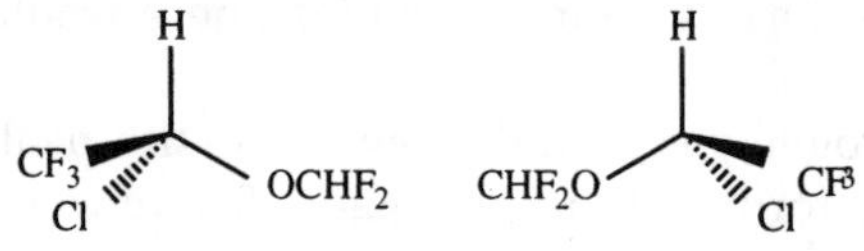
H
CF_3
Cl
$OCHF_2$
H
CHF_2O
Cl
CF3

- She mentions that she knows that halothane ($CF_3CHBrCl$) is a very popular modern anesthetic also. She asks what benefits it might have over ether compounds in a normal surgical environment, reminding you that operating rooms usually contain pure oxygen supplies? (You might want to refer to Section 5.3).
  - Ans: Ethers can form explosive peroxides in the presence of oxygen, but halothane can not. Although ethers are kept in small bottles and completely used up or discarded after each operation, and never used from an open container, accidental explosions have occurred.

CHAPTER 6

Alkenes

I. Textbook Chapter Contents

This chapter introduces alkenes, the first example of unsaturated compounds, involving a new hybridization of carbon. The second and third broad categories of reactions are also introduced—the addition reaction of alkenes and the elimination reactions used to prepare alkenes.

II. Learning Objectives

- Know the IUPAC nomenclature of alkenes and the common names of simple alkenes.
- Understand the electronic structure of alkenes, including sp^2 (trigonal) hybridization, the concept of unsaturation, and the relative stability of various kinds of alkenes.
- Understand the configurational isomerism possible in alkenes.
- Know the *E,Z* system of designation of configurational isomers.
- Write equations for the catalytic addition of hydrogen to alkenes (reduction) and be able to predict the stereochemical outcome of the *syn* addition.
- Understand the general mechanism for the addition of an electrophile to an alkene. Be able to predict the regiochemistry of the addition of unsymmetrical reagents. Know the Markovnikov rule and why it is valid.
- Write equations for the addition of hydrogen halides to alkenes.
- Write equations for the acid-catalyzed hydration of alkenes.
- Write equations for the anti-Markovnikov addition of water to alkenes, using the addition of diborane followed by oxidation of the resulting trialkylborane to an alcohol.
- Write equations for the stereospecific *anti*-addition of halogens to alkenes.
- Write equations for the *syn*-oxidation of an alkene to a vicinal diol using cold potassium permanganate.
- Write equations for the epoxidation of alkenes.
- Know the mechanism for the acid-catalyzed dehydration of alcohols to alkenes. Be able to explain the regiochemistry of such reactions (known as the Zaitzev rule).
- Know the mechanism for the base-induced dehydrohalogenation of alkyl halides to alkenes. Be able to explain the regiochemistry and the stereospecificity of the E2 elimination reaction.
- Understand the competition between elimination and substitution when an alkyl halide reacts with a nucleophile, as well as the factors controlling the ratio of products formed.

- Be able to carry out two-step syntheses involving alkyl halides, alcohols, and alkenes, applying a retrosynthetic approach.

- Be able to determine the structure of simple unknown compounds using qualitative tests and analysis of molecular formulas.

III. Glossary

addition reaction a reaction in which a reagent combines with a substrate, in this chapter an alkene. All of the atoms of both the reagent and the substrate appear in the product

alkene a family of hydrocarbons containing one or more double bonds and whose acyclic members have the general formula C_nH_{2n}

allyl group the CH_2=CH-CH_2– group

***anti* addition** an addition reaction in which the adding atoms or groups (the electrophile and the nucleophile) add to the opposite side of the double bond

anti-Markovnikov addition an addition reaction in which the product appears as though the addition occurred with a regiochemistry opposite to that predicted by the Markovnikov rule

catalytic hydrogenation the addition of hydrogen in the presence of a catalyst, typically Pt, Pd, or Raney nickel (RaNi)

***cis/trans* isomers** stereoisomers that have their substituents attached to different sides of a fixed plane of reference (a ring or a double bond)

***cis* alkene** an alkene with one substituent on each trigonal carbon with both substituents on the same side of the double bond

dehydration the reaction in which the elements of water are removed from an alcohol to form an alkene

dehydrohalogenation the reaction in which the elements of hydrogen halide are removed from an alkyl halide to form an alkene

diene a compound with two double bonds

double bond a covalent bond between two carbons in which four electrons are shared. It involves one sigma bond and one pi bond

E2 elimination a bimolecular elimination of an alkyl halide (to form an alkene) that is concerted and occurs with *anti* stereochemistry (the hydrogen and halogen leave from opposite directions)

(*E*) isomer an alkene stereoisomer in which the substituents with the highest priority on each trigonal carbon are located on opposite sides of the double bond

electrophilic addition addition to an alkene that is initiated by attack of the alkene pi electrons on an electrophile

elimination reaction a reaction in which the elements of a simple compound, typically water or a hydrogen halide, are removed from a compound to form an alkene

epoxidation the oxidation of an alkene with a peracid to form an epoxide (oxirane)

gem dihalide a compound in which two halogens are attached to a single carbon atom

hydration of alkene the addition of water across a double bond to form an alcohol, usually using an acid catalyst

hydroboration of alkenes the addition of diborane across the double bond of three equivalents of alkene to produce a trialkylborane. Oxidation of the latter produces three equivalents of alcohol, the overall result being the *anti*-Markovnikov hydration of the alkene

hydrogenation the addition of hydrogen to a multiple bond. Hydrogenation of alkenes produces alkanes

hydrohalogenation the addition of a hydrogen halide to an alkene

Markovnikov's rule an empirical rule that predicts that in the addition of an unsymmetrical reagent to an unsymmetrical alkene, the nucleophilic portion of the reagent is attached to the most highly substituted carbon. This rule is now explainable on the basis of the mechanism of electrophilic addition

methylene group the $-CH_2-$ or $CH_2=$ group

ozonolysis of alkenes the reaction of alkenes with ozone to form an ozonide; after treatment with zinc and water (a reduction) two carbonyl compounds result from the cleavage of the double bond

pi bond a bond formed by the overlap of two parallel *p* orbitals

pi orbital a molecular orbital formed by the overlap of two parallel *p* orbitals

polyene a compound with many double bonds

reduction increasing the hydrogen content or decreasing the oxygen content in a compound; reduction of alkenes implies the hydrogenation of alkenes

regiochemistry the orientation of a reaction with an unsymmetrical substrate

regioselective reaction a reaction which occurs to form preferentially, though not necessarily exclusively, one of two possible positional isomers

stereospecific a reaction that occurs with predictable stereochemistry to produce a single stereoisomer

stereospecific addition an addition reaction that occurs with predictable stereochemistry, forming either *syn* or *anti* addition products, but not both

***syn* addition** an addition reaction in which both adding atoms or groups (the electrophile and the nucleophile) add to the same side of the double bond

***trans* alkene** an alkene with one substituent on each trigonal carbon and with the two substituents on the opposite side of the double bond

trigonal hybridization the hybridization of a single *s* orbital and two *p* orbitals to form three sp^2 hybrid orbitals directed to the corners of an imaginary equilateral triangle, with an unhybridized *p* orbital oriented perpendicular to the plane of the triangle

unsaturated hydrocarbon a hydrocarbon containing one or more double or triple bonds. Such a compound can be "saturated" by the addition of hydrogen to form a saturated hydrocarbon (alkane)

vicinal dihalide a compound with a halogen attached to each of two adjacent carbons

vinyl group the CH_2=CH– group

(*Z*) isomer an alkene stereoisomer in which the substituents with the highest priority on each trigonal carbon are located on the same side of the double bond

Zaitzev rule an empirical rule which predicts that in an elimination reaction, in which two or more alkenes could be formed, the major product will be the most highly substituted alkene

IV. Summary of Reactions of Alkenes

V. Summary of Preparation of Alkenes

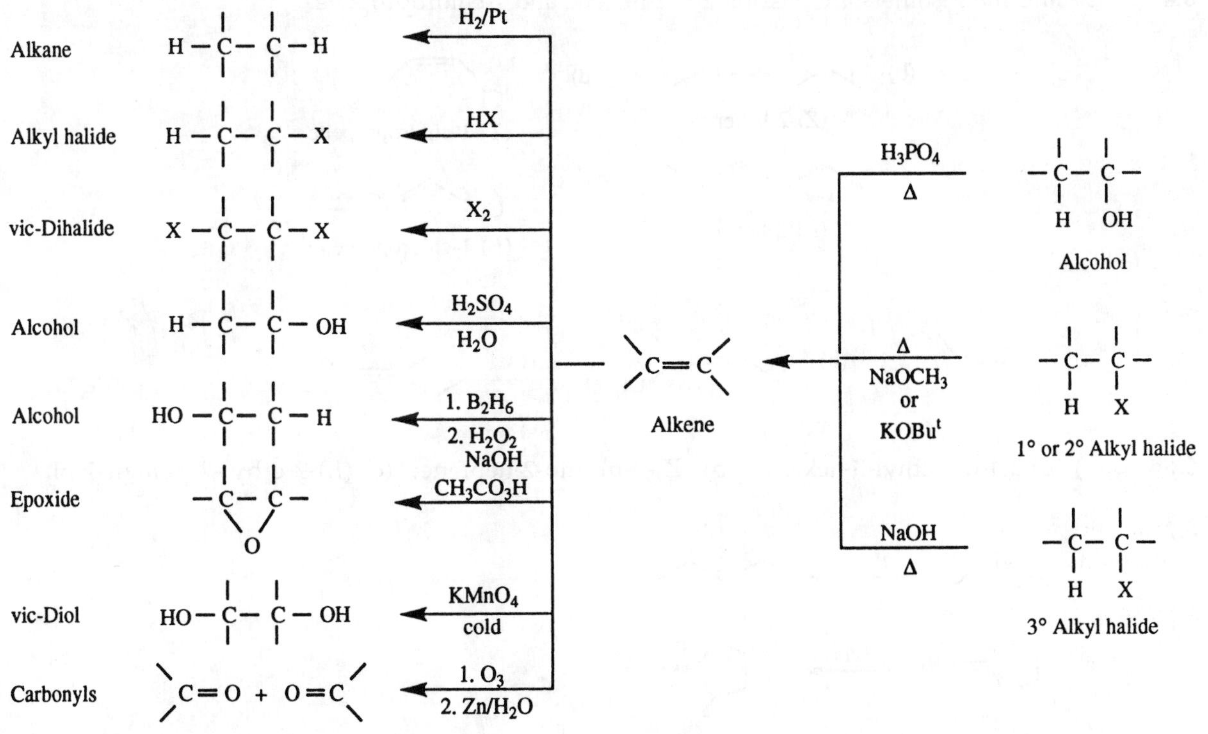

Alkane
H₂/Pt
Alkyl halide
HX
vic-Dihalide
X₂
Alcohol
H₂SO₄
H₂O
Alcohol
1. B₂H₆
2. H₂O₂
NaOH
Epoxide
CH₃CO₃H
vic-Diol
KMnO₄
cold
Carbonyls
1. O₃
2. Zn/H₂O
Alkene
H₃PO₄
Δ
Alcohol
Δ
NaOCH₃
or
KOBuᵗ
1° or 2° Alkyl halide
NaOH
Δ
3° Alkyl halide

VI. Solutions to Problems

For "**How to Solve a Problem**," refer to pages 188, 199, 201, 206, 211, 213, 218, and 220.

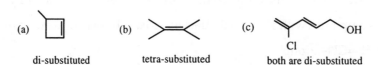

6.1

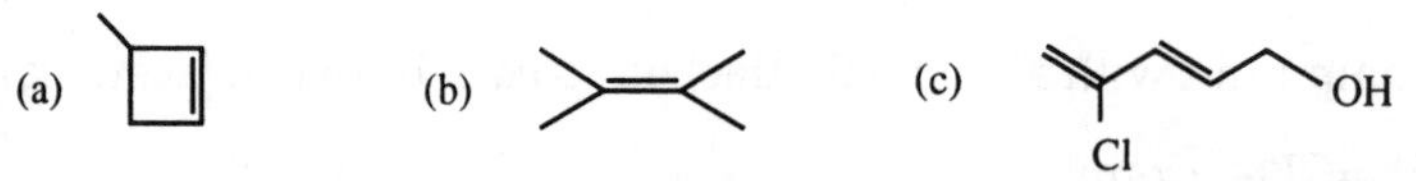
(a)
(b)
(c)
OH
Cl

di-substituted — tetra-substituted — both are di-substituted

6.2 (a) 3-bromo-4-methylcyclopentene (di-substituted); (b) 2-methyl-2-pentene (tri-substituted); (c) 1-ethyl-1,4-cyclohexadiene (tri- and di-substituted).

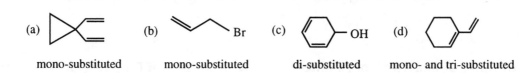

6.3

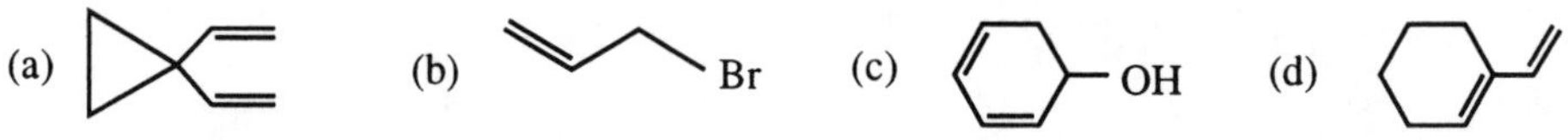
(a)
(b)
Br
(c)
OH
(d)

mono-substituted — mono-substituted — di-substituted — mono- and tri-substituted

6.4 *Cis* and *trans* isomers are possible for 2-hexene and 1-chloropropene.

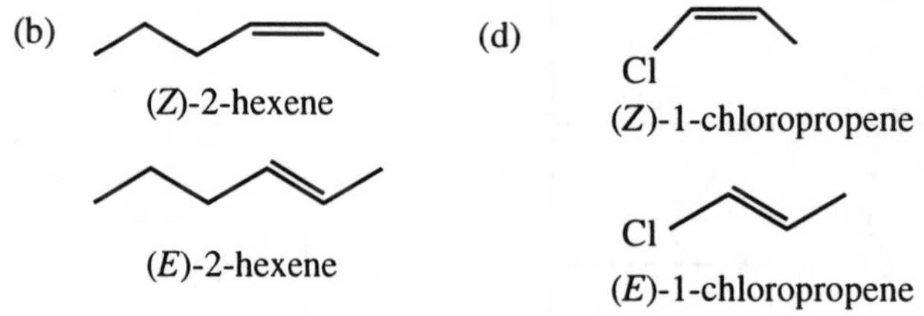
(b)
(Z)-2-hexene
(E)-2-hexene
(d)
Cl
(Z)-1-chloropropene
Cl
(E)-1-chloropropene

6.5

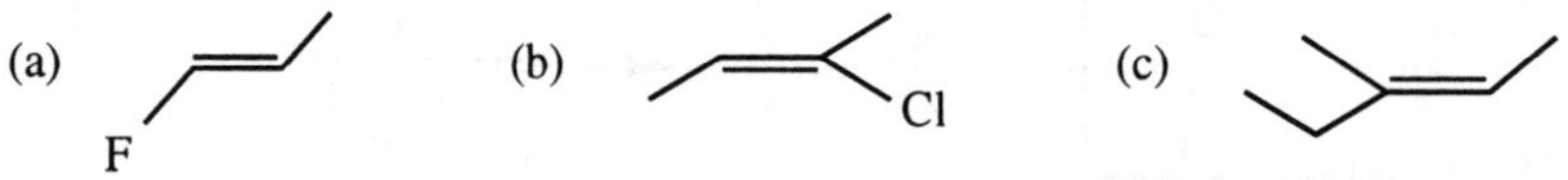
(a)
F
(b)
Cl
(c)

6.6 (a) (*E*)-3,4-dimethyl-3-hexene; (b) (*Z*)-3-bromo-2-heptene; (c) (*E*)-2-ethyl-2-penten-1-ol.

6.7

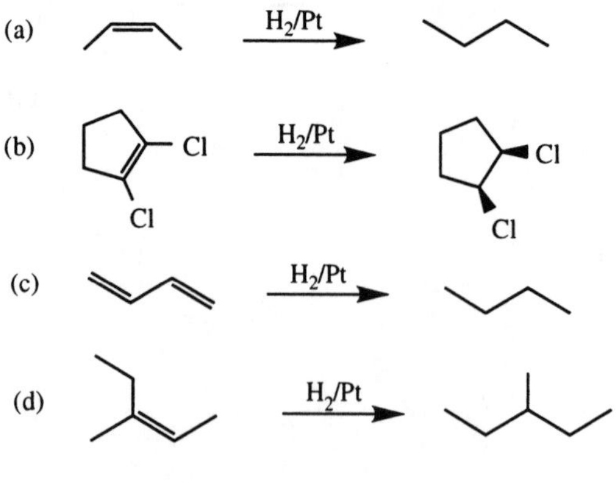
(a)
H2/Pt
(b)
Cl
Cl
H2/Pt
Cl
Cl
(c)
H2/Pt
(d)
H2/Pt

6.8

(a) 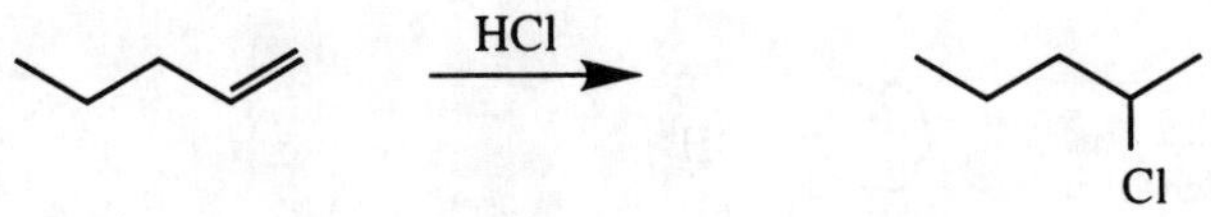
HCl
Cl

(b) 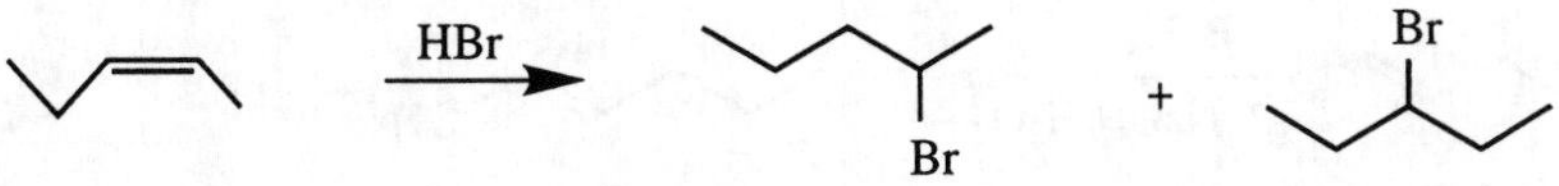
HBr
Br
+
Br

(c) 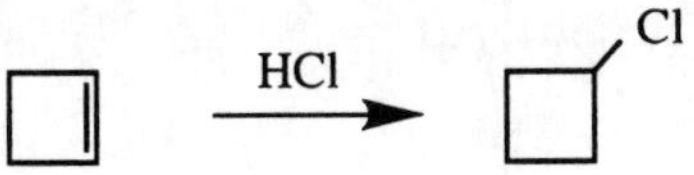
HCl
Cl

6.9

(a) 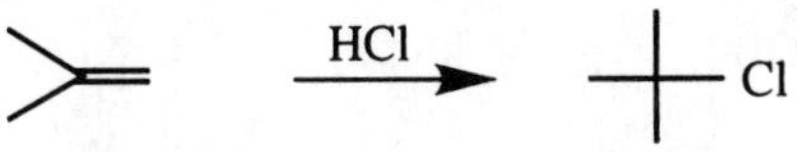
HCl
Cl

isobutylene (2-methylpropene) — *t*-butyl chloride

(b) 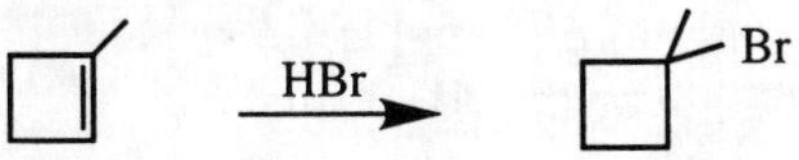
HBr
Br

1-methylcyclobutene — 1-bromo-1-methylcyclobutane

(c) 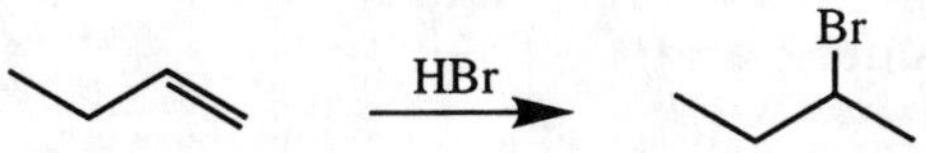
HBr
Br

1-butene — 2-bromobutane

6.10

(a) 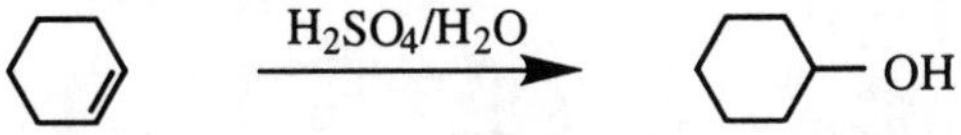
H2SO4/H2O
OH

(b) 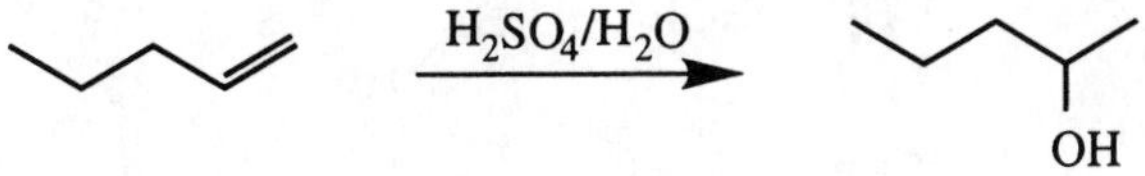
H2SO4/H2O
OH

(c) 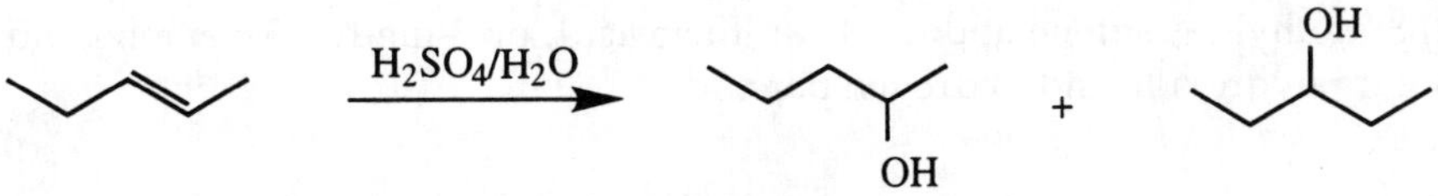
H2SO4/H2O
OH
+
OH

(d) 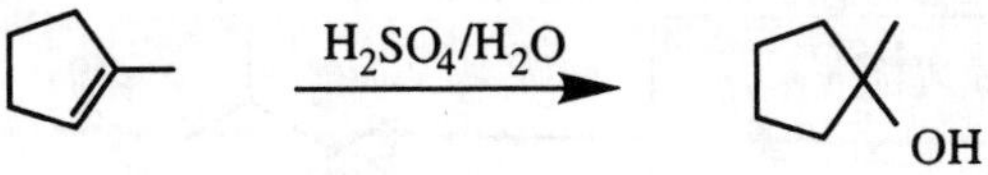
H2SO4/H2O
OH

6.11

(a) 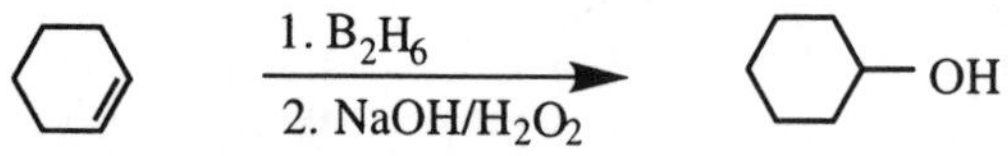

(b) 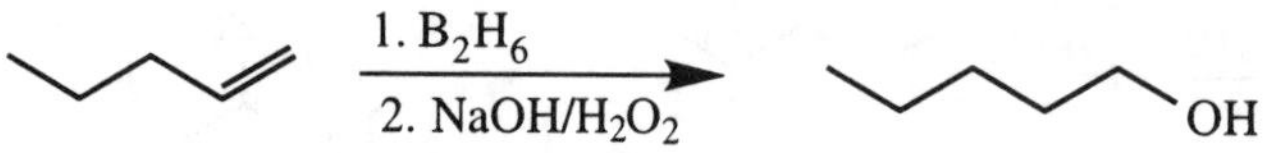

(c) 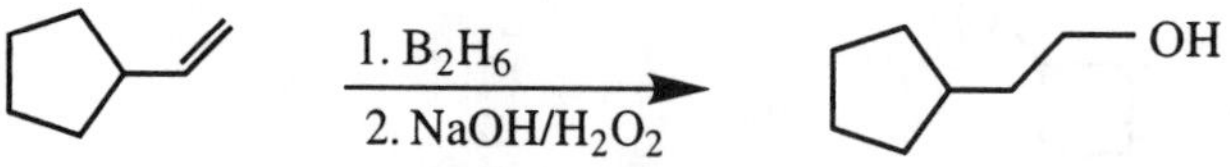

(d) 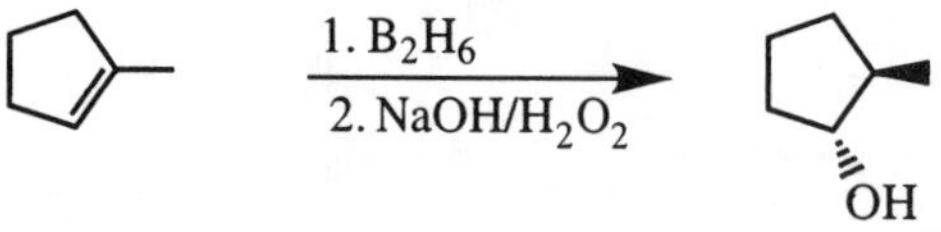

6.12 (a) Isobutylene (2-methylpropene) and dilute sulfuric acid;

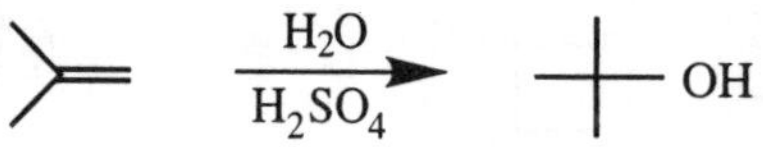

(b) 1-methylcyclohexene and dilute sulfuric acid;

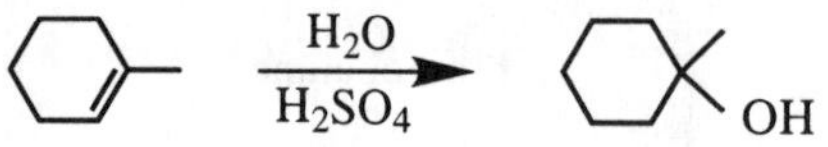

(c) 1-methylcyclohexene and diborane, then sodium hydroxide and hydrogen peroxide;

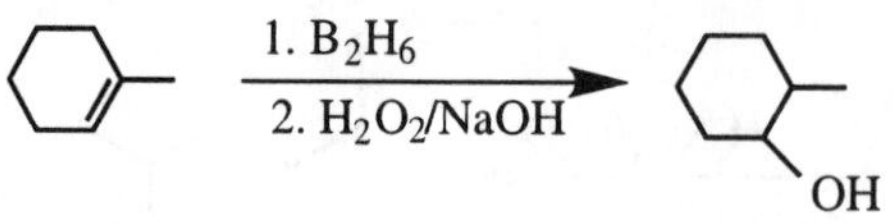

(d) 3-methyl-1-pentene and dilute sulfuric acid, **or** 3-methyl-2-pentene and diborane, then sodium hydroxide and hydrogen peroxide.

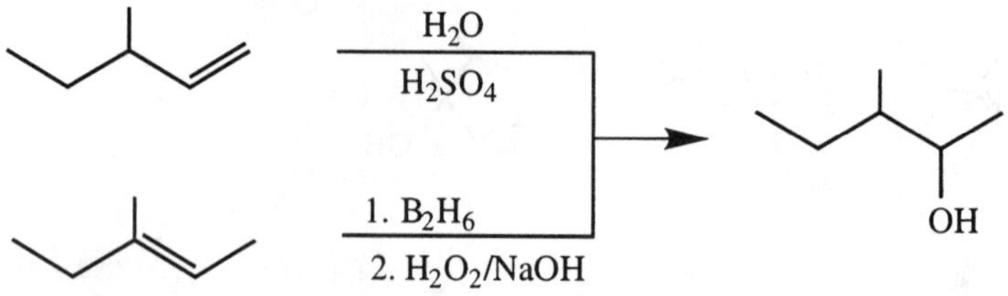

6.13 All of these reactions produce racemic mixtures, that is both enantiomers in equal amounts. Careful inspection reveals that one isomer is the mirror image of the other isomer (flip the right hand isomer 180° to prove this to yourself).

(a)

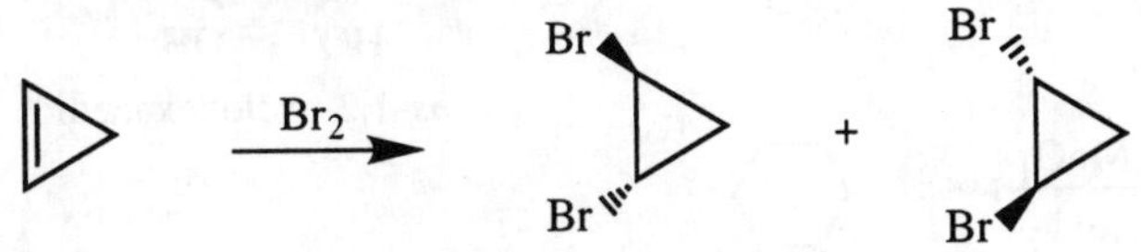
Br_2
Br
Br
+
Br
Br

(b)

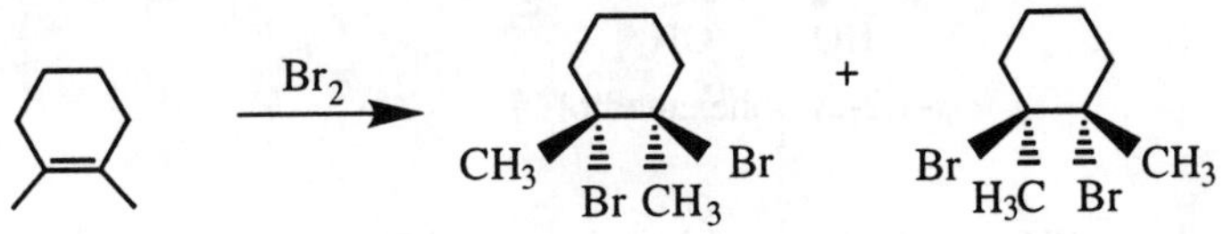
Br_2
CH_3
Br CH_3
Br
+
Br
H_3C Br
CH_3

(c)

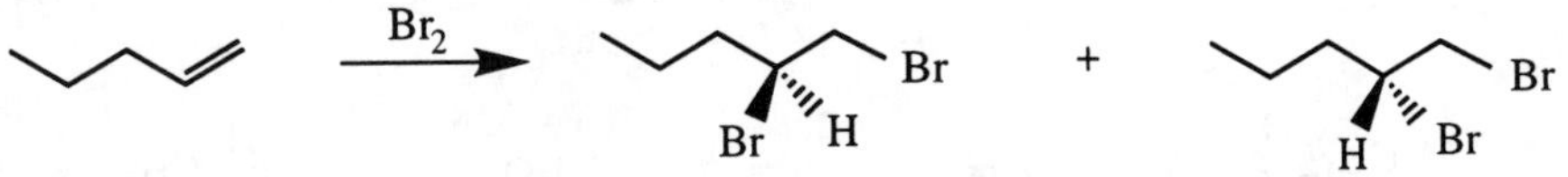
Br_2
Br
Br
H
+
Br
H
Br

(d)

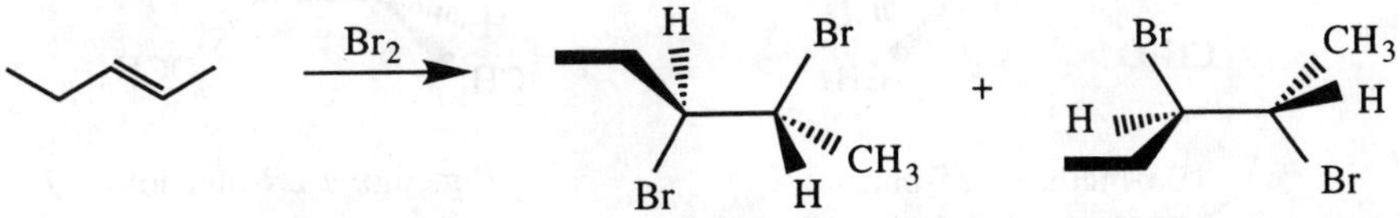
Br_2
H
Br
Br
CH_3
H
+
Br
CH_3
H
H
Br

6.14

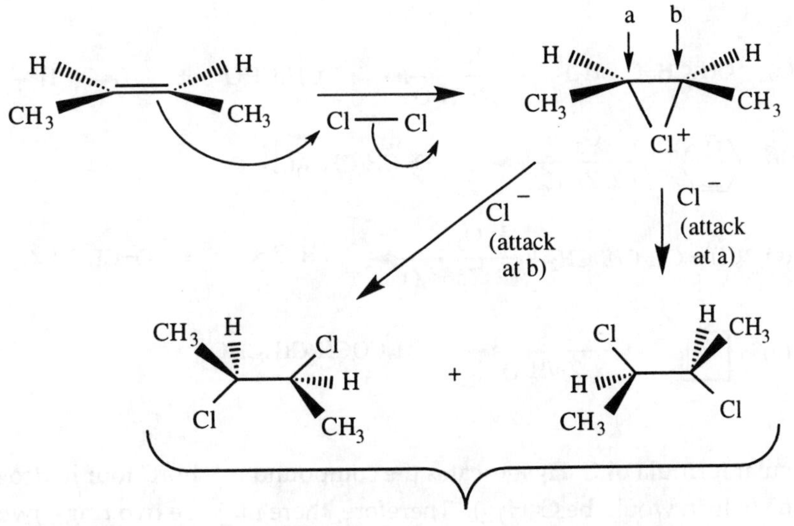
H
CH_3
H
CH_3
Cl
Cl
a
b
H
CH_3
H
CH_3
Cl^+
Cl^-
(attack
at b)
Cl^-
(attack
at a)
CH_3
H
Cl
H
Cl
CH_3
+
Cl
H
CH_3
H
CH_3
Cl

a pair of enantiomers (a racemic mixture)

6.15

(a) 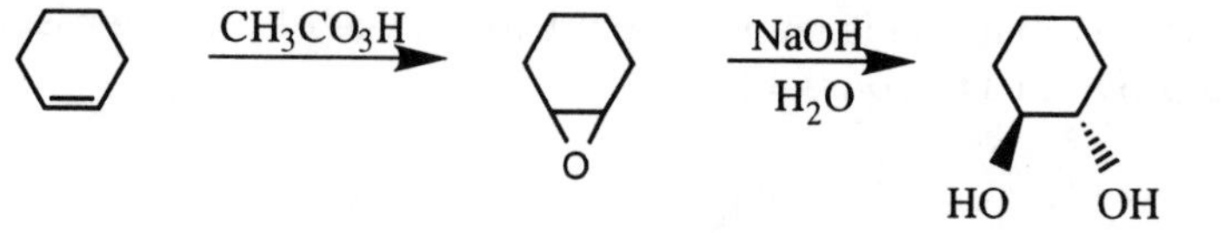
CH3CO3H
NaOH
H2O
O
HO OH

trans-1,2-cyclohexanediol

(b) 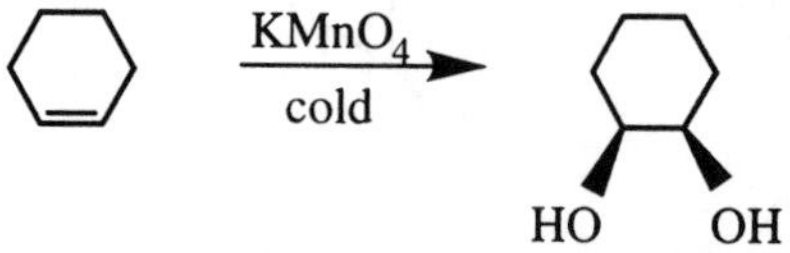
KMnO4
cold
HO OH

cis-1,2-cyclohexanediol

(c) 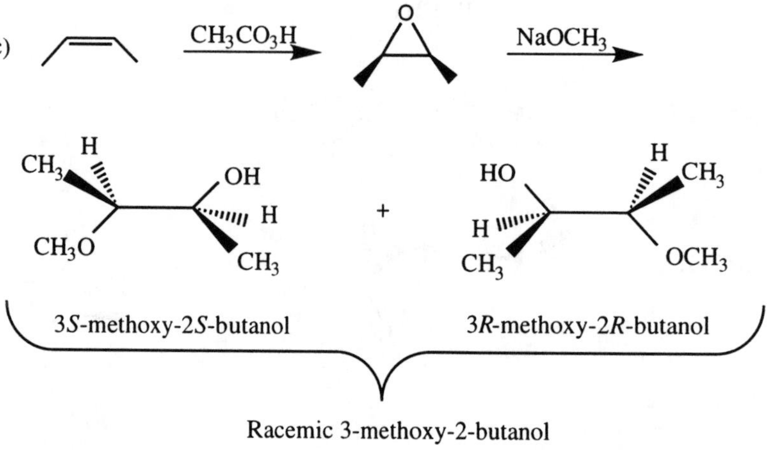
CH3CO3H
O
NaOCH3
H
CH3
OH
H
CH3O
CH3
+
HO
H
CH3
OCH3
3S-methoxy-2S-butanol
3R-methoxy-2R-butanol
Racemic 3-methoxy-2-butanol

6.16

(a) $CH_3CH{=}C(CH_3)_2 \xrightarrow[\text{2. Zn/H}_2\text{O}]{\text{1. O}_3} CH_3CHO + O{=}C(CH_3)_2$

(b)  $\xrightarrow[\text{2. Zn/H}_2\text{O}]{\text{1. O}_3} O{=}CH(CH_2)_4CH{=}O$

(c) $CH_2{=}CH\text{-}CH{=}CH_2 \xrightarrow[\text{2. Zn/H}_2\text{O}]{\text{1. O}_3} 2\ H_2C{=}O + O{=}CHCH{=}O$

(d)  $\xrightarrow[\text{2. Zn/H}_2\text{O}]{\text{1. O}_3} CH_3COCH_2CH_2CHO$

6.17 The molecular formula of C_5H_8 indicates the compound is "short" four hydrogens from being a C_5 alkane (which would be C_5H_{12}). Therefore, there must be two rings, two double bonds, or one of each in the structure. Since it only absorbs one equivalent of hydrogen, and therefore forms C_5H_{10}, the original compound must contain only one double bond, and therefore one ring. Since only a single compound was obtained upon ozonolysis, which cleaves a double bond, the two "ends" of the double bond must be connected. In other words, it must be a cyclic compound which contains the double bond in the ring and for which the following are possible structures:

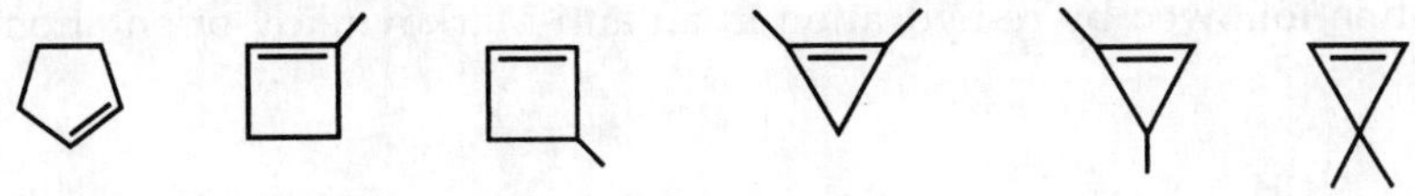

Additional experiments, usually spectroscopic (see Chapter 11), would be required to distinguish between these possibilities.

6.18

(a) 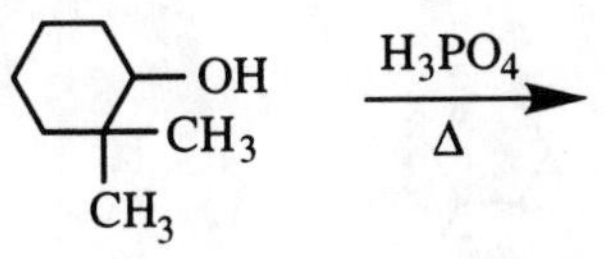

(b) 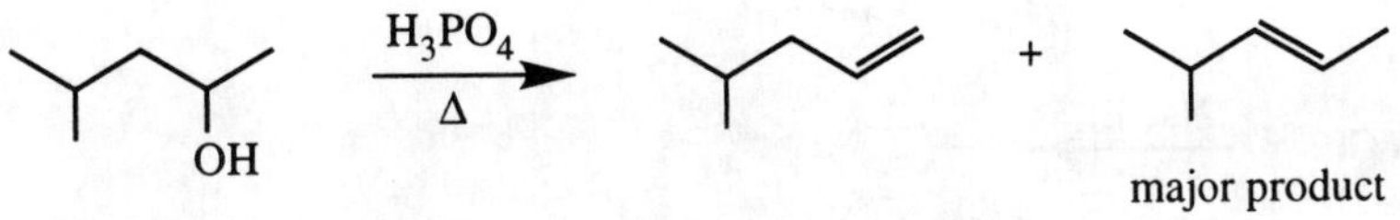

(c) 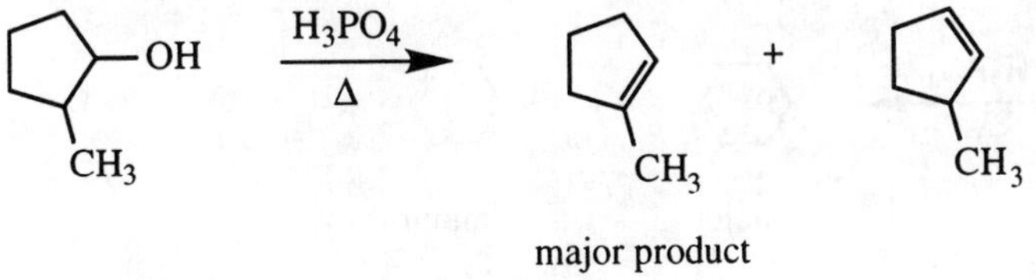

6.19

(a) 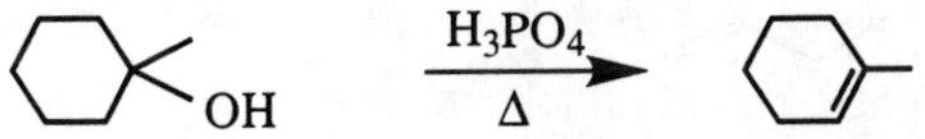

(b) 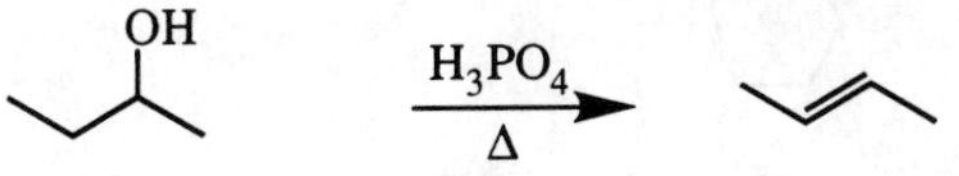

(c) 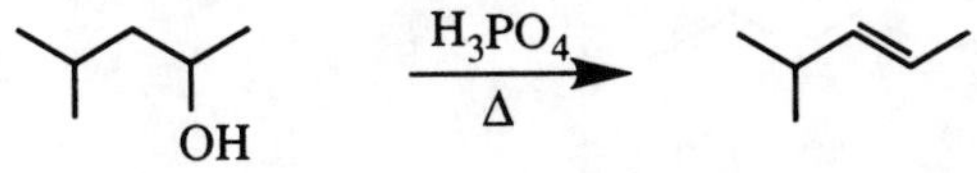

6.20 The challenge is to literally "move" a hydroxyl group from one carbon to an adjacent carbon. Of course, this cannot be done directly. However, alcohols can be converted into alkenes which can be re-converted into alcohols with pre-determined regioselectivity. Therefore a dehydration followed by re-hydration in an anti-Markovnikov orientation accomplishes the goal.

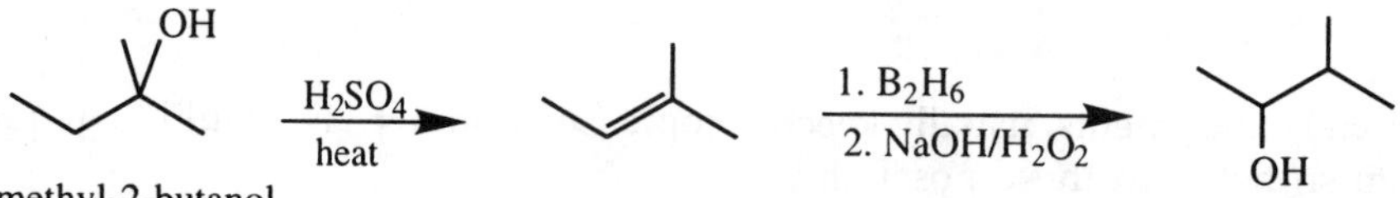
OH
H_2SO_4
heat
1. B_2H_6
2. NaOH/H_2O_2
OH

2-methyl-2-butanol   3-methyl-2-butanol

6.21

(a)

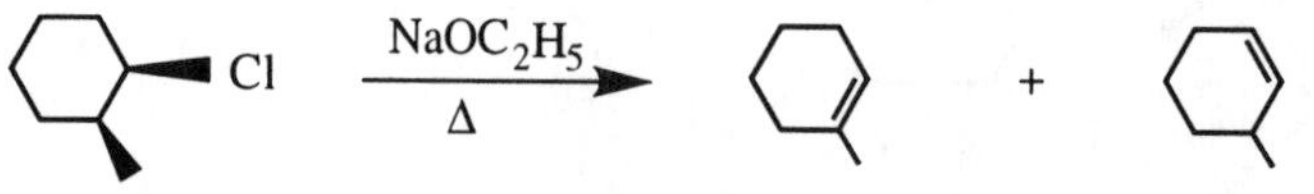
Cl
$NaOC_2H_5$
Δ
+

major   minor

(b)

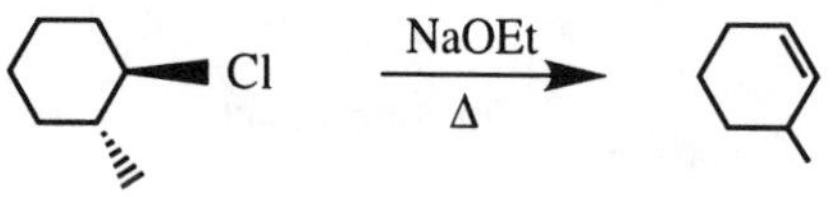
Cl
NaOEt
Δ

(c)

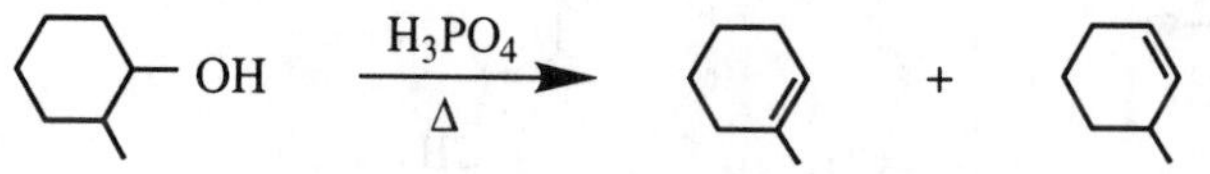
OH
H_3PO_4
Δ
+

major   minor

6.22

(a)

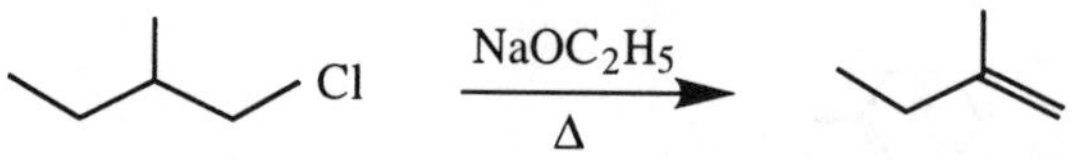
Cl
$NaOC_2H_5$
Δ

(b)

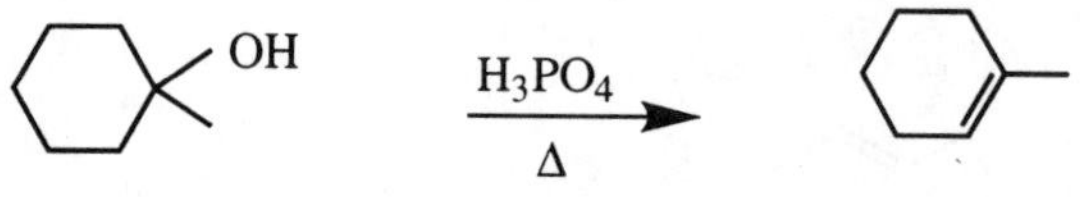
OH
H_3PO_4
Δ

(c)

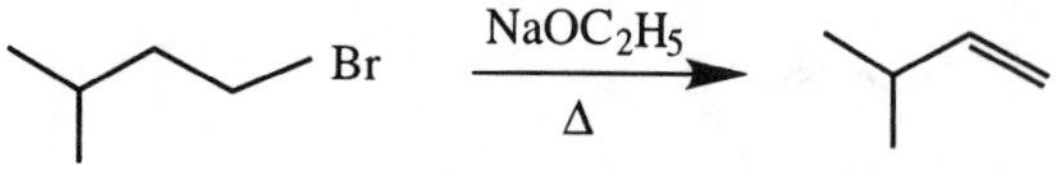
Br
$NaOC_2H_5$
Δ

6.23

(a) 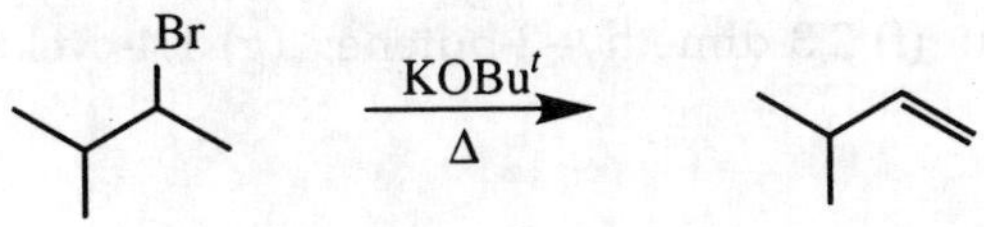
Br
KOBu^t
Δ

(b) 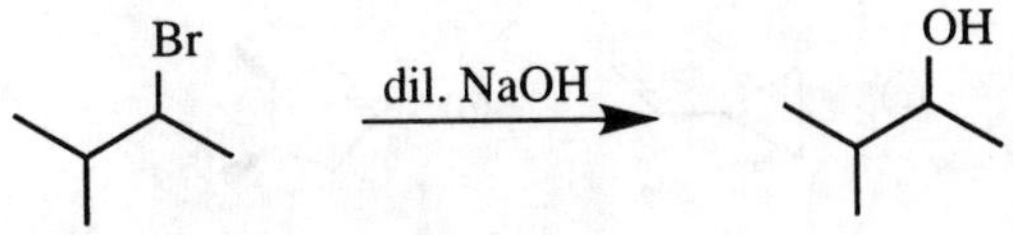
Br
dil. NaOH
OH

(c) 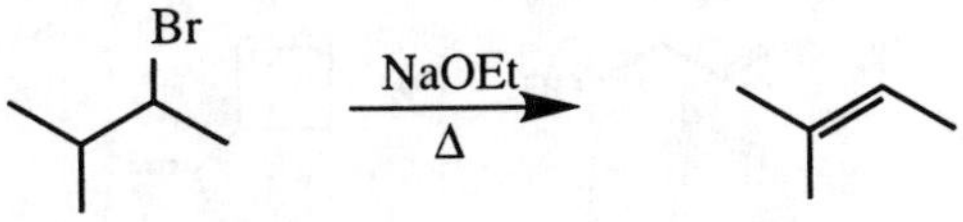
Br
NaOEt
Δ

6.24

(a) 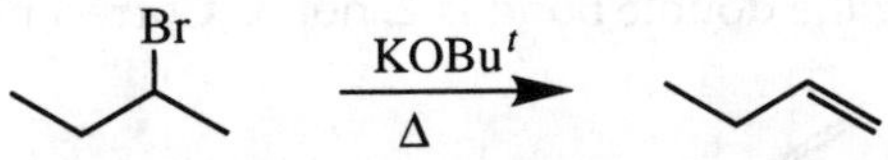
Br
KOBu^t
Δ

(b) 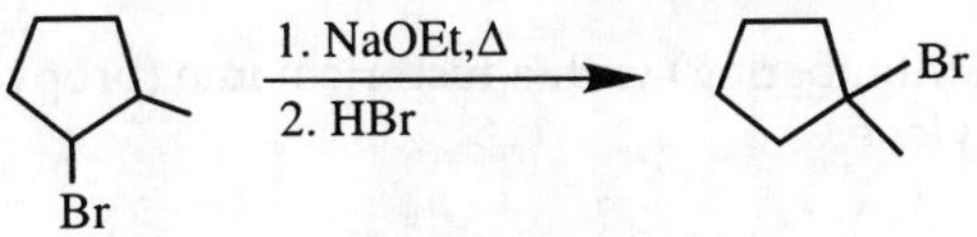
1. NaOEt,Δ
2. HBr
Br
Br

(c) 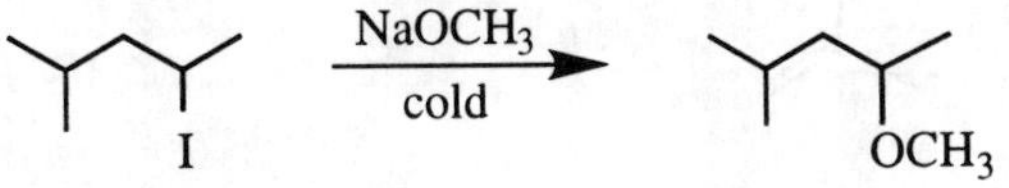
NaOCH$_3$
cold
I
OCH$_3$

(d) 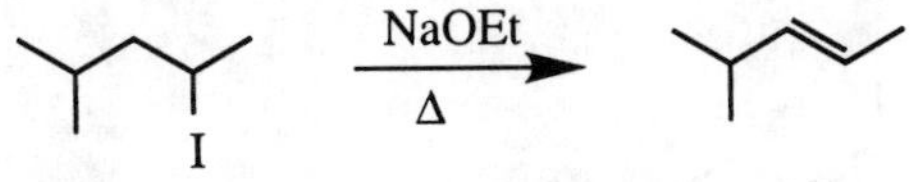
NaOEt
Δ
I

6.25

(a) 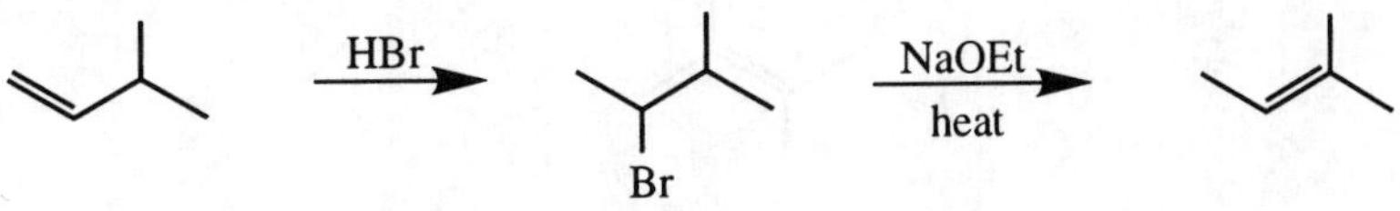
HBr
Br
NaOEt
heat

(b) 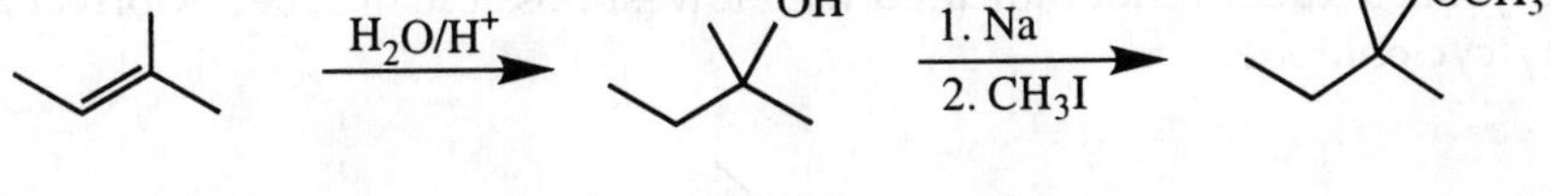
H$_2$O/H$^+$
OH
1. Na
2. CH$_3$I
OCH$_3$

(c) 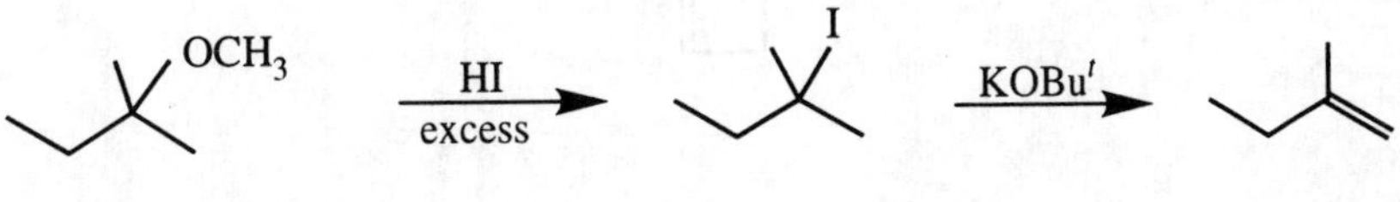
OCH$_3$
HI
excess
I
KOBu^t

6.26 (a) 2-pentene; (b) (*E*)-5-methyl-2-hexene; (c) 1,2-dimethylcyclopentene; (d) (Z)1-bromo-2-chloro-1-butene; (e) 5-hexen-2-ol; (f) 2,3-dimethyl-2-butene; (g) 1,4-cyclohexadiene; (h) 3-methyl-1-pentene.

6.27

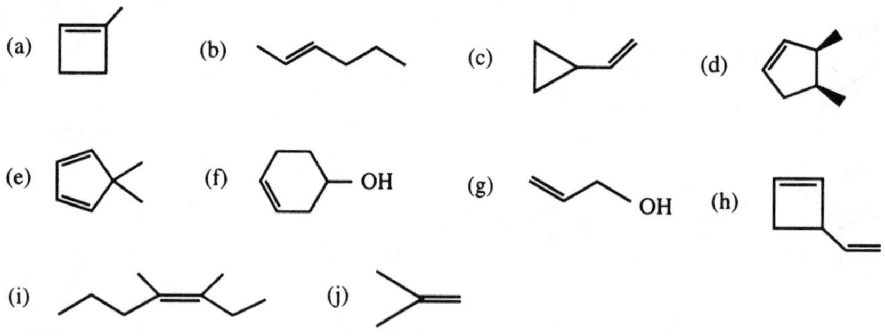
(a)
(b)
(c)
(d)
(e)
(f)
OH
(g)
OH
(h)
(i)
(j)

6.28 (a) The lowest possible number for locating the double bond is 2, not 3. Correct name is *cis*-2-pentene.

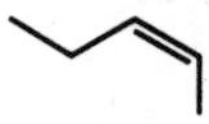

(b) Name mixes the IUPAC system (numbering) with a historic name (propylene). Correct name is 2-methylpropene or isobutylene.

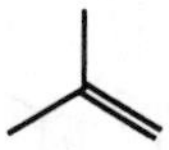

(c) Use of "*trans*" doesn't indicate which groups are trans. Correct name is *E*-3-methyl-3-hexene.

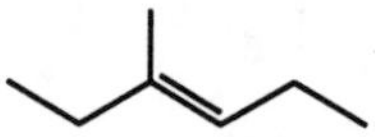

(d) Ethene is not the longest possible chain containing the double bond - it is butene. Correct name is 2,3-dimethyl-2-butene.

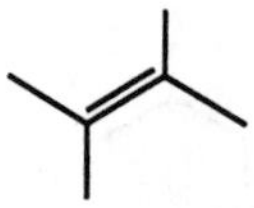

(e) Methyl substituent is not indicated with lowest possible number. Correct name is 1-methylcyclobutene.

(f) Lowest possible numbers are not used. Correct name is 3,4-dibromocyclopentene.

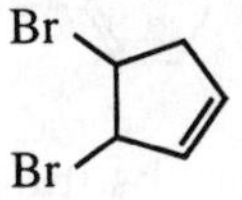

(g) Longest chain is hexene, not pentene. Correct name is 2-hexene.

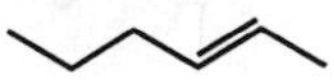

(h) Alcohol functional group must carry lowest possible number. Correct name is 3-penten-1-ol.

(i) Double bonds should carry lowest possible numbers. Correct name is 5,5-dimethyl-1,3-cyclohexadiene.

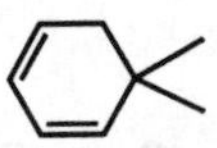

(j) Longest chain is not butene. Correct name is 1,3-hexadiene.

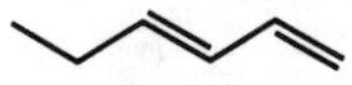

6.29 The formula C_4H_8 represents a hydrocarbon which is two hydrogens "short" of being an alkane. Therefore, it must contain either a double bond or a carbocyclic ring. The alkenes could be derived from a butane skeleton or an isobutane skeleton, and four different compounds are possible, two of which are *cis-trans* isomers of each other. The carbocyclic compounds could only have either a three- or four-membered ring.

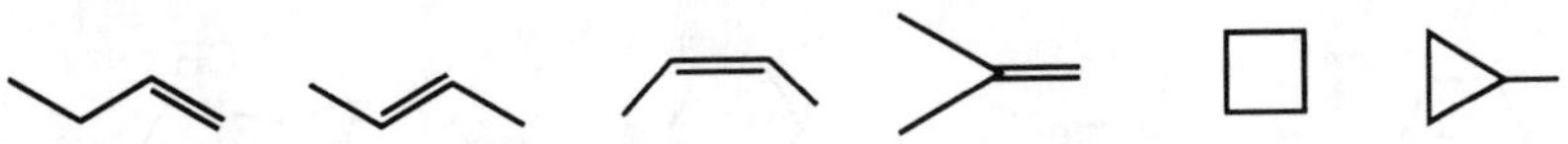

6.30 The alkenes in problem 6.29 contain the following number of substituents on their double bonds, respectively: one, two, two, two.

6.31 (a) 2-methyl-1-butene: is a di-substituted alkene rather than a mono-substituted alkene.

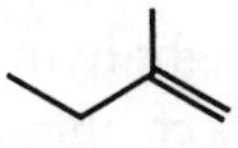

(b) *E*-2-pentene: The substituents are on opposite sides of the alkene resulting in less steric hindrance.

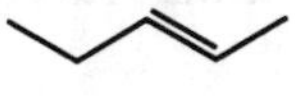

(c) 1-methylcyclohexene: is a tri-substituted alkene rather than a disubstituted alkene.

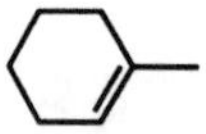

(d) 2,3-dimethyl-2-butene: is a tetra-substituted alkene rather than a tri-substituted alkene.

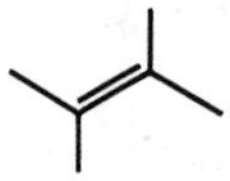

(e) *trans*-3,4-dimethylcyclobutene: the two methyl groups are oriented away from each other, thereby lowering the steric hindrance.

6.32 The highest priority group on each double bond is indicated by the small arrow:

(a)
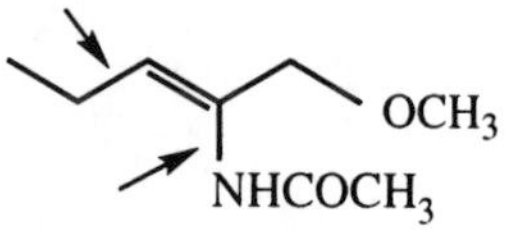
OCH3
NHCOCH3
(b)
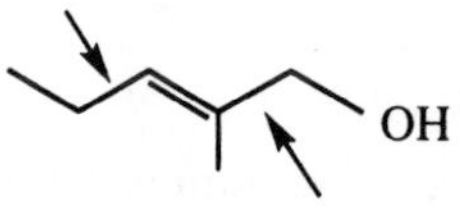
OH
(c)
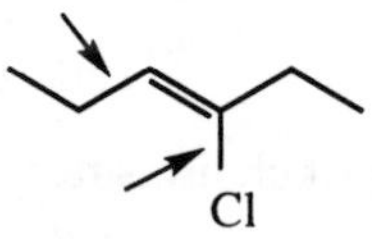
Cl

Z *E* *Z*

6.33 There are only two configurational isomers of 1,2-dimethylcyclohexane, the *cis*- and the *trans*-. The hydrogenation process occurs by two hydrogen atoms being "delivered" to the alkene from the catalyst surface. Thus, they approach the alkene from the same side. In order to form a *trans* isomer the hydrogens must be "delivered" from the opposite sides of the ring and that is physically impossible with these catalytic surfaces. Thus, the only product is the *cis* isomer.

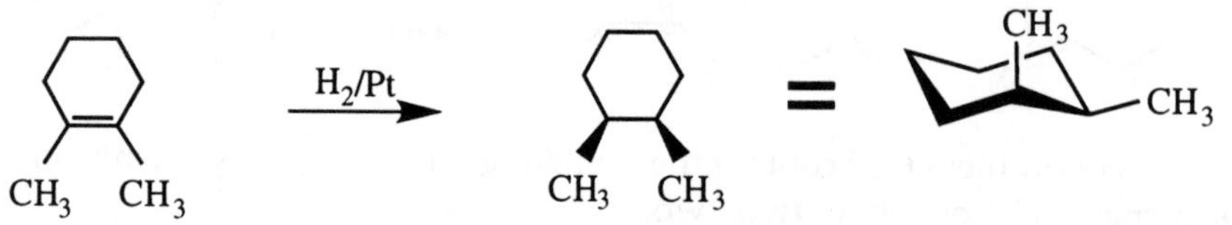
CH3 CH3
H2/Pt
CH3 CH3
=
CH3
CH3

cis-1,2-dimethylcyclohexane

6.34 Caryophyllene, $C_{15}H_{24}$, is "short" eight hydrogens from being a saturated acyclic alkane ($C_{15}H_{32}$). Therefore, it must contain a combination of four rings or double bonds (excluding consideration of triple bonds at this point). Since hydrogenation adds four hydrogens there must have been two double bonds present. By difference, therefore, it must contain two rings. Therefore, it can be concluded that caryophyllene is a bicyclic diene.

6.35

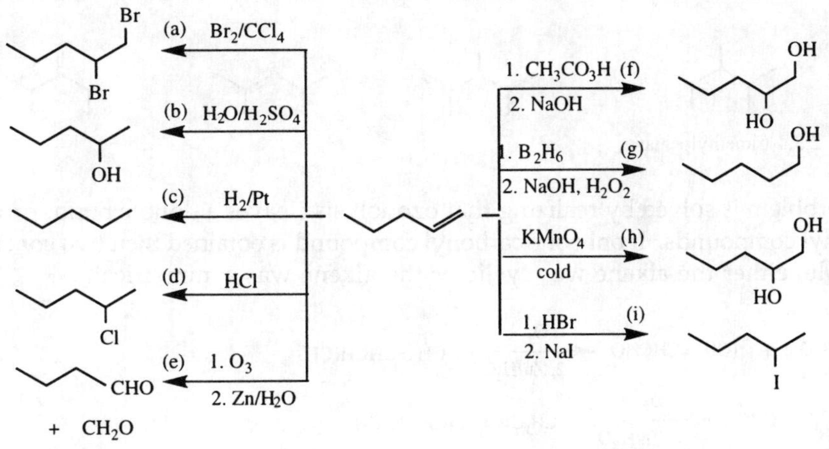

6.36

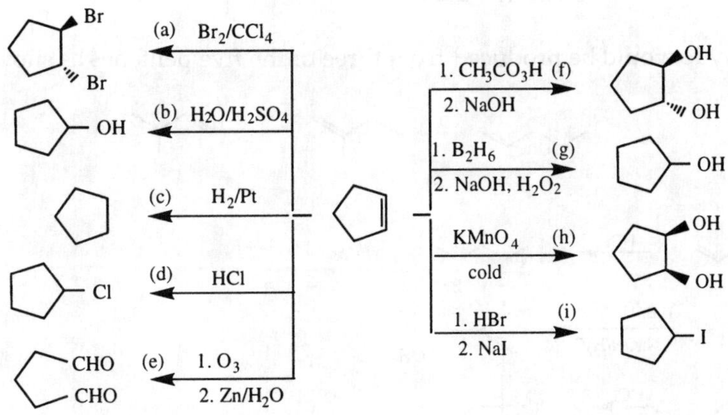

6.37

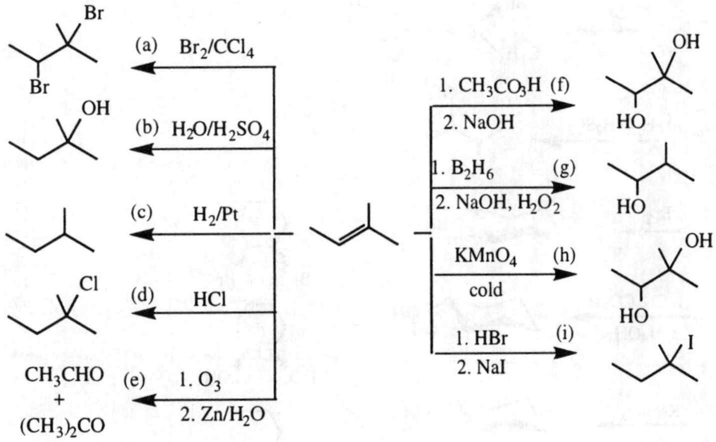

6.38 Three constitutionally isomeric alkenes could produce 2,3,4-trimethylpentane.

2,3,4-trimethylpentane

6.39 This problem is solved by realizing that ozonolysis cleaves a double bond, producing two carbonyl compounds. If only one carbonyl compound is obtained then two conclusions are possible, either the alkene was cyclic or the alkene was symmetrical.

(a) $CH_2O + (CH_3)_2CHCHO \xleftarrow[\text{2. Zn/H}_2\text{O}]{\text{1. O}_3} CH_2{=}CHCH(CH_3)_2$

(b) $CH_3CH_2CHO \xleftarrow[\text{2. Zn/H}_2\text{O}]{\text{1. O}_3} CH_3CH_2CH{=}CHCH_2CH_3$

(c) $O{=}CHCH_2CH_2CH{=}O \xleftarrow[\text{2. Zn/H}_2\text{O}]{\text{1. O}_3}$ 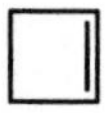

6.40 Formaldehyde would be produced from three of the five pentenes as shown below:

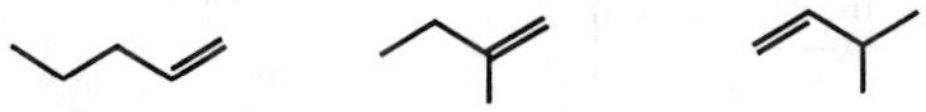

6.41

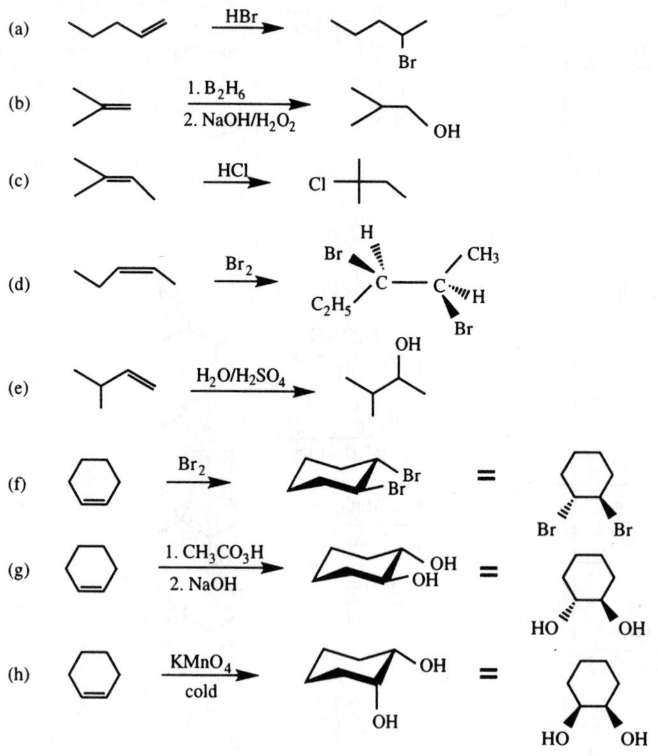
(a)
HBr
Br
(b)
1. B_2H_6
2. $NaOH/H_2O_2$
OH
(c)
HCl
Cl
(d)
Br_2
H
Br
CH_3
C
C
H
C_2H_5
Br
(e)
H_2O/H_2SO_4
OH
(f)
Br_2
Br
Br
=
Br
Br
(g)
1. CH_3CO_3H
2. NaOH
OH
OH
=
HO
OH
(h)
$KMnO_4$
cold
OH
OH
=
HO
OH

6.42

(a) 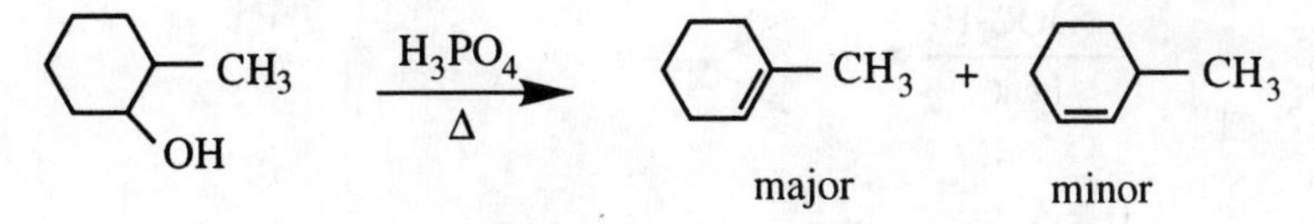
CH3
OH
H3PO4
Δ
CH3
+
CH3
major
minor

(b) $CH_3CH_2CH_2CH_2OH \xrightarrow[\Delta]{H_3PO_4} CH_3CH_2CH{=}CH_2$

(c) $CH_3CH_2CHOHCH_3 \xrightarrow[\Delta]{H_3PO_4} \underset{\text{major}}{CH_3CH{=}CHCH_3} + \underset{\text{minor}}{CH_3CH_2CH{=}CH_2}$

(d) 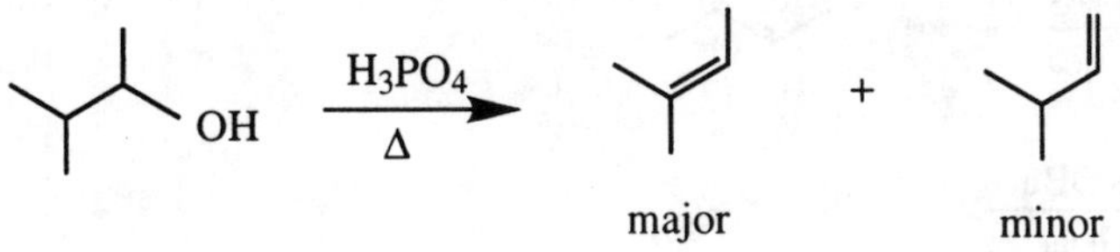
OH
H3PO4
Δ
+
major
minor

6.43

(a) $CH_3CH_2C(OH)(CH_3)_2 \xrightarrow[\Delta]{H_2SO_4} CH_3CH{=}C(CH_3)_2$

(b) 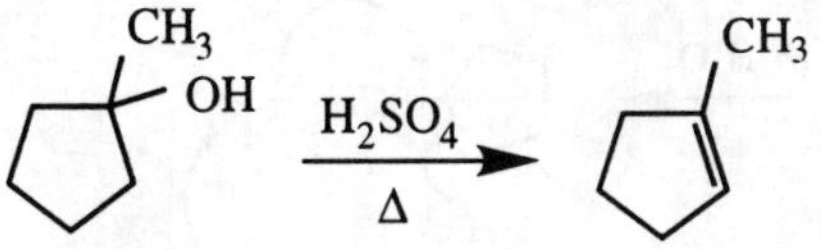
CH3
OH
H2SO4
Δ
CH3

(c) 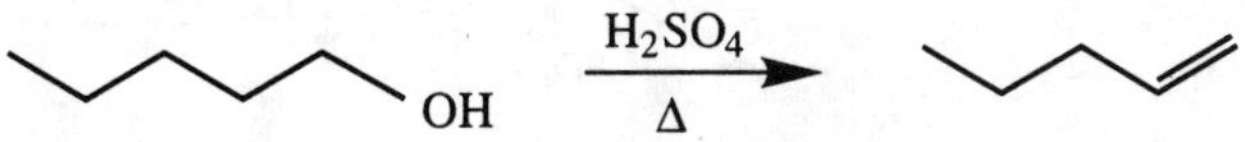
OH
H2SO4
Δ

(d) 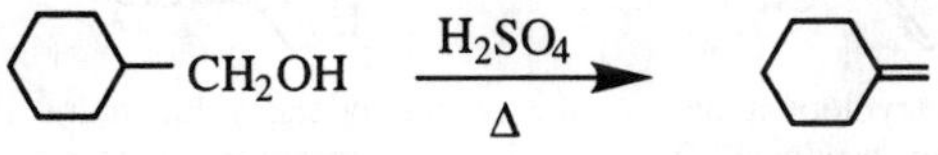
CH2OH
H2SO4
Δ

6.44

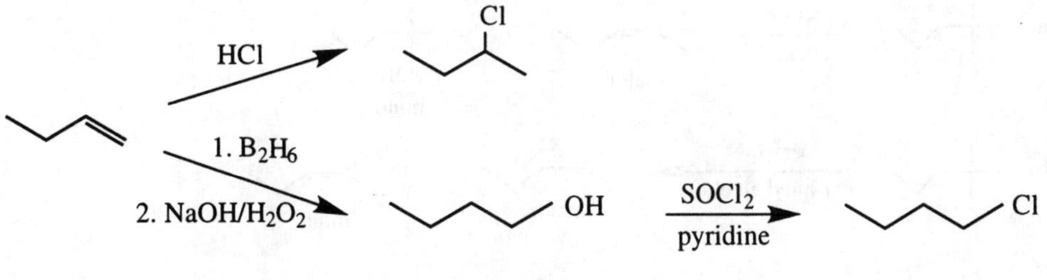
Cl
HCl
1. B2H6
2. NaOH/H2O2
OH
SOCl2
pyridine
Cl

6.45

(a) 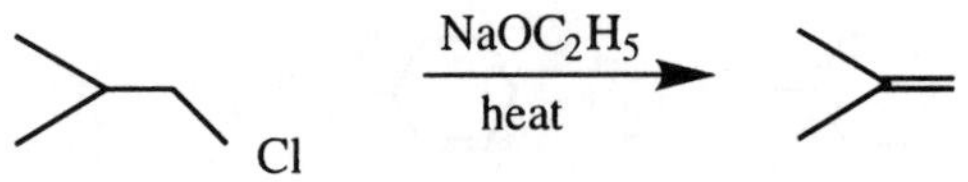
Cl
NaOC₂H₅
heat

(b) 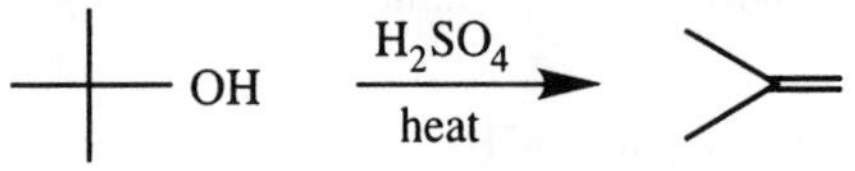
OH
H₂SO₄
heat

(c) 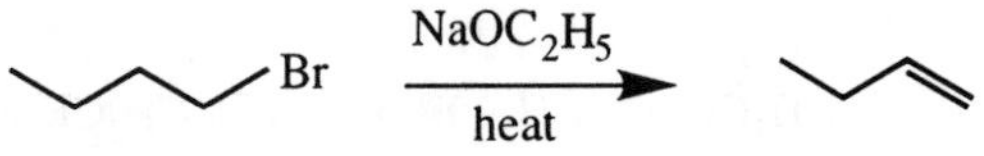
Br
NaOC₂H₅
heat

(d) 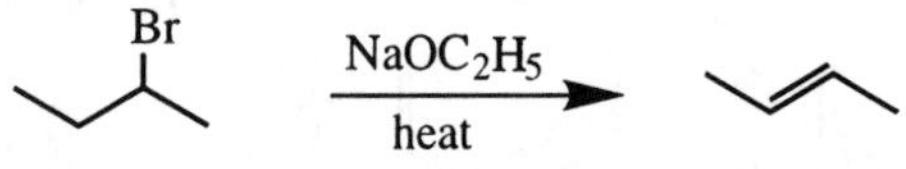
Br
NaOC₂H₅
heat

(e) 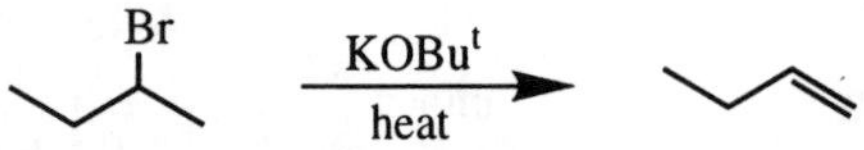
Br
KOBuᵗ
heat

6.46 Two products are possible in this dehydration reaction. 1-Methylcyclopentene is expected to be the major product because it has the most stable double bond, being tri-substituted. Methylenecyclopentane has a di-substituted double bond.

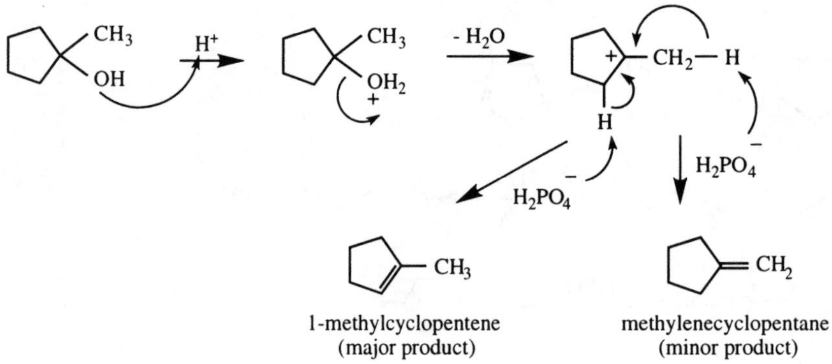
CH₃
OH
H⁺
CH₃
OH₂
+
- H₂O
+
CH₂— H
H
H₂PO₄⁻
H₂PO₄⁻
CH₃
1-methylcyclopentene
(major product)
CH₂
methylenecyclopentane
(minor product)

6.47

(a) 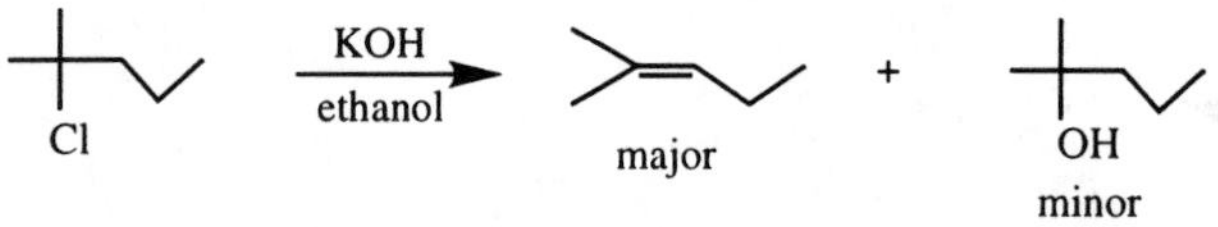
Cl
KOH
ethanol
major
+
OH
minor

(b) 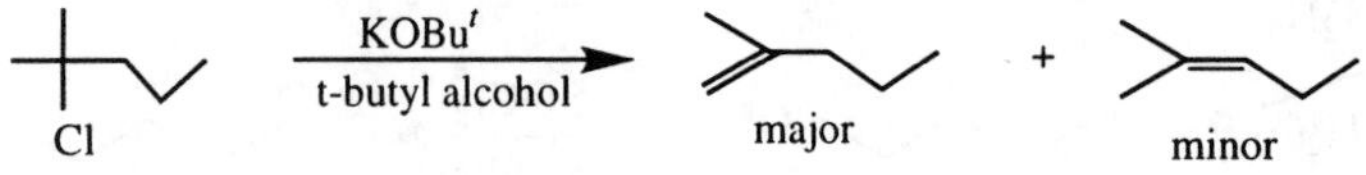
Cl
KOBuᵗ
t-butyl alcohol
major
+
minor

(c) 
Cl
NaOC₂H₅
ethanol
major
+
minor

6.48

(a) 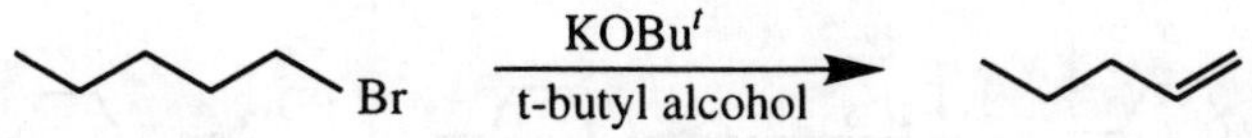
Br
KOBu^t
t-butyl alcohol

(b) 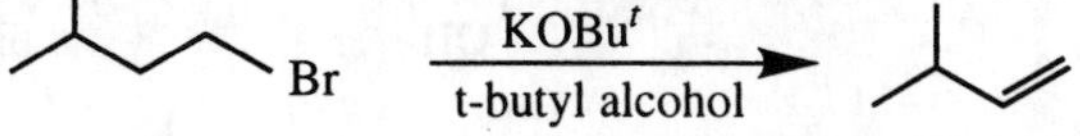
Br
KOBu^t
t-butyl alcohol

(c) 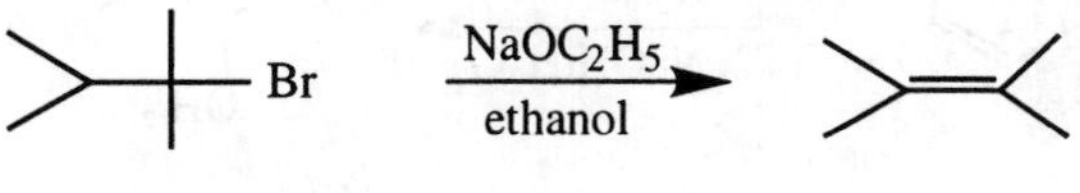
Br
$NaOC_2H_5$
ethanol

(d) 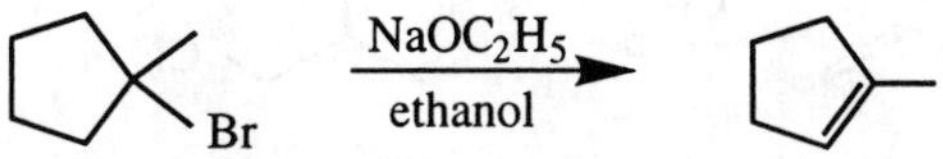
Br
$NaOC_2H_5$
ethanol

6.49 There are no *cis-trans* isomers for myrcene or for limonene. There are four *cis-trans* isomers for farnesol, two each at the C2-3 and C6-7 double bonds. There will be a 2*Z*,6*Z*-, a 2*Z*,6*E*-, a 2*E*,6*E*-, and a 2*E*,6*Z*- isomer. Farnesol itself is named 3,7,11-trimethyl-2*E*,6*E*,10-dodecatrien-1-ol.

6.50

(a) 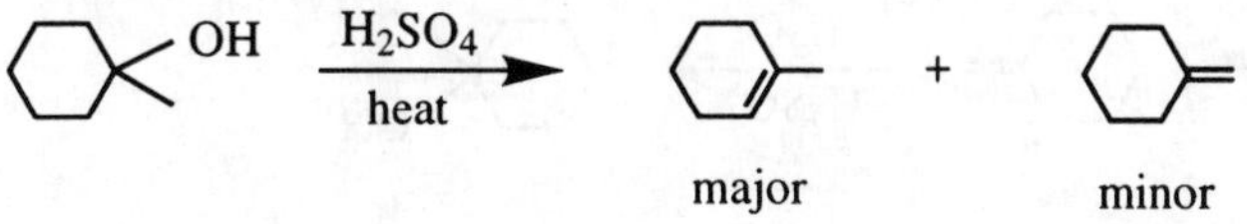
OH
H_2SO_4
heat
+
major
minor

(b) 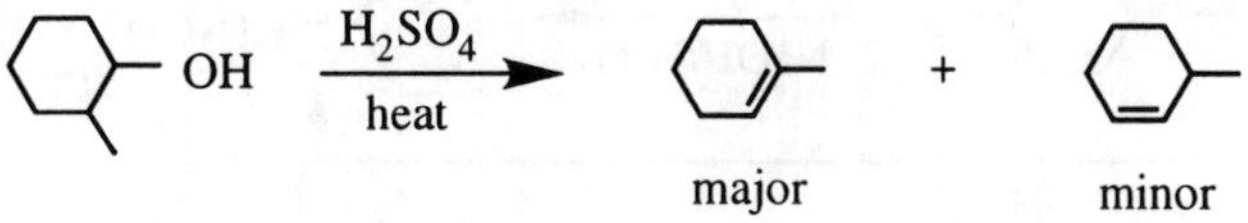
OH
H_2SO_4
heat
+
major
minor

(c) 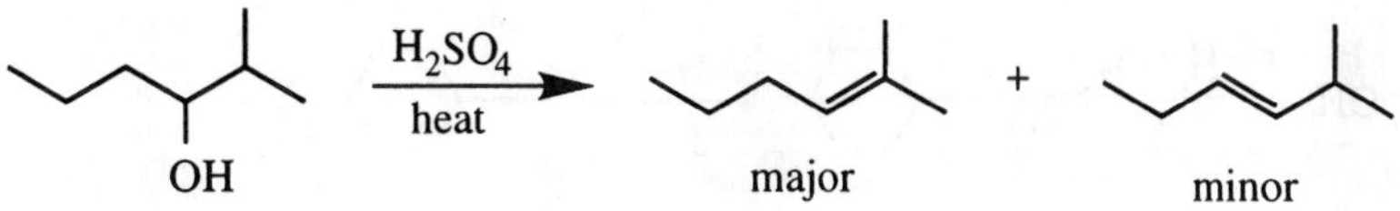
OH
H_2SO_4
heat
+
major
minor

(d) 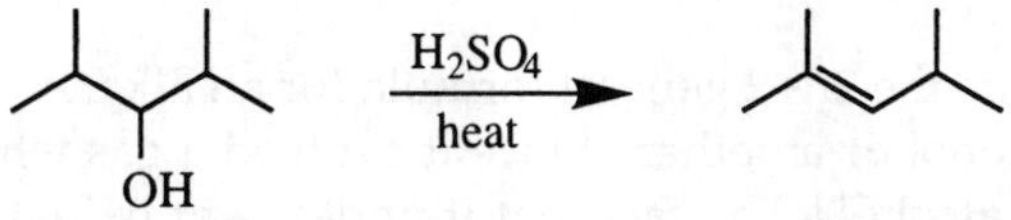
OH
H_2SO_4
heat

6.51 (a) there are two *cis-trans* isomers for oleic acid: *cis* and *trans*.

(b) There are four *cis-trans* isomers for linoleic acid: *cis-cis, cis-trans, trans-cis,* and *trans-trans.*

(c) There are eight *cis-trans* isomers for linolenic acid: *cis-cis-cis, cis-cis-trans, cis-trans-cis, cis-trans-trans, trans-trans-trans, trans-trans-cis, trans-cis-trans,* and *trans-cis-cis.*

6.52

(a) 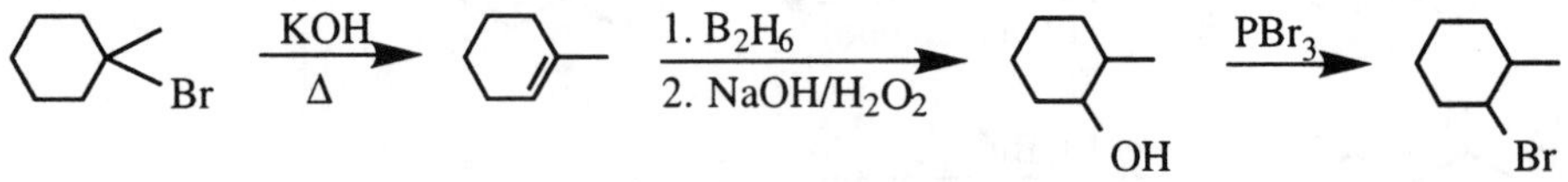
Br
KOH
Δ
1. B_2H_6
2. $NaOH/H_2O_2$
OH
PBr_3
Br

(b) 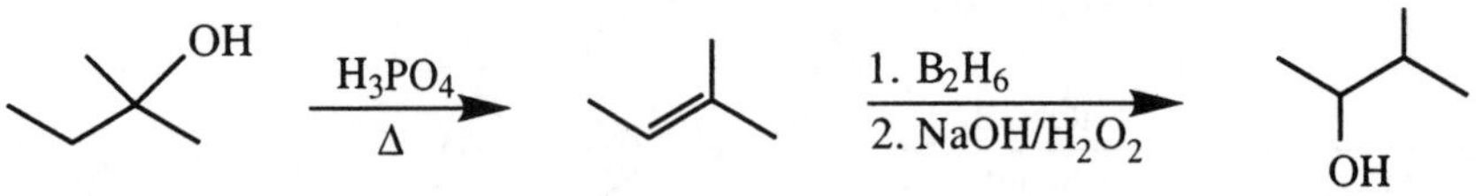
OH
H_3PO_4
Δ
1. B_2H_6
2. $NaOH/H_2O_2$
OH

(c) 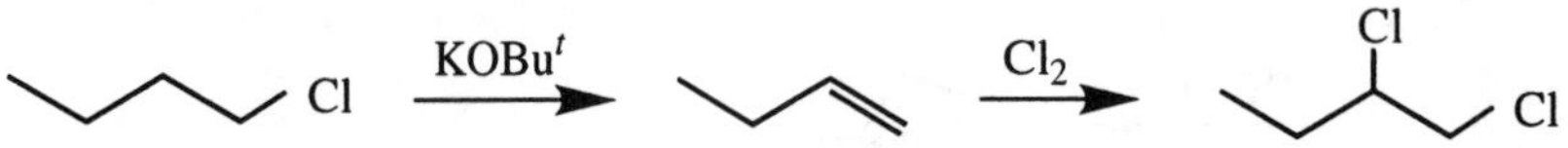
Cl
$KOBu^t$
Cl_2
Cl
Cl

(d) 
OH
H_3PO_4
Δ
$KMnO_4$
cold
OH
OH

(e) 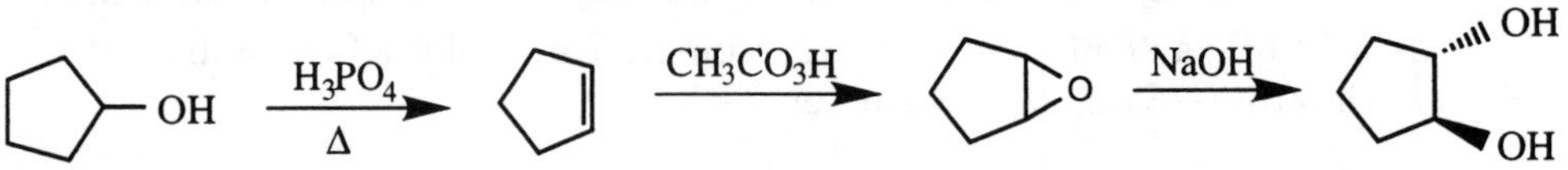
OH
H_3PO_4
Δ
CH_3CO_3H
O
NaOH
OH
OH

(f) 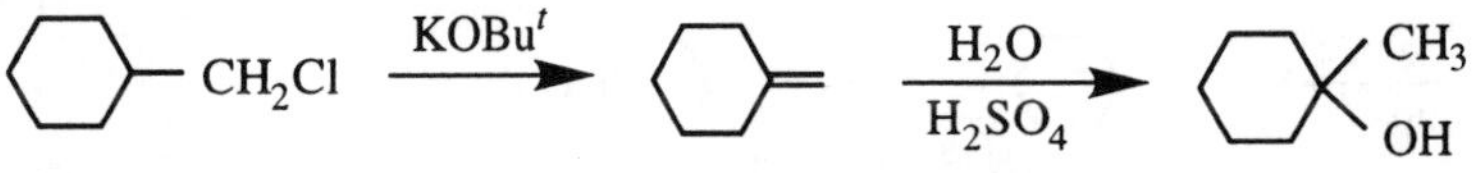
CH_2Cl
$KOBu^t$
H_2O
H_2SO_4
CH_3
OH

(g) 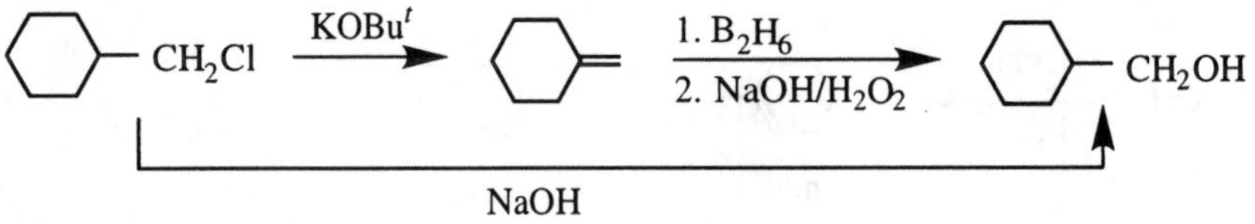
CH_2Cl
$KOBu^t$
1. B_2H_6
2. $NaOH/H_2O_2$
CH_2OH
NaOH

(h) 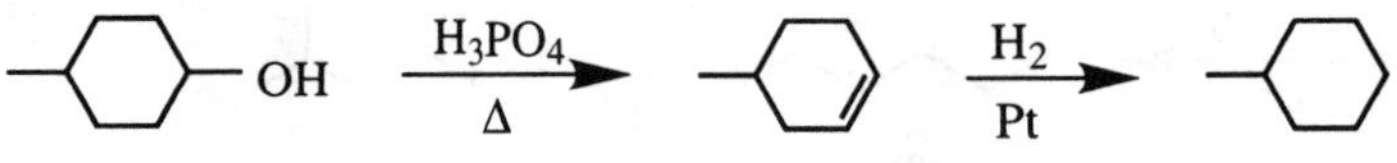
OH
H_3PO_4
Δ
H_2
Pt

6.53 The unknown's molecular formula fits the 2n+2 general formula for an alkane. It contains a single oxygen, indicating it is an alcohol or an ether. Since it evolved a gas when reacted with metallic sodium it must be an alcohol. The fact that it underwent oxidation with sodium dichromate means it must be a primary or secondary alcohol. This is confirmed by the reaction with concentrated sulfuric acid (dehydration conditions) in which the unknown loses H_2O to afford C_4H_8, an alkene. The fact that there are no isomers of the alkene formed means water could be eliminated from the alcohol in only a single direction - this means it must either be a primary alcohol or a symmetrically-substituted alcohol. Hydrogenation of the alkene produced the parent alkane, a butane, of which there are only two constitutional isomers.

Two structures best fit the provided evidence, *n*-butyl alcohol and isobutyl alcohol. The evidence provided does not permit distinguishing between these two isomers.

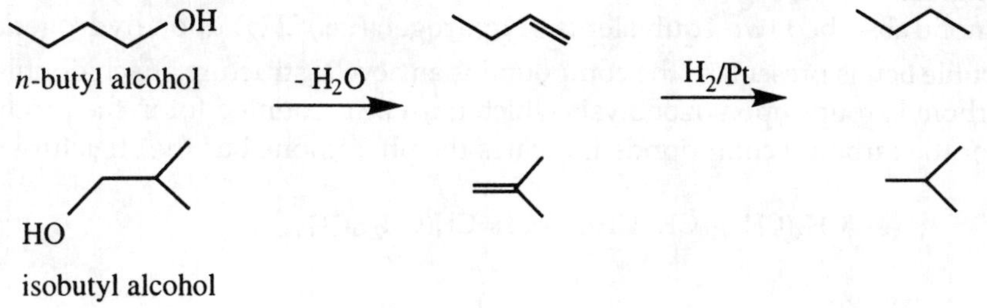
OH
n-butyl alcohol
- H2O
H2/Pt
HO
isobutyl alcohol

6.54

(a) 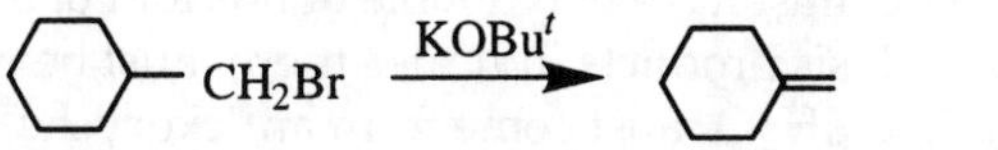
CH2Br
KOBu^t

(b) 
Br
KOBu^t

(c) 
Br
KOBu^t

6.55

(a) 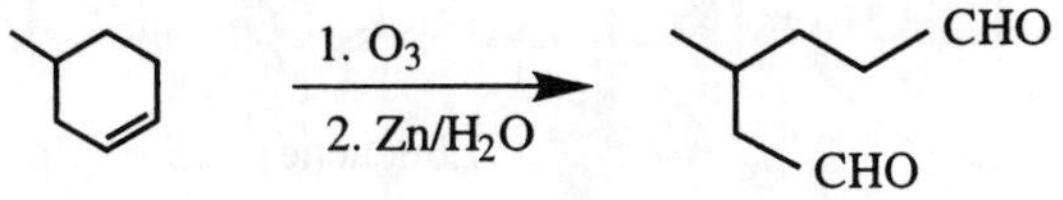
1. O3
2. Zn/H2O
CHO
CHO

(b) 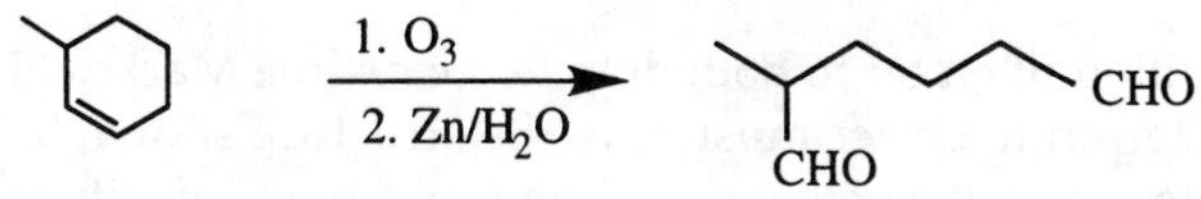
1. O3
2. Zn/H2O
CHO
CHO

6.56 Since the alkyl bromide reacted slowly with both sodium iodide and silver nitrate it probably is a secondary bromide. Reaction with sodium ethoxide resulted in the elimination of HBr and the formation of two alkenes. Therefore the bromide is attached to a secondary carbon which has different substituents on each side of it. On the basis of the ozonolysis products the structure of the alkenes **Y** and **Z** is as shown below.

$(CH_3)_2C{=}CHCH_2CH_3$	$(CH_3)_2CHCH{=}CHCH_3$	$(CH_3)_2CHCHBrCH_2CH_3$
Y	**Z**	**X**

The only alkyl halide structure which can produce both **Y** and **Z** upon dehydrohalogenation is compound **X**, which is a secondary bromide.

6.57 The formula indicates the pheromone is "short" four hydrogens from an alkane structure ($C_{21}H_{44}$) and so has a combination of two double bonds or rings. The bromine and permanganate reactions indicates that at least one double bond is present. Since the pheromone absorbed two equivalents of hydrogen (i.e., $2H_2$) upon hydrogenation there were two double bonds present, so the compound is an acyclic structure. Each double bond produces two carbonyl groups upon ozonolysis which must be accounted for in the products. Piecing together the carbonyl compounds indicates the pheromone has the structure shown:

$$CH_3(CH_2)_{10}CH{=}CHCH_2CH{=}CH(CH_2)_4CH_3$$

6.58 Based on its molecular formula limonene is six hydrogens "short" of an alkane structure, indicating the presence of a combination of three double bonds and/or rings. Since it absorbs only two equivalents of hydrogen limonene must have two double bonds and one six-membered ring. Examination of the ozonolysis products indicates there must be one double bond in the ring and one not in the ring (the CH_2O must come from an "exocyclic" double bond, one not involved in a ring). The three carbonyl groups in the tricarbonyl compound could arise from two different ring structures (connections from **A** or **B**), only one of which (**A**) results in a six-membered ring. Therefore, the structure of limonene results from connection **A** is as shown below.

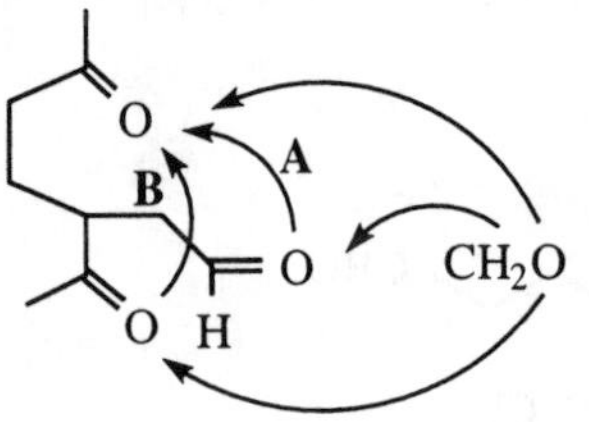
O
A
B
O
CH₂O
O H

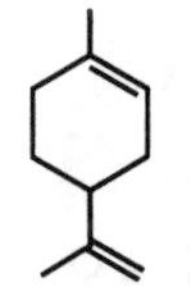

Limonene

6.59 Hydration results in the addition of water to both double bonds in a Markovnikov orientation. Therefore the "terpin hydrate" must have the structure shown below. It contains no stereocenters. However, the newly added ring-hydroxyl substituent could be oriented either cis- or *trans*- to the existing C_3 side chain. Thus, two configurational isomers will be formed.

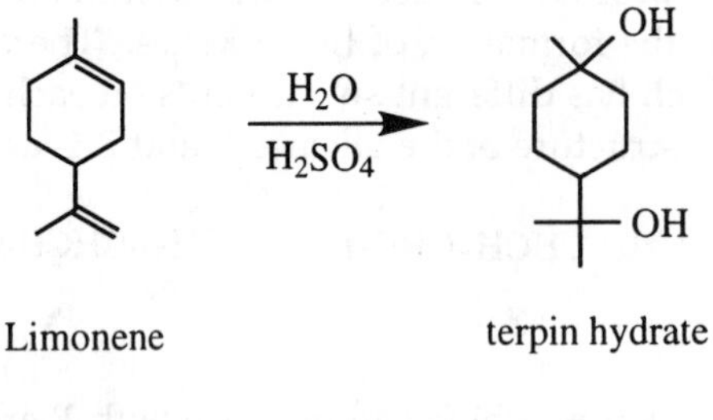
H₂O
H₂SO₄
OH
OH
Limonene
terpin hydrate

6.60 Compound **A**, the ozonolysis product from α-pinene, contains all ten original carbon atoms - no carbons were lost. Therefore, ozonolysis resulted in ring cleavage, with the double bond being endocyclic (that is, within the ring) and being located where the carbonyl groups are now found. Therefore, α-pinene has the structure shown below.

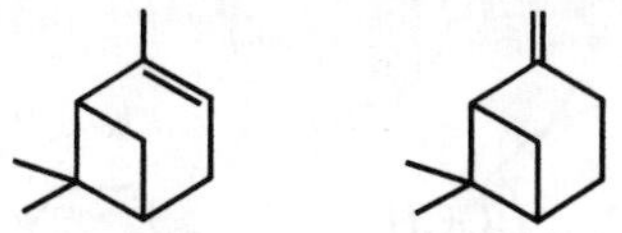

α-pinene β-pinene

Compound **B**, from β-pinene, has only nine of the ten original carbons. Therefore, one carbon must have been lost as formaldehyde (CH_2O). The double bond must been from the ring to a methylene group located exocyclic (that is, outside the ring) to the ring and located as shown in the structure of β-pinene shown above.

6.61 All of the possible alkene isomers of C_5H_{10} are shown in (a), with the asterisk indicating 2-methylpentene can exist as two stereoisomers as shown in (b).

(a) $CH_3CH_2CH_2CH{=}CH_2$ $CH_3CH_2\overset{*}{C}H{=}CHCH_3$ $(CH_3)_2C{=}CHCH_3$

$(CH_3)_2CHCH{=}CH_2$ $CH_3CH_2C(CH_3){=}CH_2$

(b)  

trans-2-pentene *cis*-2-pentene

6.62 An alkene is protonated by an acid and this example is facile because of the stability of the *t*-butyl carbocation which is formed. The carbocation then completes its octet by reacting with the nucleophilic methanol, the only nucleophile (other than the very weak bisulfate anion, HSO_4^-) in the solution. Loss of a proton from the oxonium ion forms *t*-butyl methyl ether (known as the gasoline additive MTBE in the petroleum industry).

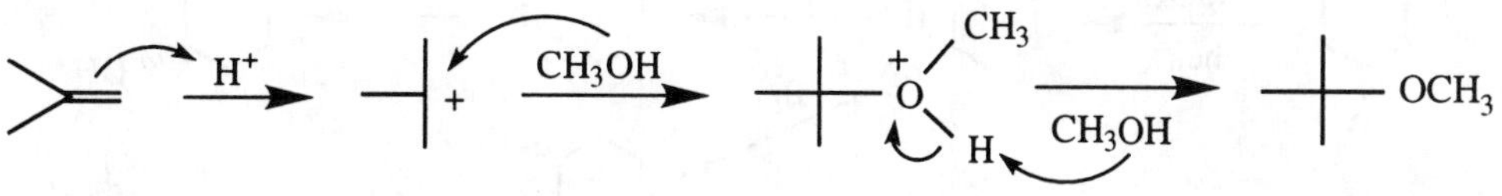

H⁺
CH₃OH
CH₃
H
CH₃OH
OCH₃

6.63 An alkyl halide usually has two potential fates in the presence of a nucleophile, substitution or elimination. In both instances bromide is expelled. Cyclohexyl bromide is a secondary bromide so both reactions are feasible: methanol is a modest nucleophile, and methoxide is a strong nucleophile. The elimination reaction is favored by heating with a strong nucleophile which attacks a proton resulting in an E2-elimination to afford cyclohexene as the major product. Use of the modest nucleophile methanol results in the S_N2 substitution reaction predominating, affording cyclohexyl methyl ether as the major product.

E2 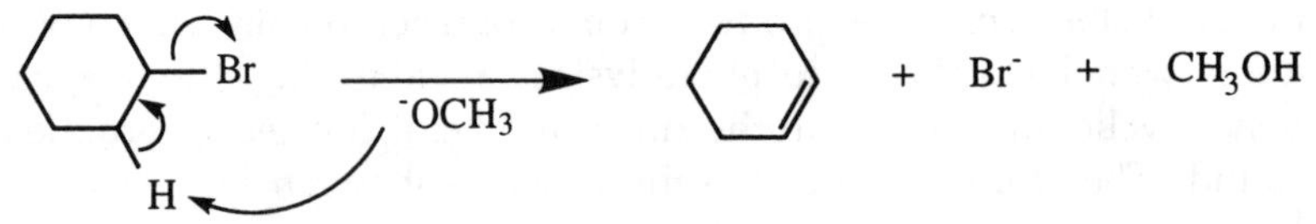

S_N2 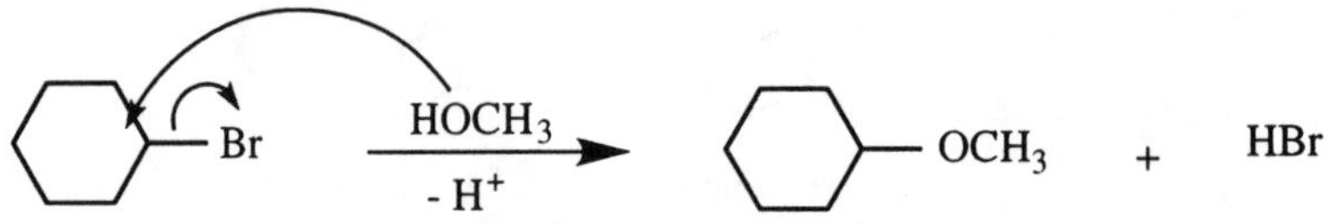

6.64 Five different alkenes (constitutional isomers) can be derived from 2,3-dimethylpentane. The names and structures are as follows:
A 3,4-dimethyl-1-pentene; **B** 3,4-dimethyl-2-pentene; **C** 2-ethyl-3-methyl-1-butene; **D** 2,3-dimethyl-2-pentene; **E** 2,3-dimethyl-1-pentene.
Configurational isomers (*cis-trans* isomers) exist only for structural isomer **B** and they are shown as **B-*E*** and **B-*Z***. **D** should be the most stable constitutional isomer because it is tetra-substituted.

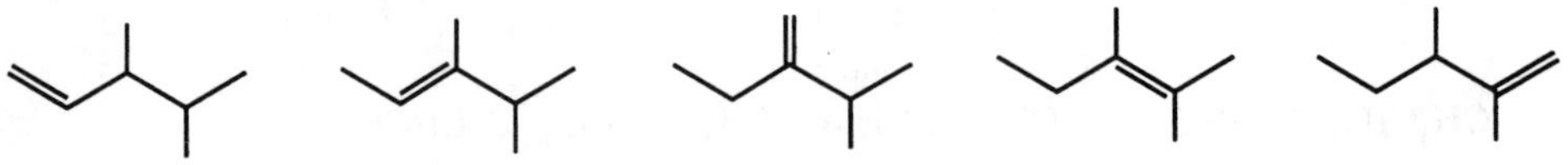

A **B** **C** **D** **E**

B-*E* **B-*Z***

6.65

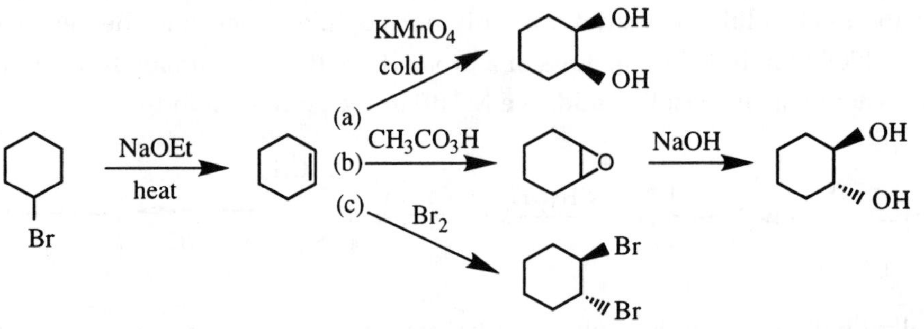

(d) 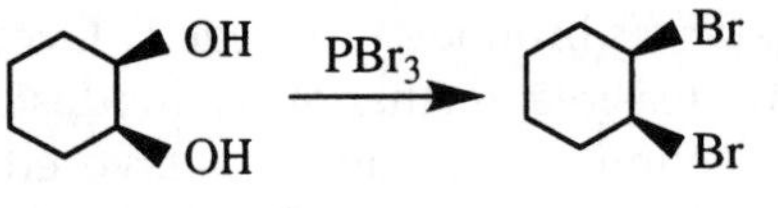

(from (a))

(e) 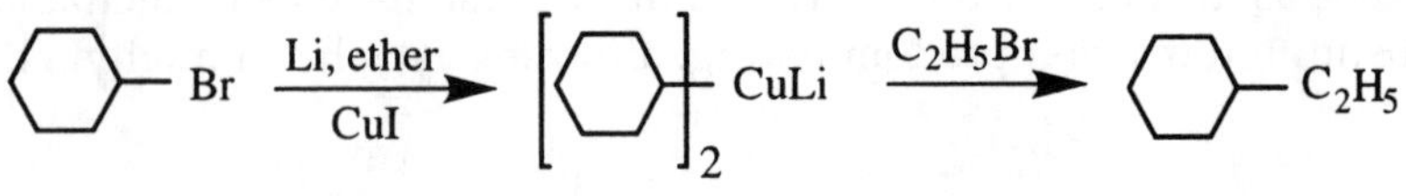

6.66 The formula C_5H_8O indicates **A** is short four hydrogens from the alkane formula C_5H_{12} so it has two double bonds and/or rings. It contains an oxygen which must be part of an ether or an alcohol group. Since **A** reacts with sodium it contains an alcohol group. The reaction with sodium produces an alkoxide and its treatment with methyl iodide must afford a methyl ether (**B**) via a Williamson reaction. The reaction of **A** and **B** with bromine and permanganate indicates at least one double bond is present. The fact that only one equivalent of hydrogen is consumed (to form **C**) indicates **A** contains one double bond and a ring. **C** must be saturated after hydrogenation and therefore its oxidation with permanganate or Jones' reagent indicates it is a primary or secondary alcohol (recall a tertiary alcohol cannot be oxidized). Thus, to this point it is known that **A** is a cyclic unsaturated five carbon primary or secondary alcohol.

Reaction of **A** with PBr_3 affords an alkyl bromide (**E**) (note in the formula an OH has been replaced by a Br) and treatment of the latter with sodium ethoxide effected a dehydrohalogenation (note the loss of HBr) to afford an alkene **F**, C_5H_6. Ozonolysis of **A** produced a single compound which indicates the double bond is in the ring. The fact that **F** afforded two compounds each with two aldehyde groups indicates that **F** contained two double bonds and both were within the ring - the only way for this to be the case with a five carbon compound is for the ring to be a five-membered ring.

One compound which fits these observations is a five-membered ring compound containing a double bond and carrying an alcohol substituent, such as compound **A** shown below.

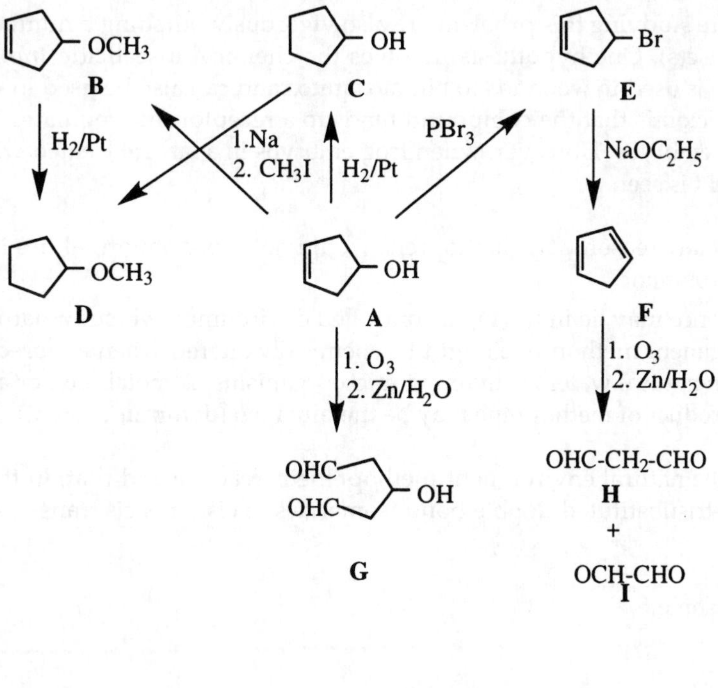
OCH3
B
OH
C
Br
E
H2/Pt
1.Na
2. CH3I
H2/Pt
PBr3
NaOC2H5
OCH3
D
OH
A
F
1. O3
2. Zn/H2O
1. O3
2. Zn/H2O
OHC
OHC
OH
G
OHC-CH2-CHO
H
+
OCH-CHO
I

VII. Conceptual Problem

Frogs: The New "Canary" in the Mine?

You work for your state's wildlife management office. Increasingly, reports of sightings of deformed frogs in local ponds have crossed your desk. Just as canaries were once used to warn miners of poor air quality in the mines, so frogs may serve to warn us about environmental degradation.

Your initial research tells you that the first cases of deformed frogs were reported in Minnesota. Similar reports now have been documented from almost every state. The deformities included extra legs, malformed or missing legs, and other severe defects. One of the most common abnormalities is the absence of a hind limb. Your task is to consider hypotheses for "natural" causes, as well as chemically induced causes (that is, those that might result from human intervention in the environment) for such deformities.

■ Can you propose any non-chemically induced, or "natural" causes for these observations of deformities?

- Ans: natural causes could include naturally occurring biota (e.g., parasites) in the water or exposure to increased UV radiation.

Researchers who are studying this problem are also vigorously pursuing a number of hypotheses as to the possible cause(s). One hypothesis involves the chemical insecticide *trans,trans*-(S)-methoprene, which is used in wetlands to kill mosquitos and can also be used in various sprays to kill fleas. The suspicion is that the compound binds to a receptor that regulates limb development in developing frog embryos. However, when frog embryos in a lab are treated with methoprene, normal development is seen.

■ Can you think of any reason why methoprene would not cause abnormalities in the lab, but might in a natural environment?

- Ans: The difference may lie in having a controlled environment versus a natural one. In the natural environment methoprene might be chemically altered when exposed to sunlight or when placed in natural waters containing microorganisms. A metabolite or an environmental degradation product of methoprene may be the mutagen (deforming agent).

You learn that in the natural environment methoprene is reactive and that, in the presence of sunlight, the trans-trisubstituted double bond isomerizes to cis. This cis,trans-isomer may be mutagenic.

■ Draw that new isomer

- Ans:

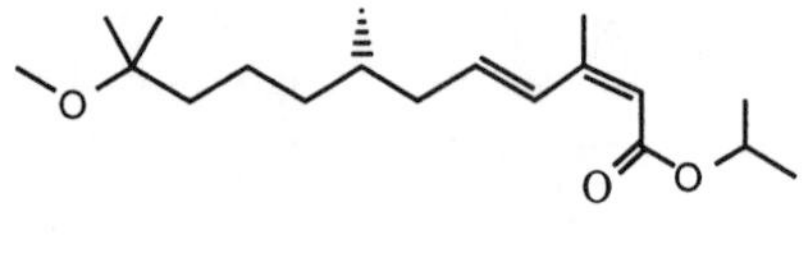
O
O
O

CHAPTER 7

Alkynes

I. Textbook Chapter Contents

This chapter introduces the second family of unsaturated compounds, alkynes, that are compounds with a triple bond and *sp* hybridization of carbon.

II. Learning Objectives

- Know the IUPAC nomenclature of alkynes and the naming of simple alkynes. Distinguish between internal and terminal alkynes.
- Understand the nature of the *sp* hybridization of alkynes and the implications for reactions and stereochemistry.

- Understand the acidity of terminal alkynes and the nucleophilicity of the alkynide anions which result from loss of a proton.

- Write equations for the catalytic hydrogenation of alkynes to form *cis*-alkenes or alkanes.

- Write equations for the metal-ammonia reduction of alkenes to form *trans*-alkenes.

- Write equations for the oxidation of alkynes to carboxylic acids. Be able to use this reaction to deduce the structure of unknown alkynes.

- Be able to synthesize alkynes from acetylene using initial formation of an alkynide anion followed by its use in an S_N2 substitution reaction with a primary or secondary alkyl halide.

- Carry out three-step syntheses involving alkynes, alkenes, alcohols, and alkyl halides.

III. Glossary

alkylation of an alkyne replacement of a terminal hydrogen of an alkyne with an alkyl group

alkyne a compound containing a triple bond and whose acyclic members have the general formula C_nH_{2n-2}

alkynide a carbanion formed by removal of a proton from a terminal alkyne carbon

***anti* addition** an addition reaction in which the adding atoms or groups (the electrophile and the nucleophile) add to the opposite side of the multiple bond

hydrogenation the addition of hydrogen

internal alkyne an alkyne with no hydrogens attached to an *sp* hybridized carbon; the triple bond is not at the end of a chain

linear hybridization the hybridization of a single *s* orbital and a single *p* orbital to form two *sp* hybrid orbitals aligned 180° to each other (linear), with two unhybridized *p* orbitals oriented perpendicular to the linear *sp* orbitals and orthogonal to each other

pheromone a chemical excreted in very small amounts by plants or animals that serves as a method of communication, most often within the same species. Examples are sex pheromones and alarm pheromones

***syn* addition** an addition reaction in which both adding atoms or groups (the electrophile and the nucleophile) add to the same side of the multiple bond

terminal alkyne an alkyne with at least one hydrogen attached to an *sp* hybridized carbon; the triple bond is at one end of a chain

triple bond a covalent bond between two carbon atoms in which six electrons are shared; it involves one sigma bond and two pi bonds

IV. Summary of Reactions of Alkynes

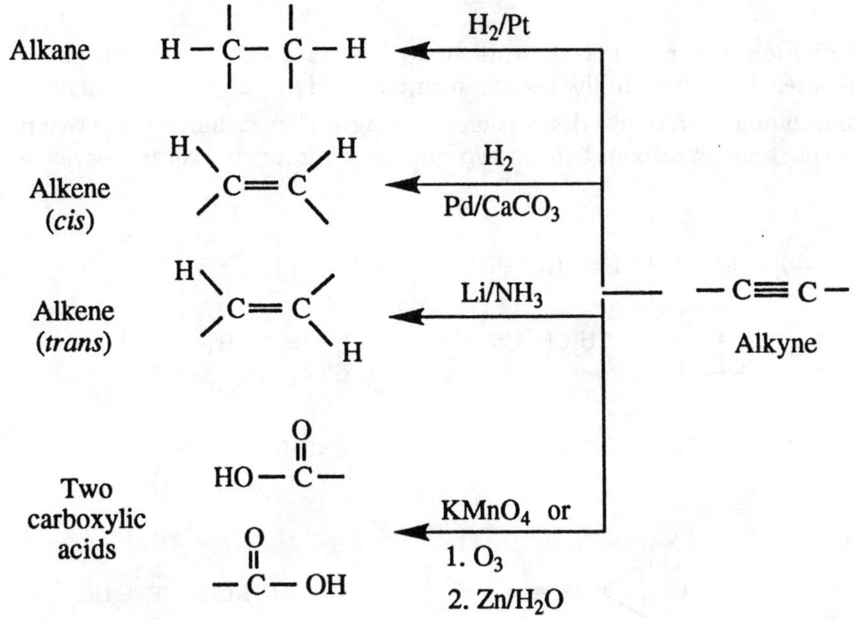

Alkane

$$H - \overset{|}{\underset{|}{C}} - \overset{|}{\underset{|}{C}} - H \xleftarrow{\quad H_2/Pt \quad}$$

Alkene
(*cis*)

$$\underset{}{\overset{H}{\diagdown}} C = C \overset{H}{\diagup} \xleftarrow[\quad Pd/CaCO_3 \quad]{\quad H_2 \quad}$$

Alkene
(*trans*)

$$\underset{}{\overset{H}{\diagdown}} C = C \underset{H}{\diagdown} \xleftarrow{\quad Li/NH_3 \quad} \qquad - C \equiv C -$$

Alkyne

Two
carboxylic
acids

$$HO - \overset{O}{\overset{||}{C}} -$$

$$- \overset{O}{\overset{||}{C}} - OH \xleftarrow[\substack{1.\ O_3 \\ 2.\ Zn/H_2O}]{\quad KMnO_4 \ \ or \quad}$$

V. Summary of Preparation of Alkynes

$$H - C \equiv C - H \xrightarrow{\quad NaNH_2 \quad} \left[H - C \equiv C^- \ Na^+ \right] \xrightarrow{\quad R - Br \quad} H - C \equiv C - R$$

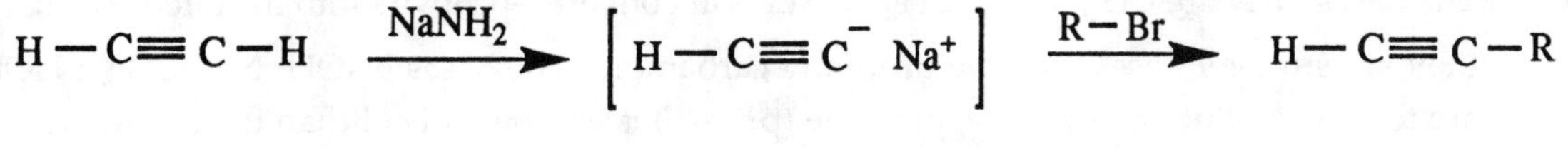

VI. Solutions to Problems

For "**How to Solve a Problem,**" review pages 233, 240, and 243

7.1 Both molecular formulas indicate the hydrocarbons are four hydrogens "short" of being an alkane. Thus, they fit the general formula C_nH_{2n-2} and must contain either a triple bond, or a combination of two double bonds or rings. They cannot contain two rings because there are not enough carbons to form two rings (a minimum of six carbons normally are required).

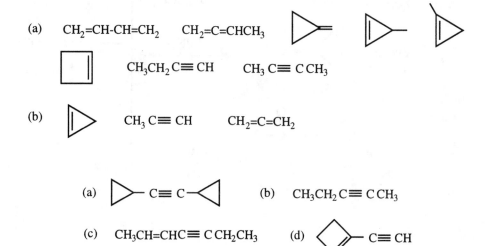

(a) CH_2=CH-CH=CH_2 CH_2=C=$CHCH_3$ 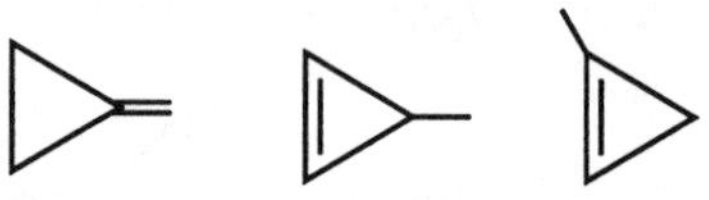

 $CH_3CH_2C\equiv CH$ $CH_3C\equiv CCH_3$

(b)  $CH_3C\equiv CH$ CH_2=C=CH_2

7.2

(a) 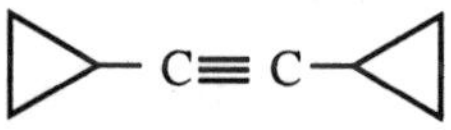   (b) $CH_3CH_2C\equiv CCH_3$

(c) CH_3CH=$CHC\equiv CCH_2CH_3$ (d) 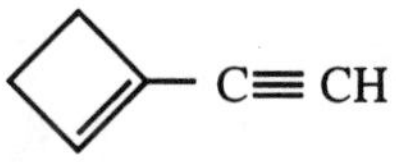

7.3 (a) (*E*)-3-penten-1-yne; (b) 3-methylcyclooctyne; (c) 1-ethynyl-2-vinylcyclobutane.

7.4 An *sp* hybrid carbon is more electronegative than an sp^2 hybrid carbon than a sp^3 hybrid carbon. The more electronegative carbon will be the more stable carbanion. Therefore, the order of acidity is as follows:
(c) ethynylcyclobutane > (b) vinylcyclobutane >
(a) ethylcyclobutane

7.5 The bases $NaNH_2$, CH_3Li, and CH_2=CHLi will convert 1-propyne into its anion because they are stronger bases than the propynyl carbanion. The bases NaOH, $NaOCH_3$, $NaOBu^t$ are too weak. Put another way, propyne (pK_a 25) is a stronger acid than the conjugate acids of these bases, ammonia (pK_a 33), methane (pK_a 50), and ethene (pK_a 44):

$$CH_3C\equiv CH + NaNH_2 \rightleftharpoons CH_3C\equiv C^- \; Na^+ + NH_3$$

$$CH_3C\equiv CH + CH_3Li \rightleftharpoons CH_3C\equiv C^- \; Li^+ + CH_4$$

$$CH_3C\equiv CH + CH_2{=}CHLi \rightleftharpoons CH_3C\equiv C^- \; Li^+ + CH_2{=}CH_2$$

7.6

(a) $CH_3C{\equiv}CCH_2CH_3 \xrightarrow[Pt]{H_2} CH_3CH_2CH_2CH_2CH_3$

(b) $CH_3CH_2C{\equiv}CH \xrightarrow[Pd/CaCO_3]{H_2} CH_3CH_2CH{=}CH_2$

(c) 
CH3 C≡CCH2CH3
Na/NH3

(d) 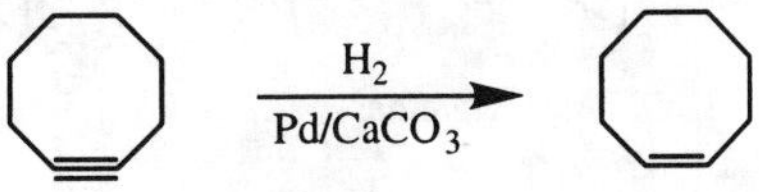
H2
Pd/CaCO3

7.7

(a) $CH_3C{\equiv}CCH_3 \xrightarrow{O_3} 2\,CH_3COOH$
2-butyne

(b) $CH_3CH{=}CHCH_2C{\equiv}CCH_3 \xrightarrow{O_3} CH_3CHO + OHCCH_2COOH + CH_3COOH$
2-hepten-5-yne

(c) 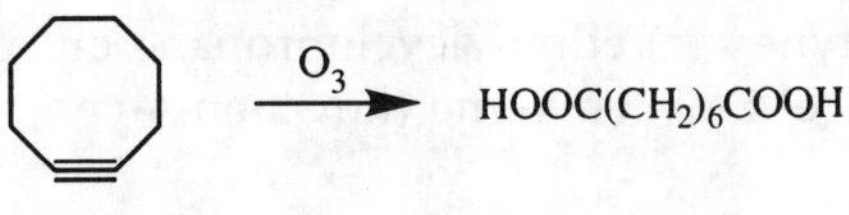
O3
HOOC(CH2)6COOH
cyclooctyne

(d) $CH_3C{\equiv}CH \xrightarrow{KMnO_4} CH_3COOH + CO_2$
propyne

7.8

(a) $HC{\equiv}CH \xrightarrow[2.\ C_4H_9Br]{1.\ NaNH_2} C_4H_9C{\equiv}CH \xrightarrow[2.\ CH_3Br]{1.\ NaNH_2} C_4H_9C{\equiv}CCH_3$

(b) 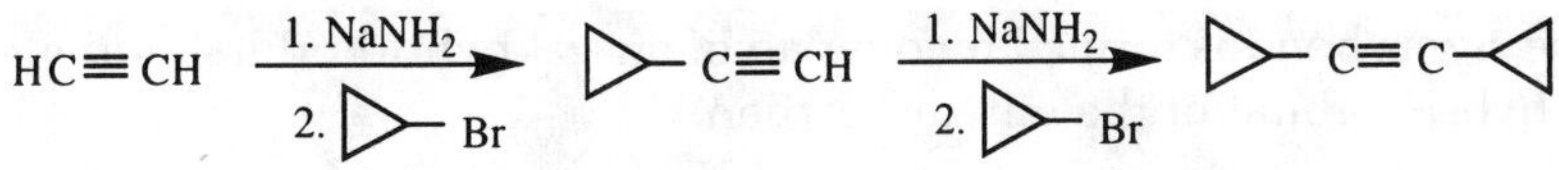
HC≡CH
1. NaNH2
2.
Br
C≡CH
1. NaNH2
2.
Br
C≡C

(c) 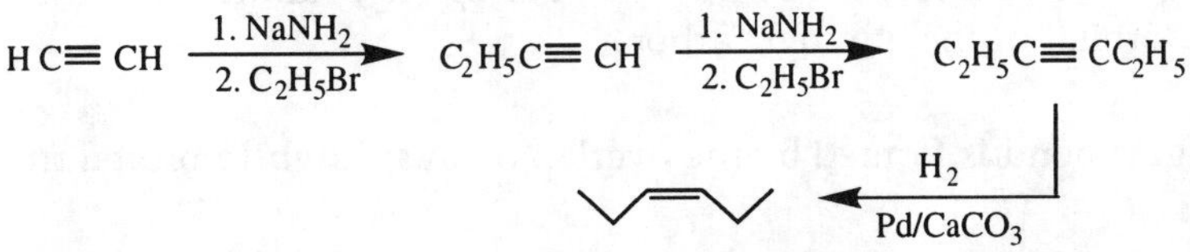
HC≡CH
1. NaNH2
2. C2H5Br
C2H5C≡CH
1. NaNH2
2. C2H5Br
C2H5C≡CC2H5
H2
Pd/CaCO3

(d) 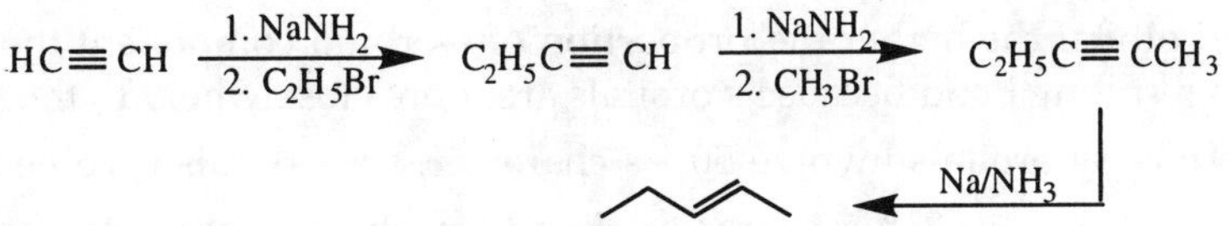
HC≡CH
1. NaNH2
2. C2H5Br
C2H5C≡CH
1. NaNH2
2. CH3Br
C2H5C≡CCH3
Na/NH3

7.9

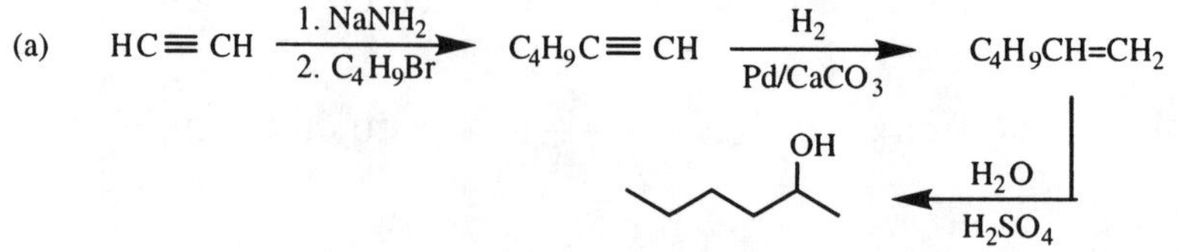
(a)
HC≡CH
1. NaNH2
2. C4H9Br
C4H9C≡CH
H2
Pd/CaCO3
C4H9CH=CH2
H2O
H2SO4
OH

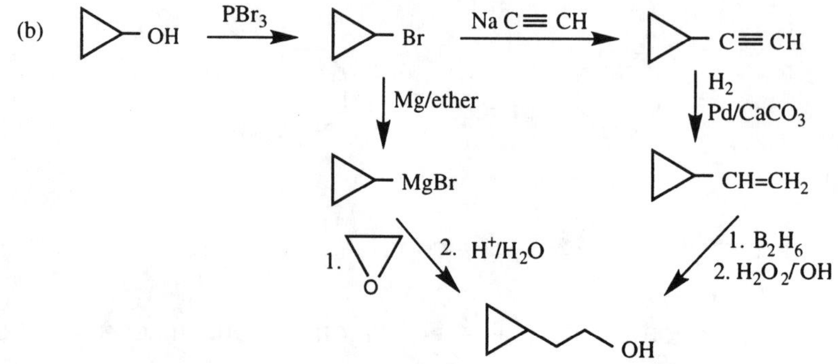
(b)
OH
PBr3
Br
Na C≡CH
C≡CH
Mg/ether
H2
Pd/CaCO3
MgBr
CH=CH2
1.
O
2. H+/H2O
1. B2H6
2. H2O2/-OH
OH

7.10 (a) 1-heptyne; (b) 3,3-dimethyl-1-butyne; (c) ethynylcyclopropane or cyclopropylacetylene; (d) 2-butyne; (e) 2-hexen-4-yne (hex-2-en-4-yne); (f) 3-butyn-1-ol (but-3-yn-1-ol).

7.11

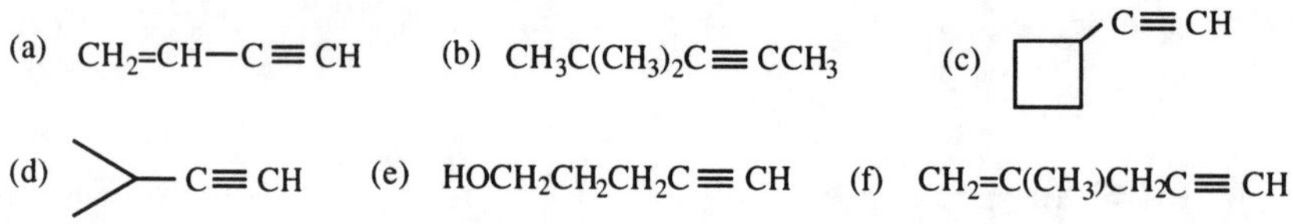
(a) CH2=CH—C≡CH
(b) CH3C(CH3)2C≡CCH3
(c)
C≡CH
(d)
C≡CH
(e) HOCH2CH2CH2C≡CH
(f) CH2=C(CH3)CH2C≡CH

7.12 (a) The sigma bond is formed by overlap of an sp^3 hybrid orbital of the methyl carbon and an *sp* hybrid orbital of the ethynyl carbon.

(b) The sigma bond is formed by overlap of an sp^2 hybrid orbital of the vinyl carbon with an *sp* hybrid orbital of the ethynyl carbon.

(c) The sigma bond is formed by the overlap of an sp^2 hybrid orbital from each of the vinyl carbons.

7.13 In a hybrid orbital the higher the proportion of s-orbital component the shorter is the length of a resulting bond because *s* orbitals are more closely held to the nucleus than are *p* orbitals. Thus, *sp* orbitals involve 50% *s* character, sp^2 orbitals involve 33% *s* character, and sp^3 orbitals involve 25% *s* character. Bond lengths increase in the order $sp < sp^2 < sp^3$ orbital.

The bond in (b) is shorter than that in (a) because while both involve overlap of an *sp* hybrid orbital of the ethynyl carbon, (b) involves overlap with an sp^2 hybrid orbital while (a) involves overlap with a longer sp^3 hybrid orbital. The bond in (c) is longer than that in (b) because while both involve overlap of an sp^2 hybrid orbital of one vinyl carbon, (c) involves overlap with the sp^2 orbital of a second vinyl carbon while (b) involves overlap with the shorter *sp* hybrid orbital of an ethynyl carbon.

7.14

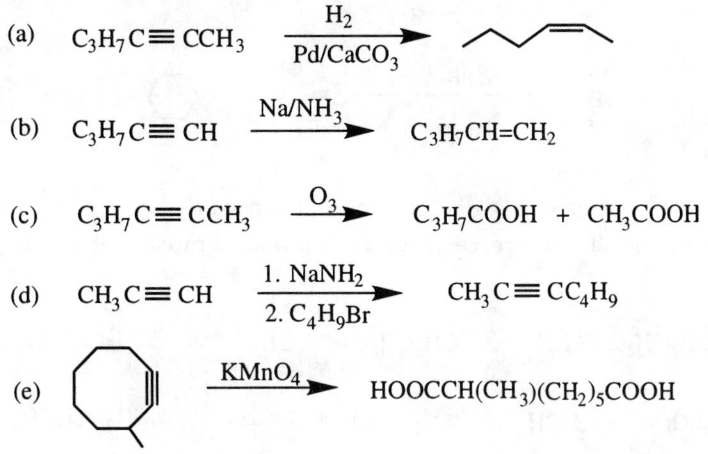
(a) C3H7C≡CCH3
H2
Pd/CaCO3
(b) C3H7C≡CH
Na/NH3
C3H7CH=CH2
(c) C3H7C≡CCH3
O3
C3H7COOH + CH3COOH
(d) CH3C≡CH
1. NaNH2
2. C4H9Br
CH3C≡CC4H9
(e)
KMnO4
HOOCCH(CH3)(CH2)5COOH

7.15

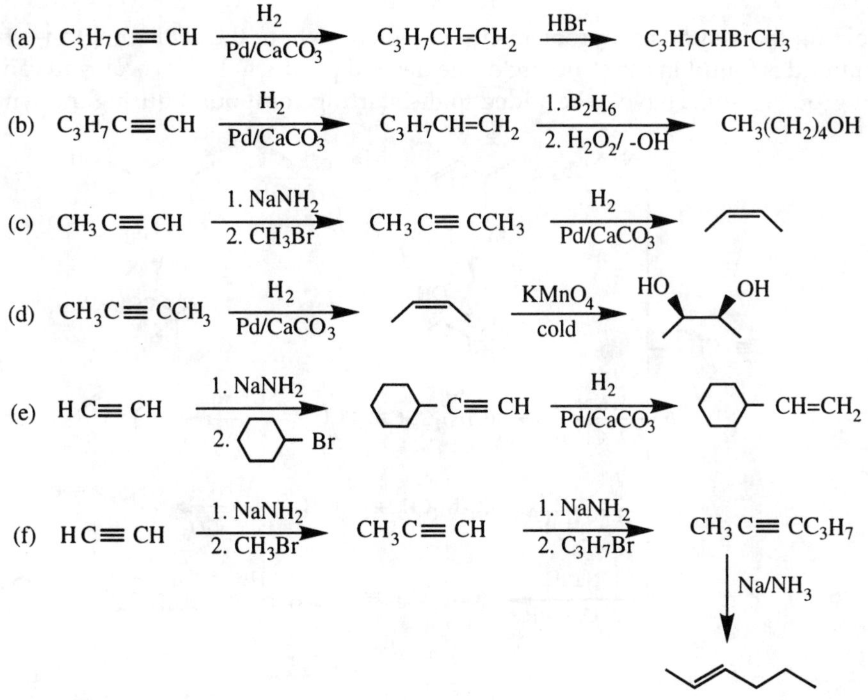
(a) C3H7C≡CH
H2
Pd/CaCO3
C3H7CH=CH2
HBr
C3H7CHBrCH3
(b) C3H7C≡CH
H2
Pd/CaCO3
C3H7CH=CH2
1. B2H6
2. H2O2/ -OH
CH3(CH2)4OH
(c) CH3C≡CH
1. NaNH2
2. CH3Br
CH3C≡CCH3
H2
Pd/CaCO3
(d) CH3C≡CCH3
H2
Pd/CaCO3
KMnO4
cold
HO
OH
(e) HC≡CH
1. NaNH2
2.
Br
C≡CH
H2
Pd/CaCO3
CH=CH2
(f) HC≡CH
1. NaNH2
2. CH3Br
CH3C≡CH
1. NaNH2
2. C3H7Br
CH3C≡CC3H7
Na/NH3

7.16

(a) $HC\equiv CH \xrightarrow[2.\ C_2H_5Br]{1.\ NaNH_2} CH_3CH_2C\equiv CH$

(b) $HC\equiv CH \xrightarrow[2.\ CH_3Br]{1.\ NaNH_2} HC\equiv CCH_3 \xrightarrow[2.\ CH_3Br]{1.\ NaNH_2} CH_3C\equiv CCH_3$

(c) 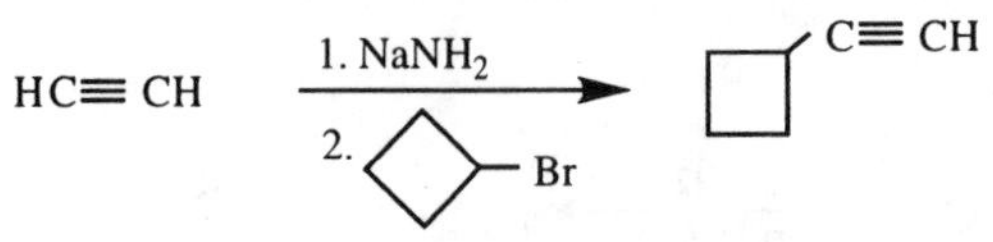
HC≡ CH
1. NaNH2
2.
Br
C≡ CH

(d) 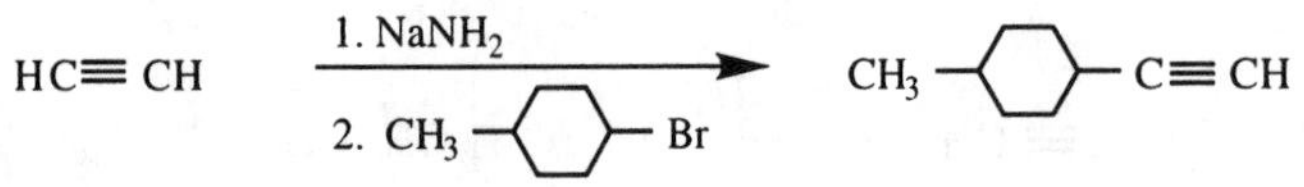
HC≡ CH
1. NaNH2
2. CH3
Br
CH3
C≡ CH

7.17 The molecular formula C_5H_8 fits the general formula C_nH_{2n-2}. It is four hydrogens "short" of being an alkane. Therefore, each acyclic compound must contain a triple bond or two double bonds.

$CH_3CH_2CH_2C\equiv CH$	$CH_3CH_2C\equiv CCH_3$	$CH_3CH(CH_3)C\equiv CH$
$CH_2=CH\text{-}CH=CHCH_3$	$CH_2=C(CH_3)CH=CH_2$	$CH_2=CHCH_2CH=CH_2$
$CH_2=C=CHCH_2CH_3$	$CH_2=C=C(CH_3)_2$	$CH_3CH=C=CHCH_3$

7.18 In solving these synthesis problems first envision where the skeleton of the starting compound is found in the structure of the desired product. In that way you can identify what groups/atoms have to be added to the starting compound during the synthesis.

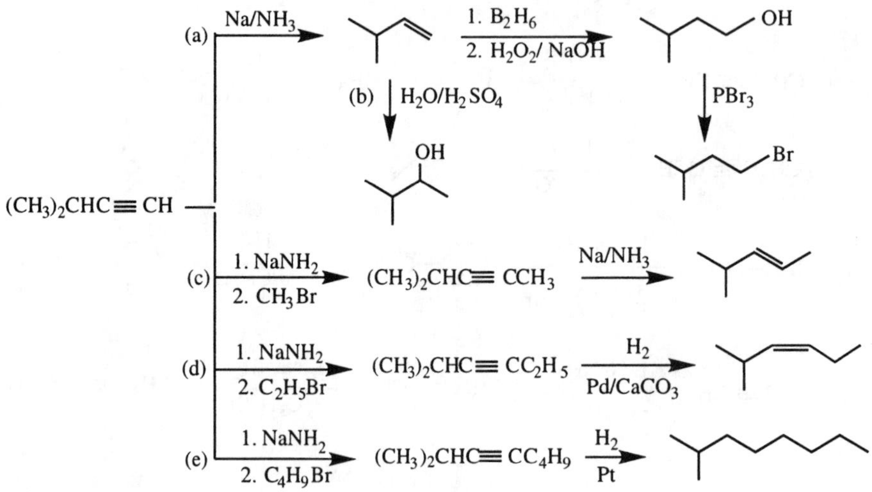
(a)
Na/NH3
1. B2H6
2. H2O2/ NaOH
OH
(b)
H2O/H2SO4
PBr3
OH
Br
(CH3)2CHC≡ CH
(c)
1. NaNH2
2. CH3Br
(CH3)2CHC≡ CCH3
Na/NH3
(d)
1. NaNH2
2. C2H5Br
(CH3)2CHC≡ CC2H5
H2
Pd/CaCO3
(e)
1. NaNH2
2. C4H9Br
(CH3)2CHC≡ CC4H9
H2
Pt

7.19 The formula C_5H_8 indicates there are two double bonds, two rings, one triple bond, or one double bond and a ring in each compound. Reaction of all three compounds with bromine and permanganate indicates there must be at least one double bond or triple bond in each - there cannot be two rings. Since **A** and **B** afford pentane upon hydrogenation they can have no rings and so each has either a triple bond or two double bonds. Further they must be straight-chain compounds. **C** must contain one ring since it absorbed only one equivalent of hydrogen and, by difference, must contain one double bond.

(a) **Possibilities for A and B:**

$CH_3CH_2CH_2C{\equiv}CH$	$CH_2{=}C{=}CHCH_2CH_3$	$CH_2{=}CH\text{-}CH{=}CHCH_3$
$CH_3CH_2C{\equiv}CCH_3$	$CH_3CH{=}C{=}CHCH_3$	$CH_2{=}CHCH_2CH{=}CH_2$

Possibilities for C:

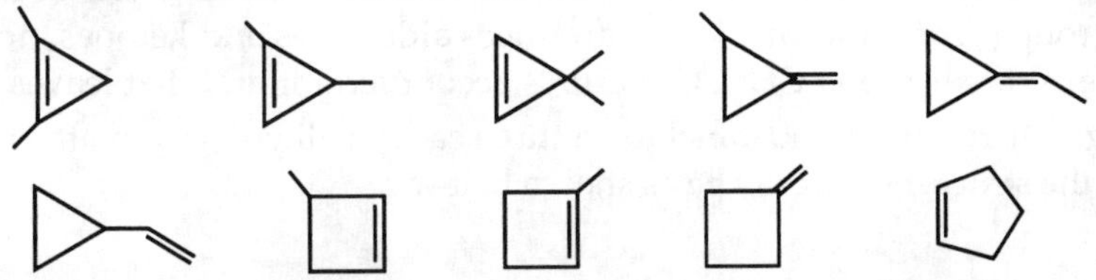

(b) Since **A** produced $CH_3CH_2CH_2COOH$, which contains four of the five carbons, it cannot have two points of unsaturation. Therefore, it must be the terminal alkyne shown here. Similarly, since **B** produced two carboxylic acids accounting for all five carbons upon oxidation, it must be an internal alkyne as shown here.

$CH_3CH_2CH_2C{\equiv}CH$	$CH_3CH_2C{\equiv}CCH_3$
A	**B**

(c) Since ozonolysis of C produced $OHC(CH_2)_3CHO$ it must be cyclopentene.

C

7.20 The challenge is to add a three carbon unit to a cyclohexane ring. Carbon-carbon bonds are readily formed by an S_N2 substitution of a carbanion on an alkyl halide. Therefore, use of an alkyne precursor to produce a three-carbon carbanion will produce the desired carbon skeleton. Hydrogenation will afford the desired propylcyclohexane.

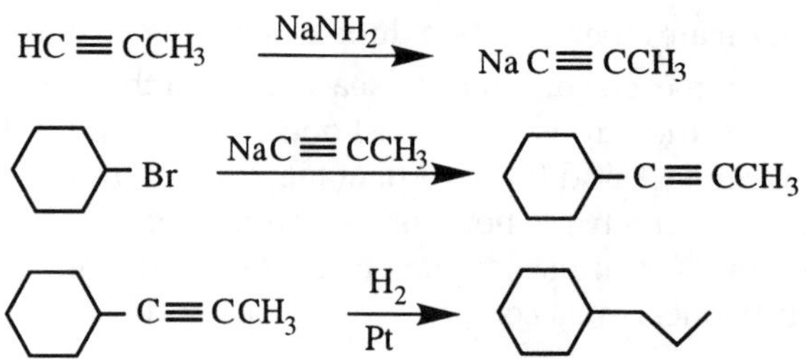

7.21 The formula weight of C_3H_4 is 40. Since the molecular weight is 80 the molecular formula is twice the empirical formula, C_6H_8. On the basis of the molecular formula the compound is "short" six hydrogens from the parent alkane. Since it reacted with bromine and permanganate it contains double and/or triple bonds. Since it absorbed only two equivalents of hydrogen (which would form C_6H_{12}) it contains a ring and either one triple bond or two double bonds. Acetic acid must have originated from the ozonolysis of an alkyne carrying a methyl group (ozonolysis of alkenes produces aldehydes and ketones, not carboxylic acids). Therefore, a three-carbon CH_3CC group is accounted for and that leaves only three carbons for a ring. Therefore, **W** must include a three carbon alkyne group attached to a cyclopropyl ring and the structure can only be as shown below:

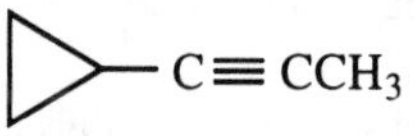

W

7.22

(a) 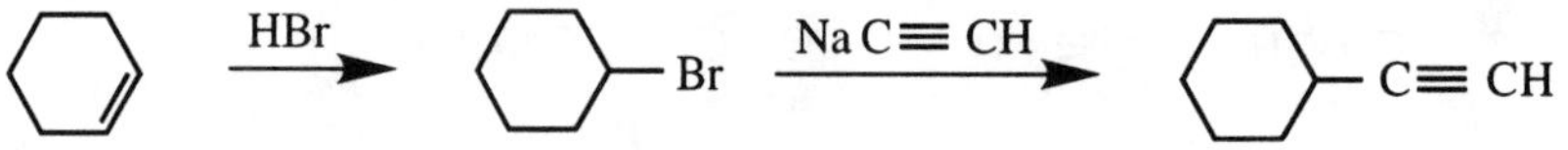

(b) $$CH_3CH_2CH{=}CH_2 \xrightarrow{HBr} CH_3CH_2CHBrCH_3 \xrightarrow{NaC\equiv CH} CH_3CH_2CH(CH_3)C\equiv CH$$

(c) $$(CH_3)_2C{=}CH_2 \xrightarrow[2.\ H_2O_2/^{-}OH]{1.\ B_2H_6} (CH_3)_2CHCH_2OH \xrightarrow{PBr_3} (CH_3)_2CHCH_2Br \xrightarrow{Na\,C\equiv CH} (CH_3)_2CHCH_2C\equiv CH$$

(d) $$CH_2{=}CH_2 \xrightarrow{HBr} CH_3CH_2Br \xrightarrow{Na\,C\equiv CH} CH_3CH_2C\equiv CH \xrightarrow[2.\ CH_3Br]{1.\ NaNH_2} CH_3CH_2C\equiv CCH_3$$

VII. Conceptual Problem

Pheromones: A Cheap Date

You work for the agricultural extension service of a large university. In increasing numbers, the owners of the farms and orchards in the surrounding community have come in seeking advice because the conventional insecticides that were once effective in controlling crop-destroying pests are losing their effectiveness. Many of the insects targeted have developed a resistance to the insecticides and it takes more insecticide to control the population, which means more time and money spent by these growers. They are also concerned about the long-term environmental impact of increased insecticide use.

The extension service agrees to oversee a community-based pest management program that will involve the integrated use of insecticides and pheromones. The first prong of the attack involves using synthetic pheromones that mimic the sex pheromones of the female pests. Pheromone dispensers are put out at the time when mating is known to occur. In the presence of so much pheromone, the males are confused as to the whereabouts of the females and less mating occurs.

■What are some of the advantages of using mating disruption as a means of pest control?

- Ans: Helps minimize pesticide resistance. Targets a specific pest and so does not harm beneficial insects. No pesticide residue or run off.

■Some of the growers are concerned that the pheromone will also attract females and increase the likelihood of infestation. How do you allay their fears?

- Ans: The synthetic pheromone is unique in structure, specifically attractive to the male pest. It will not attract females into the area.

■They also ask whether a pheromone might be designed that would be effective for closely related species of pests. What factors would determine that likelihood?

- Ans: The synthetic pheromone used would have to effectively mimic the sex pheromone of each species. There would need to be a strong similarity in the structural features, including chirality and overall three-dimensional shape. It is unlikely a single compound would attract more than one species.

■What are some of the disadvantages of using pheromones in this way, as compared to conventional insecticides?

- Ans: The conventional method offers a "blanket" approach, that is the insectide is applied relatively quickly, over a wide area, and affects several species of pests at the same time. Pheromone use is selective as to species. Because the phermones are tied to certain behaviors of the pests they control, the user must know the appropriate time to put out the pheromones and also where the targeted pest will most likely be found so that the pest will "find" the lures and traps set out.

CHAPTER 8

Conjugated Dienes

I. Textbook Chapter Contents

This chapter examines the reactions of one kind of diene. It introduces the concept of resonance stabilization and applies it to the phenomenon known as conjugate addition to dienes. The unique stability of allylic carbocations is also encountered.

II. Learning Objectives

- Be able to distinguish between conjugated, isolated, and cumulated dienes.
- Understand the electronic structure of conjugated dienes and the phenomenon known as conjugation.
- Write equations for the addition of hydrogen bromide to a conjugated diene, explaining the formation of 1,2- and 1,4-adducts.
- Write equations for the addition of bromine to a conjugated diene, explaining the formation of 1,2- and 1,4-adducts.

- Understand the concept of resonance stabilization, especially its application to the stability of the allyl carbocation.

- Become familiar with the family of compounds known as terpenes and how their structure incorporates the isoprene unit. Distinguish between monoterpenes, sesquiterpenes, diterpenes, triterpenes, and tetraterpenes.

III. Glossary

1,2-adduct the result of an addition reaction in which the adding entities are attached to adjacent carbons (called carbons 1 and 2); this typically occurs with addition to an isolated alkene but may also result from addition to one double bond of a conjugated diene.

1,4-adduct the result of an addition reaction in which the adding entities are attached to non-adjacent carbons (called carbons 1 and 4) separated by two other carbons (carbons 2 and 3); such adducts typically result from addition reactions with conjugated dienes.

allyl carbocation CH_2=CH-CH_2^+, a carbocation which can be envisioned as resulting from dissociation of allyl bromide to a carbocation in an S_N1 reaction; this is a resonance stabilized carbocation resulting from conjugation of the carbocation with the double bond.

allylic carbocation a carbocation that has a double bond conjugated to the carbocation, thereby providing resonance stabilization

diterpene a C_{20} terpene based on four isoprene units

conjugate addition an addition reaction with a conjugated diene to produce a 1,4-adduct

conjugated diene a diene in which the double bonds are separated by one single bond. This means that each of the four carbons of the diene system is sp^2 hybridized and therefore has a *p* orbital capable of pi overlap

conjugated polyene a compound with multiple double bonds in which each double bond is separated from another by one single bond. There is an alternating sequence of carbon-carbon double bonds and single bonds

conjugation when there is at least a three carbon structural segment in which each carbon is sp^2 hybridized and therefore has a *p* orbital capable of pi overlap

contributing structure the structure of a species which does not exist, but which represents one of several localized structures; the hybrid of all such structures is the actual structure of a molecular species. Such contributing structures differ only in the positions of electrons, and not in the positions of atoms

cumulated diene a diene in which two carbon-carbon double bonds are adjacent and are not separated by a single bond

delocalization the spreading of electron density over a structural unit; the delocalization in a resonance hybrid is over a pi orbital-containing conjugated system

diene a compound with two double bonds

essential oils naturally occurring compounds, most of which are members of the terpene family and which contain the essence or flavor of the plant

heat of hydrogenation the energy evolved when hydrogen is added to a structural unit such as an alkene

isolated diene a diene in which the double bonds are separated by more than one single bond

isoprene $CH_2=C(CH_3)-CH=CH_2$, a C_5 hydrocarbon which serves as the building block in terpenes

isoprenoid compounds compounds whose structure is based on multiple isoprene segments joined together

monoterpene a C_{10} terpene based on two isoprene units

natural rubber a polymer of isoprene which contains only *cis* double bonds

polyene a compound with many double bonds

resonance hybrid the actual structure of a compound stabilized by resonance, and which is a hybrid of the various contributing structures

resonance theory a theory which states that whenever a molecule or ion can be represented by two or more structures that differ only in the positions of the electrons, stabilization results

resonance stabilization the stabilization afforded a molecule or reactive intermediate by delocalization of electrons through contributing structures

sesquiterpene a C_{15} terpene based on three isoprene units

steroids a group of naturally occurring compounds with a tetracyclic ring structure called the steroid nucleus (three fused six-membered rings and a single fused five-membered ring)

terpenes a large family of natural products, most of which are relatively non-polar, and which contain structures based on sequential polymerization of isoprene

tetraterpene a C_{40} terpene based on eight isoprene units

triterpene a C_{30} terpene based on six isoprene units

IV. Summary of Reactions of Conjugated Dienes

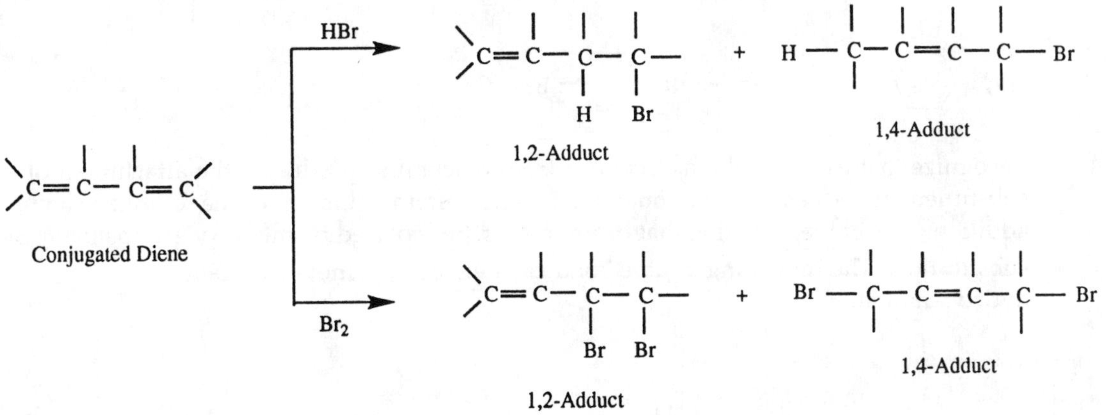
HBr
H
Br
1,2-Adduct
H
Br
1,4-Adduct
Conjugated Diene
Br₂
Br
Br
1,2-Adduct
Br
Br
1,4-Adduct

V. Solutions to Problems

For "**How to Solve a Problem,**" review pages 257 and 259

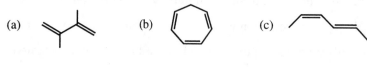

8.1

(a) 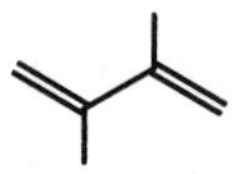 (b) 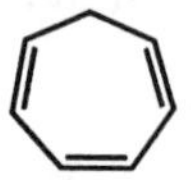 (c) 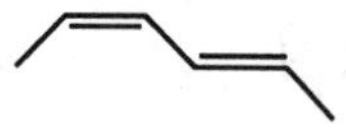

(d) 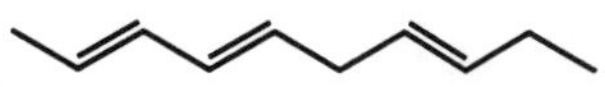

8.2

(a) 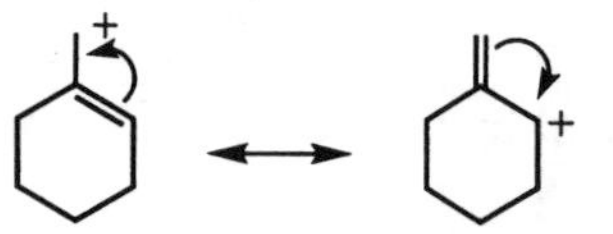 (b) 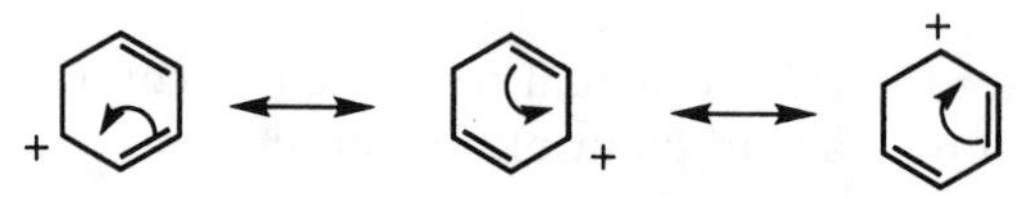

(c) 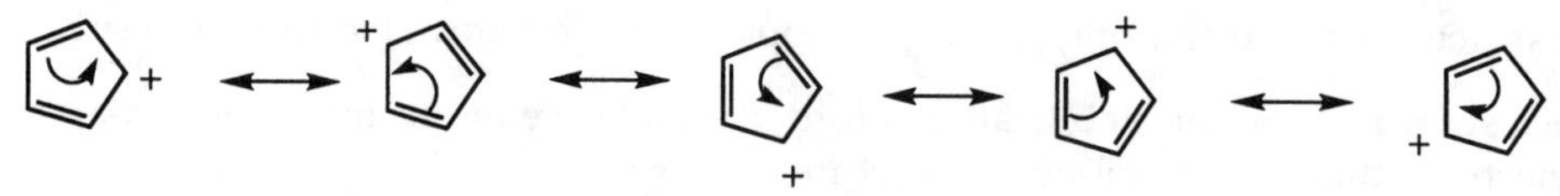

8.3

(a) 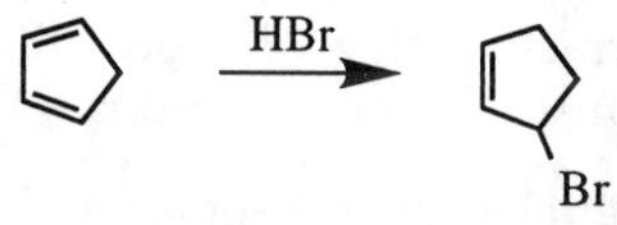
HBr
Br

(b) 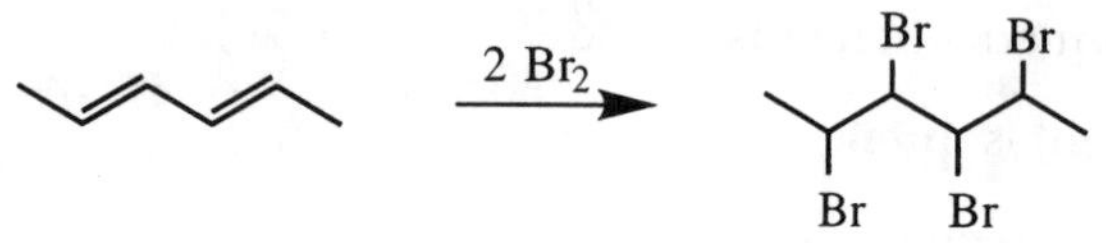
2 Br_2
Br Br
Br Br

(c) 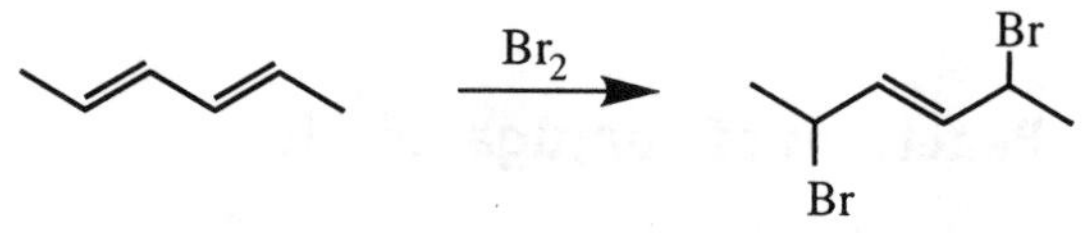
Br_2
Br
Br

(d) 
Br_2
Br
Br

8.4 Recognize that the overall major change from reactant to product is the attachment of a substituent at both ends of the conjugated diene system. This is the clue to utilize conjugate addition of bromine, realizing that bromines can be replaced by methoxy groups using S_N2 substitution. The remaining double bond can be readily removed by catalytic hydrogenation.

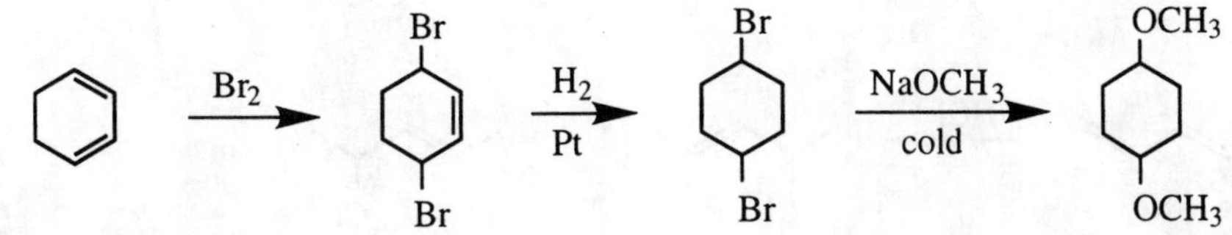
Br₂
Br
Br
H₂
Pt
Br
Br
NaOCH₃
cold
OCH₃
OCH₃

8.5 (a) 2*E*,4*E*-heptadiene
(b) 1,3,5-cyclooctatriene
(c) 5-methyl-1,3-cyclohexadiene
(d) 5,5,-dimethyl-1,3-cyclopentadiene.

8.6

(a) 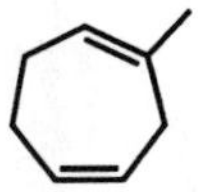

(b) 

(c) 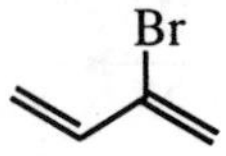
Br

(d) 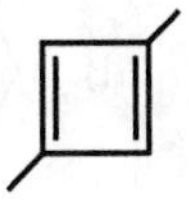

8.7

(a) 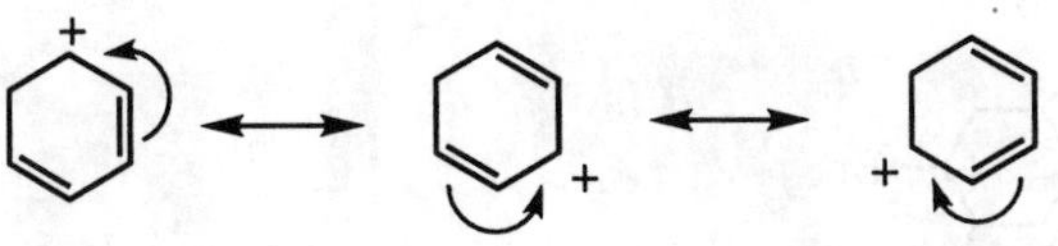

(b) 

(c) 
CH₂
CH₂

8.8

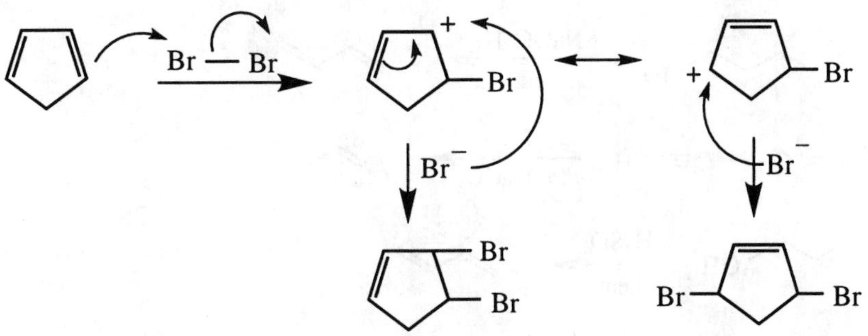
Br — Br
Br
Br⁻
Br
Br⁻
Br
Br
Br
Br

1,2-adduct 1,4-adduct

8.9

a) 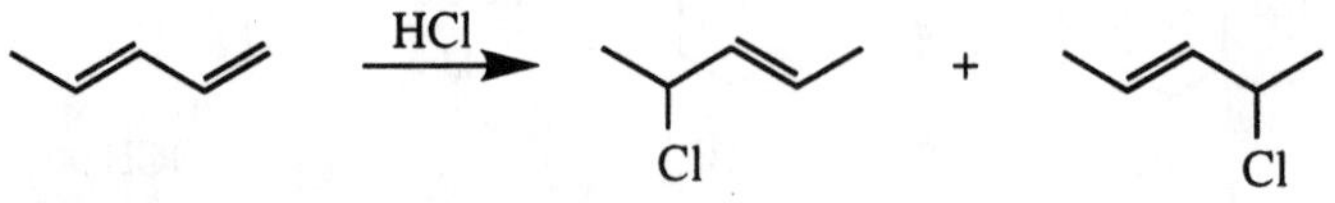
HCl
+
Cl
Cl

b) 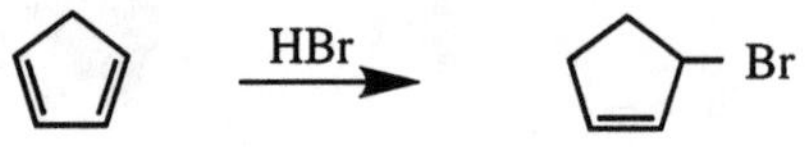
HBr
Br
(same product from 1,2- and 1,4-addition!)

c) 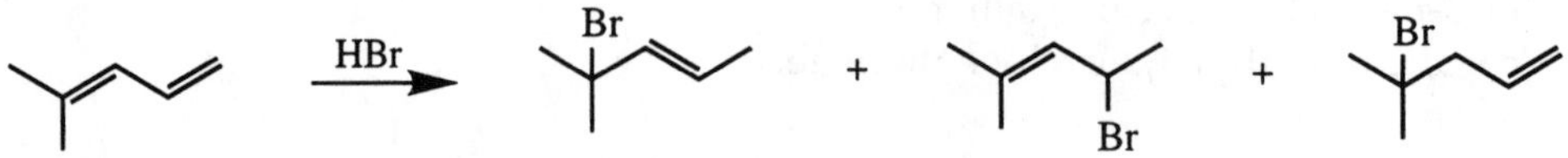
HBr
Br
+
Br
+
Br
major product

d) 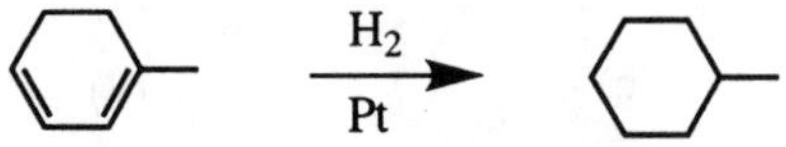
H_2
Pt

e) 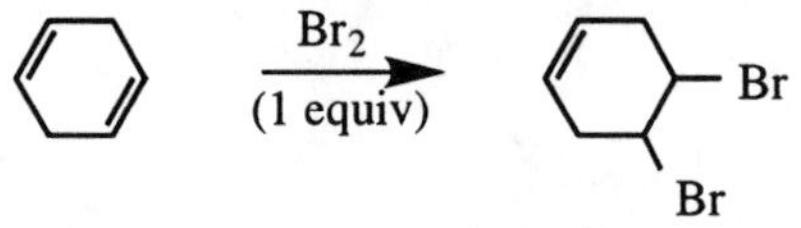
Br_2
(1 equiv)
Br
Br

f) 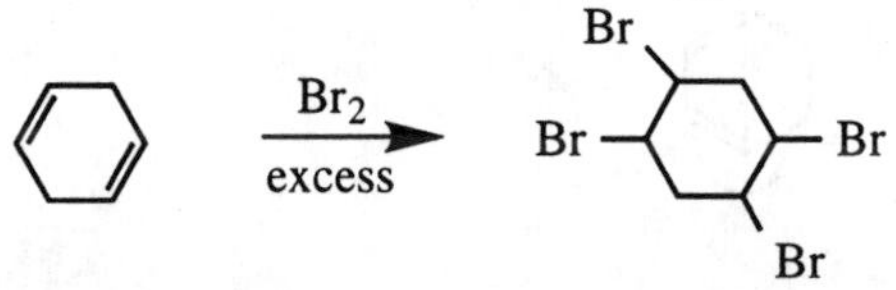
Br_2
excess
Br
Br
Br
Br

g) 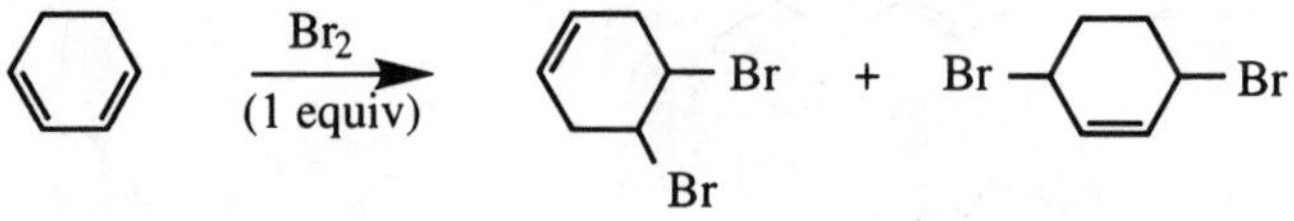
Br_2
(1 equiv)
Br
Br
+
Br
Br

h) 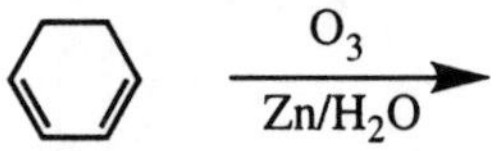
O_3
Zn/H_2O
$OHC(CH_2)_2CHO$ + OHC-CHO

8.10

(a) 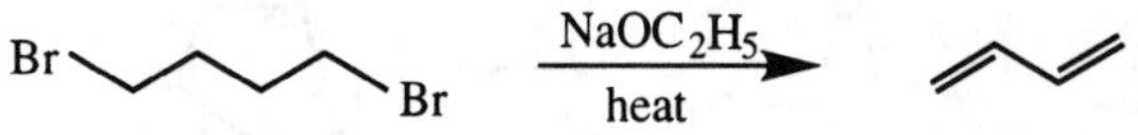
Br
Br
$NaOC_2H_5$
heat

(b) $CH_2 = CH-C\equiv CH$ 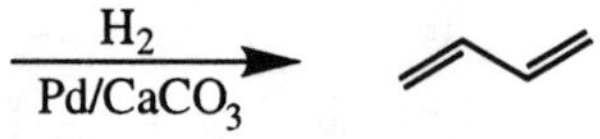
H_2
$Pd/CaCO_3$

(c) 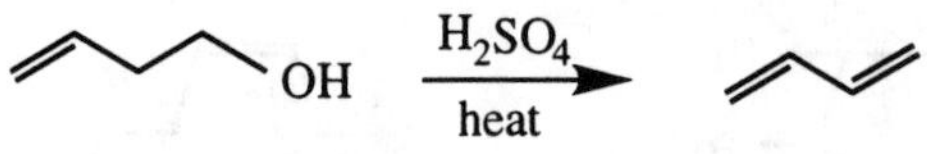
OH
H_2SO_4
heat

(d) 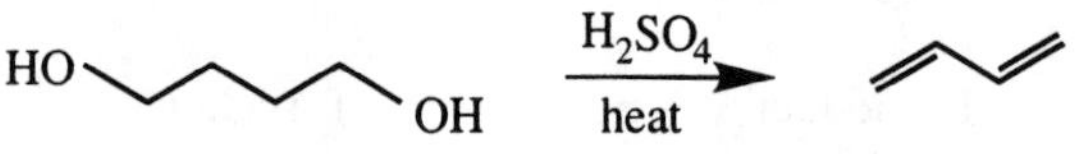
HO
OH
H_2SO_4
heat

8.11 The reaction of an alkyl bromide with silver nitrate is an S_N1 reaction, the silver "pulling off" the bromide (to form silver bromide precipitate) leaving behind a carbocation (see Section 3.4.4). The stability of the carbocation determines the rate at which silver bromide is formed. 1-Bromopropane has to form a primary carbocation for this reaction to occur, and the relative instability of a primary carbocation makes the reaction difficult and slow. By contrast, allyl bromide has to form an allyl carbocation for the reaction to occur. Allyl carbocations are relatively stable due to resonance so form readily, making the silver bromide reaction rapid with allyl bromide.

8.12 Resonance structure **B** should be the major contributing structure because it is an allylic tertiary carbocation whereas structure **A** is an allylic secondary carbocation. Tertiary carbocations are more stable than secondary carbocations due to hyperconjugation.

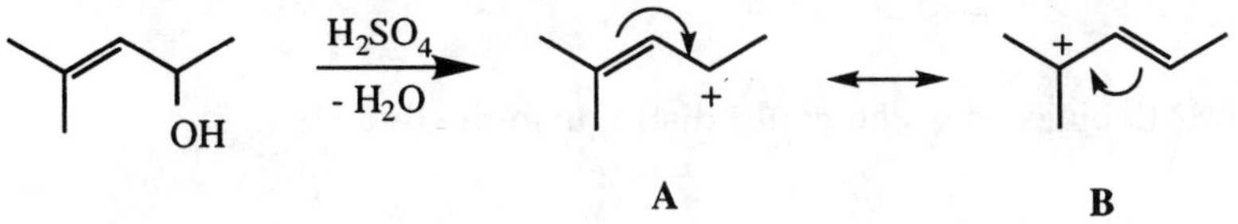

H_2SO_4
$- H_2O$
OH
+
+
A
B

8.13 2-Cyclohexen-1-ol reacts readily with sulfuric acid because the oxonium ion very readily loses water to form a stabilized carbocation, an allylic carbocation. The dehydration reaction is completed by loss of a proton from the only available carbon, forming the stable conjugated diene.

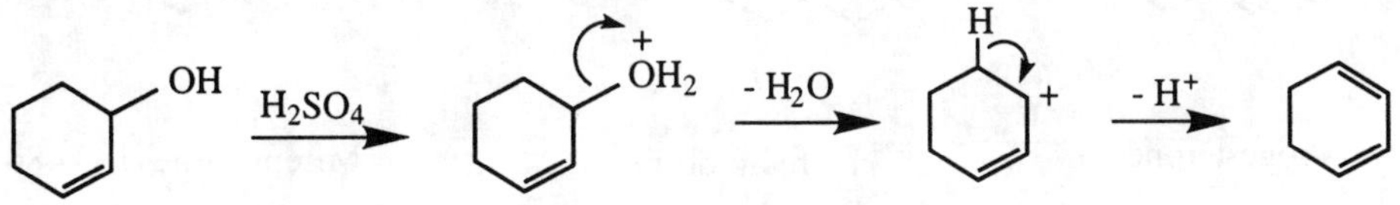

OH
H_2SO_4
$\overset{+}{O}H_2$
$- H_2O$
H
+
$- H^+$

8.14

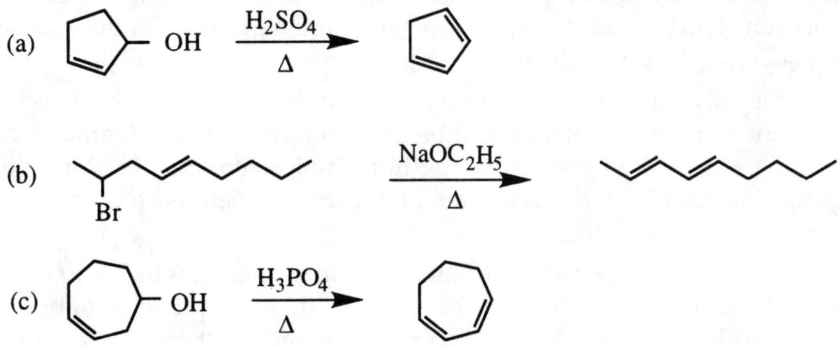

(a)
OH
H_2SO_4
Δ
(b)
Br
$NaOC_2H_5$
Δ
(c)
OH
H_3PO_4
Δ

VI. Conceptual Problem

TESTING...1,2,3

You have just started working at a laboratory that conducts drug testing for the Federal Drug Administration. Your supervisor decides to test your knowledge of organic chemistry. He places three pills before you and says that one is the birth-control pill norethindrone, one is RU-486 (mifepristone, the "morning after" pill), and the other is progesterone (used in estrogen therapy). He asks whether you know a simple way to distinguish the three compounds using chemical tests.

■ What would you tell him? Explain how you could distinguish the three drugs.

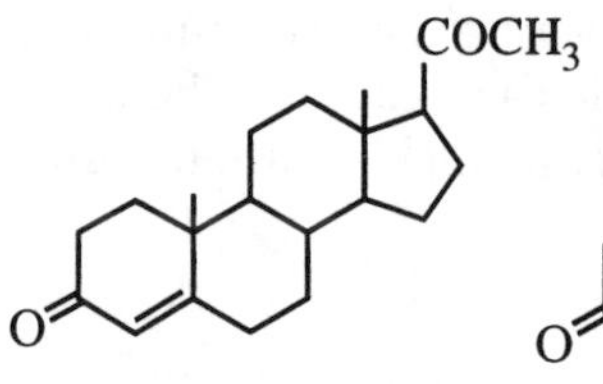
COCH$_3$
O

Progesterone

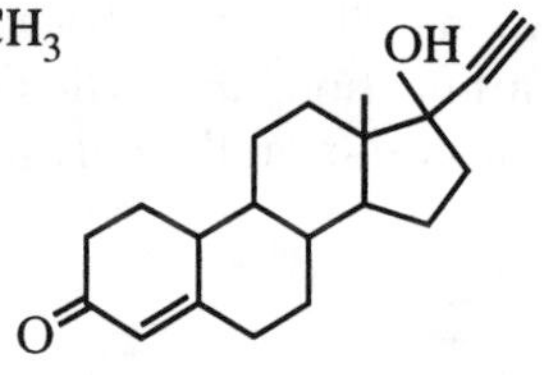
OH
O

Norethindrone

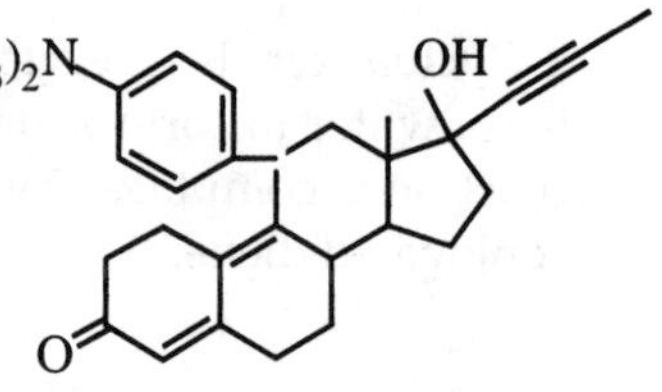
(CH$_3$)$_2$N
OH
O

Mifepristone (RU 486)

- Ans: Examine the structures carefully to identify the functional groups present in each. Progesterone has ketone and alkene groups; Norethindrone has ketone, alkene, alcohol, and alkyne groups; Mifepristone has ketone, diene, alcohol, and amine groups. On the basis of this analysis there are two separate means of distinguishing the three compounds:
  1. Since mifesterone is the only compound containing nitorgen its presence can be detected by qualitative analysis for nitrogen. (Note: as will be indicated in chapter 12, amines are basic so this will be the only compound to be soluble in dilute hydrochloric acid.) Norenthindrone has an alcohol group (detectable by the evolution of hydrogen when reacted with sodium metal) whereas progesterone does not.
  2. The threee compounds could be reacted quantitatively with bromine, which should add to the alkene, diene, and alkyne groups. Progesterone would add one equivalent of bromine, norethindrone would add three equivalents of bromine, and mifepristone would add four equivalents of bromine.

CHAPTER 9

Aromatics

I. Textbook Chapter Contents

This chapter introduces a completely different carbon skeleton, that of compounds derived from benzene (C_6H_6). All previous families encountered are classified as aliphatic compounds, but benzenoid compounds are known as aromatic compounds. In addition, related compounds also showing the property of aromaticity are introduced. A new reaction, electrophilic aromatic substitution, and its mechanism are described.

II. Learning Objectives

- Understand the concept of aromaticity and be able to explain the unique stability of benzene and its derivatives, known as arenes.

- Know the meaning of resonance stabilization, resonance energy, aromaticity, Hückel rule, heteroaromatic compound.

- Be able to name benzenoid compounds using the IUPAC and common systems. Designate di-substituted derivatives as ortho, meta, or para isomers. Know the phenyl and benzyl group.

- Understand the general mechanism for electrophilic aromatic substitution.

- Write equations for the halogenation, nitration, and sulfonation of benzene.

- Write equations for the Friedel-Crafts alkylation and acylation of benzene.

- Understand why certain substituents on a benzene ring are activators and others are deactivators of further electrophilic substitution on the ring.

- Understand why certain substituents on a benzene ring are ortho-para directors and others are meta directors for further electrophilic substitution on the ring.

- Understand the mechanistic relationship between the activating effect and directing effect exerted by a substituent already on a benzene ring.
- Be able to use knowledge of the directing and activating effects of substituents to plan multi-step syntheses of di- and tri-substituted benzenes from benzene.
- Know how to name phenols.
- Understand why phenols are weak Brønsted acids and how other ring substituents affect the acidity of a substituted phenol.
- Understand the activating effect of a phenolic hydroxyl group and how this can be moderated by conversion to an ester group.
- Write equations for the preparation of substituted phenols by electrophilic aromatic substitution.
- Understand how carbocations formed adjacent to a benzene ring (benzylic carbocations) are especially stabilized by resonance, and therefore form readily. Know how this accounts for the ready formation of alkenylbenzenes in elimination reactions, and the regiochemistry of electrophilic addition to alkenyl benzenes.
- Write reactions to account for the oxidation of alkylbenzenes to benzoic acids using hot potassium permanganate.
- Be familiar with the concept of polynuclear aromatic hydrocarbons, and recognize a few simple members.
- Be familiar with the concept of heterocyclic aromatic compounds, and recognize a few simple compounds. Also, become familiar with the heterocyclic aromatic compounds known as purines and pyrimidines which appear as bases in DNA and RNA.

III. Glossary

activator a group that, when attached to a benzene ring, causes an electrophilic aromatic substitution to occur faster than on benzene itself

acylium cation the ion RCO^+

alkaloids naturally occurring nitrogenous bases, some of which are heteroaromatics

alkenyl benzene a benzenoid compound with a carbon-carbon double bond conjugated with the ring

Ar a generalized representation for an aryl group

arenes aromatic hydrocarbons

aryl group an aromatic group such as phenyl (C_6H_5–)

aromatic compound a cyclic, planar, highly unsaturated, conjugated and resonance stabilized compound

aromaticity a special stability of aromatic compounds associated with a planar cyclic structure containing *p* orbitals on each ring atom and having a Hückel number (4n + 2) of electrons

aromatic sextet a continuous pi orbital containing six electrons which confers aromaticity on the ring structure

benzene the compound C_6H_6, considered the parent benzenoid compound

benzenoid a compound which contains a benzene ring

benzyl the group $C_6H_5CH_2$–

benzylic the position adjacent to the ring in an alkylbenzene

Buckminsterfullerene also known as "buckyball," this compound of formula C_{60} is a soccer-ball-shaped aromatic compound which is another form of elemental carbon, in addition to graphite and diamond. It contains continuously fused rings, 20 six-membered and 12 five-membered

Clemmensen reduction a process for reduction of a carbonyl group (when attached to a benzene ring) to a methylene group using zinc amalgam in hydrochloric acid

deactivator a group that, when attached to a benzene ring, causes an electrophilic aromatic substitution to occur slower than on benzene itself

directing effect the influence of a substituent already on a benzene ring in directing an incoming electrophile to specific positions on the ring (that is, the substituent influences the regiochemistry of the electrophilic aromatic substitution)

DNA bases four heteroaromatic compounds that occur in DNA - adenine, guanine, cytosine, and thymine

electrophilic aromatic substitution the replacement of a hydrogen on a benzene ring by a substituent, the mechanism proceeding by attack of the ring by an electrophilic reagent

Friedel-Crafts acylation reaction of an acyl halide with a benzenoid compound in the presence of a Lewis acid (usually AlX_3) resulting in the replacement of an aryl hydrogen with an acyl group

Friedel-Crafts alkylation reaction of an alkyl halide with a benzenoid compound in the presence of a Lewis acid (usually AlX_3) resulting in the replacement of an aryl hydrogen with an alkyl group

graphite a form of elemental carbon whose structure is a large "sheet" of continuously-fused benzene rings

halogenation the substitution of a halogen onto a benzene ring

heteroaromatic an aromatic compound containing a heteroatom in the ring

Hückel rule an empirical rule stating that 4n+2 pi electrons (where n = 0 or a whole number) in a cyclic, planar structure with continuous overlap of p orbitals confers aromatic character on the compound

m-director a substituent which directs an attacking electrophile mainly to the meta position on a benzene ring

meta position the 3 position on a benzene ring

nitration the substitution of a nitro group onto a benzene ring

o,p-director a substituent which directs an attacking electrophile mainly to the ortho and para positions on a benzene ring

ortho position the 2 position on a benzene ring

PAH an abbreviation used for polynuclear aromatic hydrocarbon

para position the 4-position on a benzene ring

phenols aromatic compounds with one or more –OH groups attached to the ring

phenoxide anion C_6H_5O–, the anion resulting from removal of a hydroxyl proton from phenol

phenyl a C_6H_5– group

polynuclear aromatic hydrocarbon a hydrocarbon which has two or more benzene rings fused together. Examples include naphthalene (2 rings) and phenanthrene (3 rings)

RNA bases four heteroaromatic compounds that occur in RNA - adenine, guanine, cytosine, and uracil

resonance energy the energy by which a compound is stabilized due to resonance

sulfonation the substitution of a sulfonic acid group onto a benzene ring

surfactant a surface active agent, a compound with a hydrophilic end and a lipophilic end which bridges the interface between an aqueous and an organic layer

IV. Summary of Reactions of Aromatic Compounds

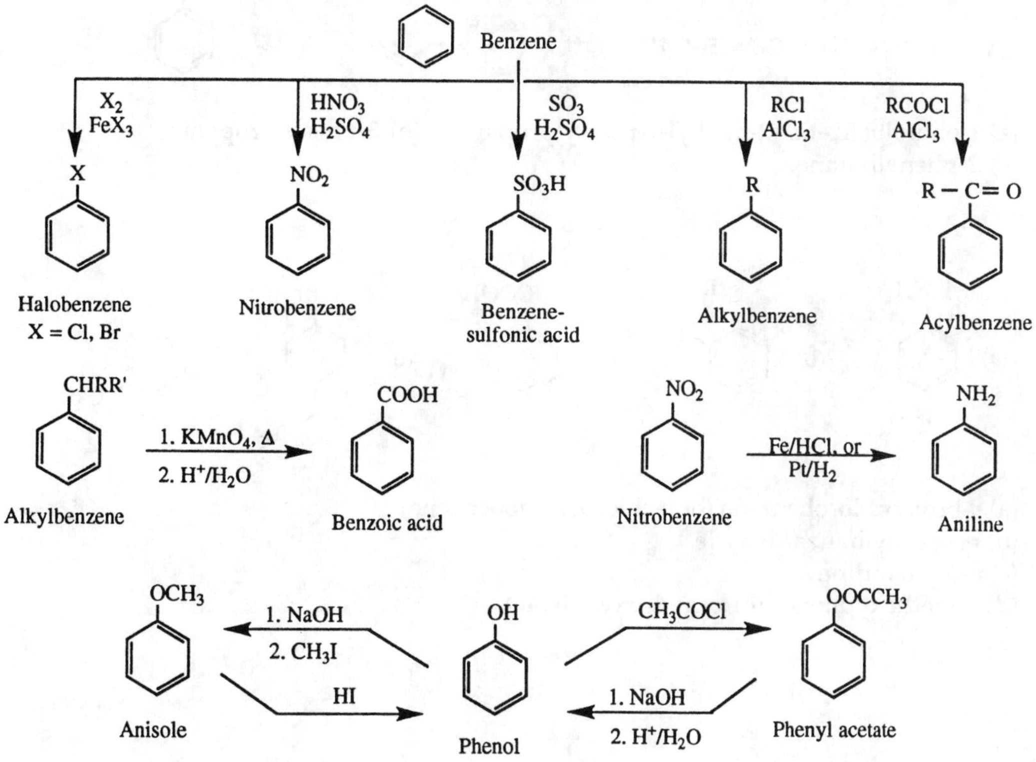
Benzene
X2
FeX3
HNO3
H2SO4
SO3
H2SO4
RCl
AlCl3
RCOCl
AlCl3
X
NO2
SO3H
R
R – C= O
Halobenzene
X = Cl, Br
Nitrobenzene
Benzene-
sulfonic acid
Alkylbenzene
Acylbenzene
CHRR'
1. KMnO4, Δ
2. H+/H2O
COOH
Alkylbenzene
Benzoic acid
NO2
Fe/HCl, or
Pt/H2
NH2
Nitrobenzene
Aniline
OCH3
1. NaOH
2. CH3I
HI
OH
CH3COCl
OOCCH3
1. NaOH
2. H+/H2O
Anisole
Phenol
Phenyl acetate

V. Solutions to Problems

For "**How to Solve a Problem**," review pages 274, 287, 295, 297, 302, and 310)

9.1 Since the six carbon-carbon bonds in benzene are identical, we can represent its structure by a hexagon with a ring (representing six electrons) enclosed. This means that two ring carbons carrying a bromine atom in dibromobenzenes can have zero, one, or two carbon-carbon bonds between them. There are only those three possibilities.

A representation of benzene

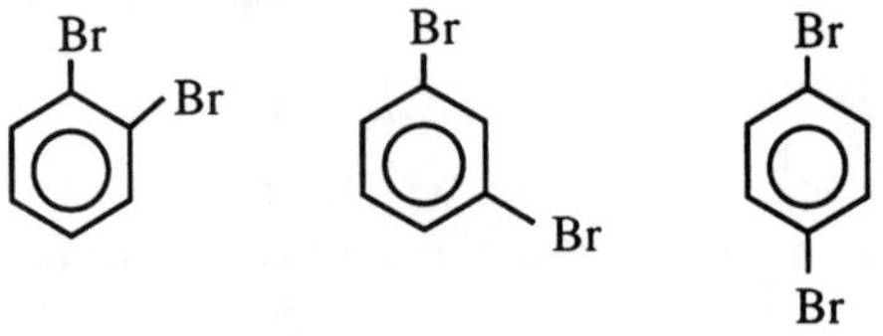

Br
Br
Br
Br
Br
Br

Three different dibromobenzenes

9.2

(a) 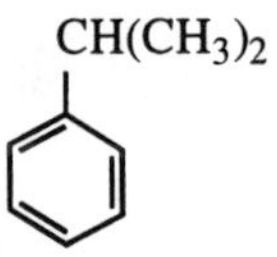
CH(CH3)2

(b) 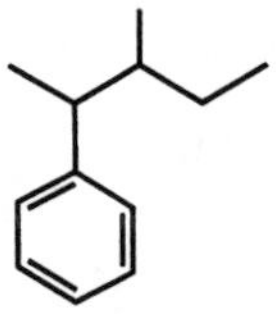

(c) 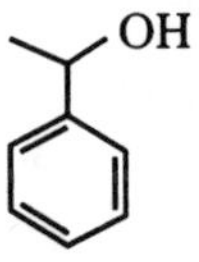
OH

(d) 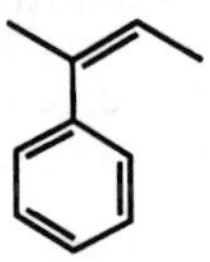

(e) C_6H_5-CH=CH-CH=CH-C_6H_5

(f) 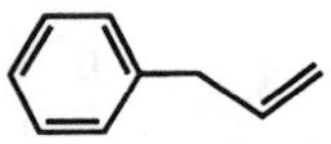

(g) 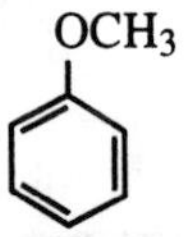
OCH3

9.3 (a) isobutylbenzene (2-methyl-1-phenylpropane); (b) 3-phenylpropyne; (c) 2-phenylbutane.

9.4

(a) 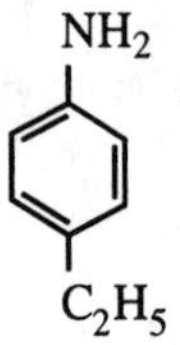

NH2
C2H5

(b) 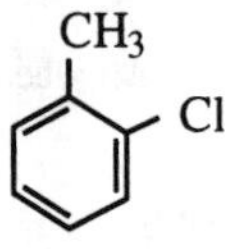

CH3
Cl

(c) 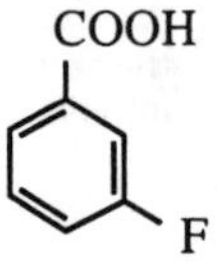

COOH
F

(d) 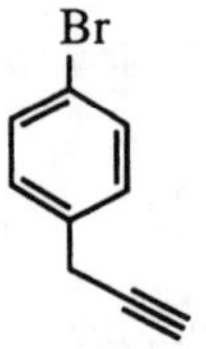
Br

(e) 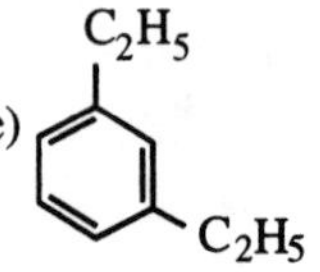

C2H5
C2H5

9.5 (a) *p*-bromochlorobenzene (or *p*-chlorobromobenzene)
(b) *m*-methylbenzaldehyde
(c) *o*-nitroaniline
(d) *o*-methoxyphenol (or *o*-hydroxyanisole).

9.6

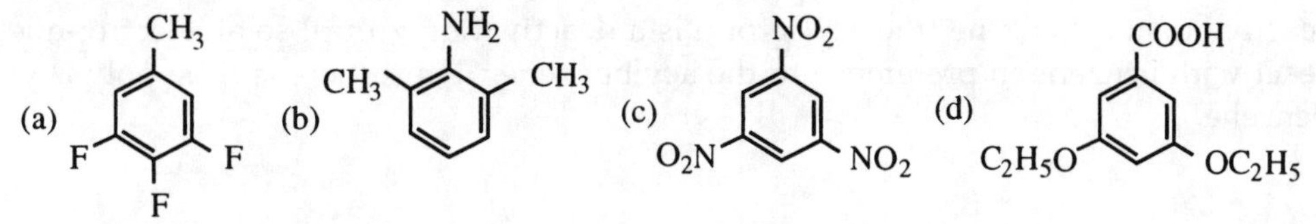
(a)
CH_3
F
F
F
(b)
NH_2
CH_3
CH_3
(c)
NO_2
O_2N
NO_2
(d)
COOH
C_2H_5O
OC_2H_5

9.7 (a) 3,4-dimethoxybenzenesulfonic acid; (b) 4-chloro-2-fluoro-6-iodonitrobenzene; (c) 4-ethyl-5-hydroxy-2-methylbenzoic acid; (d) 3,4,5-tribromobenzaldehyde.

9.8

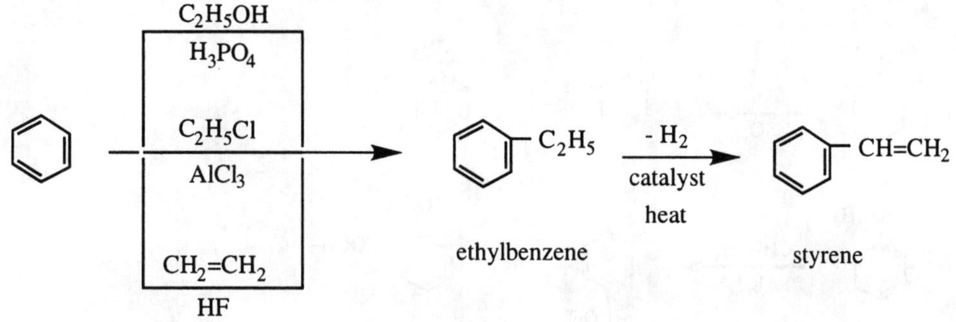
C_2H_5OH
H_3PO_4
C_2H_5Cl
$AlCl_3$
$CH_2{=}CH_2$
HF
C_2H_5
ethylbenzene
$-H_2$
catalyst
heat
$CH{=}CH_2$
styrene

9.9

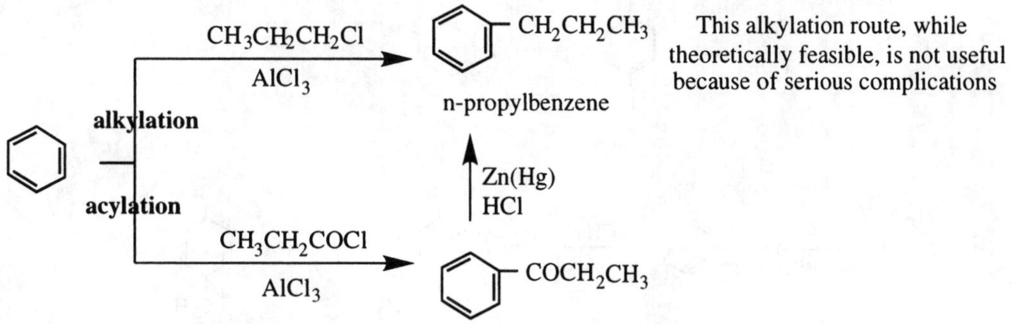
$CH_3CH_2CH_2Cl$
$AlCl_3$
$CH_2CH_2CH_3$
n-propylbenzene
This alkylation route, while theoretically feasible, is not useful because of serious complications
alkylation
acylation
Zn(Hg)
HCl
CH_3CH_2COCl
$AlCl_3$
$COCH_2CH_3$

9.10 Reference to Table 9.1 provides information on the relative activating effect of substituents. The orders of reactivity are as follows:
(a) aniline > acetanilide; (b) ethylbenzene > acetophenone; (c) anisole > toluene; (d) aniline > nitrobenzene; (e) toluene > bromobenzene.

9.11 In alkylation, the first substitution produces an alkylbenzene. Thereafter, the solution contains a mixture of the product alkylbenzene and benzene. Since the alkyl group is an activating group, the alkylbenzene is **more** reactive than is benzene so a second electrophile will react with the alkylbenzene in preference to benzene, thereby producing a dialkylbenzene. The product dialkylbenzene is more reactive than is the alkylbenzene or benzene. Therefore, the dialkylbenzene is converted into trialkylbenzene more readily than benzene is converted into alkylbenzene. In summary, alkylation of benzene tends to produce considerable proportions of poly-alkylated benzene.

In acylation of benzene, the first substitution produces an acylbenzene. Thereafter, the solution contains a mixture of the product acylbenzene and benzene. The acylbenzene is **less** reactive than is benzene (the acyl group is a deactivating group) so an electrophile will react with benzene in preference to the acylbenzene. Thus, there is little poly-acylation of benzene.

9.12

(a)
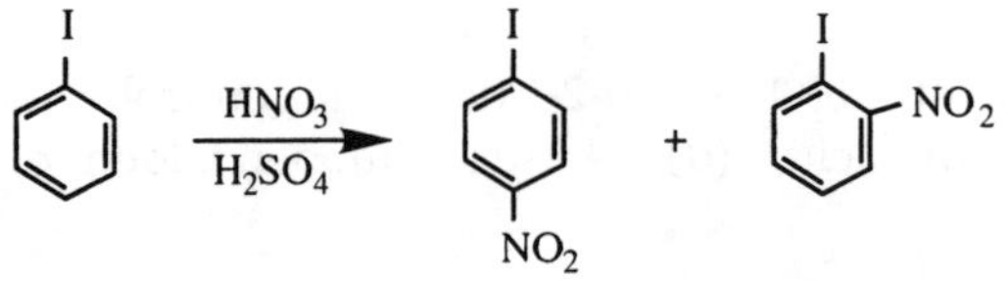

(b)
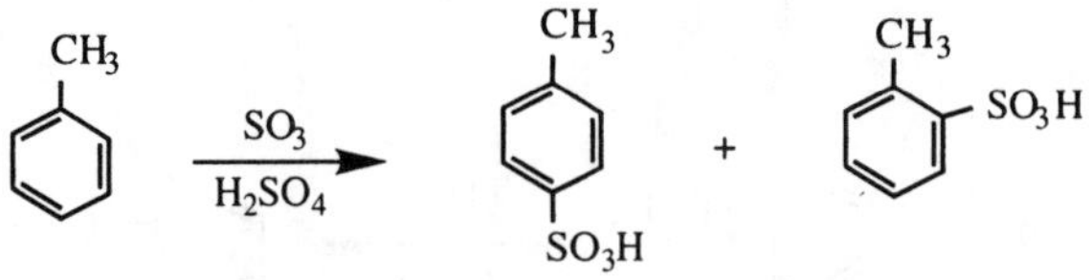

(c)
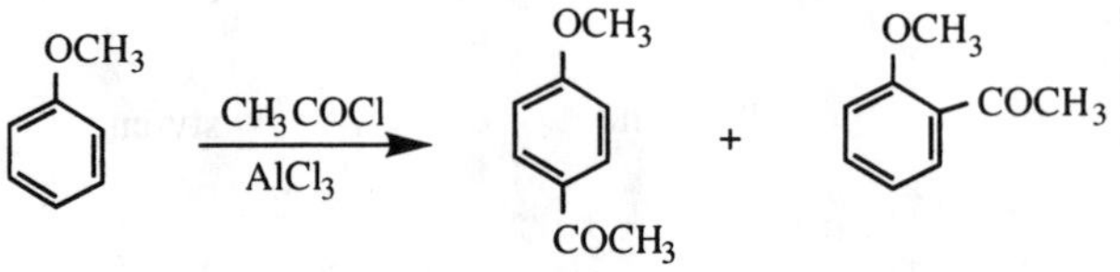

(d)
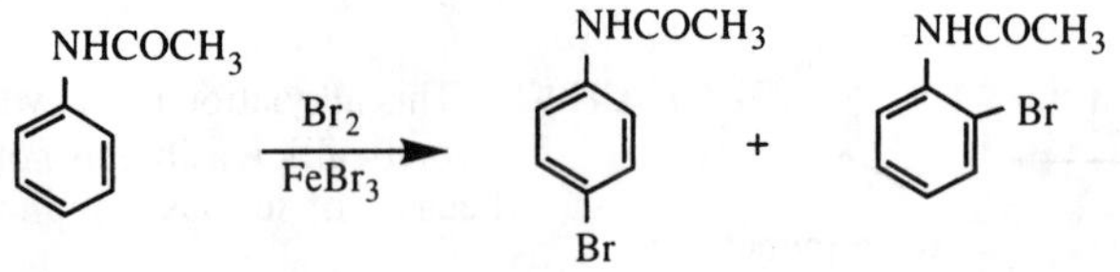

9.13

(a)
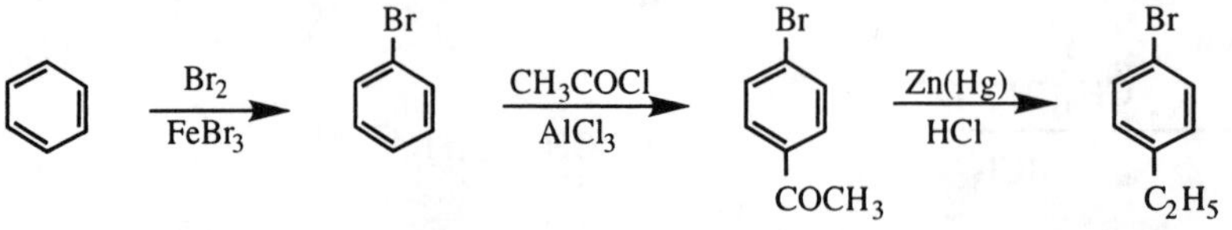

(b)
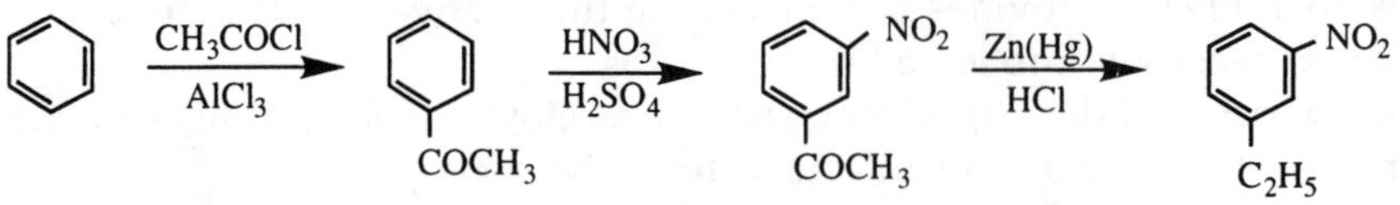

(c)
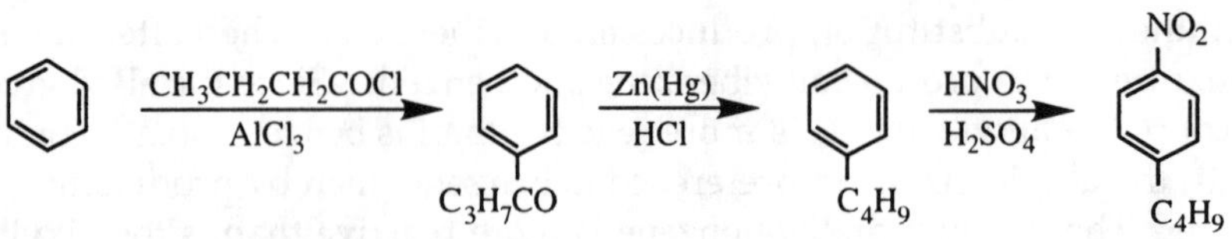

(d)
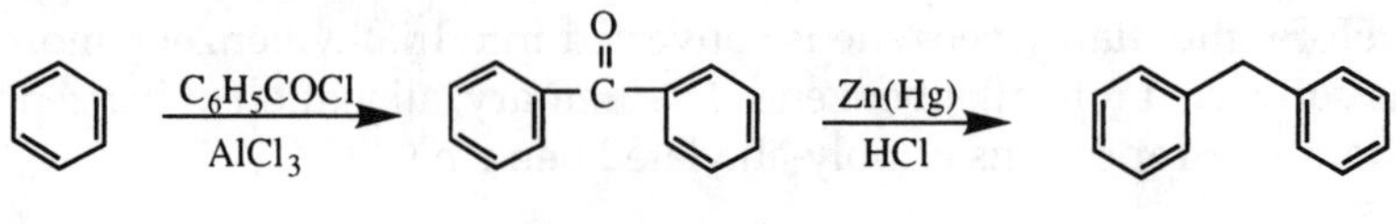

9.14

(a) 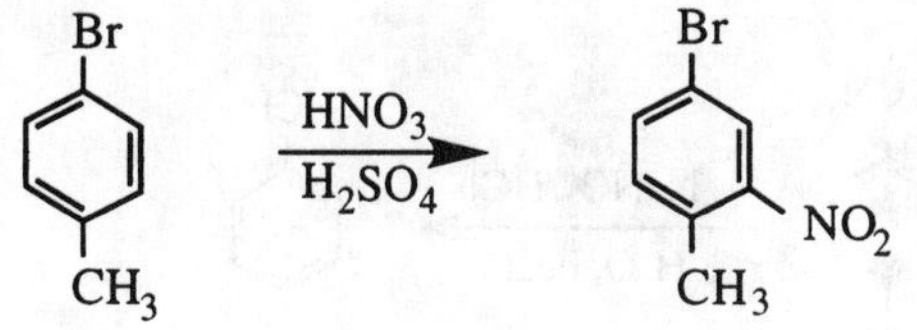

(b) 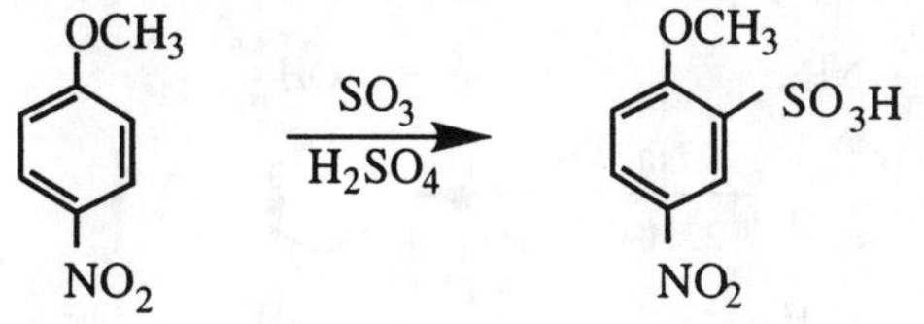

(c) 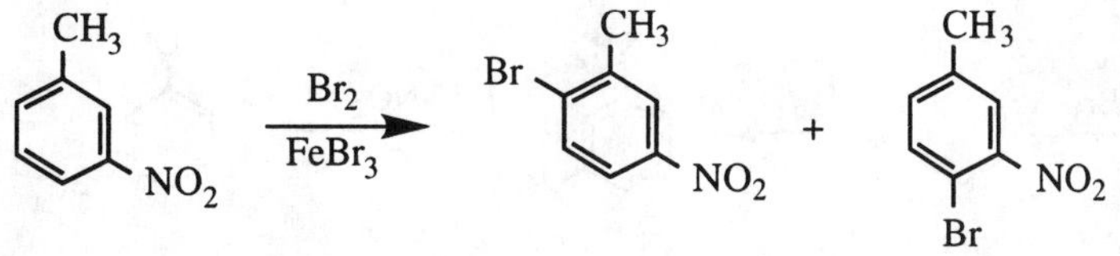

9.15

(a) 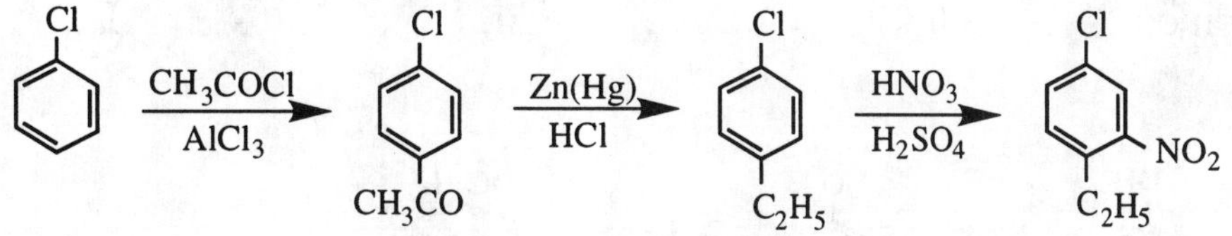

(b) 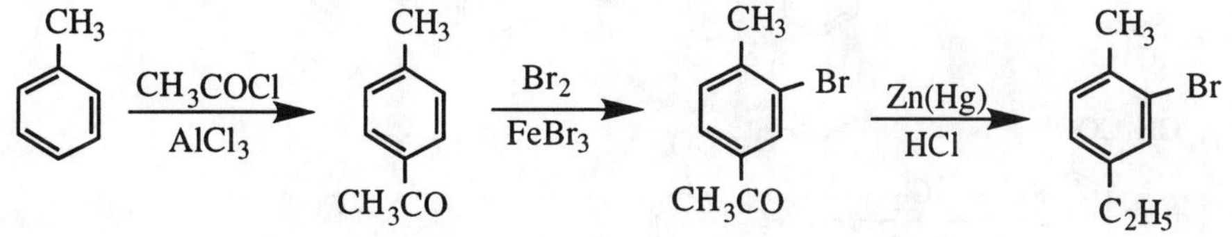

(c) 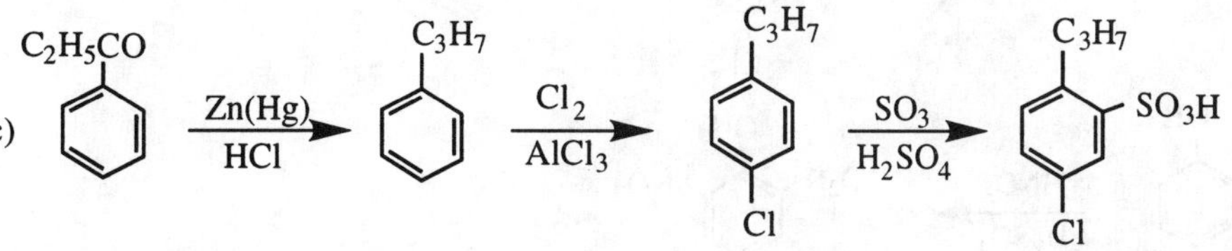

9.16 The most acidic phenol will be that which carries the most powerful electron withdrawing group(s), because these groups will better delocalize the negative charge of the phenoxide anion. The acidity orders are:

(a) *p*-nitrophenol > *p*-chlorophenol
(b) *o*-iodophenol > *p*-iodophenol
(c) *p*-acetylphenol > *p*-ethylphenol

9.17

(a) 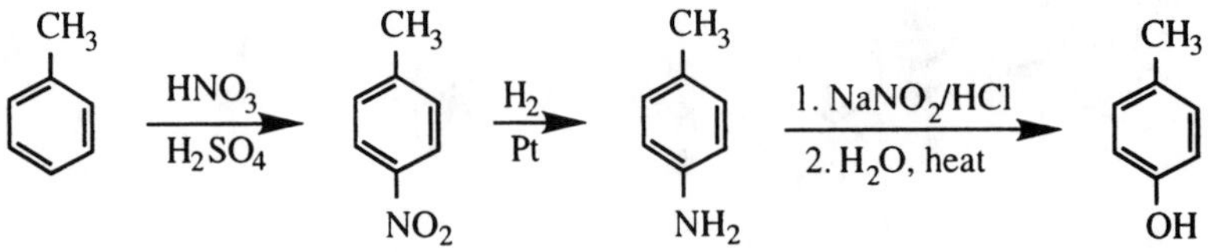
CH3
HNO3
H2SO4
CH3
NO2
H2
Pt
CH3
NH2
1. NaNO2/HCl
2. H2O, heat
CH3
OH

(b) 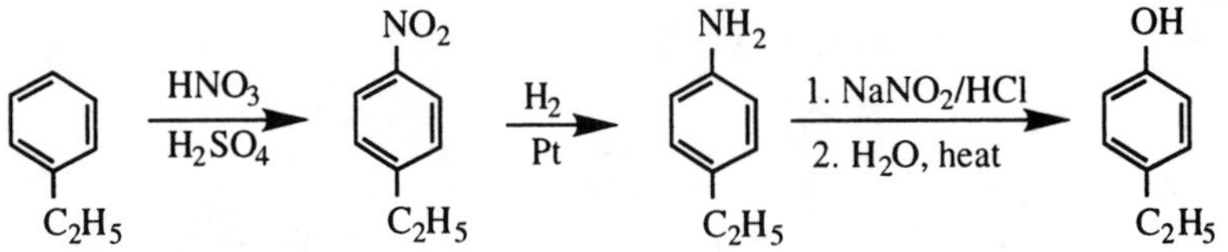
C2H5
HNO3
H2SO4
NO2
C2H5
H2
Pt
NH2
C2H5
1. NaNO2/HCl
2. H2O, heat
OH
C2H5

(c) 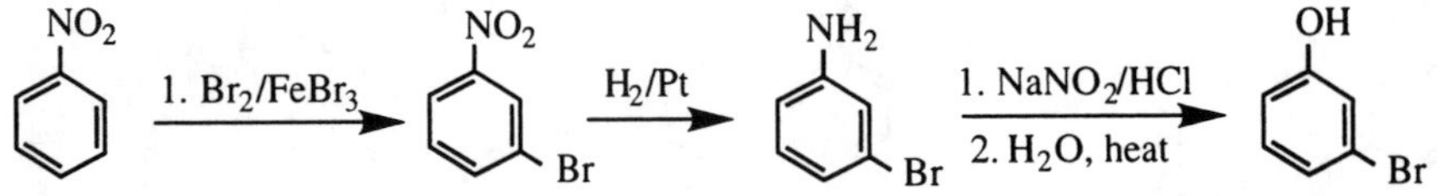
NO2
1. Br2/FeBr3
NO2
Br
H2/Pt
NH2
Br
1. NaNO2/HCl
2. H2O, heat
OH
Br

(d) 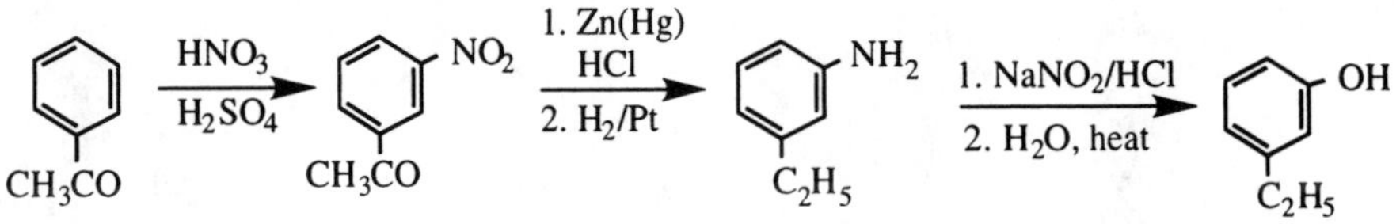
CH3CO
HNO3
H2SO4
NO2
CH3CO
1. Zn(Hg)
HCl
2. H2/Pt
NH2
C2H5
1. NaNO2/HCl
2. H2O, heat
OH
C2H5

9.18

(a) 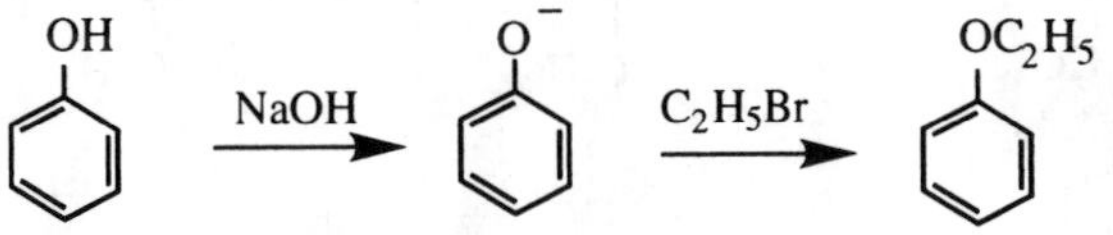
OH
NaOH
O−
C2H5Br
OC2H5

(b) 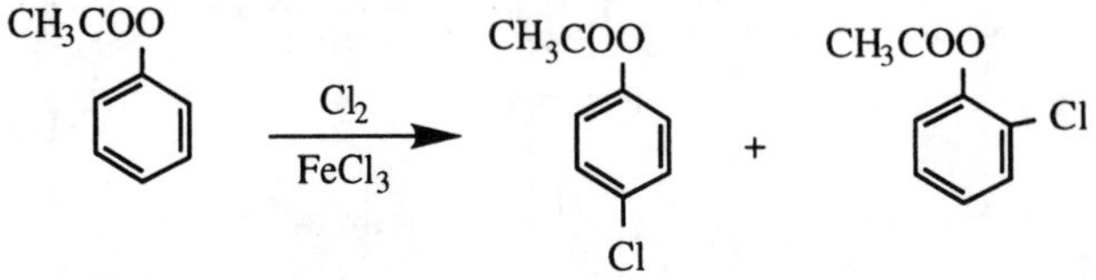
CH3COO
Cl2
FeCl3
CH3COO
Cl
+
CH3COO
Cl

(c) 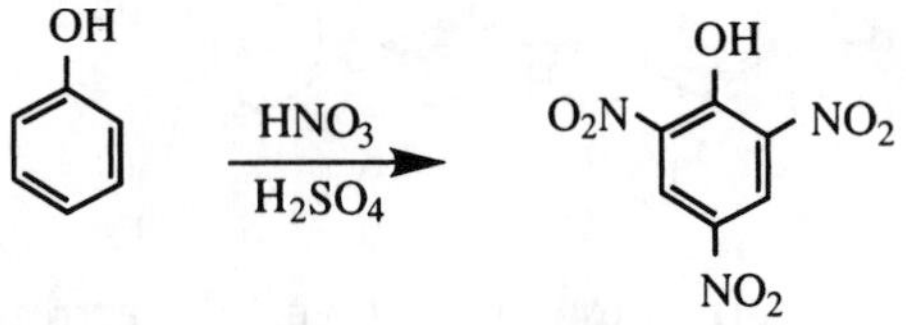
OH
HNO3
H2SO4
OH
O2N
NO2
NO2

(d) 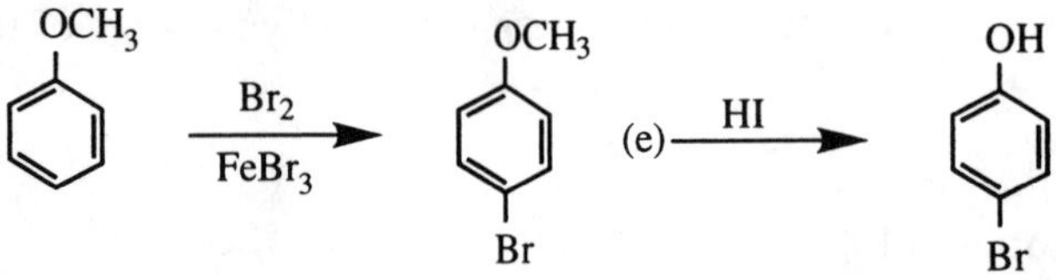
OCH3
Br2
FeBr3
OCH3
Br
(e)
HI
OH
Br

(major product)

9.19

(a) $C_6H_5CH{=}CHCH_3 \xrightarrow{HBr} C_6H_5CHBrCH_2CH_3$

(b) $C_6H_5CH{=}CHCH_3 \xrightarrow{H_2O/H_2SO_4} C_6H_5CHOHCH_2CH_3$

9.20

(a) 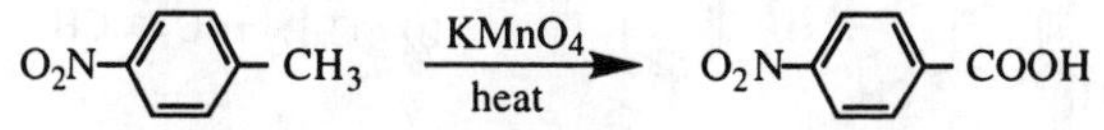

(b) 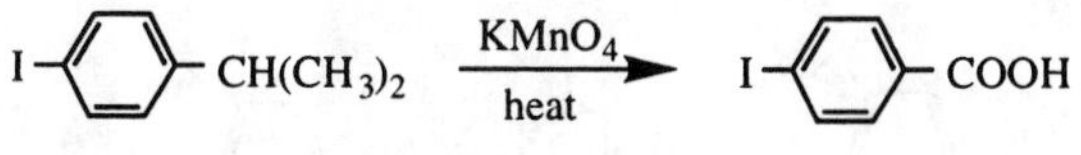

(c) 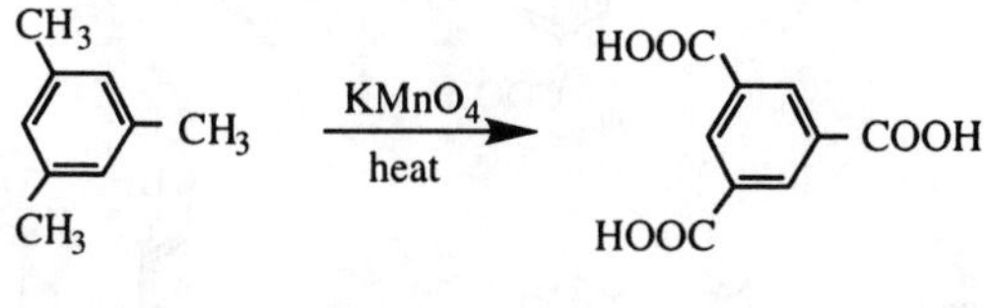

(d) 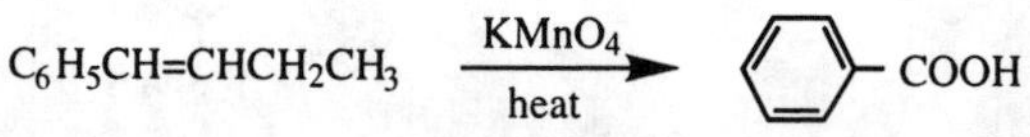

(e) 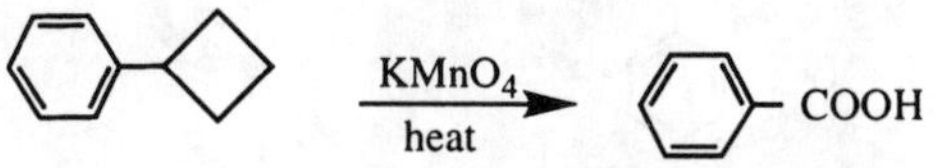

9.21 The formula $C_{10}H_{12}$ indicates the presence of five rings/and or multiple bonds (it is ten hydrogens short of being a C_{10} alkane). Since **A** does not react with bromine or permanganate there can be no normal double or triple bonds in **A**, so the presence of a benzene ring is suspected. A benzene ring accounts for the absence of eight hydrogens, so there also must be another ring present. Since strong oxidation produces phthalic acid, there are only two points of attachment of substituents on the benzene ring, and they must be ortho to each other, leading to partial structure **B** for the unknown. Thus, a saturated ring must be attached to benzene in compound **A**, and several structures are possible for **A** as shown below. The evidence given does not permit distinguishing between these four possible structures.

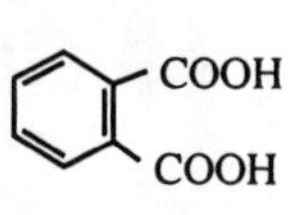
COOH
COOH

phthalic acid

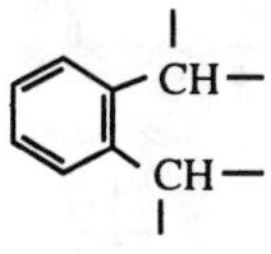
CH—
CH—

B

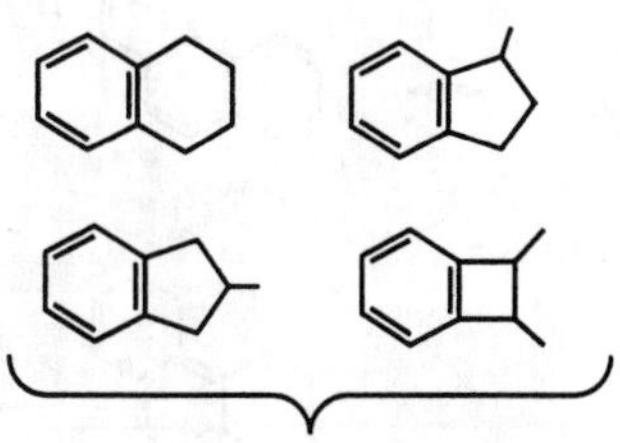

A

9.22

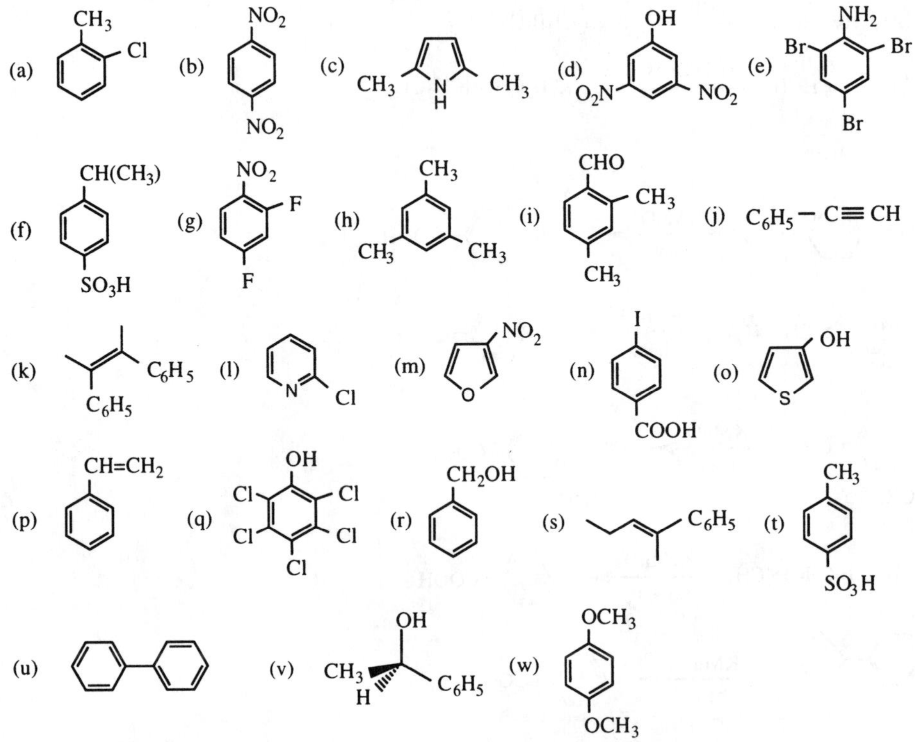

9.23 (a) (*E*)-1-phenyl-2-hexen-1-ol; (b) *m*-fluoronitro-benzene; (c) 3-methylfuran; (d) *p*-isopropylbenzaldehyde; (e) 3,4,5-trimethylbenzoic acid; (f) 3,5-dibromoanisole; (g) 3-bromopyridine; (h) *m*-fluorophenol; (i) *o*-methylbenzenesulfonic acid (*o*-toluenesulfonic acid); (j) *p*-ethylaniline; (k) *cis*-1,2-diphenylethene ((*Z*)-1,2-diphenylethene); (l) 3-phenylpyrrole.

9.24

(a)

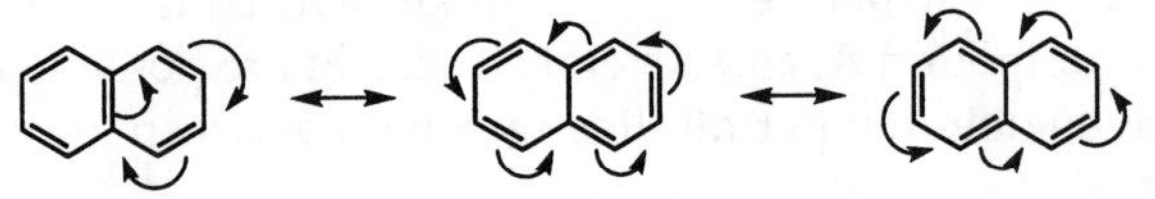

(b)

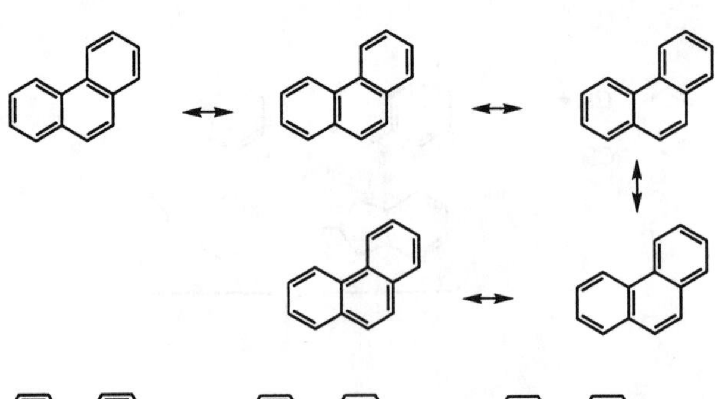

(c)

9.25 There are two mono-nitro derivatives of napthalene (a) and three mono-nitro derivatives of anthracene (b).

(a)

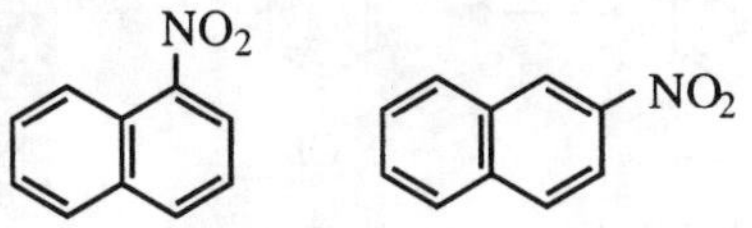

NO_2
NO_2

(b)

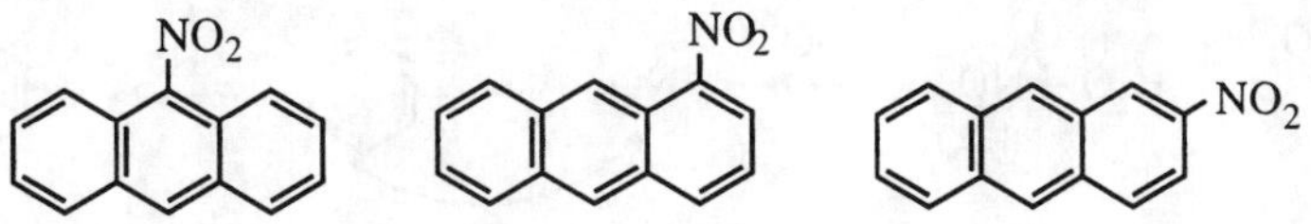

NO_2
NO_2
NO_2

9.26 (a) non-aromatic because it has eight π-electrons, not fitting the Huckel rule of 4n+2 π -electrons.
(b) non-aromatic because it has eight π-electrons (not 4n+2).
(c) non-aromatic because it has twelve π-electrons (not 4n+2).
(d) aromatic because it has 6 π-electrons (4x1 + 2).
(e) non-aromatic because it has four π-electrons (not 4n+2).
(f) aromatic because it has 14 π-electrons (4x3 + 2).
(g) non-aromatic because the six π-electrons are not in a "closed shell." In other words, in the eight-membered ring there are two tetrahedral carbons so there is not a "continuous π system." It is not a fully conjugated system and the π-electrons cannot be delocalized over the entire ring.
(h) aromatic because it has six π-electrons (4x1 + 2).

9.27

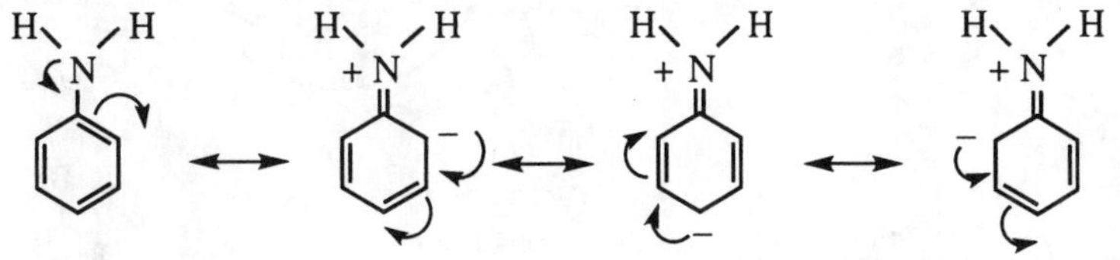

9.28

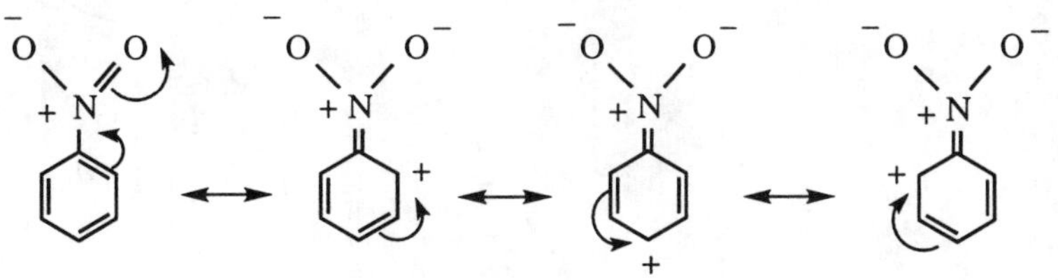

9.29

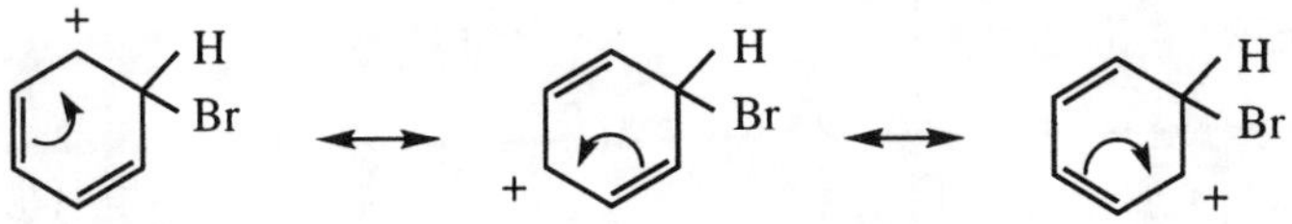

H
Br
H
Br
H
Br

9.30

a) 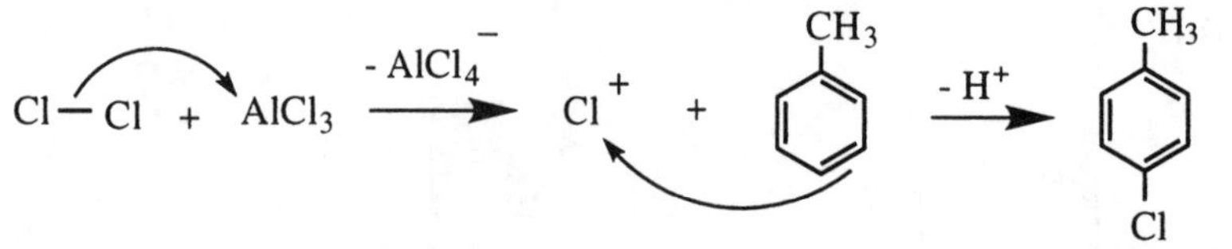
Cl—Cl + AlCl3
- AlCl4
Cl
CH3
- H+
CH3
Cl

b) 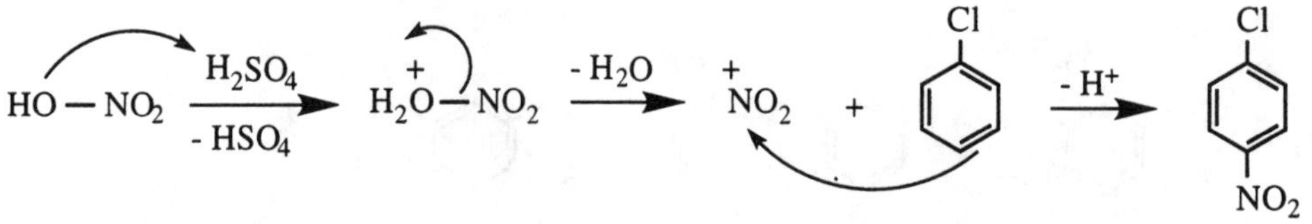
HO—NO2
H2SO4
- HSO4
H2O—NO2
- H2O
NO2
Cl
- H+
Cl
NO2

c) 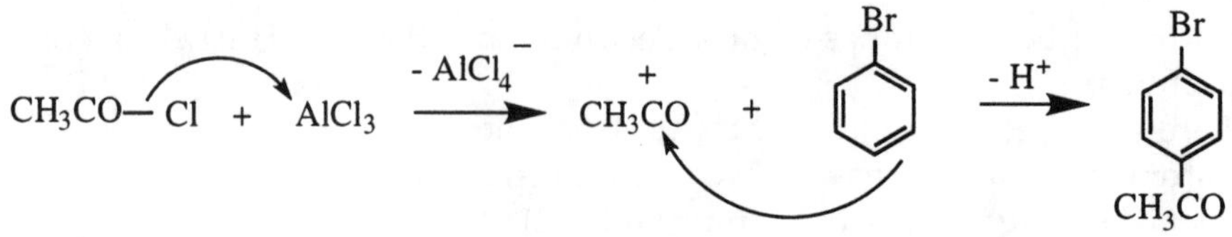
CH3CO—Cl + AlCl3
- AlCl4
CH3CO
Br
- H+
Br
CH3CO

d) 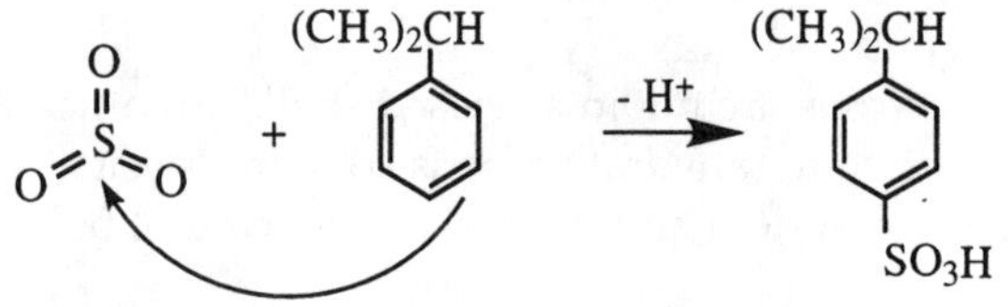
O
S
O
O
(CH3)2CH
- H+
(CH3)2CH
SO3H

e) 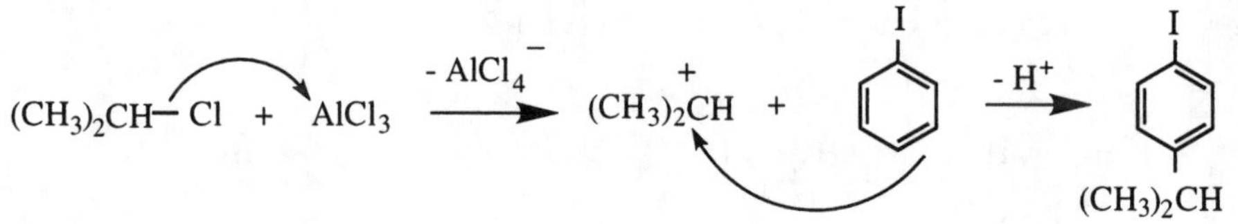
(CH3)2CH—Cl + AlCl3
- AlCl4
(CH3)2CH
I
- H+
I
(CH3)2CH

f) 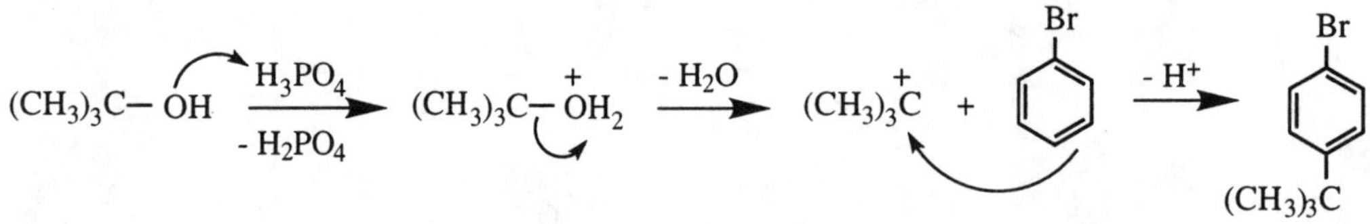
(CH3)3C—OH
H3PO4
- H2PO4
(CH3)3C—OH2
- H2O
(CH3)3C
Br
- H+
Br
(CH3)3C

9.31

(a) 

(b) 

(c) 

(d) 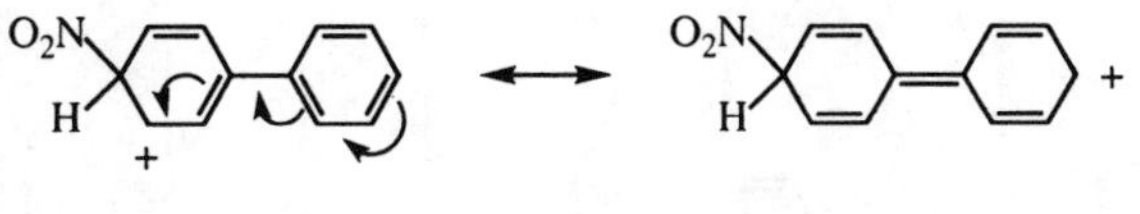

(e) 

9.32

(a) 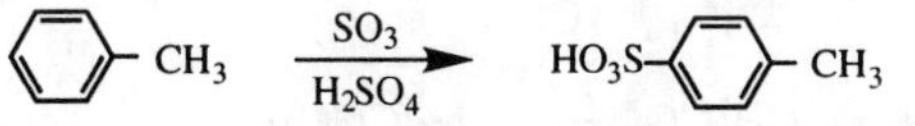

(b) 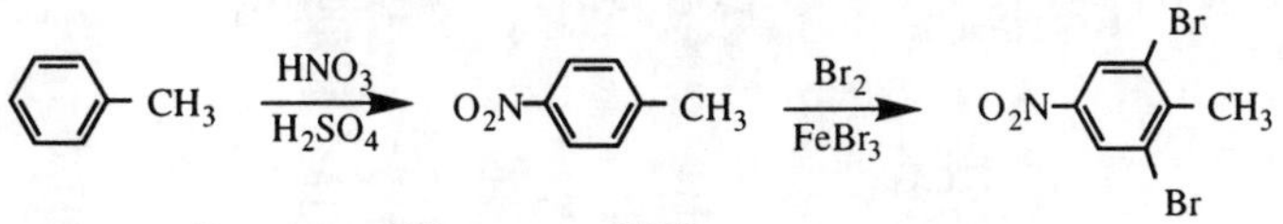

(c) 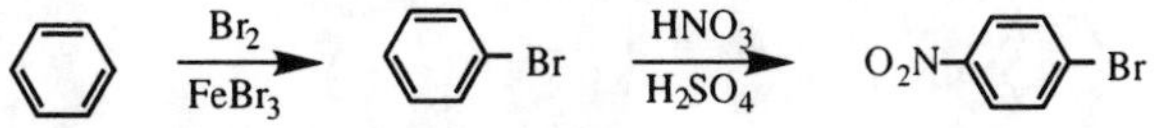

(d) 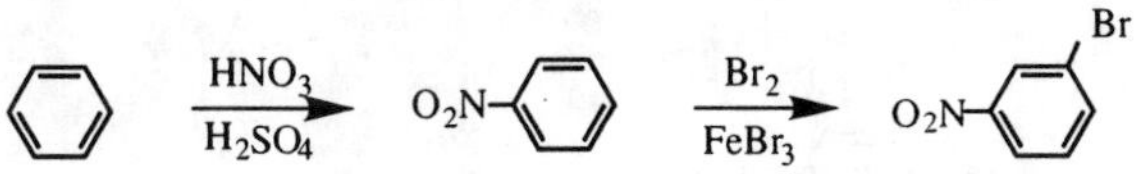

(e) 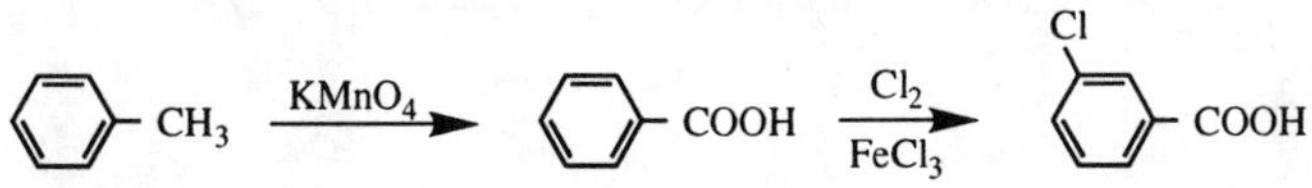

(f) 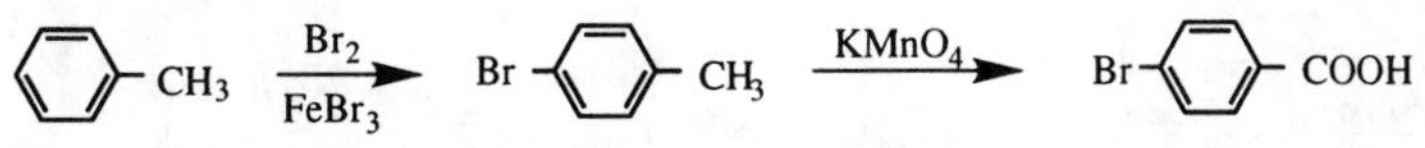

(g) 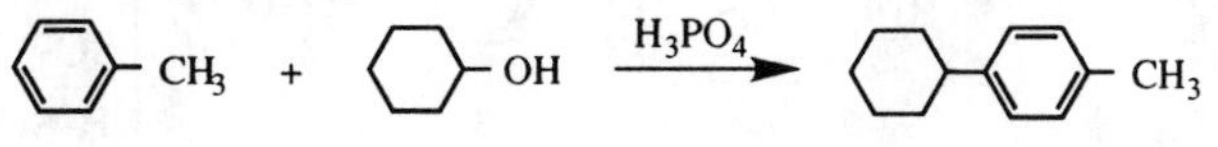

(h) 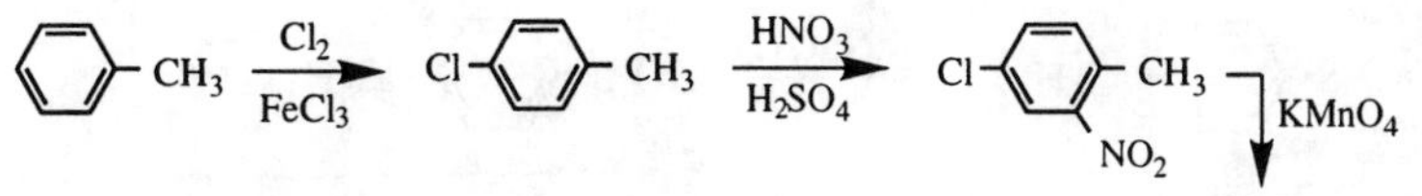

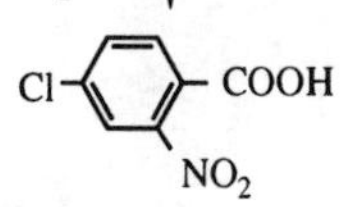

(i) 

9.33 The reactivity increases to the right in each series:

(a) 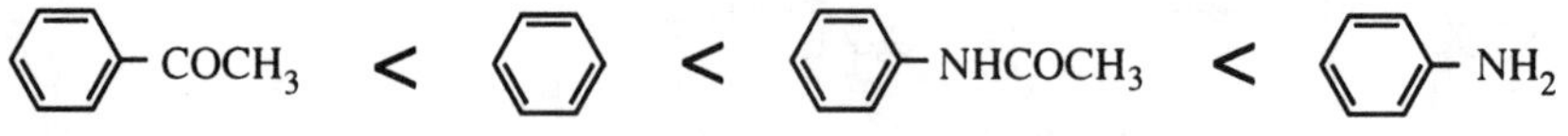
COCH3
<
<
NHCOCH3
<
NH2

(b) 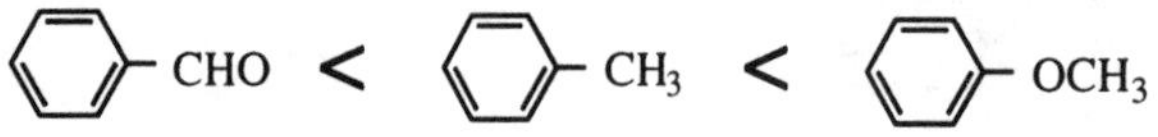
CHO
<
CH3
<
OCH3

(c) 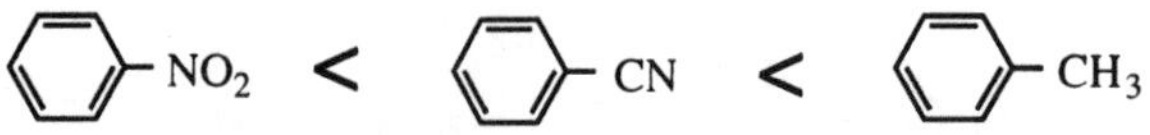
NO2
<
CN
<
CH3

9.34

(a) 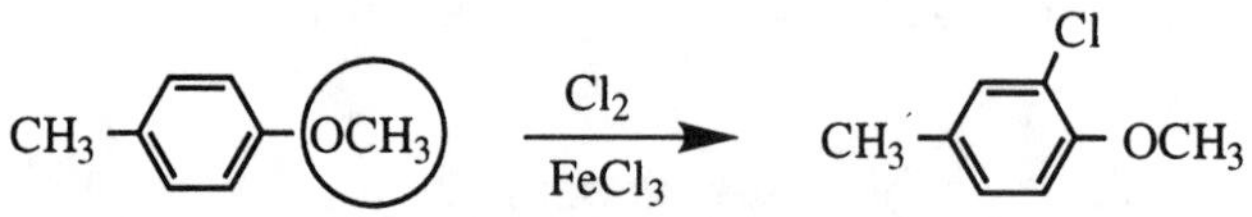
CH3
OCH3
Cl2
FeCl3
CH3
Cl
OCH3

(b) 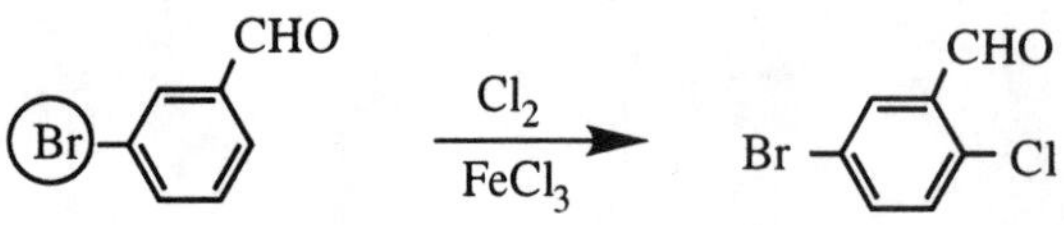
Br
CHO
Cl2
FeCl3
Br
CHO
Cl

(c) 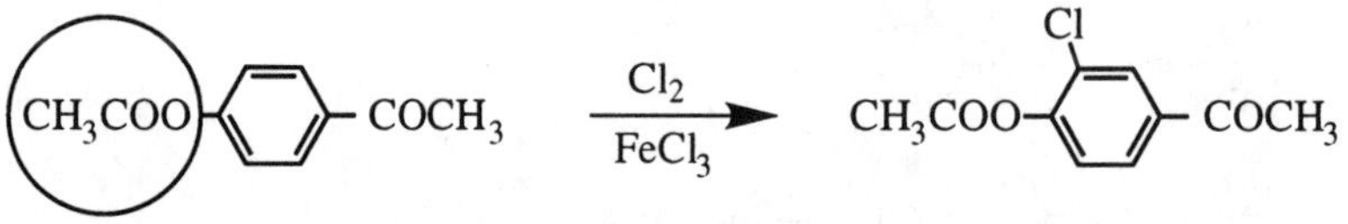
CH3COO
COCH3
Cl2
FeCl3
CH3COO
Cl
COCH3

(d) 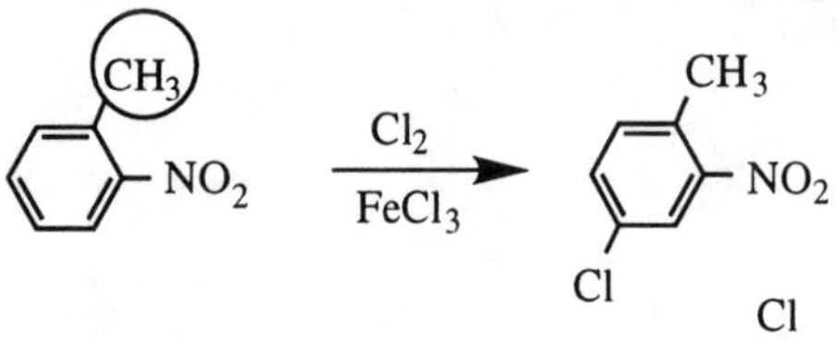
CH3
NO2
Cl2
FeCl3
CH3
NO2
Cl

(e) 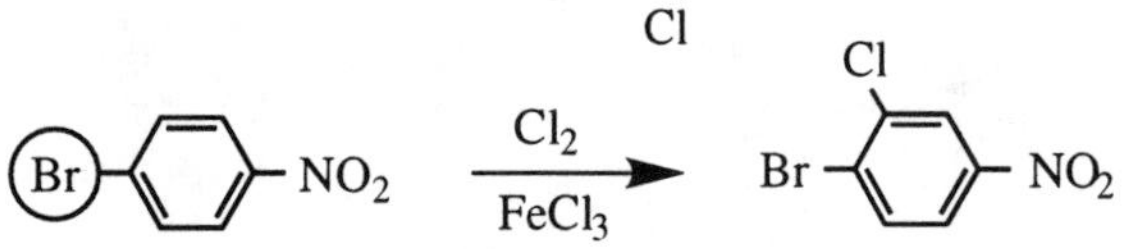
Br
NO2
Cl2
FeCl3
Cl
Br
NO2

***9.35**

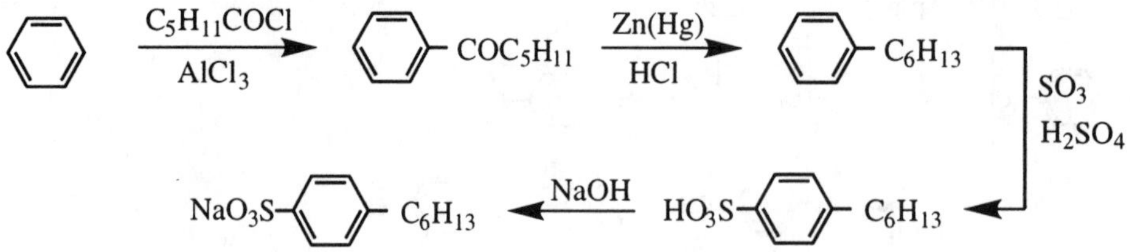
C5H11COCl
AlCl3
COC5H11
Zn(Hg)
HCl
C6H13
SO3
H2SO4
HO3S
C6H13
NaOH
NaO3S
C6H13

9.36 *p*-Nitrophenol is more acidic than *p*-methoxyphenol because the *p*-nitrophenoxide anion is stabilized by resonance delocalization to the nitro group whereas the *p*-methoxy group de-stabilizes the phenoxide anion. The more stable is the phenoxide anion, the more easily it forms and the more acidic is the parent phenol.

9.37

(a) 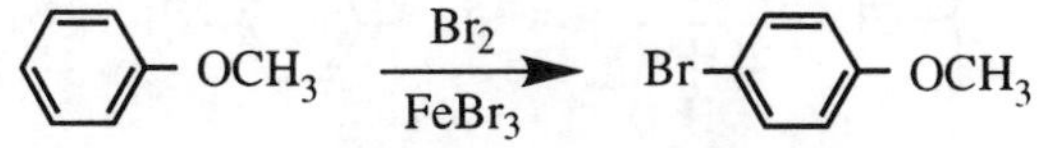

(b) 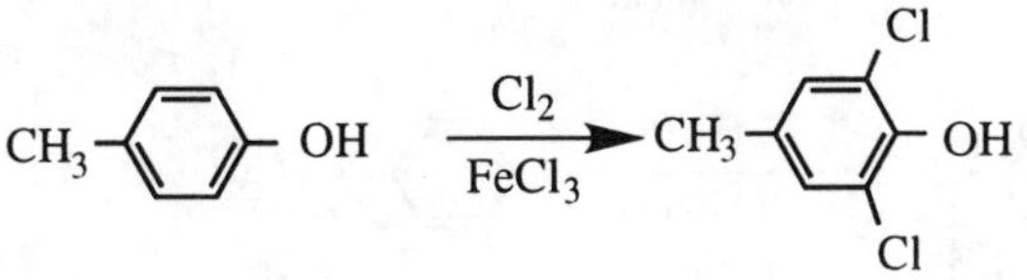

(c) 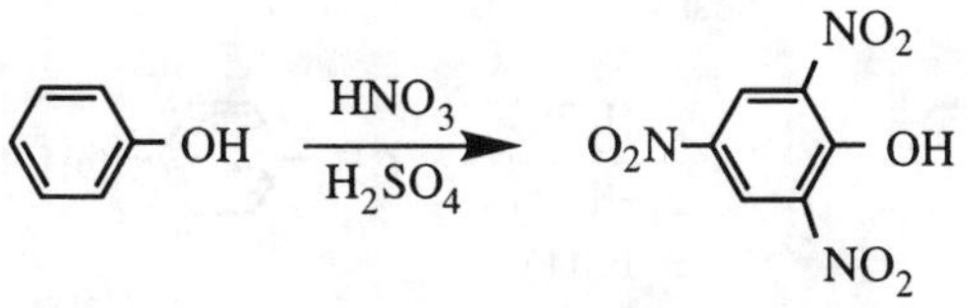

(d) 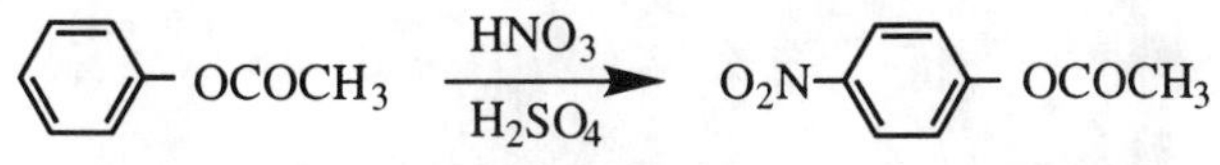

9.38 The key to this, and most other organic separations, is to find a way to make one component temporarily water-soluble, and then to physically separate (using a separatory funnel) the water and ether layers. The final steps are the recovery of each compound individually from the separate layers. In this instance, the phenolic compound is converted to the water-soluble sodium salt using aqueous sodium hydroxide - the phenolic compound is sufficiently acidic for proton removal but the alcohol is not.

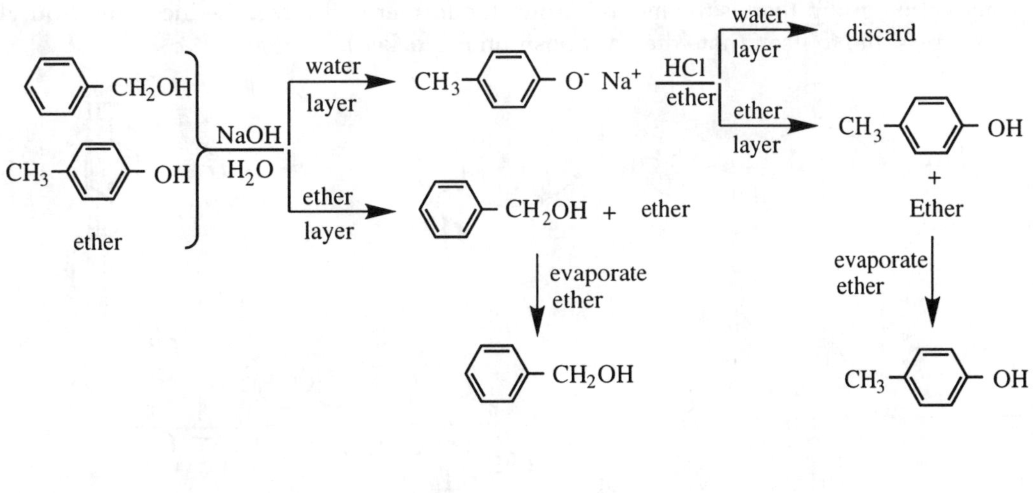

9.39

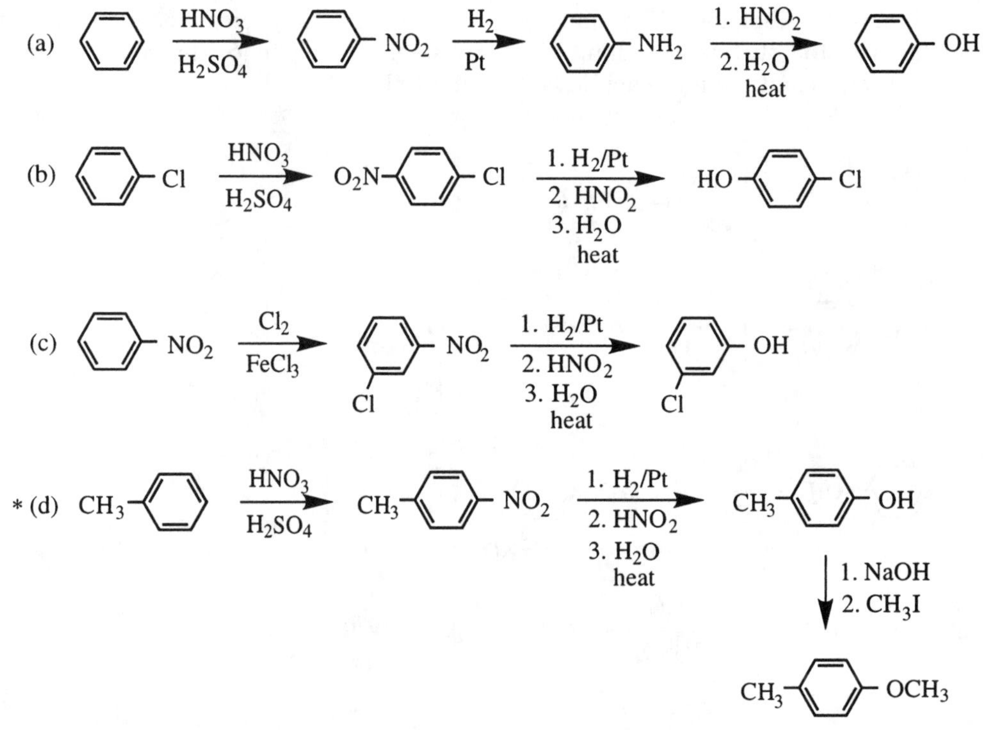

9.40 In order to attach a group to an aromatic ring it has to be converted to an electrophile because electrophilic aromatic substitution is the standard means of substituting on an aromatic ring. Propene can be protonated, as can any alkene, to produce a carbocation, in this instance the relatively stable *t*-butyl carbocation, which will effect a Friedel-Crafts alkylation. Since the aromatic ring carries two substituents a judgement must be made of which will serve as the controlling directing group. Since the hydroxyl is a much stronger activating group than is the methyl group the former will direct the incoming *t*-butyl groups ortho to itself (note the para position is blocked).

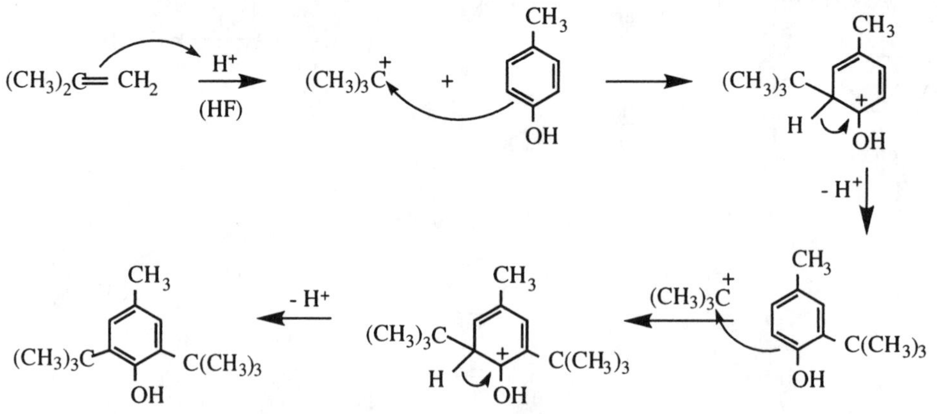

BHT

9.41

(a) 
CH=CH2
HBr
dark
CHBrCH3

(b) 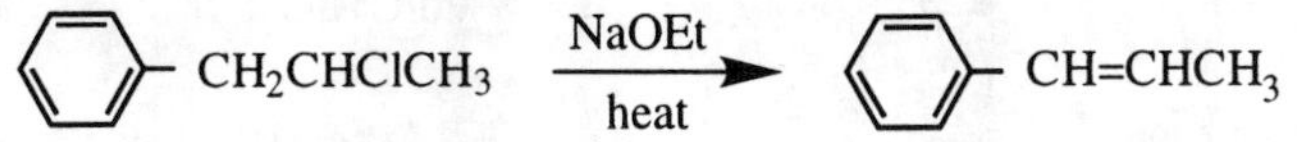
CH2CHClCH3
NaOEt
heat
CH=CHCH3

(c) 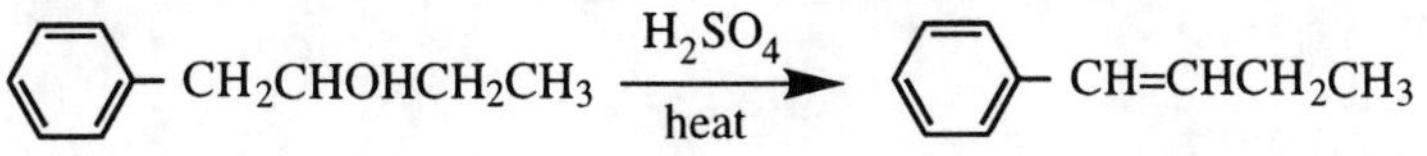
CH2CHOHCH2CH3
H2SO4
heat
CH=CHCH2CH3

(d) 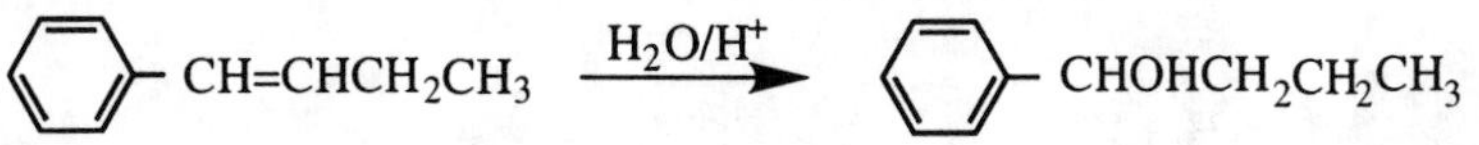
CH=CHCH2CH3
H2O/H+
CHOHCH2CH2CH3

(e) 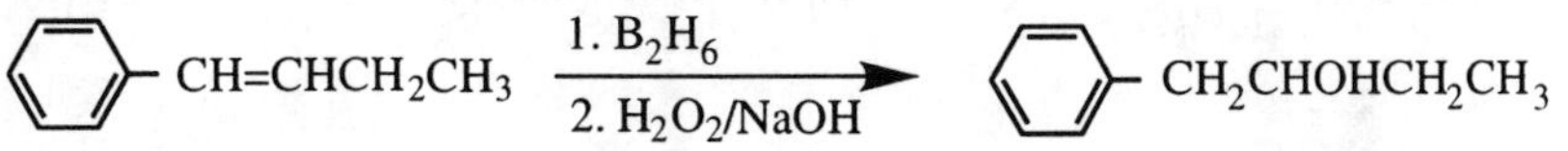
CH=CHCH2CH3
1. B2H6
2. H2O2/NaOH
CH2CHOHCH2CH3

(f) 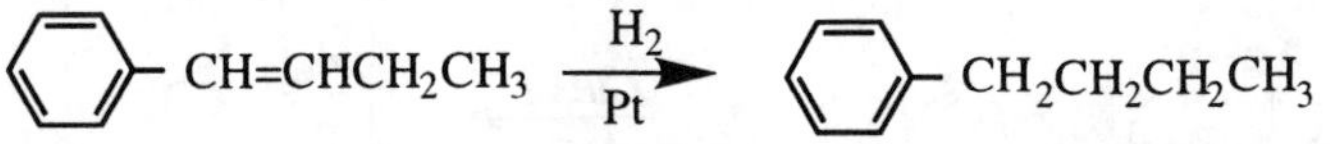
CH=CHCH2CH3
H2
Pt
CH2CH2CH2CH3

(g) 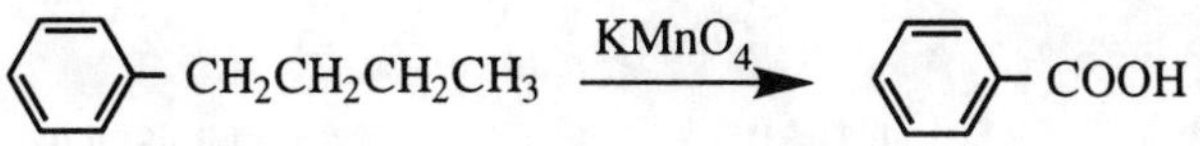
CH2CH2CH2CH3
KMnO4
COOH

9.42 3-Bromobenzoic acid is not an appropriate starting material for producing 3-bromo-5-nitrobenzoic acid by nitration because the bromine group would control the location of the incoming nitronium cation, and would direct it to the 4- and 6-positions. 3-Nitrobenzoic acid is an appropriate starting material because both the carboxyl group and the nitro group will direct the incoming bromous cation to the 5-position (meta to these two substituents).

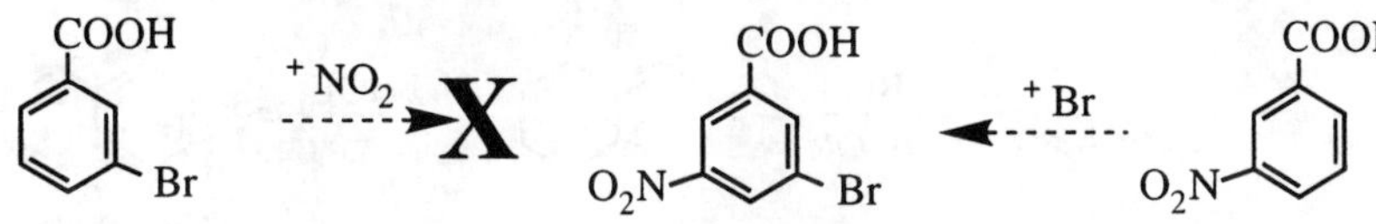
COOH
Br
+NO2
X
COOH
O2N
Br
+Br
COOH
O2N

3-bromo-5-nitrobenzoic acid

9.43

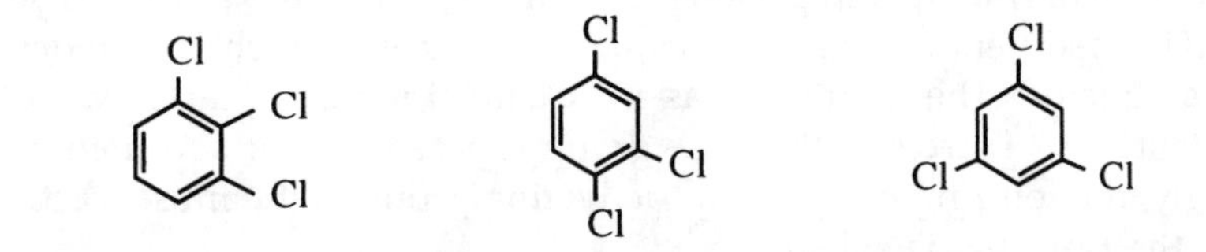
Cl
Cl
Cl
Cl
Cl
Cl
Cl
Cl
Cl

1,2,3-trichlorobenzene 1,2,4-trichlorobenzene 1,3,5-trichlorobenzene

9.44

(a) 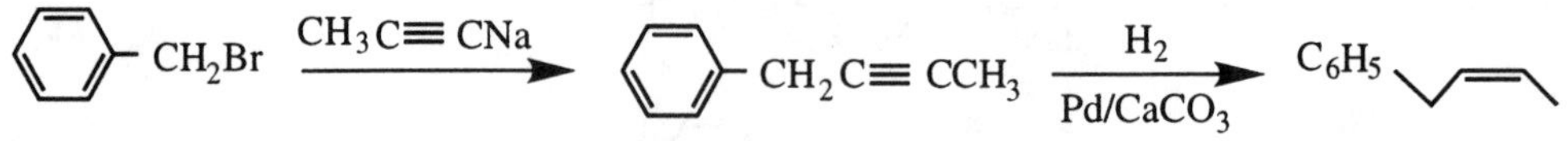

(b) 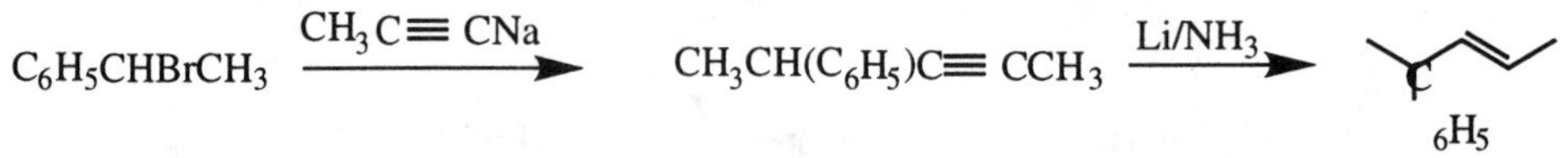

(c) $C_6H_5CH{=}CHCH_3 \xrightarrow{H_2O/H^+} C_6H_5CHOHCH_2CH_3$

d) $C_6H_5CH{=}CHCH_3 \xrightarrow[2.\ H_2O_2/NaOH]{1.\ B_2H_6} C_6H_5CH_2CHOHCH_3$

9.45

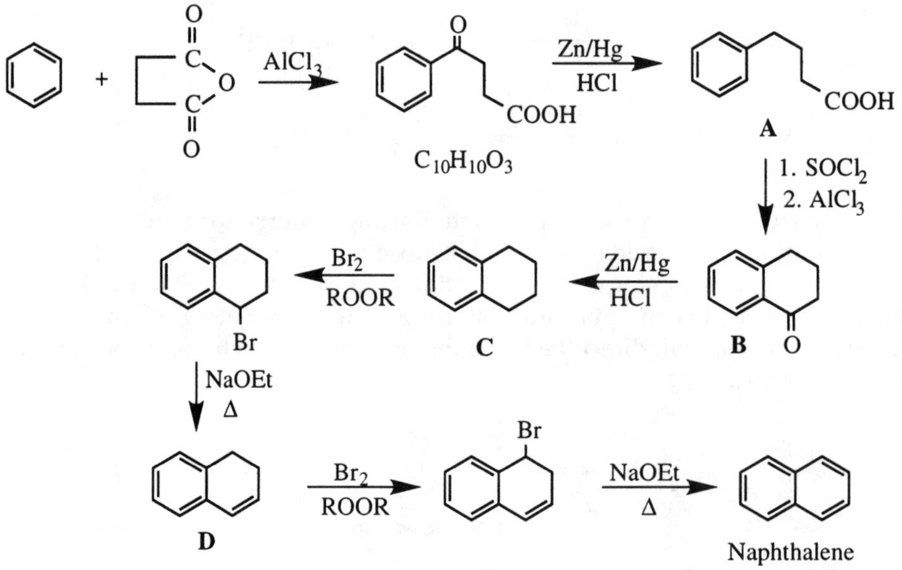
AlCl$_3$
COOH
C$_{10}$H$_{10}$O$_3$
Zn/Hg
HCl
A
1. SOCl$_2$
2. AlCl$_3$
B
C
Br$_2$
ROOR
Br
NaOEt
Δ
D
Naphthalene

9.46 Since there are two benzenoid rings each could be mono-brominated. The issue is whether one ring will be brominated in preference to the other and the answer is yes. The left ring has an -NH substituent carrying a lone pair of electrons which is a moderate activator and ortho-para director. The right ring has a -CO substituent, the carbonyl carbon being electron deficient. Therefore, the -CO- group is a deactivator and meta director. Accordingly, the left ring carrying the activating group is the most reactive and is, therefore, the ring that is substituted.

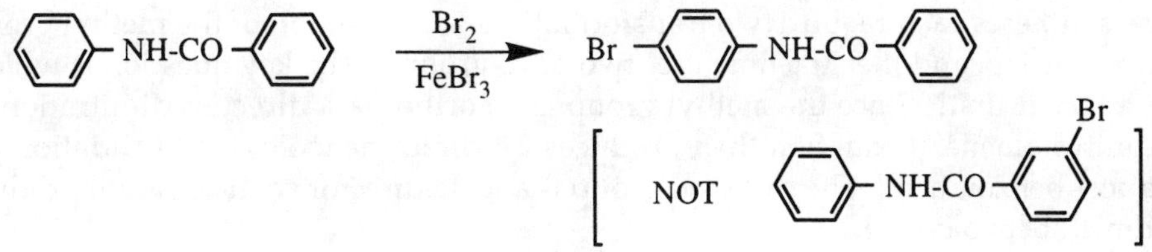

9.47

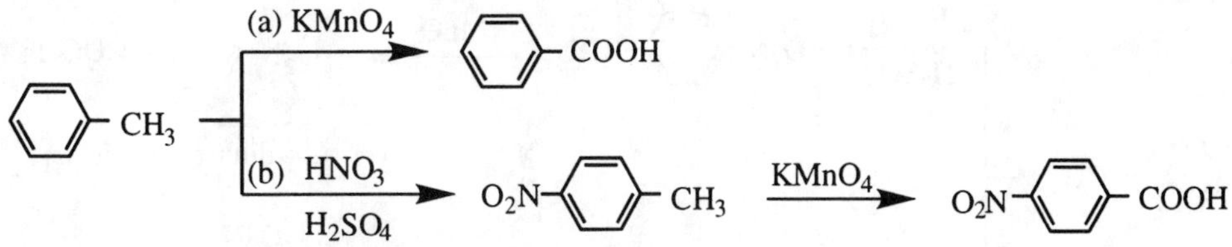

9.48 (a) *p*-Methylbenzyl bromide is solvolyzed rapidly by methanol because it readily forms the carbocation intermediate essential in a S_N1 reaction. It forms a carbocation readily because the latter is stabilized by resonance, being a benzylic carbocation.

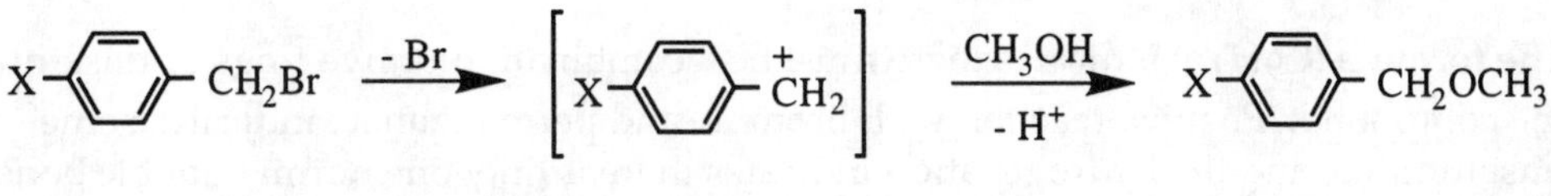

Relative rates: X = CH_3O > CH_3 > NO_2

(b) The solvolysis is faster with a *p*-methoxy group because the latter can provide electron density to the ring making the benzylic carbocation even more stable. The reaction is slower with a *p*-nitro group because the latter de-stabilizes the benzylic carbocation because of its electron withdrawing character.

9.49 The aromatic sextet represents the requirement of having six electrons in *p*-orbitals in a closed shell. Pyridine has six such electrons, one from each of the five carbons and one from the nitrogen, all as represented in the double bonds shown. Therefore, the lone pair of electrons on nitrogen are not involved in the closed shell and they are available for protonation as for any other amine. Therefore, pyridine is basic.

By contrast, to form an aromatic sextet in pyrrole requires one electron from each of the four carbons (i.e., from the two double bonds shown) but also both unshared electrons from nitrogen. Therefore, these unshared electrons are involved in the aromatic sextet and unavailable for protonation. Protonation of the nitrogen would require destruction of the aromatic sextet and foregoing the resonance stabilization energy associated therewith.

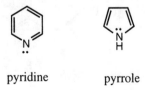

pyridine pyrrole

9.50 These syntheses each require two transformations - conversion of the methyl group to a carboxyl group, and the attachment of two nitro groups. The key question is which should occur first? Since the methyl group is an ortho-para director, di-nitration produces 2,4-dinitrotoluene. Oxidation then produces 2,4-dinitrobenzoic acid. Oxidation of toluene produces benzoic acid. The carboxyl group is a meta director so di-nitration produces 3,5-dinitrobenzoic acid.

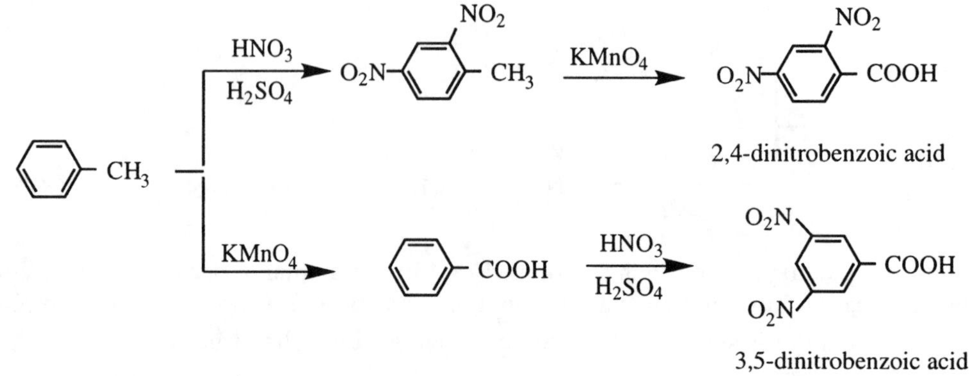

NO2
HNO3
H2SO4
O2N
CH3
KMnO4
COOH
2,4-dinitrobenzoic acid
O2N
KMnO4
COOH
HNO3
H2SO4
O2N
3,5-dinitrobenzoic acid

9.51 The formula (C_9H_{10}) indicates there must be a combination of five rings or unsaturations in the compound. Positive reaction with bromine and permanganate indicates some unsaturation, and the hydrogenation indicates there is only one normal double bond present. Therefore, the remaining four unsaturations/rings indicate the probable presence of a benzenoid ring. Vigorous oxidation, a reaction which leaves benzenoid rings intact and removes side chains except for a carboxyl group, produces $C_7H_6O_2$ which must be benzoic acid (C_6H_5COOH). Therefore, the three carbons unaccounted for (after the six are assigned to a benzenoid ring) all are part of a single side chain (otherwise there would be two carboxyl groups on the ring). The production of formaldehyde (CH_2O) upon ozonolysis indicates the presence of a CH_2= group on the benzenoid side chain. At this point it can be deduced that **A** can only be structure **E** or **F**. The fact that **D** is produced by acetylation determines its structure and means that **A** can only be structure **E**.

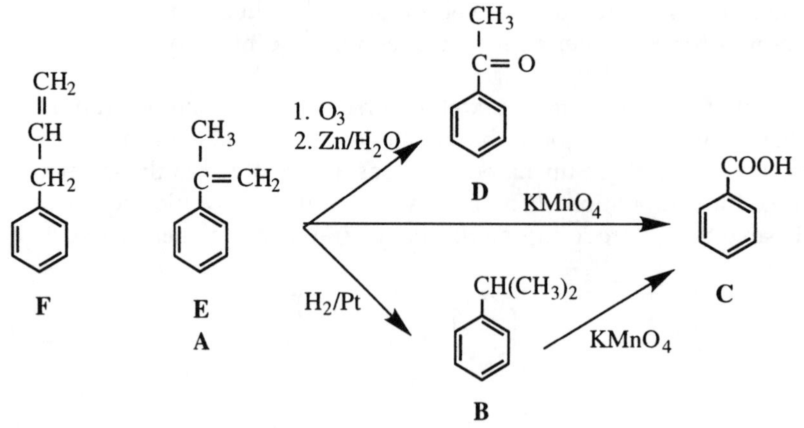

CH2
CH
CH2
F
CH3
C=CH2
E
A
1. O3
2. Zn/H2O
CH3
C=O
D
KMnO4
COOH
C
H2/Pt
CH(CH3)2
B
KMnO4

9.52

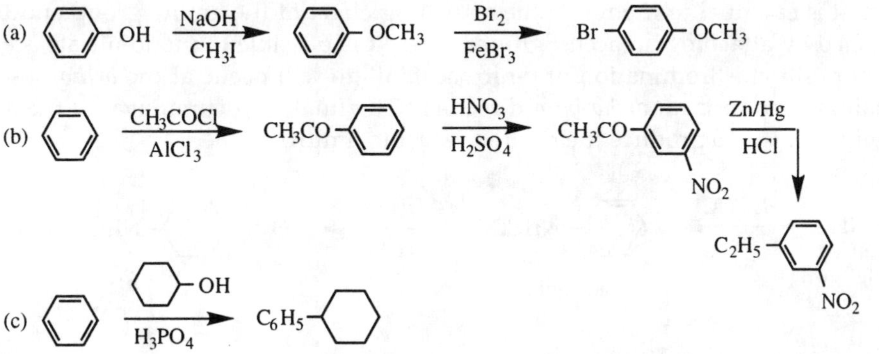
(a)
OH
NaOH
CH_3I
OCH_3
Br_2
$FeBr_3$
Br
OCH_3
(b)
CH_3COCl
$AlCl_3$
CH_3CO
HNO_3
H_2SO_4
CH_3CO
NO_2
Zn/Hg
HCl
C_2H_5
NO_2
(c)
OH
H_3PO_4
C_6H_5

9.53 Nitration will occur fastest on the ring which provides the most stable arenium cation. The bromo group is a deactivator because of its high electronegativity. Thus, the bromo-substituted ring provides the least stable arenium cation. The dominant product is 4-bromo-4'-nitrodiphenyl, derived from attack of nitronium ion on the unsubstituted ring.

9.54 The difference in the reactivity of aniline and acetanilide is due to the difference in the extent to which the $-NH_2$ (amino) and $-NHCOCH_3$ (acetamido) substituents release electrons to stabilize the arenium cation. Both substituents have a nitrogen atom attached directly to the ring, and the unshared electrons of nitrogen are available to delocalize the positive charge in the arenium cation formed during electrophilic bromination.

In the case of aniline the amino unshared electrons are able to be fully shared with the ring to stabilize the arenium cation. There is no other competition for these electrons. However, in the case of the acetamido group the unshared electrons of nitrogen also are attracted by the carbonyl group due to its polarization away from the ring (path **a**). Therefore, the unshared electrons on nitrogen are less available to the ring in acetanilide (path **b**) than in aniline. Therefore, aniline is more reactive in electrophilic bromination than is acetanilide and is therefore susceptible to tri-substitution.

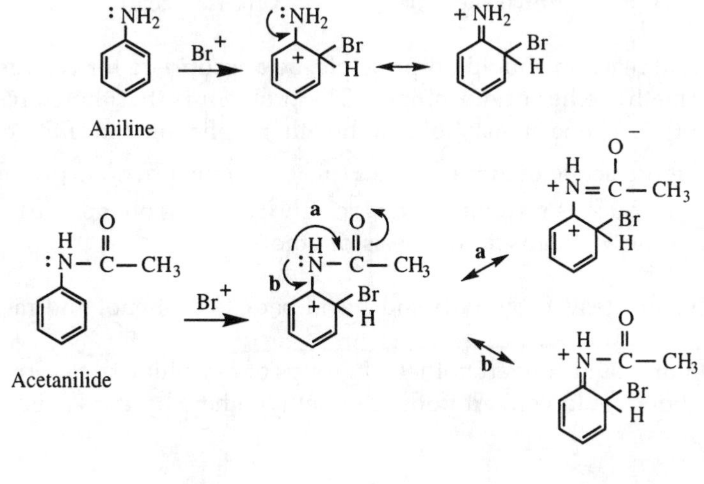
Aniline
Acetanilide
Br^+
Br
H
a
b

***9.55** Recognize that any substitution reaction on aniline will lead to poly-substitution because of the strong activating effect of the amino group (as strong as that of the hydroxyl group). Therefore, it is essential to moderate the activating effect of the amino group and this is accomplished by attaching an acetyl group. Then it is possible to mono-nitrate acetanilide in the *para* position. Bromination of *p*-nitroacetanilide will occur at the *ortho* position (the acetamido group is an *ortho-para* director). The final step is removal of the acetyl group by hydrolysis to produce the desired 2-bromo-4-nitroaniline.

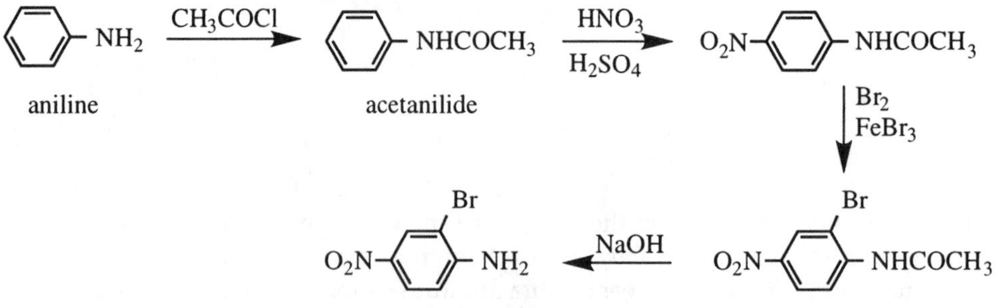
NH2
CH3COCl
aniline
NHCOCH3
acetanilide
HNO3
H2SO4
O2N
NHCOCH3
Br2
FeBr3
Br
O2N
NHCOCH3
NaOH
Br
O2N
NH2
2-bromo-4-nitroaniline

9.56 The formula weight of C_4H_5 is 53, so **W** must have a molecular formula of C_8H_{10} (molecular weight 106). This formula implies the presence of four unsaturations and/or rings. Since **W** did not react with bromine or permanganate it has no normal unsaturations. Therefore, the presence of a benzenoid ring is suspected and only two carbons are left unaccounted for. The structures $C_6H_5CH_2CH_3$ (ethylbenzene) and $C_6H_4(CH_3)_2$ (*o*-xylene [*o*-dimethylbenzene], *m*-xylene, or *p*-xylene) are therefore suspected for **W**. **X** produced by oxidation of **W** most likely is benzoic acid (C_6H_5COOH) which indicates that the benzene ring of **W** has only a single substituent. By these conclusions **W** is confirmed to be ethylbenzene.

CH2CH3
COOH

W (ethylbenzene) **X** (benzoic acid)

9.57 The Williamson reaction should, in principle, be appropriate for converting morphine to codeine (the methyl ether of morphine). The problem is that there are two hydroxyl groups in morphine, one an alcohol and the other a phenol. Since the phenolic hydroxyl (pK_a ~ 10) is more acidic than the alcohol (pK_a ~ 16) the phenolic proton can be removed selectively with aqueous sodium hydroxide. The resulting phenoxide can be used as a nucleophile in the Williamson synthesis of ethers.

Methyl ethers are cleaved by hydroiodic acid back to a phenol and methyl iodide.

Metallic sodium would convert both -OH groups of morphine to oxyanions and the addition of methyl iodide would convert both into methyl ethers by the Williamson synthesis.

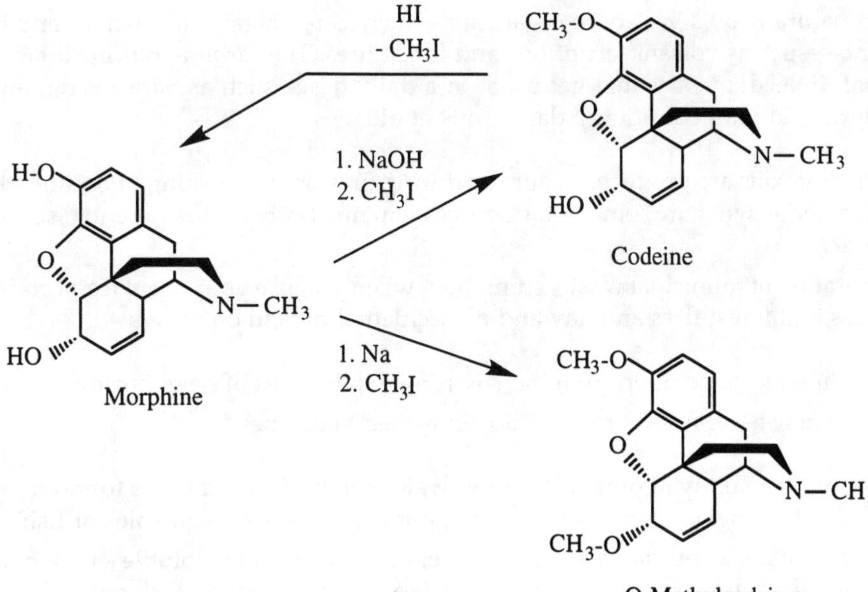
HI
- CH_3I
1. NaOH
2. CH_3I
1. Na
2. CH_3I
Morphine
Codeine
O-Methylcodeine

VI. Conceptual Problem

Dioxins: Up in Smoke

You have recently been hired by the state environmental office as an environmental engineer. The major focus of your job is to establish tougher but practicable standards that ensure a substantial decrease in the dioxin levels in the state, particularly in the larger cities. You soon realize that part of your job will also entail public relations, for a series of small chemical accidents in the last year has put dioxins in the news. You attend a local hearing to discuss one such chemical accident where the citizens are justifiably upset and demand that ALL dioxins be eliminated. As a citizen, you share their concern; as an engineer, you discuss how realistic such a goal would be. What many people do not realize is that the general term "dioxins" applies not to just a single compound, but to a family of chlorinated compounds derived from the parent compound dioxin (compound A). The most prominent member of that class of compounds is 2,3,7,8-tetrachlorodioxin (compound B).

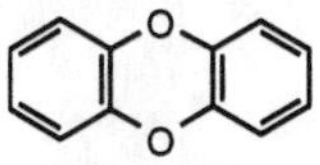

Compound A

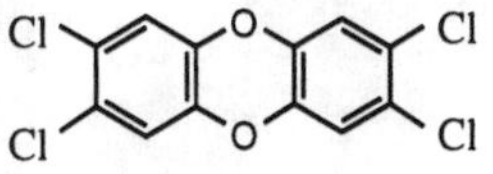

Compound B

Any and/or all hydrogens on the parent dioxin rings can be replaced by chlorines, which means there are a huge number of different compounds in the dioxin family. Many halogenated compounds are produced naturally by a variety of organisms—such as red algae and plants—and by natural physical events—such as volcanic eruptions and forest fires. The carbon-chlorine bond is not innately lethal. Indeed, plastics that get used on a daily basis, such as Saran Wrap and polyvinylchloride, are not considered dangerous at all!

■ Knowing that dioxins are produced naturally during fires or any burning of organic chlorine-containing material, what are some of the sources you must consider as potential sources of dioxins in your state?

- Ans: incineration of municipal waste, cremation, when you use your fireplace, wood-burning stoves, grass and forest fires and any and all accidental fires in buildings

■ Why must you seek cooperation from the environmental offices of neighboring states?

- Ans: Dioxins may become airborne and do not respect state lines.

■ Are dioxins and the family of organochlorines water soluble? Are dioxins found in food? Which foods might contain higher levels of these compounds, fruits and vegetables or fish?

- Ans: Dioxins are not appreciably water soluble, but rather are fat soluble - they have no very polar functional groups that can hydrogen bond to water molecules. Fish generally contain higher amounts because of all the fish oils which solubilize them and because of the presence of dioxins in many water effluents. Fruits and vegetables have extremely low levels of dioxins.

CHAPTER 10

Carbon Radicals

I. Textbook Chapter Contents

This chapter introduces a second type of reactive intermediate (the first being the carbocation), a carbon radical in which a carbon atom carries three sigma bonded groups and a single unpaired electron. They are intermediates in a few important reactions of organic compounds.

II. Learning Objectives

- Know the electronic structure of a carbon radical and understand the stability sequence of alkyl radicals (3° > 2° > 1).
- Know that radicals can be generated by heat, by light, and by chemical initiators.
- Be familiar with the fact that combustion of hydrocarbons occurs via a radical initiated oxidation mechanism.
- Know the chain-reaction mechanism for the radical-initiated halogenation of alkanes. Be able to apply this reaction to benzylic and allylic compounds as well.

- Write equations for the application of radical bromination for the formation of alkyl bromides from alkanes.

- Know the mechanism for the radical-initiated addition of hydrogen bromide to alkenes. Be able to account for the anti-Markovnikov regiochemistry of such additions.

- Be able to apply ionic or radical addition of HBr to alkenes as part of organic syntheses.

III. Glossary

antioxidant a reagent which inhibits autoxidation by trapping the propagating radical

autoxidation a chemical reaction that involves oxygen, proceeds via a radical chain reaction, and results in the formation of hydroperoxides

carbon radical a carbon atom with three of its four electrons participating in covalent bonds to three substituents, the fourth electron being unpaired

chain reaction a reaction that once started is self-propagating. One of the products of the propagation step is the reactant needed to make the reaction occur again with another molecule of substrate

heterolytic cleavage a bond breaking in which both electrons remain with one of the two atoms involved in the bond

homolytic cleavage a bond breaking in which one electron remains with each of the two atoms involved in the bond

hydroperoxide a compound of structure ROOH

inhibitor a reagent which interrupts the chain reaction of the autoxidation process

initiator a substance that readily forms radicals that can initiate a radical chain reaction

initiation step the first step in a chain reaction, typically the production of a radical initiator

NBS N-Bromosuccinimide, a reagent used to accomplish radical brominations, especially of allylic or benzylic positions

peracid RCO_3H, related to a carboxylic acid but containing an "extra" oxygen in an oxygen-oxygen sigma bond

peroxide a compound containing an "extra" oxygen atom in an oxygen-oxygen sigma bond. Examples are hydrogen peroxide (HOOH), alkyl hydroperoxides (ROOH), and alkyl peroxides (ROOR)

propagation step the second step in a chain reaction, typically the step that produces the desired product and regenerates the reactant needed to effect another cycle of the reaction

radical a group or atom with one or more unpaired electrons

termination step the final step of a chain reaction, a reaction that consumes a radical that otherwise would propagate the reaction

IV. Summary of Reactions Involving Carbon Radicals

1. Halogenation of alkanes

$$R\text{-}H + X_2 \xrightarrow[\Delta \text{ or ROOR}]{h\nu \text{ or}} R\text{-}X + HX \qquad X = Cl \text{ or } Br$$

2. Halogenation of allylic and benzylic compounds

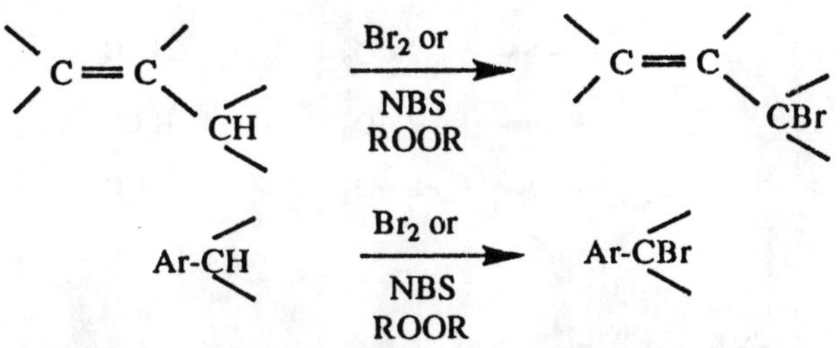
C=C
CH
Br₂ or
NBS
ROOR
C=C
CBr
Ar-CH
Br₂ or
NBS
ROOR
Ar-CBr

3. Addition of HBr to alkenes

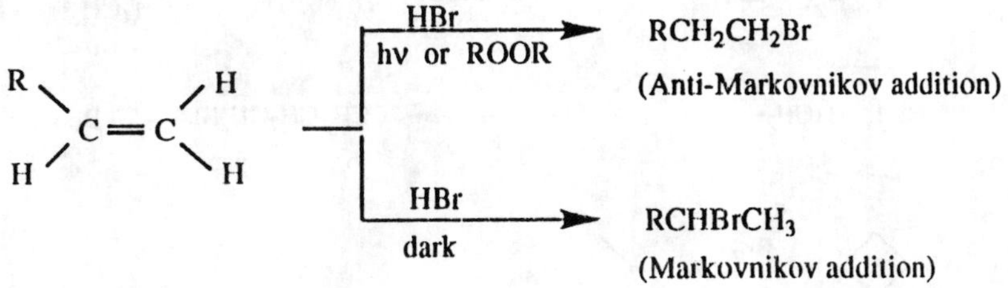
R
H
C=C
H
H
HBr
hν or ROOR
RCH₂CH₂Br
(Anti-Markovnikov addition)
HBr
dark
RCHBrCH₃
(Markovnikov addition)

V. Solutions to Problems

For "**How to Solve a Problem,**" review pages 339 and 344.

10.1 The technique for balancing an oxidation equation is to determine the number of carbons in the substrate and use that same number for the number of molecules of CO_2 produced (since each carbon will appear in the form of CO_2). Then determine the number of molecules of water produced by deducing the multiplier needed to account for all of the hydrogens in the substrate. Finally, total up the number of oxygens in the products and assign the necessary multiplier to the oxygen molecules required.

$$CH_4 + 2\,O_2 \longrightarrow CO_2 + 2\,H_2O$$

$$C_2H_4 + 3\,O_2 \longrightarrow 2\,CO_2 + 2\,H_2O$$

$$C_2H_2 + 2.5\,O_2 \longrightarrow 2\,CO_2 + H_2O$$

$$C_8H_{18} + 12.5\,O_2 \longrightarrow 8\,CO_2 + 9\,H_2O$$

10.2

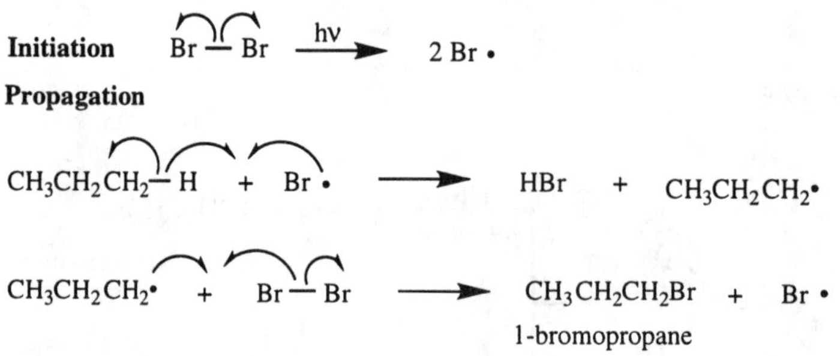
Initiation
Br — Br
hν
2 Br •
Propagation
CH3CH2CH2— H + Br •
HBr + CH3CH2CH2•
CH3CH2CH2• + Br — Br
CH3CH2CH2Br + Br •
1-bromopropane

10.3

(a)

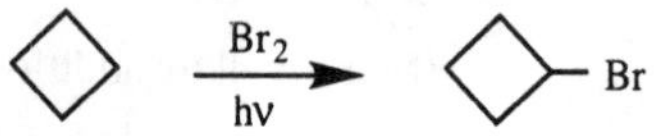
Br2
hν
Br

(b) $CH_3CH_2CH_2CH_3 \xrightarrow[h\nu]{Br_2} CH_3CH_2CH_2CH_2Br \quad CH_3CH_2CHBrCH_3$

(c)

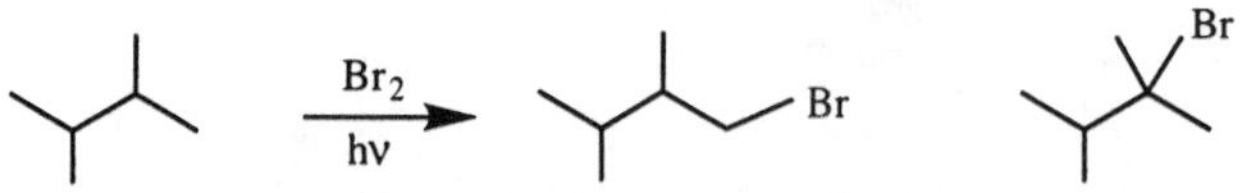
Br2
hν
Br
Br

(d)

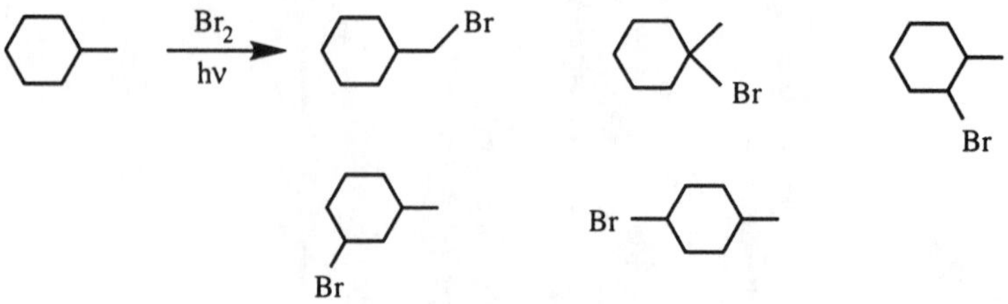
Br2
hν
Br
Br
Br
Br
Br

10.4

(a) 
hν
Br_2
Br
NaC≡CH
C≡CH
H_2
Pt
C_2H_5

(b) 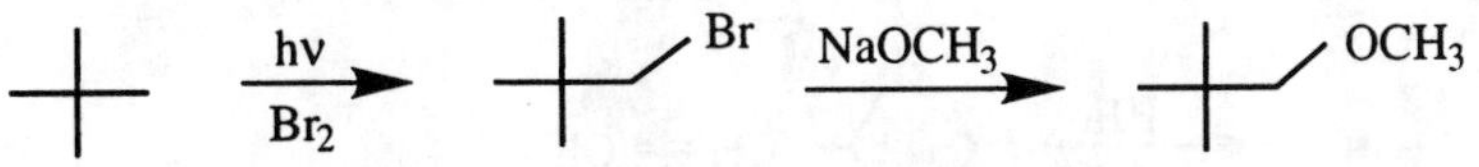
hν
Br_2
Br
$NaOCH_3$
OCH_3

(c) 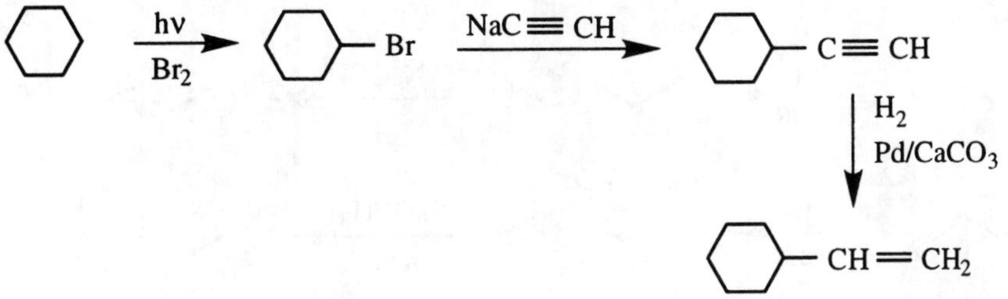
hν
Br_2
Br
NaC≡CH
C≡CH
H_2
$Pd/CaCO_3$
$CH{=}CH_2$

10.5

(a) 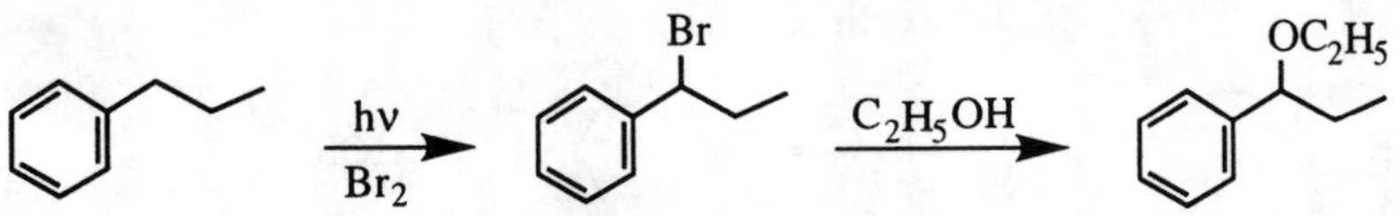
hν
Br_2
Br
C_2H_5OH
OC_2H_5

(b) 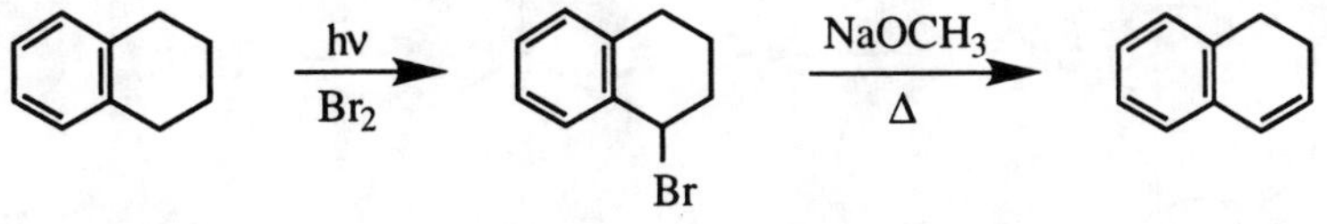
hν
Br_2
Br
$NaOCH_3$
Δ

10.6

(a) 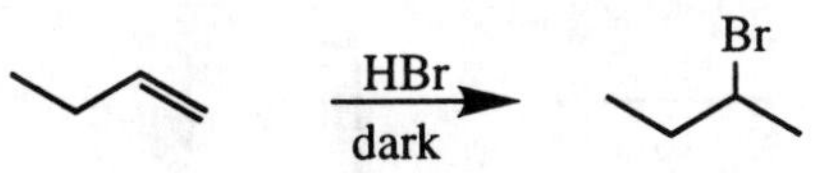
HBr
dark
Br

(b) 
HBr
ROOR
Br

(c) 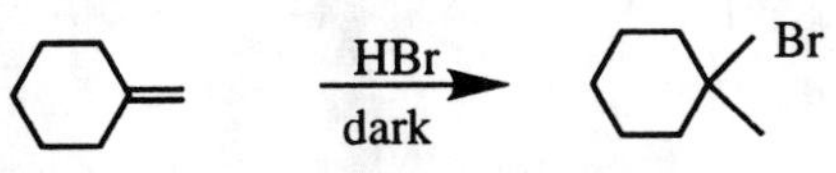
HBr
dark
Br

(d) 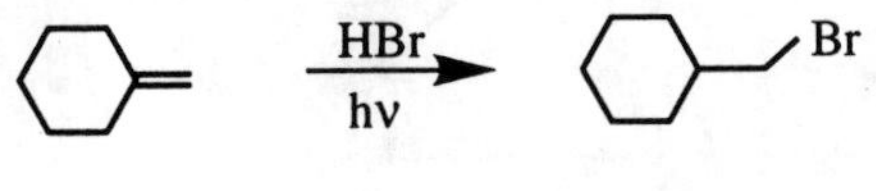
HBr
hν
Br

10.7

(a)

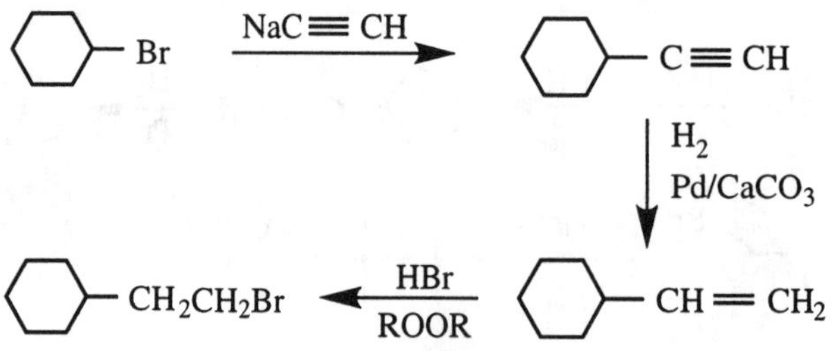
Br
NaC≡CH
C≡CH
H2
Pd/CaCO3
CH2CH2Br
HBr
ROOR
CH=CH2

(b)

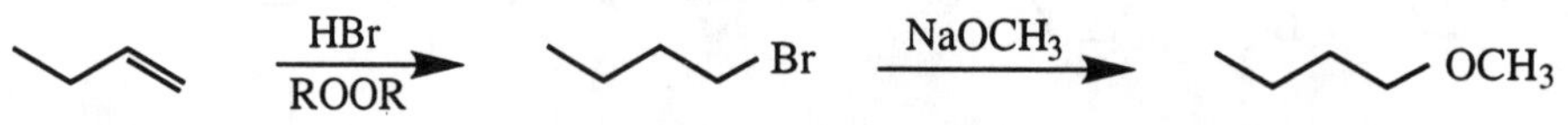
HBr
ROOR
Br
NaOCH3
OCH3

(c)

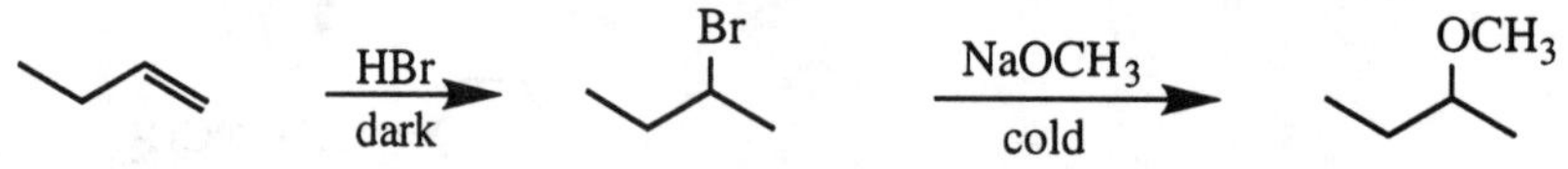
HBr
dark
Br
NaOCH3
cold
OCH3

10.8

(a)

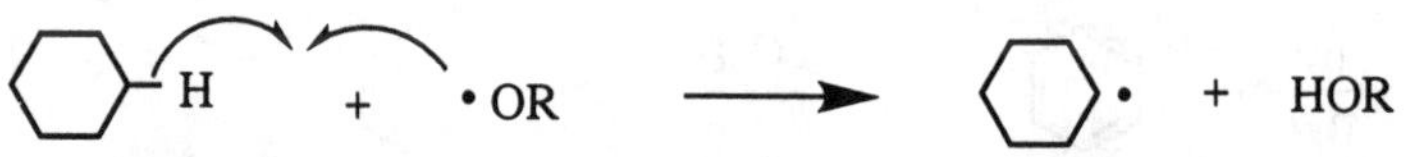
H
+
• OR
+
HOR

(b)

H
+
• OR
+
HOR

(c)

H
+
• OR
+
HOR

(d)

H
+
• OR
+
HOR

(e)

H
+
• OR
+
HOR

(f)

C6H5
H
+
• OR
C6H5
+
HOR

10.9 Radical reactions can be initiated by using heat, by using ultraviolet radiation, or by using an initiator such as a peroxide (ROOR).

10.10

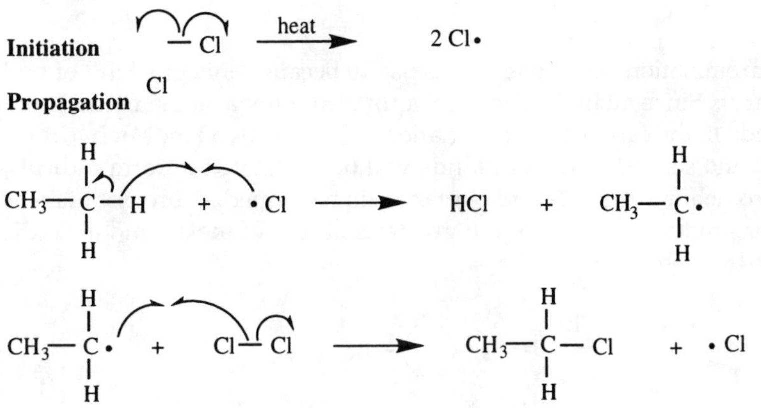

Initiation
Cl—Cl
heat
2 Cl•
Propagation
CH3—C—H + •Cl → HCl + CH3—C•
CH3—C• + Cl—Cl → CH3—C—Cl + •Cl

10.11

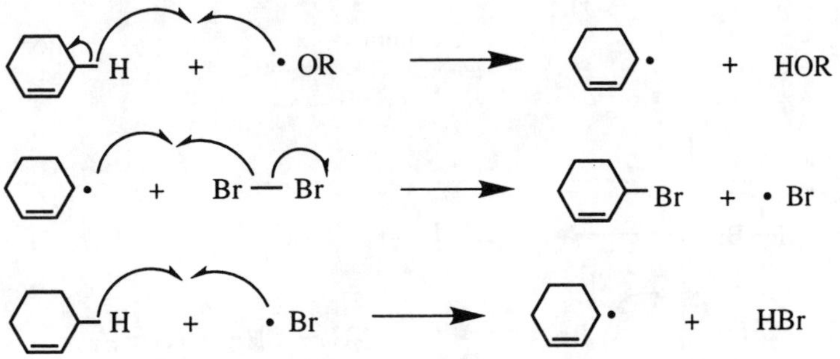

H + • OR → + HOR
+ Br — Br → Br + • Br
H + • Br → + HBr

10.12 The three possible alkyl radicals which could be formed by hydrogen abstraction from 2-pentene are shown below. The allylic radicals (**B** and **C**) will be more stable than **A** because of resonance, with **B** being the most stable because it also is secondary whereas **C** is primary. The alkyl radical (**A**) will be less stable since it is primary and not allylic. Thus, the stability sequence will be **B** > **C** > **A**.

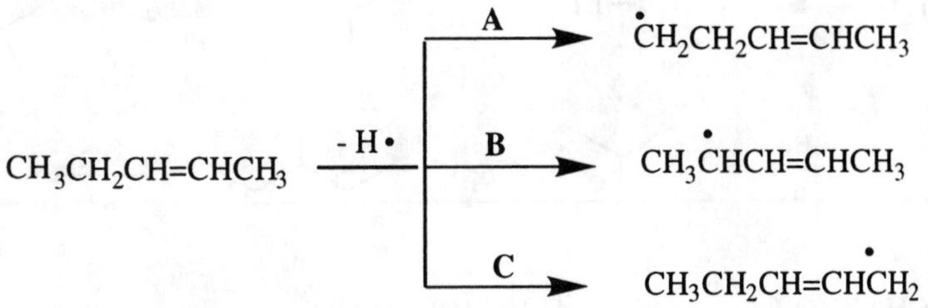

CH3CH2CH=CHCH3
- H•
A
CH2CH2CH=CHCH3
B
CH3CHCH=CHCH3
C
CH3CH2CH=CHCH2

10.13

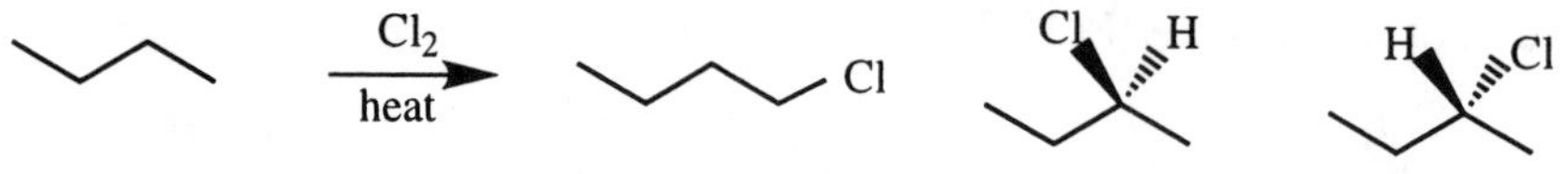
Cl2
heat
Cl
Cl
H
H
Cl

(plus polychlorinated butanes)

10.14 Radical bromination of cyclohexane is useful because only one kind of hydrogen is present (secondary). Since all hydrogens are equivalent only a single mono-bromocyclohexane will be formed. In the case of the bromination of butane, two kinds of hydrogen are present (primary and secondary). Both kinds will be abstracted to form radicals, and therefore both 1-bromobutane and 2-bromobutane will be formed. 2-Bromobutane will be formed as the major product (because of the greater stability of the secondary radical), not the desired 1-bromobutane.

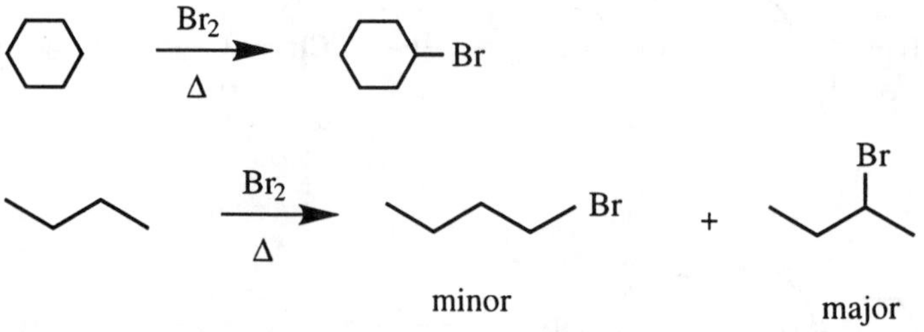
Br2
Δ
Br
Br2
Δ
Br
+
Br
minor
major

10.15

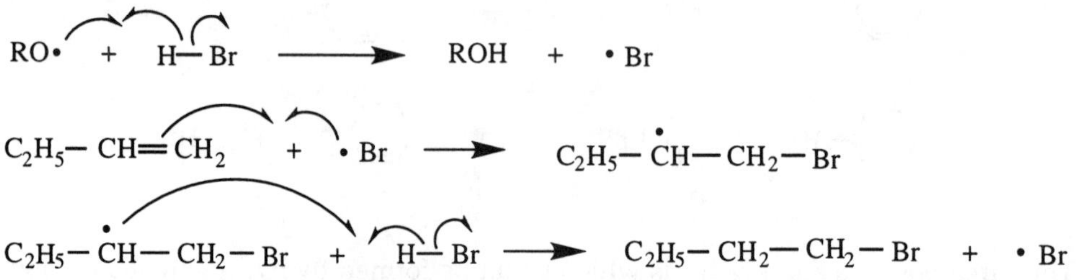
RO• + H—Br → ROH + •Br
C2H5—CH=CH2 + •Br → C2H5—ĊH—CH2—Br
C2H5—ĊH—CH2—Br + H—Br → C2H5—CH2—CH2—Br + •Br

10.16

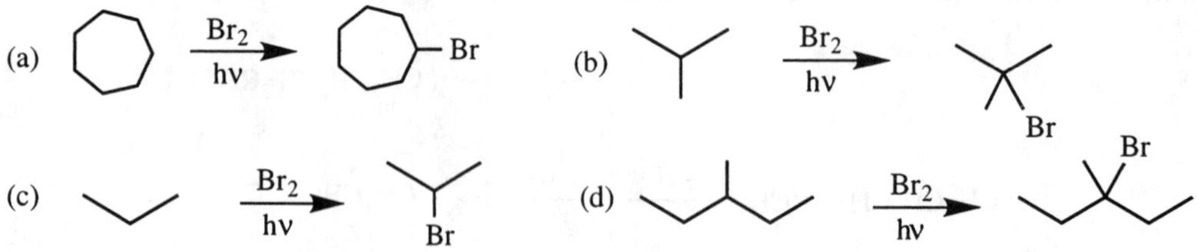
(a)
Br2
hν
Br
(b)
Br2
hν
Br
(c)
Br2
hν
Br
(d)
Br2
hν
Br

(e) $C_6H_5CH_2CH_2CH_3 \xrightarrow[h\nu]{Br_2} C_6H_5CHBrCH_2CH_3$

10.17

$$CH_3\text{-}CH_3 \xrightarrow[h\nu]{Cl_2} \underset{\text{chloroethane}}{CH_3\text{-}CH_2\text{-}Cl} \xrightarrow[h\nu]{Cl_2} \underset{\text{1,1-dichloroethane}}{CH_3\text{-}CHCl_2} + \underset{\text{1,2-dichloroethane}}{Cl\text{-}CH_2\text{-}CH_2\text{-}Cl}$$

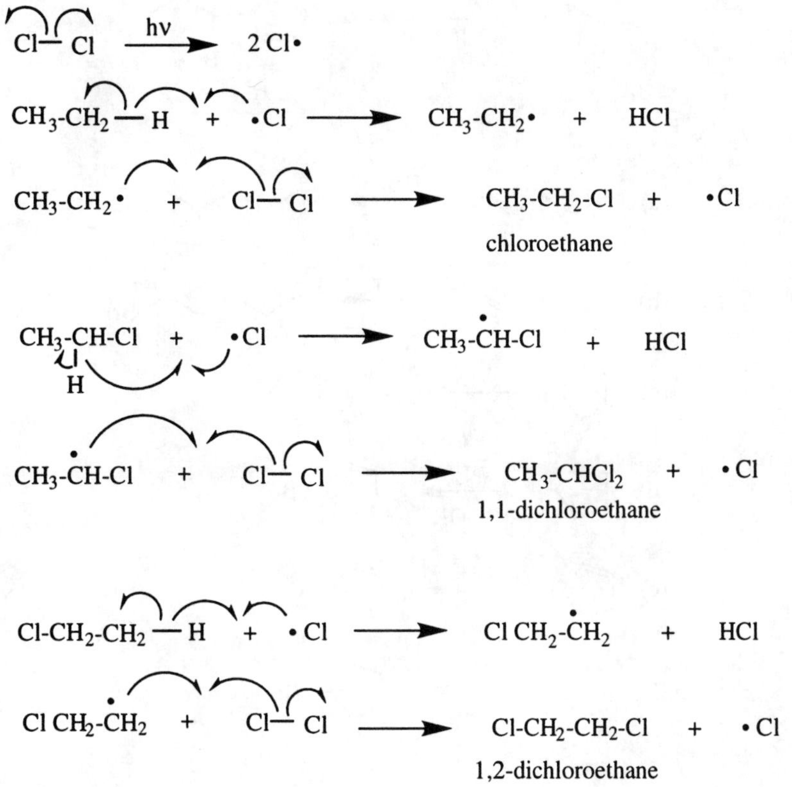

Cl—Cl → hv → 2 Cl•
CH3-CH2—H + •Cl → CH3-CH2• + HCl
CH3-CH2• + Cl—Cl → CH3-CH2-Cl + •Cl
chloroethane
CH3-CH-Cl + •Cl → CH3-ĊH-Cl + HCl
H
CH3-ĊH-Cl + Cl—Cl → CH3-CHCl2 + •Cl
1,1-dichloroethane
Cl-CH2-CH2—H + •Cl → Cl CH2-ĊH2 + HCl
Cl CH2-ĊH2 + Cl—Cl → Cl-CH2-CH2-Cl + •Cl
1,2-dichloroethane

10.18 Radical bromination involves the removal of a hydrogen atom from a carbon-hydrogen bond to produce an alkyl radical which will react with bromine. The most stable possible radical will be formed the fastest in the removal process. Therefore, the product alkyl bromide will be that resulting from the reaction of the most stable radical with bromine. There is only slight difference between the stability of a primary and secondary alkyl radical. Therefore, propane will form both primary (n-propyl) and secondary (isopropyl) radicals. It follows that a mixture of 1-bromopropane and 2-bromopropane will be produced from propane.

Propylbenzene could conceivably produce a primary, secondary, or benzylic radical. A benzylic radical is considerably more stable than a primary or secondary radical due to resonance stabilization. Therefore, it will be preferentially formed and the final product from bromination of propylbenzene will be mainly 1-bromo-1-phenylpropane.

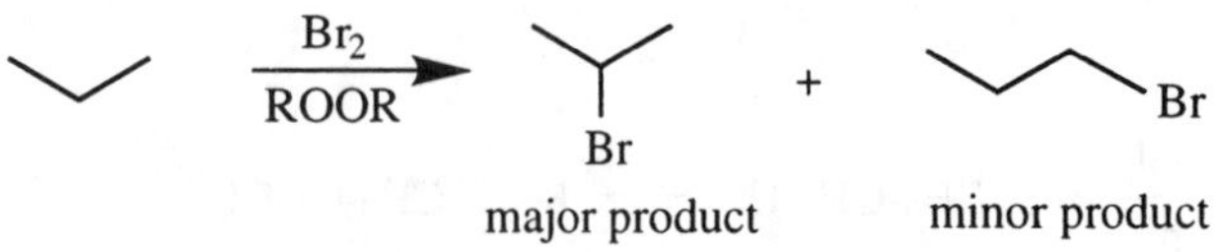

Br_2
ROOR
Br
+
Br
major product
minor product

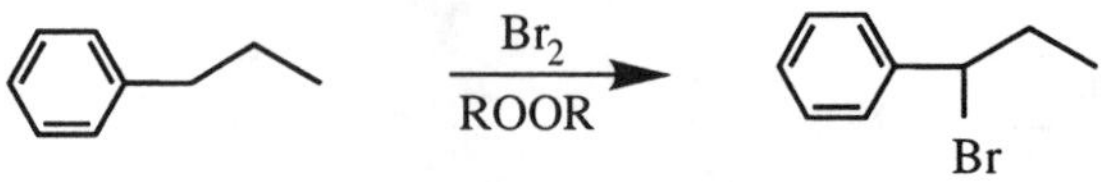

Br_2
ROOR
Br

10.19

(a) 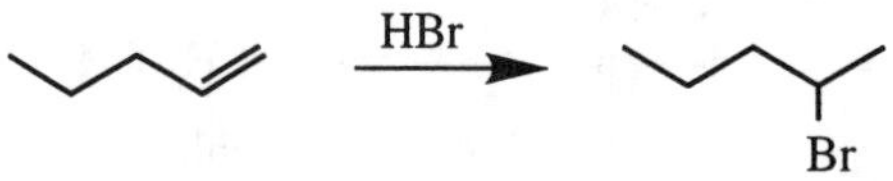

HBr
Br

(b) 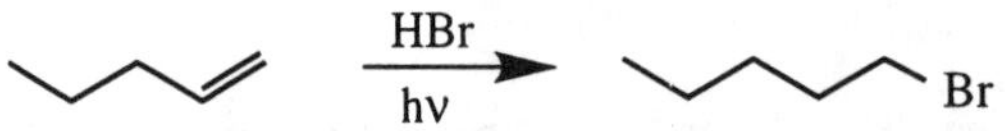

HBr
hν
Br

(c) 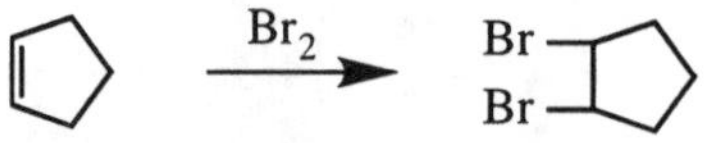

Br_2
Br
Br

(d) 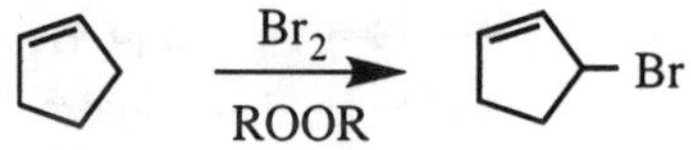

Br_2
ROOR
Br

(e) 

NBS
Br

(f) 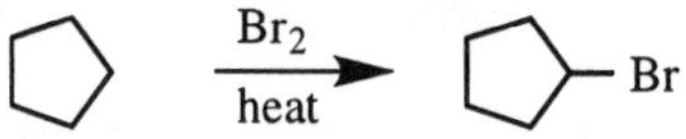

Br_2
heat
Br

10.20 The product will be allyl bromide in which bromination has occurred at the allylic position. The reaction occurs by removal of a hydrogen atom from the allylic position of propene. However, the allylic radical is resonance stabilized so there is radical character at both methylene groups of the radical intermediate. In other words, both the ^{12}C and ^{14}C terminal carbons should have equal radical character. Therefore, when the allylic radical attacks N-bromosuccinimide to remove the bromine it does so equally from the two identical contributing structures. Therefore, the allyl bromide should have about 50% of the ^{14}C on each methylene carbon.

$$^{14}CH_2{=}CH{-}CH_3 \xrightarrow{NBS} {}^{14}CH_2{=}CH{-}CH_2\cdot \longleftrightarrow \cdot{}^{14}CH_2{-}CH{=}CH_2$$

$$^{14}CH_2{=}CH{-}CH_2\cdot \xrightarrow{NBS} {}^{14}CH_2{=}CH{-}CH_2Br$$

$$\cdot{}^{14}CH_2{-}CH{=}CH_2 \xrightarrow{NBS} Br^{14}CH_2{-}CH{=}CH_2$$

10.21

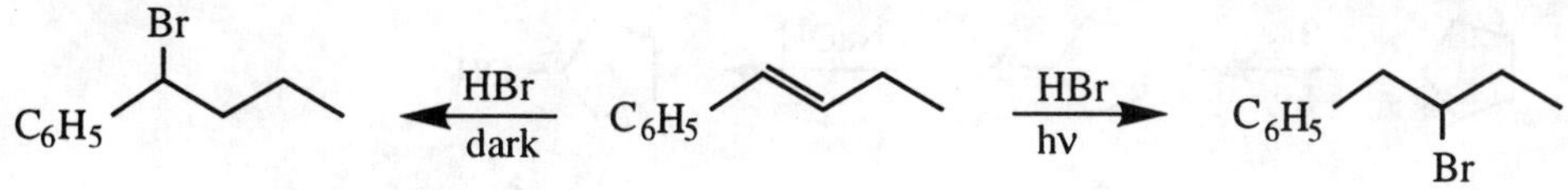
Br
HBr
dark
HBr
hν
Br

10.22

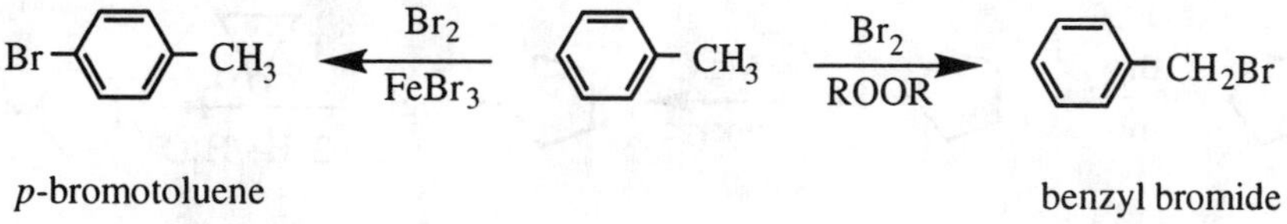
Br₂
FeBr₃
Br₂
ROOR
p-bromotoluene
benzyl bromide

***10.23**

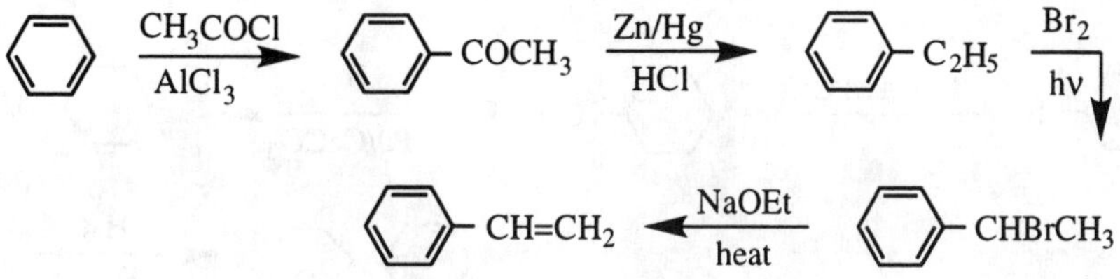
CH₃COCl
AlCl₃
COCH₃
Zn/Hg
HCl
C₂H₅
Br₂
hν
CH=CH₂
NaOEt
heat
CHBrCH₃

10.24

(a) 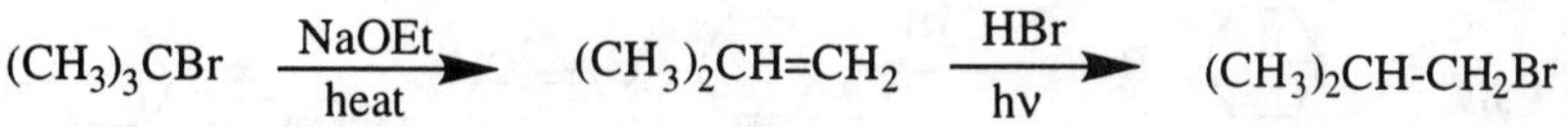
(CH₃)₃CBr
NaOEt
heat
(CH₃)₂CH=CH₂
HBr
hν
(CH₃)₂CH-CH₂Br

(b) 
CH₃CH₂CH=CH₂
NBS
CH₃CHBrCH=CH₂
NaOEt
heat
CH₂=CH-CH=CH₂

* (c) 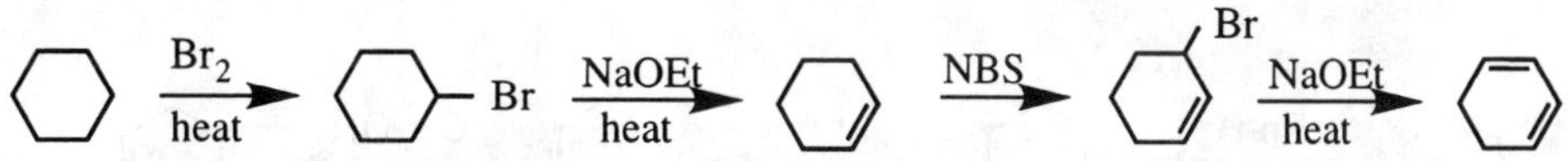
Br₂
heat
Br
NaOEt
heat
NBS
Br
NaOEt
heat

(d) 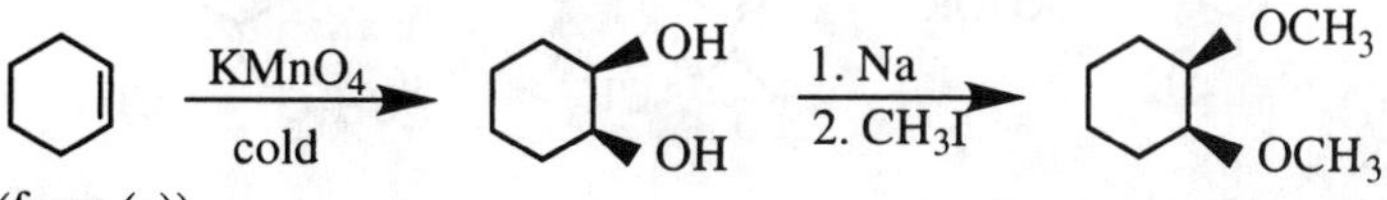
KMnO₄
cold
OH
OH
1. Na
2. CH₃I
OCH₃
OCH₃

(from (c))

(e) 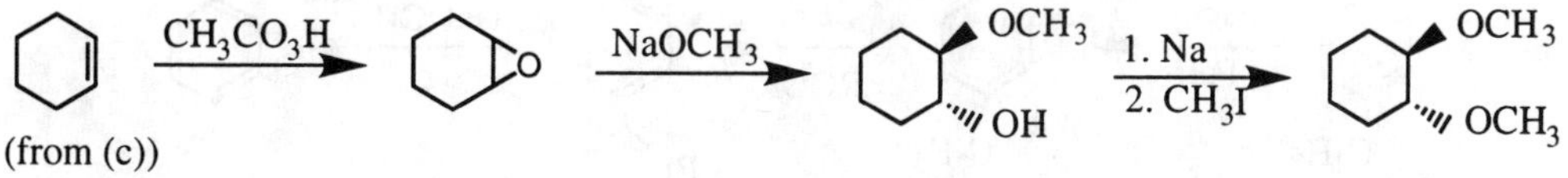
CH₃CO₃H
O
NaOCH₃
OCH₃
OH
1. Na
2. CH₃I
OCH₃
OCH₃

(from (c))

(f) 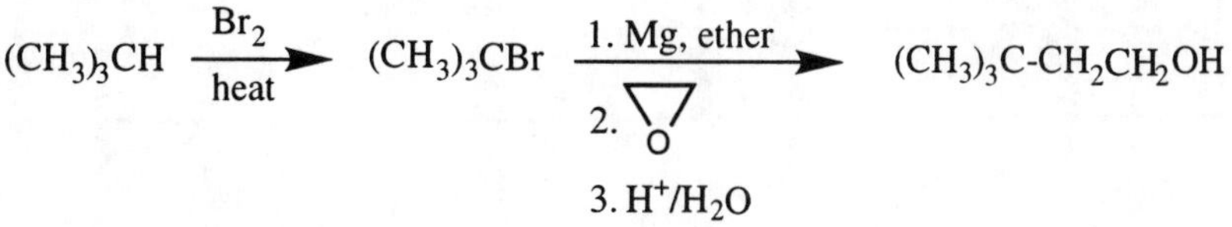
(CH₃)₃CH
Br₂
heat
(CH₃)₃CBr
1. Mg, ether
2.
O
3. H⁺/H₂O
(CH₃)₃C-CH₂CH₂OH

10.25

(a) 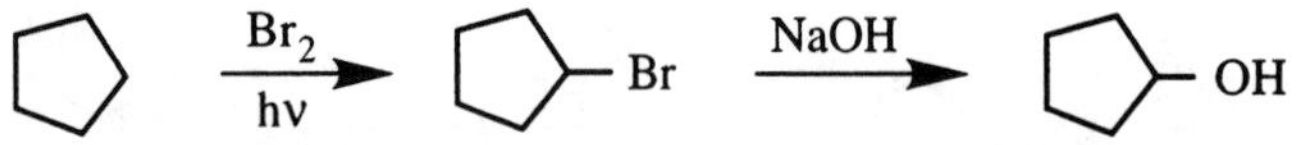
Br2
hν
Br
NaOH
OH

(b) 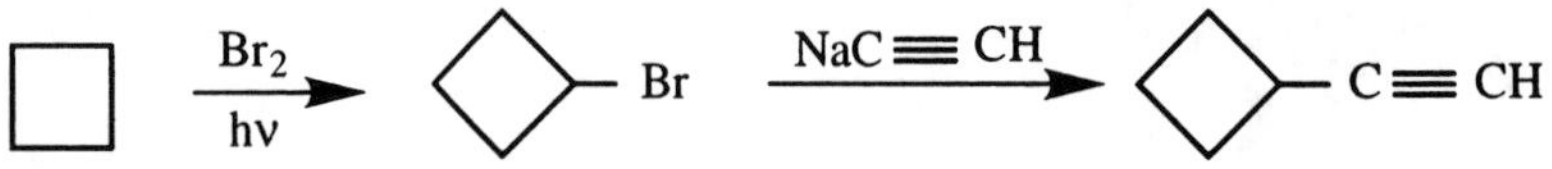
Br2
hν
Br
NaC≡CH
C≡CH

(c) 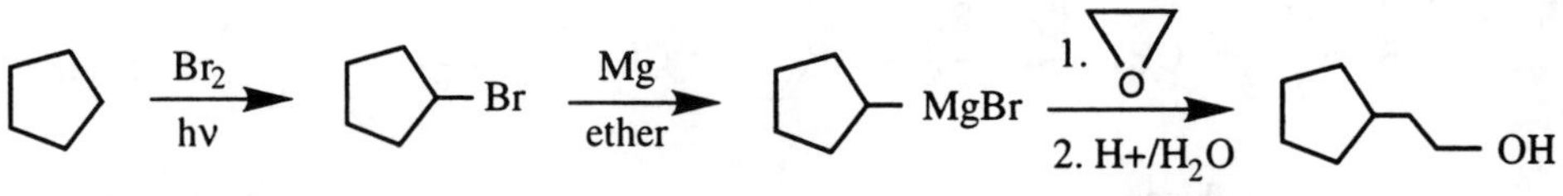
Br2
hν
Br
Mg
ether
MgBr
1.
O
2. H+/H2O
OH

(d) 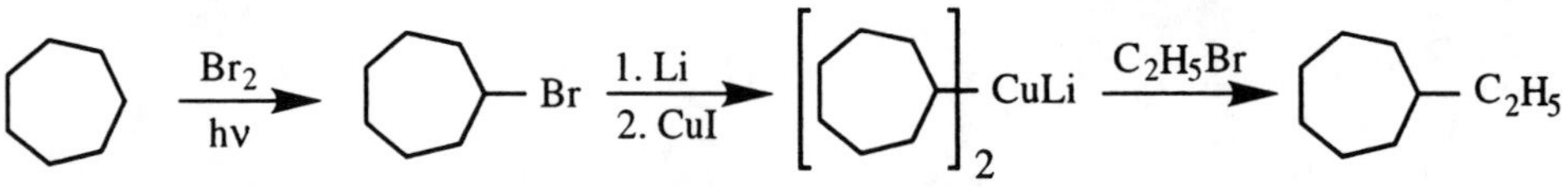
Br2
hν
Br
1. Li
2. CuI
CuLi
2
C2H5Br
C2H5

(e) 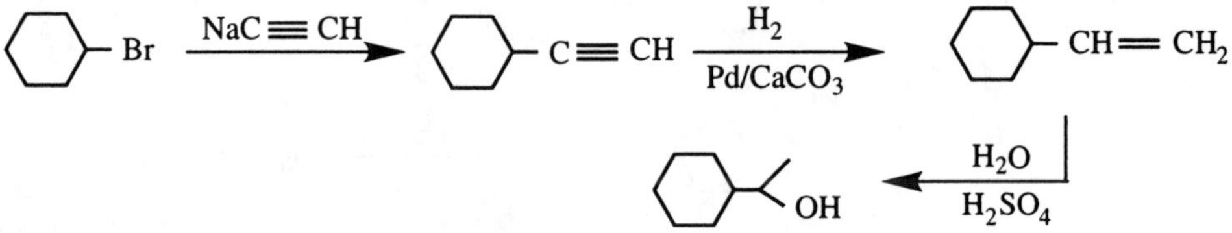
Br
NaC≡CH
C≡CH
H2
Pd/CaCO3
CH=CH2
H2O
H2SO4
OH

(f) 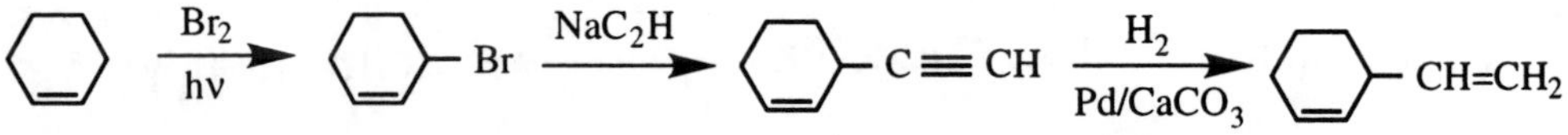
Br2
hν
Br
NaC2H
C≡CH
H2
Pd/CaCO3
CH=CH2

10.26

(a) 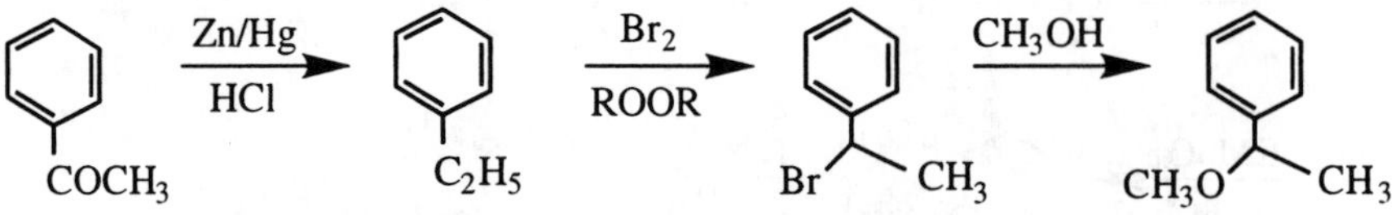
COCH3
Zn/Hg
HCl
C2H5
Br2
ROOR
Br
CH3
CH3OH
CH3O
CH3

(b) 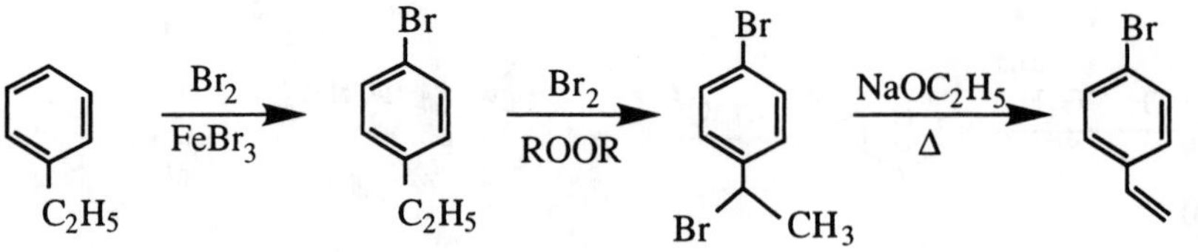
C2H5
Br2
FeBr3
Br
C2H5
Br2
ROOR
Br
Br
CH3
NaOC2H5
Δ
Br

10.27

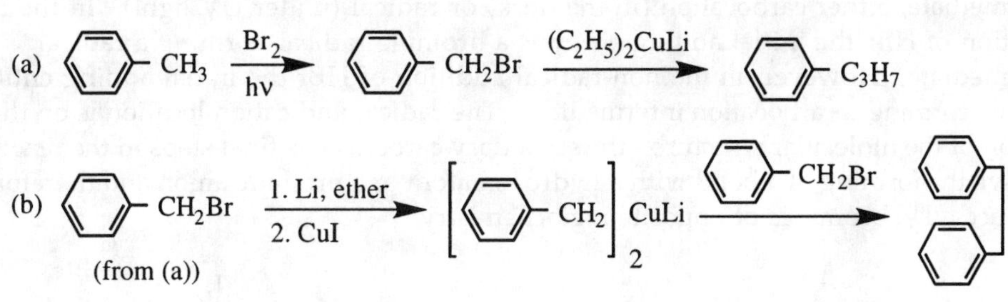

(c) $C_6H_5CH_2CH_2C_6H_5 \xrightarrow[h\nu]{Br_2} C_6H_5CHBrCH_2C_6H_5 \xrightarrow[heat]{NaOEt} C_6H_5CH{=}CHC_6H_5$

(from (b))

10.28

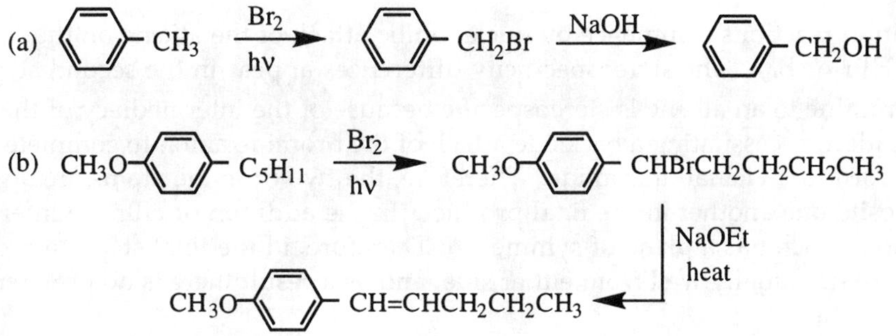

10.29

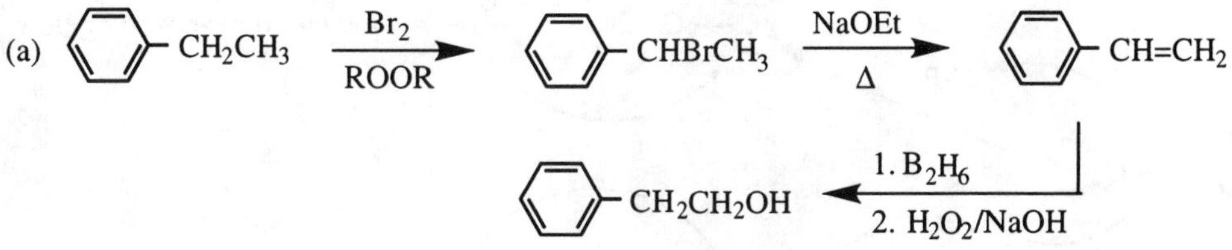

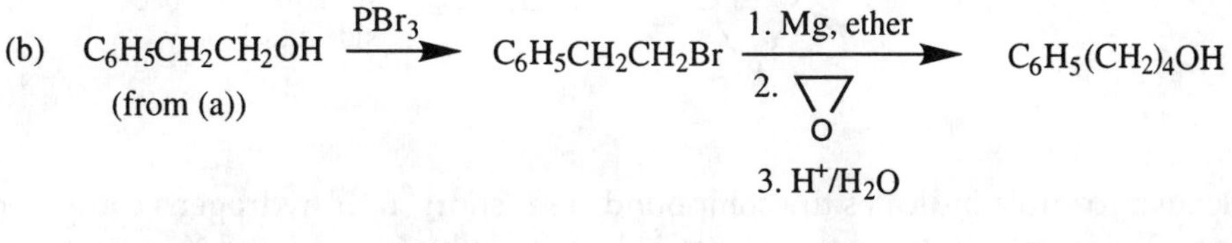

*(c) $C_6H_5CH_2CH_2Br \xrightarrow{Na\,C\equiv CH} C_6H_5CH_2CH_2C\equiv CH \xrightarrow[h\nu]{Br_2} C_6H_5CHBrCH_2C\equiv CH$

(from (b))

$C_6H_5CHBrCH_2C\equiv CH \xrightarrow[heat]{NaOEt} C_6H_5CH{=}CHC\equiv CH \xrightarrow{Li/NH_3} C_6H_5CH{=}CH\text{-}CH{=}CH_2$

10.30 (a) The regioselectivity of HBr addition is caused by the preferential stability of the intermediate, either carbocation (in the dark) or radical (under UV light). In the radical addition of HBr the initial adding entity is a bromine radical, forming a radical intermediate. However, in the non-radical addition of HBr the initial adding entity is a proton, forming a carbocation intermediate. The radical and cation location is on the same carbon of the molecular structure - the secondary carbon. The final steps in the reactions involve the forming of a bond with a hydrogen atom or a bromide anion and therefore produce alkyl bromides of opposite regiochemistry.

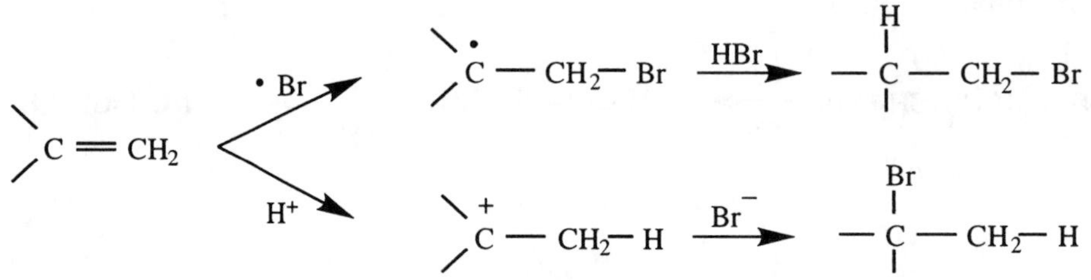
C = CH2
• Br
H+
C — CH2— Br
HBr
— C — CH2— Br
H
C — CH2— H
Br−
Br
— C — CH2— H

(b) Both addition reactions commence by nucleophilic attack of the alkene on the electrophile, HBr or Br_2. The stereospecificity differences appear in the second step. The addition of bromine to an alkene is stereospecific because of the intermediacy of the bromonium cation, necessitating a backside attack of the bromide anion to complete the addition and form the vicinal dibromide. Therefore, the two bromine atoms are always oriented opposite one another in the final product. In the addition of HBr the intermediate is a carbocation which has a plane of symmetry. Therefore, in the final step the bromide anion can approach equally well from either side, and as a result there is no preference for one side or the other.

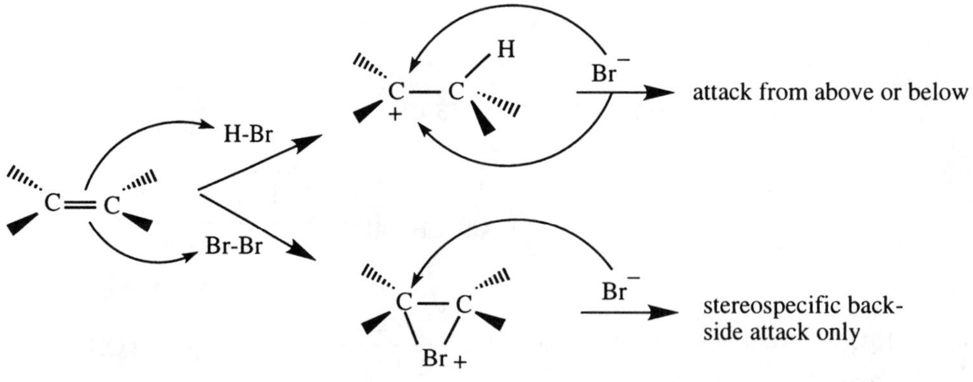
C=C
H-Br
Br-Br
H
C — C
+
Br−
attack from above or below
C — C
Br +
Br−
stereospecific back-side attack only

10.31 The molecular formula indicates the compounds are "short" four hydrogens compared to the C_5 alkane. The uptake of two equivalents of hydrogen by both **W** and **X** indicates that all the unsaturation can be removed by hydrogenation. Therefore, there are no rings present and there is one triple bond or two double bonds present in each. $KMnO_4$ oxidation will cleave any multiple bond. Since **W** produced only two carboxylic acids upon oxidation it must contain a single multiple bond, which therefore must be a triple bond. Since no carbon dioxide was produced it must have been an internal triple bond. Therefore, **W** can only have been 2-pentyne (there are no other possible structures with an internal triple bond and five carbons).

$$\underset{\text{2-pentyne}}{CH_3CH_2C{\equiv}CCH_3} \xrightarrow{KMnO_4} CH_3CH_2COOH + HOOCCH_3$$

Since **X** produced four oxidized sites there must have been two double bonds cleaved. Acetic acid (CH_3COOH) was one product indicating a $CH_3CH=$ unit must be present. The production of CO_2 indicates a terminal carbon was oxidized so a $CH_2=$ group must have been present. The two carbons unaccounted for appeared in a di-carboxylic acid which must have been HOOC-COOH, indicating a =CH-CH= unit was present. Therefore, piecing the "units" together results in the structure of **X** being 1,3-pentadiene.

$$\underset{\text{1,3-pentadiene}}{CH_3CH{=}CH{-}CH{=}CH_2} \xrightarrow{KMnO_4} CH_3COOH + HOOC{-}COOH + CO_2$$

10.32

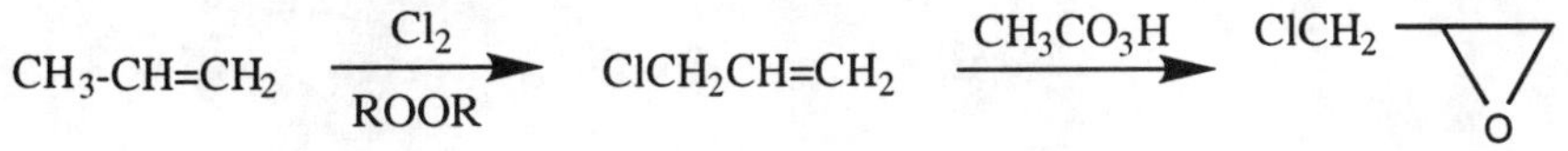

CH3-CH=CH2
Cl2
ROOR
ClCH2CH=CH2
CH3CO3H
ClCH2
O

10.33

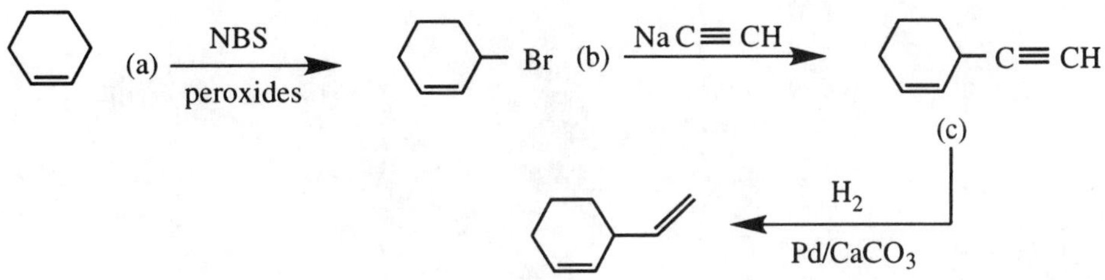

(a)
NBS
peroxides
Br
(b)
Na C≡ CH
C≡ CH
(c)
H2
Pd/CaCO3

10.34 Step **A**: bromine and UV light, or NBS and peroxide; Step **B**: $AlBr_3$ and benzene (Friedel-Crafts alkylation); Step **C**: bromine and UV light, or NBS; Step **D**: $(CH_3)_2NCH_2CH_2ONa$ obtained from the precursor alcohol and sodium.

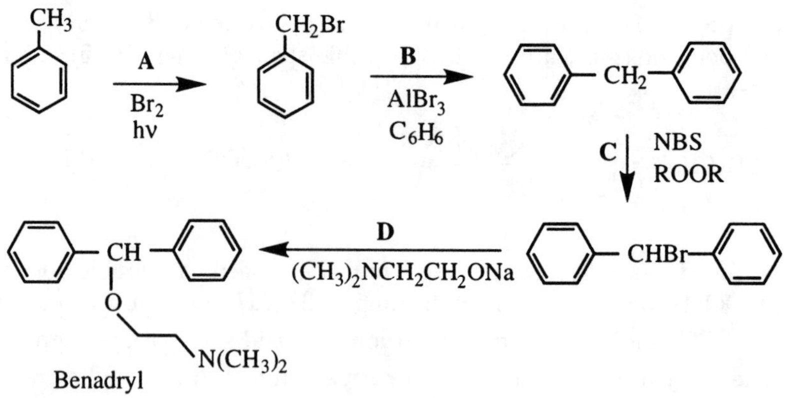
CH3
A
Br2
hv
CH2Br
B
AlBr3
C6H6
CH2
C
NBS
ROOR
D
(CH3)2NCH2CH2ONa
CHBr
CH
O
N(CH3)2
Benadryl

CHAPTER 11

Determination of Structure: Spectroscopy

I. Textbook Chapter Contents

Building on familiarity now with both aromatic and aliphatic chemistry, this chapter presents the means by which chemists determine the structure of unknown organic compounds. A number of techniques are presented within two broad categories. The first category is the historic approach to structure determination which relies on chemical reactions which will distinguish between families of compounds. The second category is the more modern approach of utilizing instrumental techniques, especially those involving molecular spectroscopy.

II. Learning Objectives

- Know how to use empirical formulas and molecular formulas to deduce the presence or absence of structural features of an unknown compound. Be able to apply the Hydrogen Deficiency Index.

- Know the chemical reactions already discussed and be able to use them to distinguish between families of compounds.

- Know the operating principle of a mass spectrometer and how it can be used to determine the molecular weight of a compound.

- Be able to detect the presence of isotopes and/or heteroatoms in a compound from the M+1 and M+2 peaks.

- Based on fragmentation analysis be able to deduce some aspects of a molecular structure.

- Know the electromagnetic spectrum and why a compound absorbs electromagnetic radiation of various frequencies. Know the general principles behind molecular spectroscopy and the significance of a spectrum.

- Know the relationship between conjugation and UV-VIS absorption. Be able to deduce aspects of a compound's structure from its VIS-UV spectrum.

- Be able to use infrared absorption peaks to determine the presence or absence of functional groups in a compound.

- Be able to use the fingerprint region of an infrared spectrum to determine the identity or non-identity of two samples.

- Using ^{1}H-NMR spectroscopy determine the number of different kinds of hydrogen in a compound, and the number of each kind.

- Using the chemical shift values in ^{1}H-NMR spectra determine the kind of hydrogen present in a structure.
- Use spin-spin splitting patterns in ^{1}H-NMR spectra to help determine the structure of an unknown compound.
- Use ^{13}C-NMR spectra to determine the number of different kinds of carbon in a compound.
- For a given compound predict the MS, UV-VIS, IR, ^{1}H-NMR and ^{13}C-NMR peaks.
- Be able to interpret peak information from all of the instrumental techniques to determine the structure of an unknown compound.

III. Glossary

chemical shift the extent to which a peak in the NMR spectrum is shifted from a reference peak (the reference usually is tetramethylsilane set at $\delta = 0$). The symbol δ is used for the chemical shift in units of ppm

complementary color the color that is transmitted through or reflected by a compound. It is the color seen by the human eye after radiation of a specific wavelength has been absorbed by a substance

coupling a phenomenon in NMR spectroscopy in which the position of resonance of a nucleus is affected by the presence of another NMR-active nucleus. This causes the peak of the nucleus being studied to be split into characteristic patterns. The detection of these patterns permits deduction of the structural environment of the nucleus in resonance

daughter ion a radical cation resulting from fragmentation of a molecular ion in mass spectrometry

decoupled electronically masking the effects of nuclei being coupled (and their NMR peaks thereby being split) by the targeting of a second RF beam at the compound being studied

downfield a direction in which a chemical shift moves when the nucleus is deshielded - a lower external field must be applied to accomplish resonance of the nucleus

electromagnetic radiation a particle (a photon) or a wave travelling at the speed of light and which may have different frequencies and, therefore, different energies

electromagnetic spectrum the range of frequencies exhibited by electromagnetic radiation

electronic transition a change in the energy level of an electron (most often a pi electron) due to absorption of energy from electromagnetic radiation. The energy level of an electronic transition usually occurs in the UV-VIS region of the spectrum

empirical formula a formula indicating which elements are present in a compound and the ratio of the number of each to the other

fingerprint region the region in the infrared from about 625 to 1550 cm^{-1} that contains many peaks and that is used mainly to compare two samples which are suspected of being identical

fragmentation the dissociation of a molecular ion into daughter ions

frequency the number of crests of an electromagnetic wave which passes a point each second. The units are cycles per second and are represented by the symbol Hz (Hertz)

functional group region a region in the infrared spectrum from 1550 to about 3500 cm^{-1} in which absorption indicates the presence of a specific functional group

functional group test a qualitative reaction that indicates the presence or absence of a particular functional group in a compound

hydrogen deficiency the number of hydrogens fewer than (2n+2) where n is the number of carbons in the molecular formula of a compound

hydrogen deficiency index (HDI) the hydrogen deficiency divided by 2. The HDI indicates the number of rings or multiple bonds present in a compound based on its molecular formula

infrared spectroscopy determination of the spectrum of a compound in the region 625 - 4000 cm^{-1} (2.5 - 16 nm)

integration a technique applied electronically to NMR spectra which calculates the area under a peak and thereby determines the ratio of the number of nuclei causing each particular peak

IR an abbreviation for infrared spectroscopy

mass spectrometry an instrumental technique for analyzing very small quantities of compounds. Information can be obtained regarding the molecular weight of the compound, the presence or absence of isotopes, and the presence or absence of structural fragments

molecular formula the actual number of atoms of each element present in a single molecule of a compound

molecular ion a radical cation resulting from the removal of one electron from a molecule, usually by mass spectrometry

molecular spectroscopy the passing of electromagnetic radiation through a sample of a compound and the determination of the absorption spectrum

MRI an abbreviation for magnetic resonance imaging, a diagnostic tool used in medicine which uses ^1H-NMR spectroscopy

MS an abbreviation for mass spectrometry

m/z the ratio of mass to charge of a radical cation (molecular ion) generated in mass spectrometry. Since z usually equals 1, the ratio reflects the molecular weight of the molecular ion

NMR an abbreviation for nuclear magnetic resonance spectroscopy

^1H-NMR spectroscopy NMR spectroscopy of hydrogen nuclei

^{13}C-NMR spectroscopy NMR spectroscopy of carbon-13 nuclei

nuclear magnetic resonance spectroscopy determination of the spectrum of a compound using radio frequency energy in the presence of a strong magnetic field

peak a position (that is, wavelength or frequency) in a spectrum at which absorption of radiation has occurred. Peaks may be sharp or broad

photon a packet of energy emitted by electromagnetic radiation. The energy of a photon is described by the relationship $E = h\nu$

radical cation a cation containing an unpaired electron resulting from loss of an electron from a neutral species

resonance when used in NMR spectroscopy the term means the condition in which the applied radio frequency energy corresponds to the energy differences between the low energy and high energy spin states of the nucleus being studied, and therefore the RF energy is absorbed

RF energy energy transmitted by radio frequency waves at wavelengths of 1 - 300 m

scanning the process of determining a spectrum, usually by measuring the intensity of absorption or transmission of energy as the wavelength is varied (scanned)

shielding the extent to which a nucleus is magnetically shielded from the externally applied magnetic field in NMR spectroscopy. A nucleus may be shielded or deshielded, relative to a reference compound, and this affects the chemical shift of the nucleus. Shielding is exerted by other nuclei and by electrons

solubility test a qualitative test to determine the solubility of a compound in various solutions, the results of which can indicate the family to which the compound belongs

spectrophotometer also called spectrometer. An instrument for producing a spectrum of a compound

spectroscopy the passing of electromagnetic radiation through a substance and the determination of the spectrum

spectrum the pattern of absorption of electromagnetic radiation. Usually reflected in a graph with the frequency or wavelength of the radiation on the x-axis and the extent of absorption on the y-axis

splitting (also called spin-spin splitting) the pattern into which a peak in resonance is split when the nucleus being studied is coupled. Typical splitting patterns are doublets, triplets, quadruplets, and multiplets

structure proof the determination of the structure of an unknown substance based on experimental observations

ultraviolet spectroscopy determination of the spectrum of a compound from about 200 nm to 400 nm

upfield a direction in which a chemical shift moves when the nucleus is shielded - a higher external field must be applied to accomplish resonance of the nucleus

UV-VIS spectroscopy abbreviation for ultraviolet-visible spectroscopy. Determination of the spectrum of a compound in the region 200-800 nm

vibrational transition the bending and stretching modes of bonds which occur with an energy found in the infrared region

visible spectroscopy determination of the spectrum of a compound from 400 nm to about 800 nm

wavelength the distance between two crests of an electromagnetic wave. The distance is measured in meters and is represented by the symbol λ (lambda)

wavenumber a reciprocal of the wavelength of absorption in the infrared region used as the x-axis in IR spectroscopy. The wavenumber is calculated by 10,000 ÷ l and shown by the symbol $\overline{\nu}$

IV. Solutions to Problems

For "**How to Solve a Problem,**" review pages 353, 354, 361, 375, 381, 383, 388, and 390.

11.1 (a) Note that the sum of the percentages equals 100%. Therefore, carbon and hydrogen are the only elements present.

Step one: Calculate the C/H ratio by dividing the percentage composition by the atomic weights: C = 83.7% ÷ 12 = 6.98
H = 16.3% ÷ 1.01 = 16.14

Step two: Divide both resulting numbers by the smallest number to produce ratios with one figure being 1.00:
C: 6.98 ÷ 6.98 = 1.0
H: 16.14 ÷ 6.98 = 2.3

Step three: If necessary multiply both numbers by a single number which brings both numbers approximately to whole units (apply liberal rounding). In this instance the multiplier 3 produces the empirical formula C_3H_7:
C: 1.0 x 3 = 3
H: 2.3 x 3 = 6.9 (round off to 7)

Step four: Calculate the formula weight of the empirical formula which in this case is (3 x 12) + (7 x 1) = 43. Divide the formula weight into the molecular weight (86 ÷ 43 = 2) which indicates the molecular formula is two times the empirical formula. Therefore, the molecular formula is C_6H_{14}.

(b) C = 77.4% ÷ 12.0 = 6.45 ÷ 1.07 = 6.0
H = 7.5% ÷ 1.01 = 7.43 ÷ 1.07 = 6.9
N = 15.0% ÷ 14.0 = 1.07 ÷ 1.07 = 1.0
Total = 99.9%

Based on calculations similar to those in (a) the empirical formula is C_6H_7N with a formula weight of 93. Division of the molecular weight of 93 by the formula weight of 93 indicates that the molecular formula is the same as the empirical formula, C_6H_7N.

(c) C = 70.6% ÷ 12.0 = 5.88 ÷ 1.47 = 4.0
H = 5.9% ÷ 1.01 = 5.84 ÷ 1.47 = 3.9
Total = 76.5%

Since the total composition accounted for is not 100% the difference is assumed to be oxygen:
100 - 76.5 = 23.5%
O = 23.5% ÷ 16.0 = 1.47 ÷ 1.47 = 1.0

Based on calculations similar to those in (a) the empirical formula is C_4H_4O which has a formula weight of 68. Since the molecular weight is twice this value the molecular formula must be twice the empirical formula, a molecular formula of $C_8H_8O_2$.

11.2 The hydrogen deficiency (HD) is the number hydrogens the compound is "short" of being an alkane. The HDI is that number divided by two. The HDI values are as follows:
(a) C_6H_{12} = 1. This value is obtained by realizing that a C_6 alkane would have a formula C_6H_{14}. Thus, C_6H_{12} is "short" two hydrogens. The index is therefore 2÷2 = 1.

(b) C_8H_{10} = 4. This compound is "short" 8 hydrogens compared to the C_8 alkane (C_8H_{18}). The index is therefore 8÷2 = 4.

(c) $C_7H_{12}O$ = 2. This compound is "short" 4 hydrogens compared to a saturated C_7 compound ($C_7H_{16}O$). The index is therefore 4÷2 = 2.

11.3 The molecular formula of C_8H_{14} has a HDI of 2. The fact that the compound reacted with bromine and permanganate indicates there is at least one double bond or one triple bond present. The fact that only one equivalent of hydrogen was absorbed indicates it must contain only one double bond. Therefore, there also must be a carbocyclic ring in the compound. In summary, C_8H_{14} contains a carbocyclic ring and includes a double bond.

11.4 (a) The compound C_7H_8 has a HDI of 4 but cannot have normal double or triple bonds because there was no reaction with bromine or hydrogen. Therefore, the HDI must be accounted for by a benzenoid ring (C_6). This leaves only one carbon unaccounted for which must be attached to that ring. Therefore, the compound must be toluene ($C_6H_5CH_3$).

(b) $C_6H_{12}O$ has no double or triple bonds even though its HDI is one. The absence of reaction with sodium indicates there is no OH group present so the oxygen must be an ether function. Therefore, the compound must have a ring which could be either carbocyclic or heterocyclic. Possibilities include the following specific seven-, six-, five-, and four-membered rings as well as numerous three-membered ring possibilities:

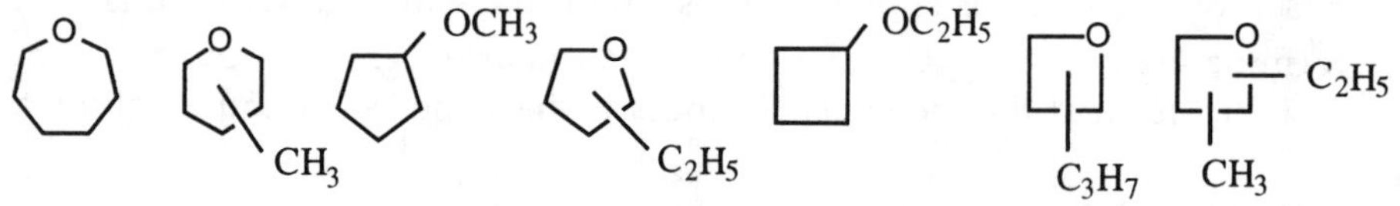

O
O
CH3
OCH3
O
C2H5
OC2H5
O
C3H7
O
C2H5
CH3

Note that the drawing of a group such as methyl on a bond protruding into the middle of a ring means that there is a methyl group on the ring but its position is unspecified.

(c) The compound $C_6H_{12}O$ with an HDI of one contains one double bond and an alcohol group.

(d) C_5H_8 with an HDI of two contains one triple bond or two double bonds. The ammoniacal silver nitrate test indicates the presence of a terminal triple bond. Therefore the compound is 1-pentyne or 3-methyl-1-butyne.

11.5 (a) C_3H_8O is a saturated alcohol (HDI = 0), and there are only two possible C_3 alcohols, *n*-propyl alcohol or isopropyl alcohol. The negative Lucas test indicates it must be a primary alcohol. Therefore, it is *n*-propyl alcohol, $CH_3CH_2CH_2OH$.

(b) C_7H_8O has an HDI of four. Since there is no detectable unsaturation it must be a benzenoid compound (this accounts for C_6H_5-, leaving only CH_3O- unaccounted for). It cannot be an alcohol on the basis of the sodium test. Therefore, the oxygen can only be an ether. There is only one possible structure, and that is phenyl methyl ether (anisole), $C_6H_5OCH_3$.

(c) C_8H_6 has an HDI of six—with this large a number a benzenoid compound (which accounts for four units of HDI) is suspected. It also has unsaturation which could be a triple bond or two double bonds. Strong oxidation produces benzoic acid ($C_7H_6O_2$), confirming the benzenoid suspicion. Further, the benzene ring can have only a single substituent. Only two carbons remain unaccounted for so the compound must contain a triple bond. The structure is phenylacetylene, C_6H_5CCH.

11.6 Molecular ions (M^+) will have the value of the molecular weight of the compounds. For (a) C_6H_{12} = 84; (b) C_3H_6BrCl = 156; (c) C_2H_7N = 45.

11.7 (a) M^+ = 122; other peak at m/z = 124 ($C_3H_7{}^{81}Br$).

(b) M^+ = 78; other peaks at m/z = 80 ($C_3H_7{}^{37}Cl$).

(c) M^+ = 58.

(d) M^+ = 73.

11.8 The peaks represent the following: 88 is the molecular ion (M^+); 73 is a M - CH_3 peak; 70 is M - H_2O (18); 59 is M - C_2H_5 (29); 55 is loss of a methyl (15) and water group (18).

11.9 (a) The molecular ion at 58 indicates no more than four carbon atoms can be present (five would require a M^+ > 60). The m/z peak at 43 (M-15) indicates loss of a methyl group and that at 29 (M-29) indicates loss of an ethyl group. The molecular weight is consistent with C_4H_{10} as the parent compound, for which isobutane and *n*-butane are the only possible structures. It cannot be isobutane [$(CH_3)_3CH$] because there is no way for an ethyl group to fragment off. Therefore, the compound is *n*-butane ($CH_3CH_2CH_2CH_3$).

(b) The m/z at 77 (M-15) indicates loss of a methyl group and that at 57 (M-35) indicates loss of a chlorine atom. The peak at m/z 57 can be accounted for by a C_4H_9 group. The latter group must be a *t*-butyl group ($(CH_3)_3C$-) since an isobutyl group ($(CH_3)_2CHCH_2$-)

would show loss of an isopropyl group and a *n*-butyl group ($CH_3CH_2CH_2CH_2$-) would show loss of an ethyl group. Therefore, the structure is *t*-butyl chloride. Since the peak at 92 is $C_4H_9{}^{35}Cl$, that at 94 is $C_4H_9{}^{37}Cl$, and those at 93 and 95 represent the ^{13}C content.

11.10 For 2-octanone the peak at m/z= 128 is the molecular ion, the peak at 129 represents the ^{13}C content, 113 represents loss of a methyl group (M-15), 85 represents loss of the CH_3CO group (M-43), and 43 represents the acetyl group (CH_3CO).

11.11 The maximum possible number of carbons is seven (7 x 12 = 84). Therefore a formula of C_7H_8 is probable and since it does not react as an alkene or alkyne, it must be a benzenoid compound. The peak at m/z = 77 represents loss of a methyl group (M-15) which would leave a group C_6H_5-. Therefore, the only feasible structure is toluene ($C_6H_5CH_3$).

11.12 The molecular formula C_9H_{10} indicates an HDI of 5 and the MS indicates the presence of a phenyl group (C_6H_5-), accounting for 4 units of unsaturation. Thus, unaccounted for is a group C_3H_5- and this group must be unsaturated or must contain a ring. The bromine test indicates **A** is not unsaturated whereas **B** is. The UV spectrum of **A** is typical for a benzene derivative which is not conjugated, whereas the longer wavelength absorption of **B** indicates there is conjugation with the ring. Therefore, the possible structures are shown below.

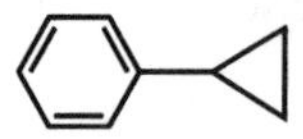

A

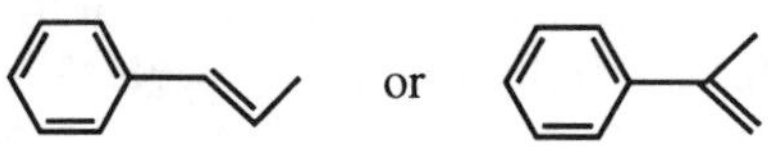

B

11.13 Any compound with a conjugated electronic system should be colored, the result of absorption of UV-VIS radiation. *p*-Nitrophenol should be colored because of the extended conjugation from the electron-donating hydroxyl group through the ring to the electron-withdrawing nitro group. 1-Phenyl-1,3,5-hexatriene also should be lightly colored because of the extensive conjugated system. 1,4-Pentadiene and vinylcyclohexane will not be colored because of the absence of a conjugated system.

11.14 Reference to Figure 11.15 indicates that
(a) for a red compound absorption is required near 500 nm;
(b) for a blue compound absorption is required near 620 nm;
(c) for a yellow compound absorption is required near 430 nm;
(d) for a green compound absorption is required near 720 nm.

11.15 The sample is *t*-butyl alcohol because it shows the strong O-H stretching peak of the alcohol near 3300 cm^{-1}.

11.16 (a) Benzaldehyde and benzoic acid both should have a strong carbonyl peak near 1700 cm^{-1}. However, only benzoic acid should have a very broad strong O-H stretching peak centered near 3300 cm^{-1}.

(b) 2-Pentyne should have a sharp moderate strength peak near 2100 cm^{-1} for the triple bond stretch whereas cyclobutene will not.

(c) Cyclohexanol will show the O-H stretching peak near 3300 cm^{-1} whereas cyclopentyl methyl ether will not.

11.17 The molecular formula $C_5H_{10}O$ has an HDI of one. The IR peak near 1725 cm^{-1} indicates this is due to a double bond in a carbonyl group (aldehyde or ketone). Since there is no NMR peak near 9.0 ppm (typical of -CHO) the compound is not an aldehyde so must be a ketone. There only two kinds of hydrogen present. The 0.9 ppm peak is a typical C-CH_3 group. The 2.6 ppm peak is typical for hydrogens on a carbon next to a carbonyl group (H-C-C=O). Therefore, a partial structure is CH_3-CH_2-CO-. Since a ketone must have carbon atoms on both sides (that is, a partial structure C-CO-C) the only feasible structure which fits these patterns is a symmetrical one with identical substituents on both sides of the carbonyl. This structure is $CH_3CH_2COCH_2CH_3$ (3-pentanone).

11.18 Since there is only a single peak for each compound there can only be a single kind of hydrogen present. The structures are as shown below:

(a) CH_3OCH_3 (b) $CH_3CCl_2CH_3$ (c) $(CH_3)_4C$ (d) $CH_3C\equiv CCH_3$

11.19 *t*-Butyl formate [$(CH_3)_3COCHO$] has two different kinds of hydrogen (CH_3- and HCO-) in the ratio of 1:9. Pivalic acid [$(CH_3)_3CCOOH$] also has two different kinds of hydrogen (CH_3- and COOH) in the same ratio 1:9. The key difference between the two is the location of the single
hydrogen as shown below - the carboxylic acid proton is at the lower field.

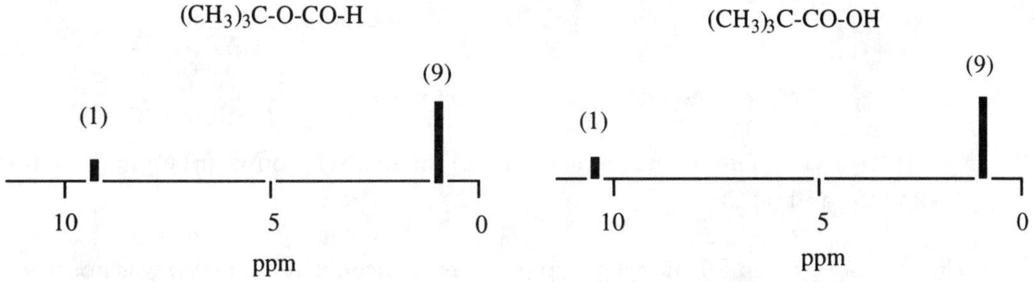
(CH3)3C-O-CO-H
(9)
(1)
10
5
0
ppm
(CH3)3C-CO-OH
(9)
(1)
10
5
0
ppm

11.20 Both compounds have a C-methyl group which is at about 0.9 ppm (area = 3), and both methyl peaks will be split into triplets by the attached methylene groups. Methyl propanoate has an O-CH_3 (area 3, unsplit) which is at 3.5 ppm whereas ethyl acetate has an O-CH_2 (area 2) at 3.5 ppm which is split into a quartet by the attached methyl group. Methyl propanoate has a CH_2-CO- (area 2, q) at 2.5 ppm whereas ethyl acetate has a CH_3-CO (area 3, s) at 2.5 ppm.

$CH_3CH_2COOCH_3$
methyl propanoate

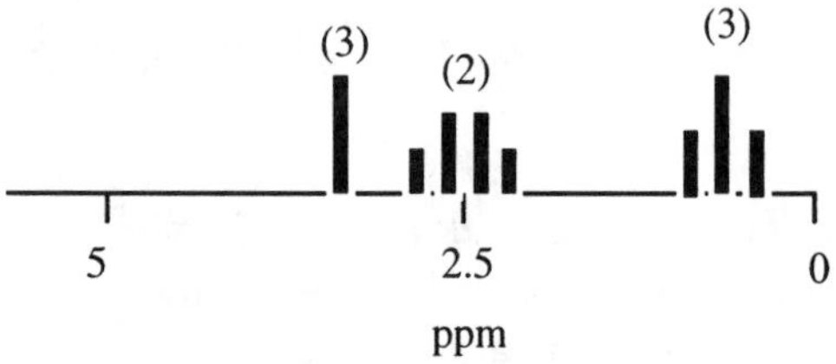
(3)
(2)
(3)
5
2.5
0
ppm

$CH_3COOCH_2CH_3$
ethyl acetate

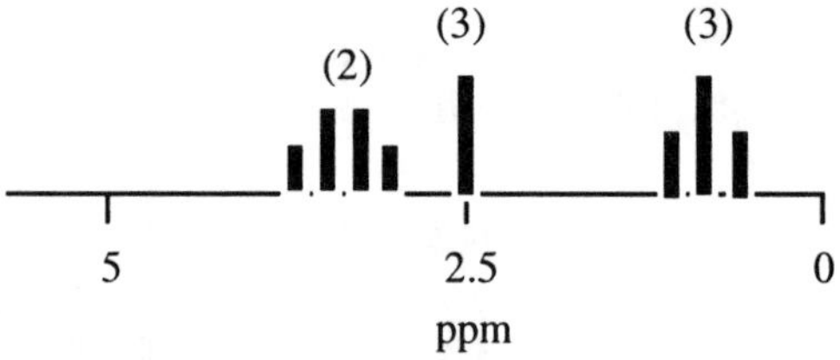
(2)
(3)
(3)
5
2.5
0
ppm

11.21

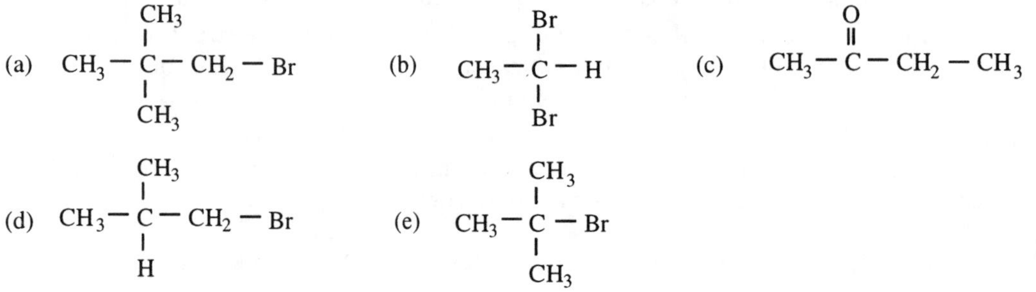
(a)
(b)
(c)
(d)
(e)

11.22 *p*-Xylene has three different kinds of carbon: (a) the two methyl groups, (b) C_1 and C_4, and (c) C_2, C_3, C_5 and C_6.

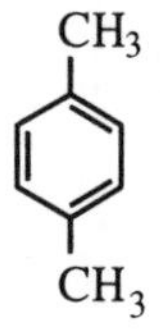

p-xylene

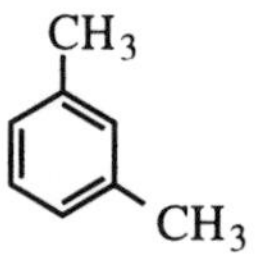

m-xylene

m-Xylene has five different kinds of carbon: (a) the methyl groups, (b) C_1 and C_3, (c) C_2, (d) C_4 and C_6, and (e) C_5.

11.23 The fact that an oxygen functional group (such as an alcohol or carbonyl) was not obvious in the IR indicates that $C_5H_{12}O$ probably is an ether. Since there are only four ^{13}C-NMR peaks two carbons must be identical. The ^1H-NMR peak at 1.0 is typical of two methyl groups on carbon, probably an isopropyl group ($(CH_3)_2CH$-). The peak at 3.4 (with area = 3) is typical of a methyl group attached to oxygen (CH_3-O-). Four carbons have been accounted for, and since the compound is an ether, the structure probably is isobutyl methyl ether $(CH_3)_2CH$-CH_2-O-CH_3. Review of the evidence in terms of this structure reveals that it is consistent.

11.24 With a molecular ion of 134 the probable number of carbons present is ten (10 x 12 = 120), in which case there would be 14 hydrogens and the molecular formula would be $C_{10}H_{14}$. The major peaks indicate the presence of a benzenoid ring (76) and one or more ethyl groups (29). The area ratios in the ^{1}H-NMR add up to only seven, so they must be doubled to account for the presence of 14 hydrogens. The peak at 7.1 is typical for a di-substituted benzene ring, consistent with the MS peak at 76. The peaks at 1.2 and 2.6 are typical of an ethyl group, and the area ratios indicate there are two ethyl groups. Therefore, the structure is a diethylbenzene. The ^{13}C-NMR spectrum confirms the presence of ethyl groups (only two kinds of aliphatic carbon) and the fact that there are only two aromatic peaks indicates the structure must be very symmetrical and is probably p-diethylbenzene.

11.25 (a) The molecular weight (210) divided by the formula weight (C_5H_{10} = 70) is three, so the molecular formula is three times the empirical formula, or $C_{15}H_{30}$.

(b) carbon = 87.50% ÷ 12.0 = 7.29 ÷ 7.29 = 1.00 x 3 = 3
hydrogen = 12.50% ÷ 1.01 = 12.38 ÷ 7.29 = 1.69 x 3 ~ 5

The empirical formula is C_3H_5 (formula weight of 41). Therefore the molecular formula is four times (164 ÷ 41 = 4) the empirical formula or $C_{12}H_{20}$.

(c) carbon = 75.95% ÷ 12.0 = 6.33 ÷ 1.27 = 4.98
hydrogen = 6.33% ÷ 1.01 = 6.27 ÷ 1.27 = 4.93
nitrogen = 17.72% ÷ 14.0 = 1.27 ÷ 1.27 = 1.00

The empirical formula is C_5H_5N (formula weight = 79). Therefore, the molecular formula also is C_5H_5N.

(d) carbon = 67.6% ÷ 12.0 = 5.63 ÷ 1.41 = 3.99
hydrogen = 9.8% ÷ 1.01 = 9.70 ÷ 1.41 = 6.88
oxygen = 22.6% ÷ 16.0 = 1.41 ÷ 1.41 = 1.00

The empirical formula is C_4H_7O (formula weight = 71). Since the molecular weight is twice the formula weight, the molecular formula must be $C_8H_{14}O_2$.

11.26 (a) The molecular formula is the same as the empirical formula (C_5H_8O). The HDI is two, requiring a combination of two double bonds, two rings, or a single triple bond. Many structures are possible, including alkenes, carbonyls, ethers, alicyclic, and heterocyclic structures. One such structure is cyclopentanone (a) shown below.

(a) 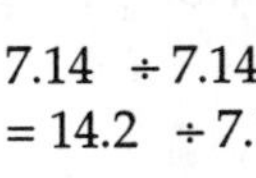
O

(b)

(b) carbon = 85.7% ÷ 12.0 = 7.14 ÷ 7.14 = 1.00
hydrogen = 14.3% ÷ 1.01 = 14.2 ÷ 7.14 = 1.99

The empirical formula is CH_2 (formula weight 14) so the molecular formula is four times (56 ÷ 14 = 4) the empirical formula, or C_4H_8. The HDI = 1 indicates the compound must have either a ring or a double bond. There are five possible structures (three alkenes and two cycloalkanes) of which cyclobutane (b) shown above is one.

11.27 (a) $C_4H_{10}O$ has an HDI of zero. Therefore, it can only be an alcohol or an ether. The test with metallic sodium would distinguish between the two, with an alcohol producing bubbles of gas as hydrogen is evolved and the ether not reacting.

(b) C_5H_{10} has an HDI of one. Therefore, it can only be an alkene or a cycloalkane. The Br_2/CCl_4 test would distinguish between the two possibilities, with an alkene reacting rapidly with bromine, removing its red-brown color, and a cycloalkane not reacting.

(c) $C_5H_{11}Br$ is a saturated alkyl halide of which there are eight possible structural isomers. Four are primary bromides, three are secondary bromides, and one is a tertiary bromide. Silver nitrate in ethanol solution would produce a rapid reaction with the tertiary halide, a slow reaction with the secondary halides, and a very slow reaction with the primary halides. Sodium iodide in acetone solution would produce a rapid reaction with the primary bromides, a moderate reaction with the secondary bromides, and a very slow reaction with the tertiary bromide. By these tests it could be determined whether the alkyl bromide was primary, secondary, or tertiary.

(d) carbon = 87.8% ÷ 12.0 = 7.32 ÷ 7.32 = 1.00 x 3 = 3
hydrogen = 12.2% ÷ 1.01 = 12.1 ÷ 7.32 = 1.65 x 3 ~ 5

The empirical formula is C_3H_5 with a formula weight of 41. The molecular weight of 82 indicates the molecular formula is C_6H_{10} which has an HDI of two. Therefore, it could be an alkyne, an acyclic diene, a cycloalkene, or a bicyclic compound. The latter compound would not decolorize bromine whereas the first three would. There are no functional group tests which would distinguish among the first three compounds since all three are unsaturated.

11.28 The unknown compound is (a) an alcohol; (b) an alkene or alkyne; (c) a primary or secondary alcohol; (d) a primary or secondary alcohol, an alkene, or an alkyne; (e) an ether; (f) a phenol; (g) an alkane, cycloalkane, or aromatic.

11.29 (a) the Lucas reagent ($HCl/ZnCl_2$) reacts quickly to form an insoluble alkyl chloride with 2-methyl-2-butanol but slowly if at all with 1-butanol.

(b) Br_2/CCl_4 adds rapidly to 1-hexene (and is decolorized) but does not react with hexane.

(c) $AgNO_3$ in ethanol produces a silver chloride precipitate rapidly with *t*-butyl chloride but slowly or not at all with *n*-butyl chloride.

(d) metallic sodium reacts with 1-butanol to evolve hydrogen gas but does not react with 1-methoxypropane.

(e) aqueous sodium hydroxide reacts with phenol to form a salt which dissolves, but there is no reaction with cyclohexanol which remains insoluble.

(f) aqueous sodium bicarbonate reacts with benzoic acid to form a salt (and evolve carbon dioxide) which dissolves whereas benzaldehyde will not react or dissolve.

11.30 **A** ($C_6H_{10}O$) has an HDI of two and the reaction with bromine and permanganate indicates it contains an alkene or alkyne function. Since only a single equivalent of hydrogen is absorbed upon catalytic hydrogenation **A** must contain a ring and an alkene group. **B** must have a formula $C_6H_{12}O$ and must be an alcohol since sulfuric acid effects dehydration to an alkene **C** (C_6H_{10}). By inference **A** also is an alcohol and produces **D** (whose formula must be C_6H_8) upon dehydration. Because of its UV absorption **D** probably is a conjugated diene, so **A** from which it is obtained must be an alkene-alcohol with the alcohol group in a position which can produce a conjugated diene upon dehydration. Since ozonolysis of **C** produced the single compound ($OHC(CH_2)_4CHO$) it must be cyclohexene which must have arisen from cyclohexanol (**B**). Cyclohexanol must have arisen by reduction of either 2-cyclohexen-1-ol or 3-cyclohexen-1-ol, both of which would afford 1,3-cyclohexadiene upon dehydration. The structures of the unknown compounds are shown below.

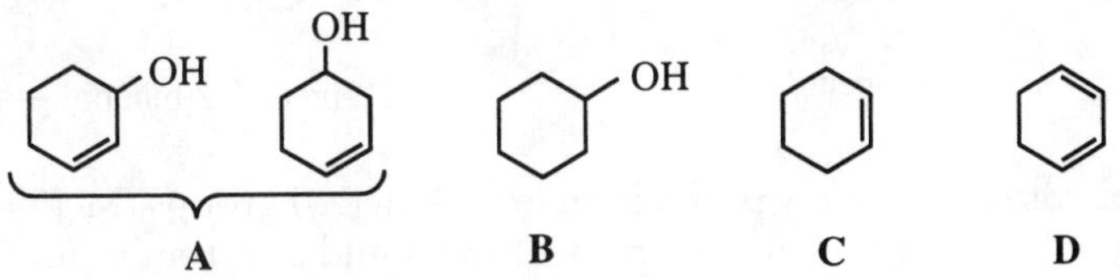
OH
OH
OH
A
B
C
D

11.31 The m/z values expected are determined by calculating the molecular weight from the molecular formula: (a) 96; (b) 126; (c) 151

11.32 (a) $M^+ = 46$; fragments at 28 (M - H_2O) and 31 (M - CH_3).

(b) $M^+ = 122$ and M + 2 = 124; fragments at 107 (M - CH_3), 79 (M - C_3H_7), and 43 (M - Br).

(c) $M^+ = 86$; fragments at 71 (M - CH_3) and 57 (M - C_2H_5).

(d) $M^+ = 106$; fragments at 77 (M - C_2H_5) and 29 (M - C_6H_5).

11.33 The peaks for 2-methylpentane are attributable as follows: 71 is M-15 from loss of a methyl group; 57 is M-29 (isobutyl) from loss of an ethyl group; 43 is M-43 (isopropyl) from loss of an *n*-propyl group; 29 is M-57 (ethyl) from loss of an isobutyl group.

$$\begin{array}{c} \quad\;\; CH_3 \\ \quad\;\; | \\ CH_3-CH-CH_2-CH_2-CH_3 \end{array}$$

2-methylpentane

11.34 The C_3H_8O unknown is an alcohol which can only be 1-propanol or 2-propanol. The MS indicates it is 1-propanol because of the presence of a m/z = 31 (M - ethyl) peak, a peak which cannot arise from fragmentation of 2-propanol.

11.35 We deduce that two bromines are present because of the M+2 and M+4 peaks (m/z = 198 has 2 x ^{79}Br; m/z = 200 has ^{79}Br + ^{81}Br; m/z = 202 has 2 x ^{81}Br). Therefore, the remainder of the structure must be m/z = 198-(2 x 79) = 40(C_3H_4) and the molecular formula must be $C_3H_4Br_2$ (HDI = one). Therefore a ring or double bond is present. Possible structures are 1,1-dibromocyclopropane, 1,2-dibromocyclopropane, 1,1-dibromopropene, 1,2-dibromopropene, 1,3-dibromopropene, 2,3-dibromopropene, and 3,3-dibromopropene.

11.36 The structures of the two alcohols (both $C_5H_{12}O$, M^+ = 88) are as shown here:

OH

1-pentanol

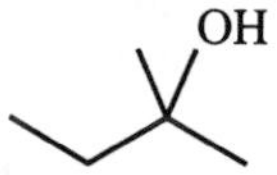
OH

2-methyl-2-butanol

Both compounds should show peaks from loss of methyl groups (M-15 = 73), ethyl groups (M-29 = 59), water (M-18 = 70). The peak at 73 should be stronger for 2-methyl-2-butanol since there are three methyl groups. Therefore, spectrum A is 1-pentanol and spectrum B is 2-methyl-2-butanol.

11.37 From 2,2-dimethylbutane (m/z = 86) the daughter ion of m/z = 57 is the *t*-butyl cation which arises from the loss of an ethyl group (m/z = 29).

$$\underset{M^{\cdot+}}{(CH_3)_3CCH_2CH_3^{\cdot+}} \longrightarrow \underset{m/z\,=\,57}{(CH_3)_3C^+} + \bullet CH_2CH_3$$

11.38 The molecular ion is 86 indicating it probably is C_6H_{14}. There are five structural isomers of C_6H_{14}. The presence of M-15 and M-29 would be expected from several isomers. However, M-43 peaks can arise only from two isomers, hexane or 2-methylpentane.

$CH_3CH_2CH_2CH_2CH_2CH_3$ — hexane

$(CH_3)_2CHCH_2CH_2CH$ — 2-methylpentane

11.39 The presence of a significant M+2 peak indicates the likelihood of chlorine or bromine being present. There are several indications the compound contains bromine: (a) the fact that the M and M+2 peaks are of approximately equivalent intensity argues for the presence of bromine isotopes (^{79}Br and ^{81}Br occur in about a 50/50 ratio whereas ^{35}Cl and ^{37}Cl occur in a ratio about 75/25); (b) if bromine is present the remainder of the compound has m/z = 77, probably the phenyl group (C_6H_5); (c) if Cl is present the remainder of the compound has m/z = 121, which doesn't provide a realistic formula for C_9 or C_{10}; (d) if there are two chlorines present the remainder of the compound has m/z = 86 which also does not produce a realistic formula. Therefore, the compound probably is C_6H_5Br (bromobenzene).

11.40 The formula C_6H_8 has HDI = 3. The hydrogenation indicates **A** and **B** are cyclohexadienes. The absence of UV absorption by **B** indicates it is a non-conjugated diene which can only be 1,4-cyclohexadiene. The UV absorption of **A** indicates it is conjugated which can only be 1,3-cyclohexadiene.

A **B**

11.41 The compounds which should absorb in the UV are those which have conjugated systems: (b) benzyl alcohol, (c) 1,3,5-hexatriene, (d) 1-phenylpropane, (e) cyclopentadiene, (g) anthracene, (i) diphenyl, and (j) diphenylmethane.

11.42 The IR spectrum of 2-methyl-1-butanol should show a strong and sharp OH stretching peak near 3300 cm^{-1}. The spectrum of t-butyl methyl ether should be blank near that wavenumber. Therefore, compound **X** is t-butyl methyl ether and compound **Y** is 2-methyl-1-butanol.

11.43 (a) the OH of 1-propanol should produce a peak near 3300 cm^{-1}.

(b) although both compounds should produce strong carbonyl peaks near 1700 cm^{-1} the benzoic acid should also produce a strong, broad peak centered near 3300 cm^{-1} for the OH group.

(c) the alkyne should produce an isolated peak near 2150 cm^{-1} whereas the diene should produce a peak near 1640 cm^{-1}.

(d) benzyl alcohol should produce a strong peak near 3300 cm^{-1}.

(e) 2-pentanone should produce a strong peak near 1700 cm^{-1}.

(f) 1-decene should produce a modest peak near 1625 cm^{-1}.

11.44 The compound was a carboxylic acid because it showed both the OH peak (3100-3400 cm^{-1}) and the carbonyl peak (1700 cm^{-1}) characteristic of carboxylic acids whereas the other two compounds would show only one of the two peaks.

11.45 The formula C_4H_8O has an HDI of one indicating the presence of a double bond or a ring. The oxygen must be in an ether functional group since a hydroxyl and carbonyl group both are absent as indicated by the IR data. The compound could be carbocyclic, heterocyclic, or alicyclic. A few of the possible structures are shown below:

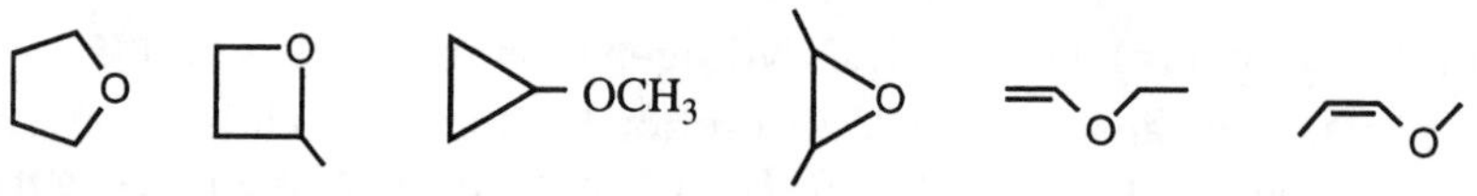
O
O
OCH_3
O
O
O

11.46 (a) 1700 cm^{-1} for the carbonyl group
(b) 2150 cm^{-1} for the alkyne group
(c) 3300 cm^{-1} for the carboxylic acid
(d) 3300 cm^{-1} for the alcohol
(e) 1625 cm^{-1} for the alkene

11.47 The progress of the reaction can be monitored by detecting the presence of the alcohol using the 3300 cm^{-1} absorption in the IR. As long as cyclopentanol remains unchanged and detectable in the IR the reaction is not complete.

11.48 (a) one peak (CH_2); (b) two peaks (CH_3 and CH_2); (c) three peaks (CH_3, CH_2, CH_2Br); (d) three peaks (CH_3, CH_2, CH); (e) three peaks (aryl-H, O-CH_3, CH_3); (f) three peaks (CH_3, CH_2, O-CH_3); (g) three peaks (CH_3, CH_2, $COCH_3$); (h) three peaks (CH_3, CH_2, $COCH_3$).

11.49

(a) CH_3OCH_3 — 3.5 ppm

(b) 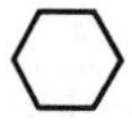 — 1.2 ppm

(c) $CH_3C{\equiv}CCH_3$ — 1.9 ppm

(d)  — 7.0 ppm

(e) $CH_3CBr_2CH_3$ — 1.4 ppm

(f) CH_3COCH_3 — 2.4 ppm

(g) $(CH_3)_3CBr$ — 1.3 ppm

(h)  — 5.0 ppm

11.50 The extent of deshielding of the methyl groups relative to TMS is related to the the electronegativity of the atom or group to which the methyl is attached. The amount of deshielding of the methyl group is as follows:

methylcyclohexane < acetone < methyl ether < methyl chloride

11.51

(a) methyl ethyl ether ($CH_3OCH_2CH_3$)

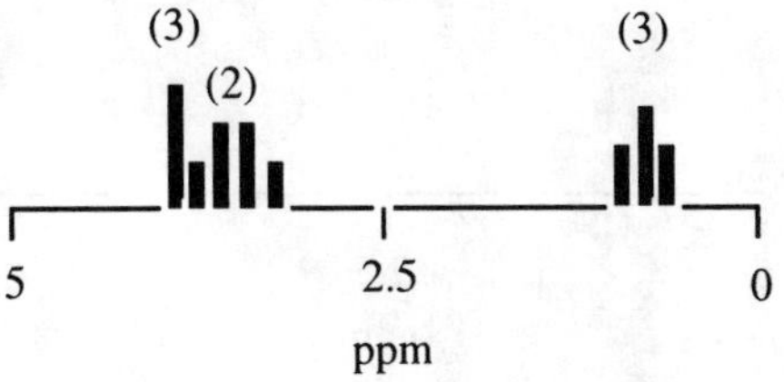
(3)
(2)
(3)
5
2.5
0
ppm

(b) ethyl bromide (CH_3CH_2Br)

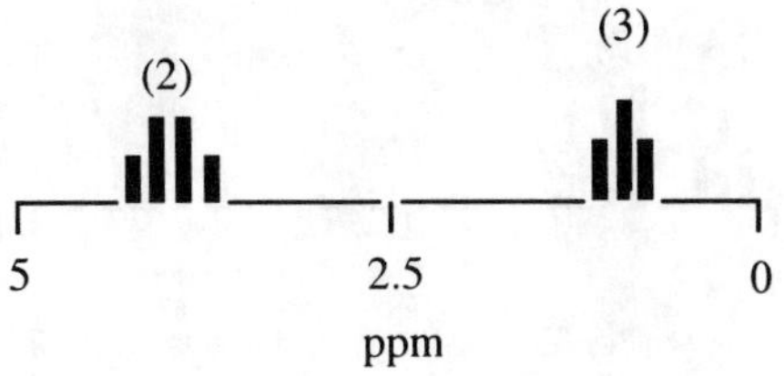
(2)
(3)
5
2.5
0
ppm

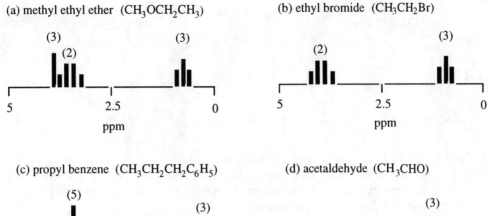

(c) propyl benzene ($CH_3CH_2CH_2C_6H_5$)

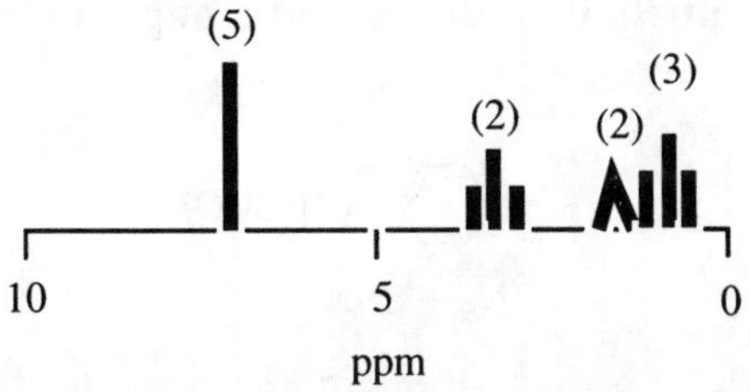
(5)
(2)
(2)
(3)
10
5
0
ppm

(d) acetaldehyde (CH_3CHO)

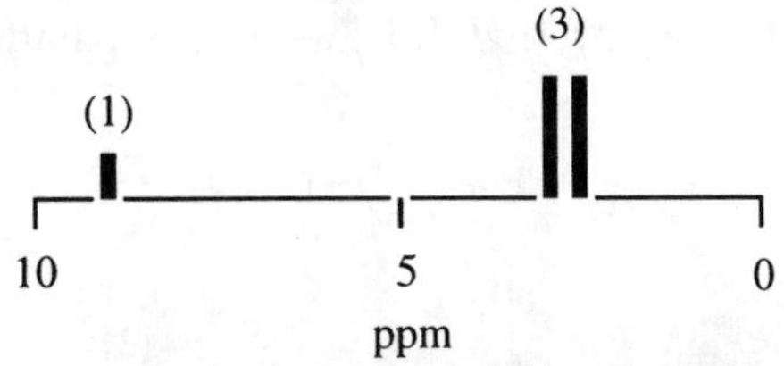
(1)
(3)
10
5
0
ppm

11.52 (a) There are three kinds of hydrogens in both compounds. The key difference is that there are two split alkoxy hydrogens (-O-CH_2-) in one compound and three unsplit (-O-CH_3) in the other compound.

CH_3CO-O-CH_2CH_3

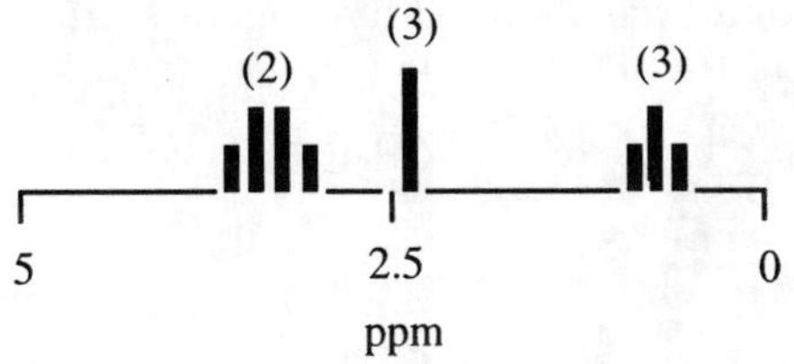
(2)
(3)
(3)
5
2.5
0
ppm

CH_3CH_2CO-O-CH_3

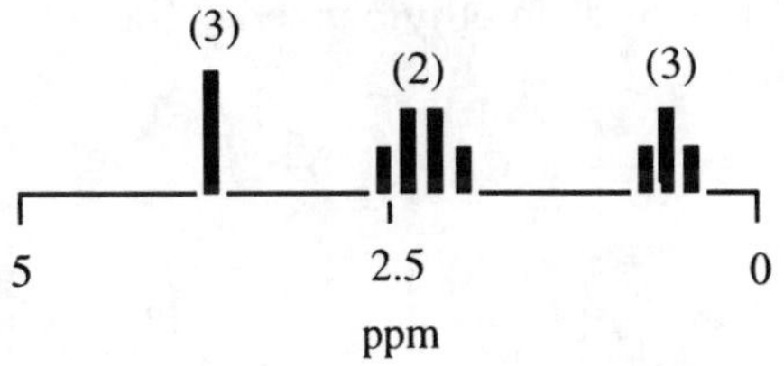
(3)
(2)
(3)
5
2.5
0
ppm

(b) The essential difference is that there are two kinds of hydrogen in 2-bromopropane and three in 1-bromopropane. There are also significant splitting and peak area differences.

$CH_3CHBrCH_3$

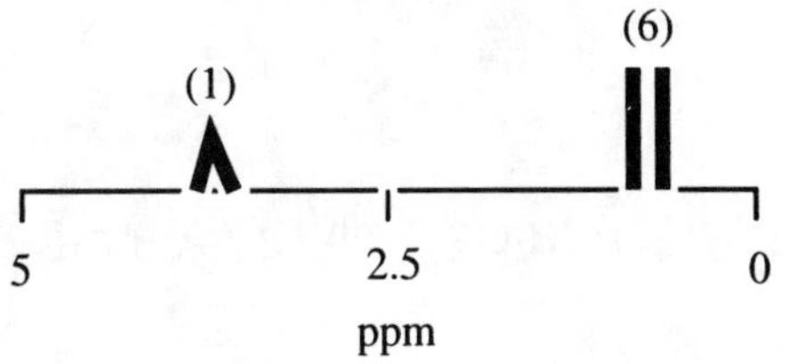
(1)
(6)
5
2.5
0
ppm

$CH_3CH_2CH_2Br$

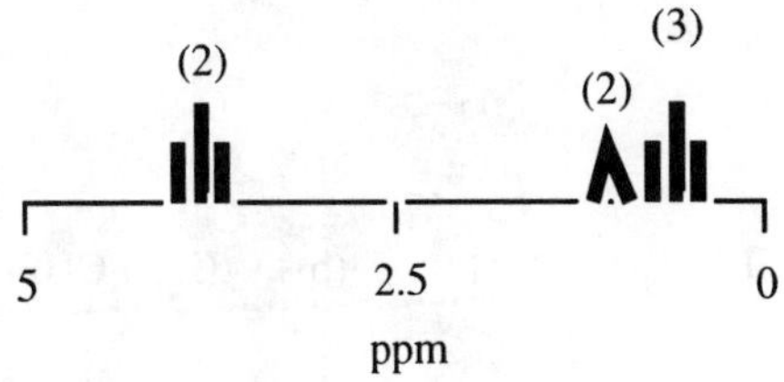
(2)
(2)
(3)
5
2.5
0
ppm

(c) The most obvious difference is the presence of two kinds of hydrogen in 1,1,2-tribromoethane but only a single kind in 1,1,1-tribromoethane.

$CH_2Br\text{-}CHBr_2$

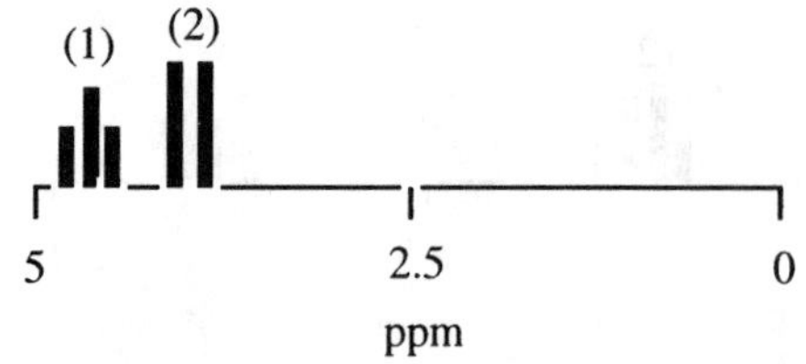
(1)
(2)
5
2.5
0
ppm

CH_3CBr_3

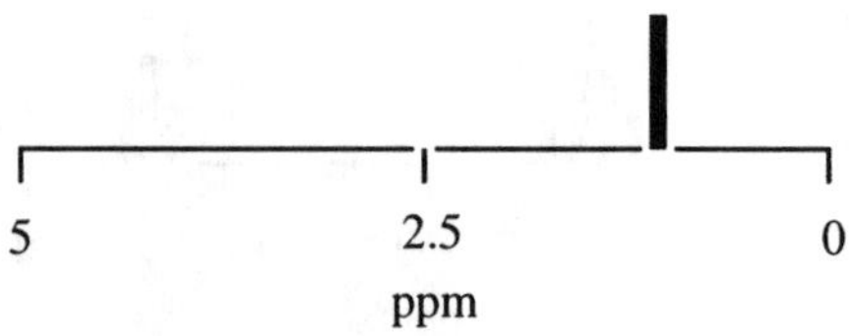
5
2.5
0
ppm

(d) Both compounds are benzenoid and both are carboxylic acids. The distinguishing feature is that one has a methylene group (area = 2) and the other has a methyl group (area = 3). The methylene is slightly more downfield than the methyl group due to having two electron-withdrawing groups attached.

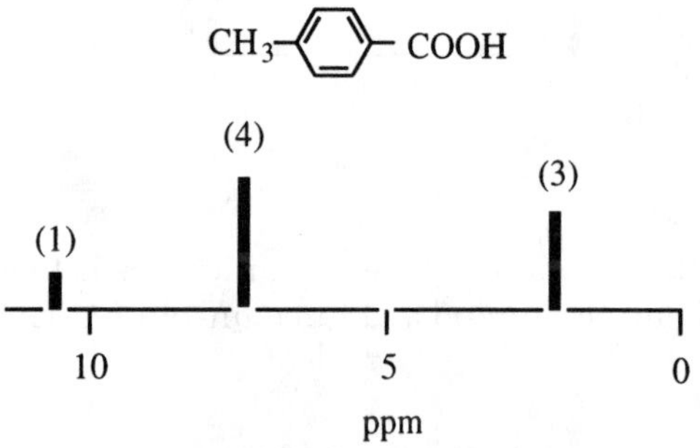
CH3
COOH
(4)
(3)
(1)
10
5
0
ppm

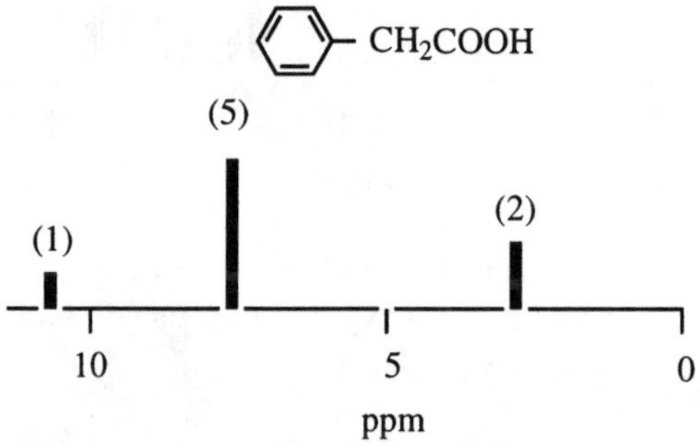
CH2COOH
(5)
(2)
(1)
10
5
0
ppm

(e) The most distinguishing feature is the presence of two kinds of hydrogen in *p*-xylene but three kinds in ethylbenzene. The latter compound has its alkyl hydrogens split.

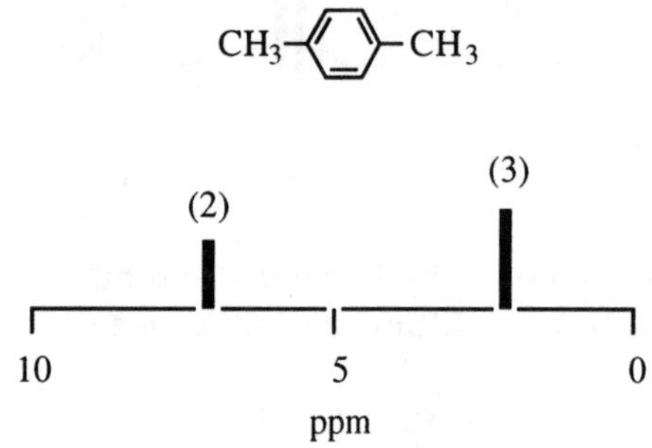
CH3
CH3
(3)
(2)
10
5
0
ppm

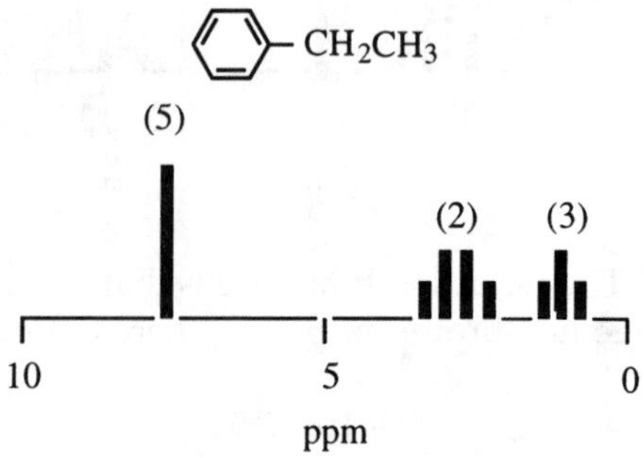
CH2CH3
(5)
(2)
(3)
10
5
0
ppm

11.53

(a) $(CH_3)_3COH$ (b) $(CH_3)_2CHBr$ (c) $(CH_3)_2CHCH_2Cl$ (d) $C_6H_5CH_2CH_3$

(e) $C_6H_5CH_2OH$ (f) CH_3CH_2COOH (g) $(CH_3)_2CHCOCH_3$ (h) $C_6H_5CHBrCH_3$

11.54 Consider how many possible compounds there are with the formula C_4H_9Br - there are only four. Write their structures and imagine the spectrum you would predict for each and compare to the given spectrum.

1-bromobutane

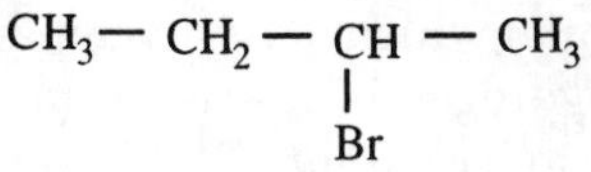

2-bromobutane

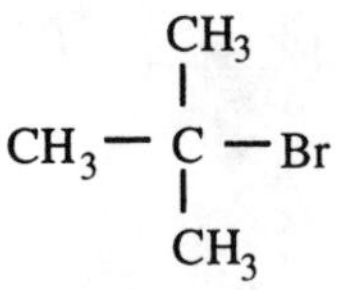

2-bromo-2-methylpropane

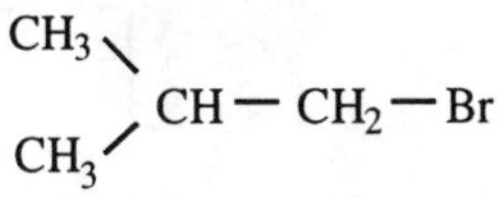

1-bromo-2-methylpropane

Analysis of the number of peaks present, their splittings, and their area ratios leads to $CH_3CHBrCH_2CH_3$ as the structure for C_4H_9Br whose ^{1}H-NMR spectrum is shown in Fig. 11.39. It shows four different sets of peaks with an area ratio of 3:3:2:1 representing a methyl triplet, a methyl doublet, a methylene multiplet, and a methinyl multiplet shifted well downfield. None of the other structures match this expected structure. First, 2-bromo-2-methylpropane should have only a sharp single peak, and so can be easily eliminated. Second, 1-bromo-2-methylpropane should have three peaks as follows: methyl doublet, methylene doublet, and methinyl multiplet, in the ratio 6:2:1, respectively, and also can be readily eliminated. 1-Bromobutane should have four peaks in the ratio 3:2:2:2 representing a methyl triplet, a methylene multiplet, another and overlapping methylene multiplet, and a downfield methylene triplet.

11.55 The assignment of spectra are as follows:

A 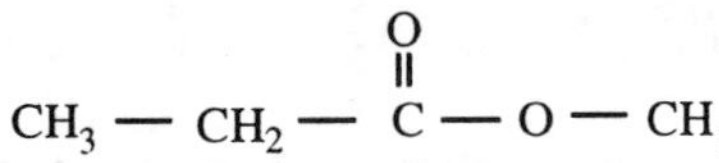

B 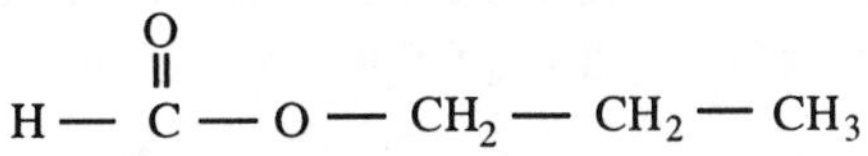

C 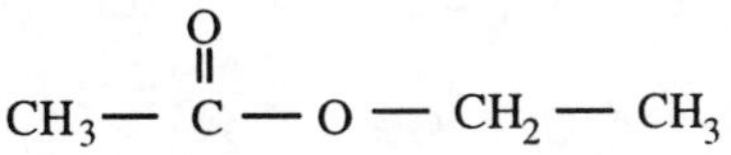

11.56 Since there are only two kinds of hydrogen the choices for the structure of $C_3H_3Cl_5$ are **A** ($Cl_2CHCHClCHCl_2$) and **B** ($ClCH_2CHClCCl_3$). The splitting patterns should be the same for these two structures. The chemical shift of the two kinds of hydrogens in **B** should be about equal (one chlorine on each carbon) whereas in **A** the chemical shift of the hydrogens on C_1 and C_3 (which should be identical and with two chlorines attached) should be more downfield than the hydrogen on C_2 which has only one chlorine attached. Therefore, the structure is **A** ($Cl_2CHCHClCHCl_2$).

11.57 The two possible dehydrochlorination products are 2-methyl-2-butene (**A**) and 2-methyl-1-butene (**B**) shown below. The ^{13}C-NMR spectra for these two alkenes are mutually exclusive and match the structures shown (e.g., **A** shows four different carbons and **B** shows five). Dehydrohalogenation normally produces the most highly substituted alkene (Zaitzev rule) which is **A**. When a sterically hindered very strong base is employed the primary hydrogen is abstracted rather than the secondary hydrogen because of steric hindrance to base approach to the latter. Therefore, alkene **B** predominates.

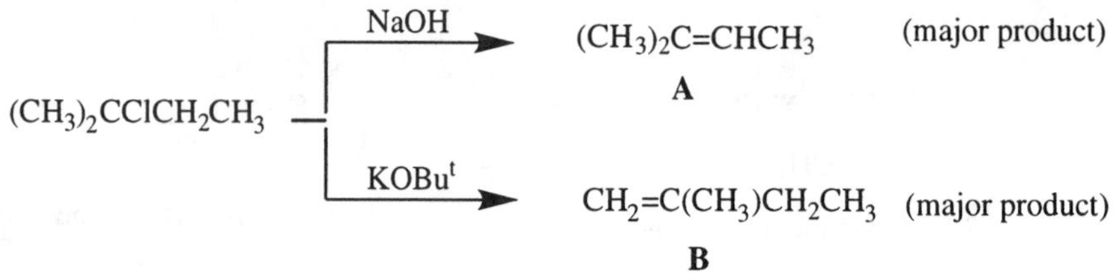
NaOH
$(CH_3)_2C{=}CHCH_3$
(major product)
A
$(CH_3)_2CClCH_2CH_3$
KOBu^t
$CH_2{=}C(CH_3)CH_2CH_3$
(major product)
B

11.58 (a) two peaks in 2-propanol; (b) five peaks in 2-chloro-2-methylpentane; (c) one peak in cyclopentane; (d) three peaks in methylcyclopropane; (e) five peaks in toluene; (f) five peaks in p-chlorobenzoic acid; (g) four peaks in m-dichlorobenzene.

11.59 Sample **A** with three peaks is 1,4-dimethylcyclohexane. Sample **B** with four peaks is 1,2-dimethylcyclohexane. Sample **C** with five peaks is 1,3-dimethylcyclohexane.

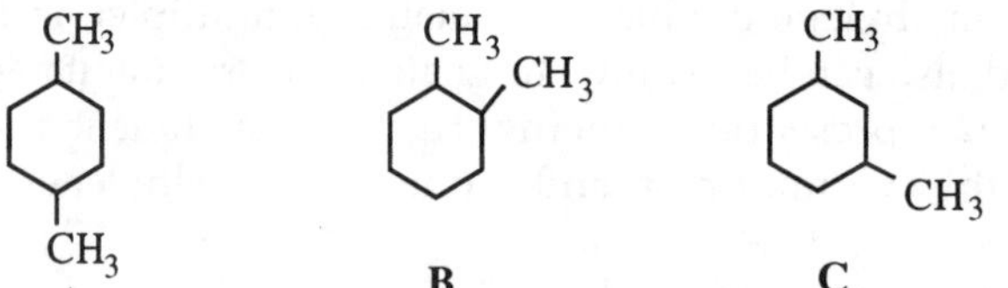
CH_3
CH_3
CH_3
CH_3
CH_3
CH_3

A	**B**	**C**
1,4-dimethyl-cyclohexane	1,2-dimethyl-cyclohexane	1,3-dimethyl-cyclohexane

11.60 The number of peaks would be as follows: 3-ethyl-1-pentanol has five peaks; 2-methyl-2-hexanol has six peaks, and 1-heptanol has seven peaks.

$CH_3CH_2CH(C_2H_5)CH_2CH_2OH$
3-ethyl-1-pentanol

$(CH_3)_2C(OH)CH_2CH_2CH_2CH_3$
2-methyl-2-hexanol

$CH_3CH_2CH_2CH_2CH_2CH_2CH_2OH$
1-heptanol

11.61 $C_5H_{12}O$ is a saturated, acyclic compound based on a HDI of zero. The IR indicates it is not an alcohol so it must be an ether. The ^{1}H-NMR indicates an O-CH_3 group (3.4 ppm) and two identical C-CH_3 groups (1.0 ppm). The other two peaks are consistent with an isobutyl group. Therefore, the structure should be $(CH_3)_2CHCH_2OCH_3$. This is consistent with the ^{13}C-NMR which shows four different kinds of carbon.

11.62 $C_8H_{10}O$ has an HDI of four, consistent with a benzenoid system. The M-15 peak indicates the presence of a methyl group and the M-18 peak indicates an alcohol. The latter is confirmed by the IR spectrum peak at 3400 cm^{-1}. The m/z peak at 77 indicates a phenyl group. The NMR peak at 7.2 ppm confirms this conclusion. Therefore all eight carbons are accounted for - six in the phenyl ring, a methyl group, and a carbon carrying the hydroxyl group. Only one structure is possible - $C_6H_5CH(OH)CH_3$. The doublet at 1.5 ppm indicates a methyl group split by an adjacent CH group. Therefore, the structure is determined to be that of 1-phenylethanol ($C_6H_5CHOHCH_3$).

11.63 The IR indicates the presence of a carbonyl group (aldehyde or ketone), and the absence of a ^1H-NMR peak for an aldehyde hydrogen near 9.5 ppm indicates it must be a ketone. The molecular ion of m/z = 86 minus the carbonyl group formula weight (28) means the rest of the molecule has a formula weight of 58, consistent only with C_4H_{10}. Therefore, the molecular formula must be CO + C_4H_{10} = $C_5H_{10}O$ (m/z = 86) and the compound is an acyclic ketone. The ^1H-NMR indicates the presence of only two kinds of hydrogen indicating the ketone must be symmetrical (consider the structure of all possible C_5 ketones for verification). The chemical shifts, areas, and splitting are consistent with an ethyl group (methyl triplet at 1.0 ppm and methylene quartet at 2.5 ppm) which means the structure must be 3-pentanone ($CH_3CH_2COCH_2CH_3$).

11.64 The MS indicates the molecular ion is m/z = 82 which is consistent with a C_6 compound which can only be C_6H_{10}. The HDI is two and there must be at least one double bond because of its reaction with bromine. The absence of absorption in the UV rules out a conjugated diene. Therefore, it could be an alkyne, a cycloalkene, or a cycloalkane with an alkene side chain. The ^1H-NMR indicates there are only two kinds of hydrogen among the ten hydrogens present. The chemical shifts, relative areas, and splittings are consistent with an ethyl group (note the familiar triplet and quartet pattern) and the molecular formula requires there be two of them. Therefore, the compound can only be 3-hexyne, the symmetrical alkyne. The MS confirms the presence of methyl (M-15) and ethyl (M-29) groups.

11.65 $C_9H_{12}O$ has an HDI of four leading to suspicion of a benzenoid ring. The ^1H-NMR confirms the presence of C_6H_5- with the peak at 7.3 ppm. Thus, only C_3H_7O remains unaccounted for. The IR peak at 3380 cm^{-1} indicates the presence of an alcohol which must be on a C_3 side chain. The NMR triplet of area 3 at 0.9 ppm indicates the presence of a methyl group split by an adjacent methylene group - therefore, there must be a fragment CH_3-CH_2- (C_2H_5-) in the side chain. Thus, only CH_2O remains unaccounted for which must include the alcohol group and which must be attached to the phenyl and ethyl groups. Therefore, the structure can only be $C_6H_5CHOHCH_2CH_3$. The methinyl group is at 4.5 ppm, the methylene group is at 1.8 ppm and the hydroxyl hydrogen is at 2.2 ppm.

11.66 The empirical formula weight of C_4H_5 is 53 but since M = 106 the molecular formula must be C_8H_{10}. The m/z at 91 indicates the loss of a methyl group (M-15). The HDI is four, leading to suspicion of a benzenoid compound. The IR peak at 1625 cm^{-1} confirms the presence of a benzenoid compound, as does the ^{1}H-NMR peak at 7.5 ppm. The relative area of the two ^{1}H-NMR peaks is 2:3 meaning there must be four aromatic hydrogens and six alkyl hydrogens. Thus, the compound is a di-substituted benzene. The singlet ^{1}H-NMR peak at 1.5 ppm is typical of a methyl group on a benzene ring, and the formula and relative areas require that there be two of them. Therefore, the compound is a xylene (dimethylbenzene). The fact that there are only three ^{13}C-NMR peaks means it must be *p*-xylene.

11.67 The empirical formula is $C_5H_{10}O$ as determined below:

carbon = 69.8% ÷ 12.0 = 5.82 ÷ 1.16 = 5.02
hydrogen = 11.6% ÷ 1.01 = 11.5 ÷ 1.16 = 9.91
oxygen = 18.6% ÷ 16.0 = 1.16 ÷ 1.16 = 1.00

Since the molecular ion is at m/z = 86 the molecular formula also is $C_5H_{10}O$ and the HDI is one. The IR spectrum indicates the presence of a carbonyl group (1720 cm^{-1}) which accounts for the HDI. The ^{1}H-NMR shows no peak near 9.5 ppm ruling out an aldehyde. Therefore, the unknown is an acyclic C_5 ketone. The M-15 peak (71) indicates the presence of a methyl group and the M-43 peak (43) indicates the possible presence of a CH_3CO- group and/or a C_3H_7- group. The singlet of area = 3 at 2.1 ppm indicates a CH_3CO group, leaving only C_3H_7 unaccounted for. The latter can only be $CH_3CH_2CH_2$- or $(CH_3)_2CH$- groups. The triplet of area = 3 at 0.9 ppm indicates it is the *n*-propyl group because the isopropyl group would show a doublet of area = 6. Therefore, without further analysis of the NMR it can be concluded that the compound is 2-pentanone ($CH_3CH_2CH_2COCH_3$).

11.68 The molecular ion is at 136 and the equally strong peak at M+2 leads to suspicion of an alkyl bromide (recall that the abundance of ^{79}Br and ^{81}Br is about equal). The alkyl group then must have m/z = 57 (M-79) and the molecular formula therefore is probably C_4H_9Br (C_4H_9 = m/z of 57). The M-15 peak indicates a methyl group but the absence of a M-29 peak indicates no ethyl group. Therefore, it cannot be 1-bromobutane or 2-bromobutane, leaving 1-bromo-2-methylpropane or 2-bromo-2-methylpropane as possibilities. The ^{1}H-NMR indicates three kinds of hydrogen with the correct splittings (doublet methyl at 1.0 ppm, doublet methylene at 3.3 ppm, and multiplet methinyl at 2.0 ppm) and area ratios (6:2:1) for 1-bromo-2-methylpropane (isobutyl bromide).

11.69 The IR peak at 3400 cm^{-1} indicates the presence of an alcohol. The molecular ion is at m/z = 74 and deducting the formula weight for the OH group (17) implies that the compound's molecular formula is C_4H_9-OH. The M-15 peak indicates a methyl group and the M-18 peak confirms an alcohol structure. The absence of a M-29 peak means it cannot be 1- or 2-butanol. The absence of a M-43 peak means it cannot be 2-methyl-1-butanol. Therefore, the compound probably is 2-methyl-2-propanol (*t*-butyl alcohol)

11.70 C_3H_8O is an alcohol as indicated by the IR peak at 3325 cm^{-1}. It can only be 1-propanol or 2-propanol because its HDI = 0. The ^{1}H-NMR indicates three kinds of hydrogen in the ratio 6:1:1 which is consistent only with that expected for 2-propanol (1-propanol would show four peak areas in the ratio 3:2:2:1).

11.71 The MS indicates the presence of a phenyl group (m/z = 77), a methyl group (M-15), and an ethyl group (M-29). The ^{1}H-NMR spectrum indicates the presence of an ethyl group (quartet methylene and triplet methyl). The ethyl and phenyl groups account for a formula weight of 77 + 29 = 106, leaving a weight of 16 unaccounted for (probably oxygen in an ether - the IR indicates it cannot be an alcohol or carbonyl). The methylene group is well downfield, indicating it likely is attached to an oxygen. Therefore, the structure of the compound is ethyl phenyl ether ($C_6H_5OCH_2CH_3$).

11.72 The m/z value for methamphetamine is 149. The IR spectrum should show phenyl absorption (1625 cm^{-1}) and the NH single peak near 3400 cm^{-1}. The ^{13}C-NMR should show eight different peaks. The ^{1}H-NMR should have the following peaks: ~7.3 ppm (aryl, 5H), ~4.0 ppm (NH, s, 1H), ~2.6 ppm (N-CH_3, s, 3H), ~2.3 ppm (CH_2, d, 2H), ~2.0 ppm (CH, m, 1H), and ~1.0 ppm (C-CH_3, d, 3H).

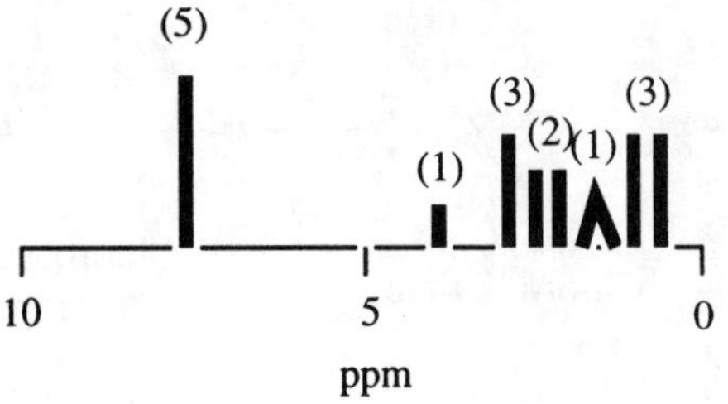
(5)
(3)
(3)
(2)
(1)
(1)
10
5
0
ppm

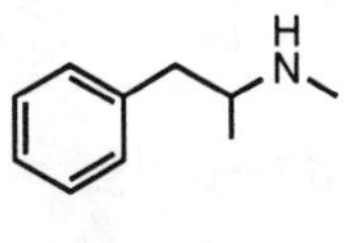

Methamphetamine

V. Conceptual Problem

PVC Under Suspicion

The poly(vinyl chloride) (PVC) monomer, chloroethene, came under suspicion as a carcinogen in 1970, when it was discovered that workers exposed to high levels of chloroethene developed liver cancer. The mode of action involves mammalian P-450 cytochrome catalysts, which causes epoxidation of chloroethene to yield chlorooxirane. At physiological pH (~2), chlorooxirane rearranges to compound A. A has an HDI of one, shows IR absorption at 1720 cm-1, and shows an 1H-NMR peak near 9 ppm. When compound A is mixed with guanine (one of the five bases involved in human DNA) a reaction occurred to form compound B and expel hydrogen chloride.

You work for an environmental "watchdog" committee and are asked by a neighborhood group to analyze air and waste water samples from a PVC manufacturing plant in their neighborhood. You perform 1H-NMR spectroscopy on the samples.

■ How many peaks would you observe in an 1H-NMR spectrum of chloroethene? What would be the approximate chemical shift of these protons?

- Ans: Two peaks. The chemical shifts would be between 4.5 and 7 ppm. The proton on carbon 1 would be more deshielded than those on carbon 2.

■ Suggest a laboratory method to convert chloroethene to chlorooxirane.

- Ans: Treatment of chloroethene with peracetic acid or perbenzoic acid

■ What would be the approximate chemical shift for the protons in chlorooxirane?

- Ans: The chemical shift for the carbon-1 proton would be between 6 and 7; that for the carbon-2 protons would be close to 3 ppm.

■ What is the structure of compounds A and B? Write a simple one-step mechanism for the formation of compound B from compound A and guanine. Is the reaction S_N1, S_N2, addition, or elimination?

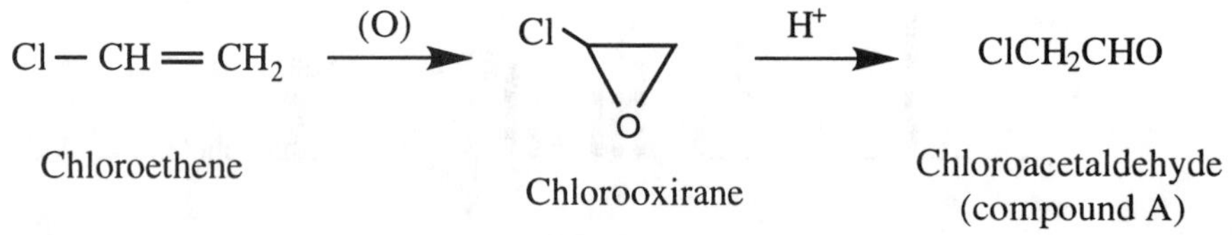
Cl — CH = CH$_2$
(O)
Cl
O
H$^+$
ClCH$_2$CHO
Chloroethene
Chlorooxirane
Chloroacetaldehyde
(compound A)

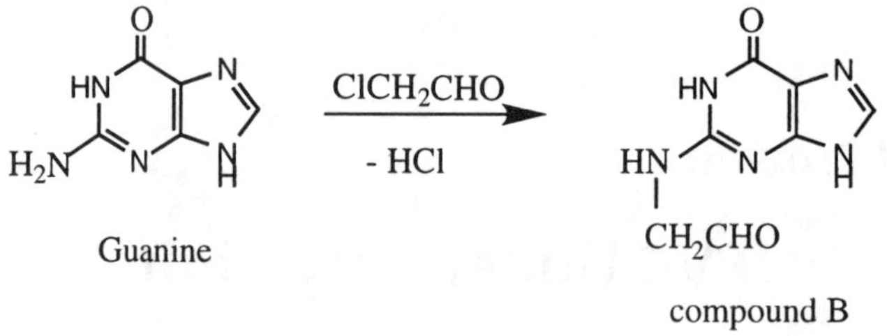
O
HN
N
H$_2$N
N
H
Guanine
ClCH$_2$CHO
- HCl
HN
CH$_2$CHO
compound B

- Ans: The reaction between guanine and compound A to form compound B is an SN2 reaction, with the amine (guanine) serving as the nucleophile and group.chlorine as the leaving group.

R-NH$_2$ = guanine

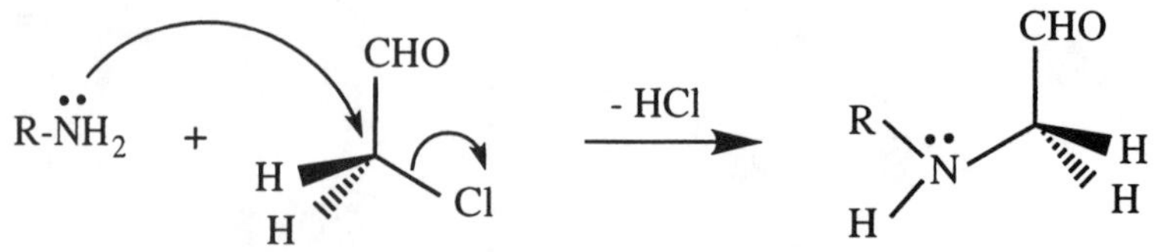
R-NH$_2$
+
CHO
H
H
Cl
- HCl
R
N
H
CHO
H
H

CHAPTER 12

Amines

I. Textbook Chapter Contents

This chapter introduces the chemistry of amines, compounds which can be considered as organic derivatives of ammonia (an alkyl or aryl group replacing one or more hydrogens of ammonia) or as derivatives of alkanes or arenes in which a -NH_2 group has replaced a hydrogen. Amines are the bases of organic chemistry.

II. Learning Objectives

- Know how to name amines as alkanamines or as derivatives of aniline (IUPAC system). Also know the common names of simple aromatic and alkyl amines.
- Be able to distinguish between primary, secondary, and tertiary amines. Be able to recognize and name quaternary ammonium salts.
- Know the electronic structure of amines and be able to account for their basicity and nucleophilicity. Be able to write an acid-base reaction involving an amine. Know how different substituents on nitrogen influence the basicity of amines and the pK_as of their conjugate acids.
- Write equations for the alkylation of amines via an S_N2 reaction. Know the limits of the application of this reaction for the synthesis of amines.
- Write equations for the acylation of amines to form amides.
- Know the diazotization reaction for primary aromatic amines.
- Write equations for the replacement of the diazonium group by a wide variety of substituents as a means of producing substituted benzenes from the corresponding anilines.
- Write reactions showing the coupling of diazonium salts with activated benzenoid compounds to form azo compounds.
- Write equations for the preparation of primary amines by alkylation of ammonia with alkyl halides.
- Write equations for the preparation of primary alkyl amines by the reduction of nitriles and azides, both having been prepared from alkyl halides.
- Write equations for the preparation of amines by the reduction of amides.
- Write equations for the preparation of aniline derivatives by the reduction of nitrobenzene derivatives.
- Be able to devise a separation scheme for a mixture of compounds which include an amine.

- Be able to determine the structure of an unknown amine based on chemical and spectroscopic information about the compound.
- Be able to plan multi-step syntheses of simple amines from other families of compounds.
- Be familiar with the nature of alkaloids and their importance in biological chemistry.

III. Glossary

acylation of amines replacement of a hydrogen on an amine with an acyl group to form an amide

alkaloids naturally occurring nitrogenous bases

alkanamine the IUPAC family name for alkyl amines

alkylation of amines replacement of a hydrogen on an amine with an alkyl group

amide a compound with an acyl group attached to an amino group and with the general structure $RCONH_2$ (the hydrogens on nitrogen also may be replaced by alkyl or aryl groups)

amine a basic compound containing trivalent nitrogen

amine conjugate acid a protonated amine which results from the reaction of an amine with a Brønsted acid

amino group the $-NH_2$ group

azides RN_3, compounds containing the azido group ($-N_3$)

azo compound a compound containing the azo group (-N=N-)

azo dyes dyes used in commerce which contain the azo group, the conjugation of which is the source of the color of the dye

coupling reaction the reaction of a diazonium ion with a reactive aromatic compound to produce an azo compound

diazonium ion an ion of structure ArN_2^+ ($Ar-N{=}N^+$)

diazotization the process of converting a primary aromatic amine into a diazonium ion

nitriles compounds containing the cyano group (-CN), such as RCN or ArCN

quaternary ammonium salt a compound containing a tetravalent nitrogen and carrying a positive charge on nitrogen

IV. Summary of Reactions of Amines

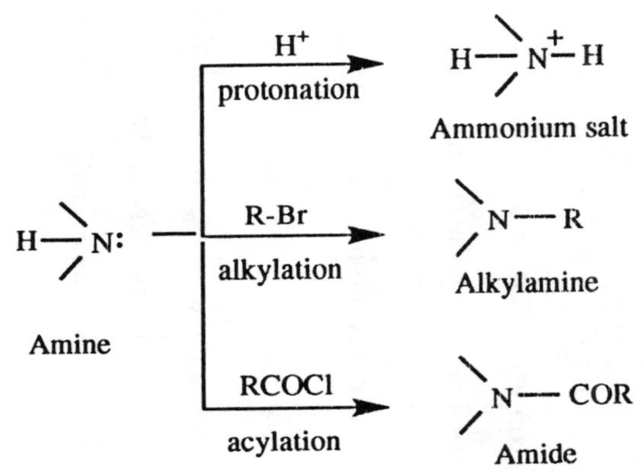
H⁺
protonation
Ammonium salt
R-Br
alkylation
Alkylamine
Amine
RCOCl
acylation
Amide

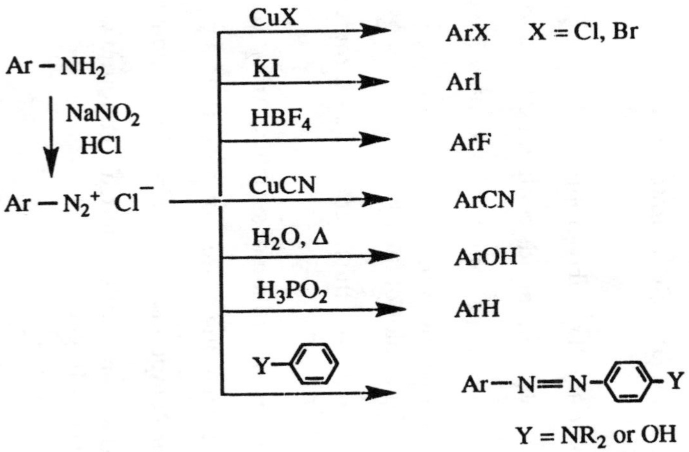
Ar – NH₂
NaNO₂
HCl
Ar – N₂⁺ Cl⁻
CuX
ArX X = Cl, Br
KI
ArI
HBF₄
ArF
CuCN
ArCN
H₂O, Δ
ArOH
H₃PO₂
ArH
Y = NR₂ or OH

V. Summary of Preparation of Amines

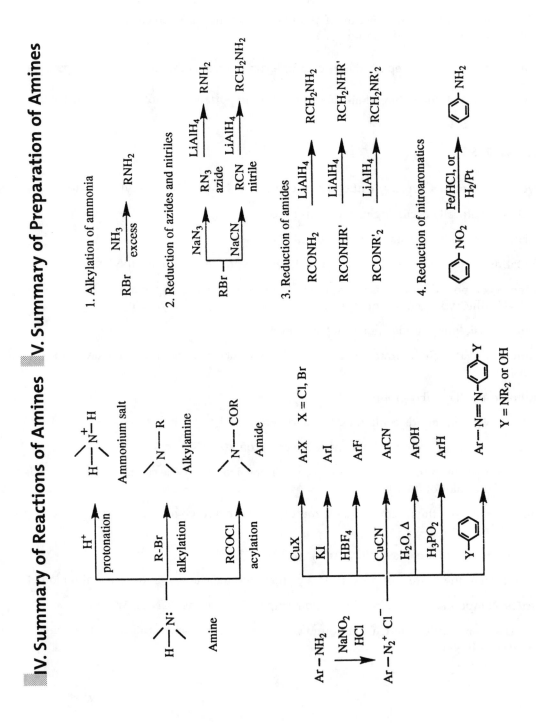

1. Alkylation of ammonia

$$RBr \xrightarrow[\text{excess}]{NH_3} RNH_2$$

2. Reduction of azides and nitriles

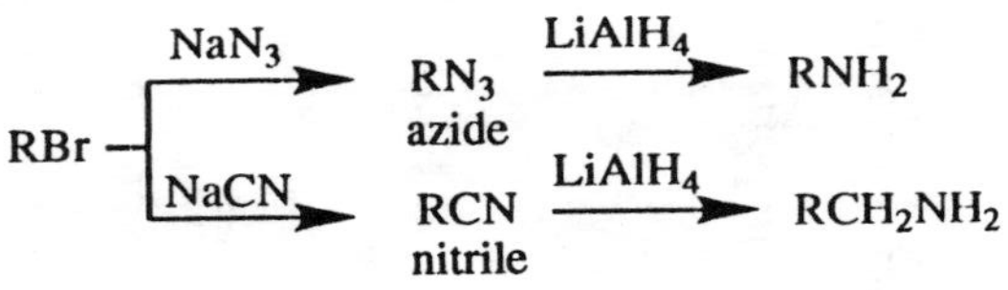
RBr
NaN₃
NaCN
RN₃
azide
RCN
nitrile
LiAlH₄
RNH₂
RCH₂NH₂

3. Reduction of amides

$$RCONH_2 \xrightarrow{LiAlH_4} RCH_2NH_2$$

$$RCONHR' \xrightarrow{LiAlH_4} RCH_2NHR'$$

$$RCONR'_2 \xrightarrow{LiAlH_4} RCH_2NR'_2$$

4. Reduction of nitroaromatics

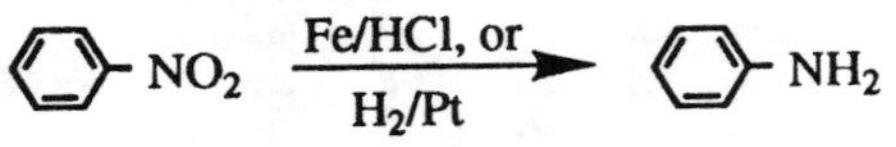
NO₂
Fe/HCl, or
H₂/Pt
NH₂

VI. Solutions to Problems

For "**How to Solve a Problem,**" review pages 405, 109, 416, 420, 422, 428, and 430)

12.1 (a) diphenylamine ($(C_6H_5)_2NH$) is secondary; (b) ethylmethylamine ($CH_3CH_2NHCH_3$) is secondary; (c) ethyldimethylamine ($CH_3CH_2N(CH_3)_2$) is tertiary; (d) aniline ($C_6H_5NH_2$) is primary; (e) propylamine ($CH_3(CH_2)_2NH_2$) is primary; (f) pyrrolidine ($(CH_2)_4NH$) is secondary.

12.2 (a) *n*-propylamine, 1-propanamine; (b) cyclopropyldimethylamine, *N,N*-dimethylcyclopropanamine; (c) cyclobutylamine, cyclobutanamine; (d) isopropylmethylamine, *N*-methyl-2-propanamine.

12.3

(a) 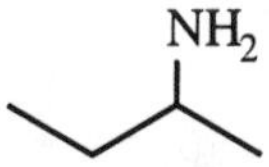

(b) 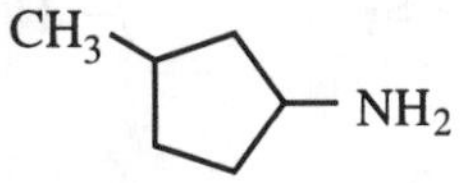

(c) 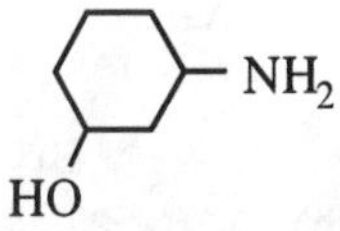

(d) 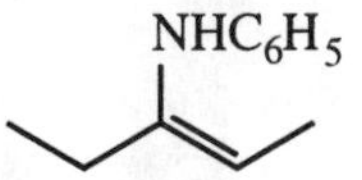

(e) 

(f) $[(CH_3)_2CH]_3N$

12.4

(a) 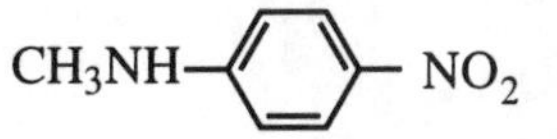

(b) 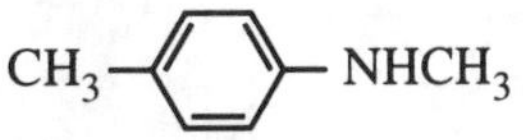

(c) 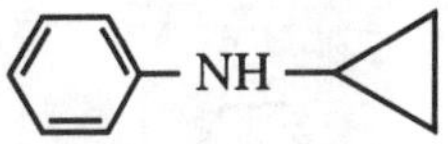

12.5 (a) diphenylamine; (b) 3,5-dimethylaniline; (c) *p*-vinyl-*N,N*-diethylaniline.

12.6 The basicity order decreases from left to right. The pK_as of the conjugate acids of the amines are shown - the smaller the pK_a, the more acidic is the amine conjugate acid (ammonium salt), and the less basic is the free amine.

(a) CH_3NH_2 > 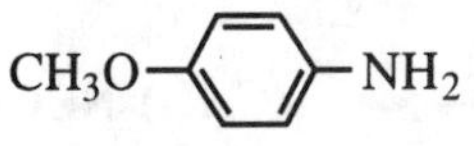 > $C_6H_5NH_2$ > 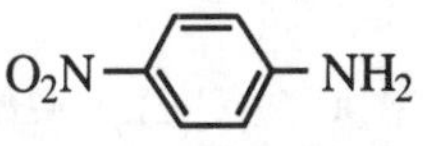

methylamine	*p*-methoxyaniline	aniline	*p*-nitroaniline
pK_a = 10.64	pK_a = 5.30	pK_a = 4.58	pK_a = 1.00

(b) $(C_2H_5)_2NH$ > 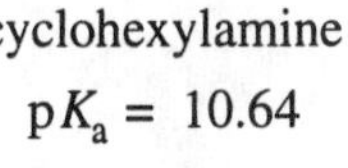

diethylamine	cyclohexylamine
pK_a = 10.98	pK_a = 10.64

12.7 The molecular weight having the odd number 73, along with the odor, indicates the presence of an amine, and the other MS peaks indicate the loss of methyl and ethyl groups. Since it cannot have more than four carbons (five carbons and nitrogen alone would have a molecular weight of 74) the molecular formula probably is $C_4H_{11}N$. The IR indicates the absence of NH absorption so it must be a tertiary amine meaning three of the four carbons must be attached to nitrogen. Therefore, by simple deduction the structure is probably ethyldimethylamine, $CH_3CH_2N(CH_3)_2$. The ^{13}C-NMR indicates only three different kinds of carbon, consistent with this formula (two different kinds of methyl - CH_3N and CH_3C - and a CH_2 group). The ^1H-NMR indicates the presence of two identical methyl groups attached to an electronegative atom (CH_3NCH_3) and an ethyl group also attached to an electronegative atom (C_2H_5N). Therefore, the unknown compound is confirmed to be $CH_3CH_2N(CH_3)_2$.

12.8

(a) 

NH2
C2H5I
excess
+
N(C2H5)3
I−

(b) 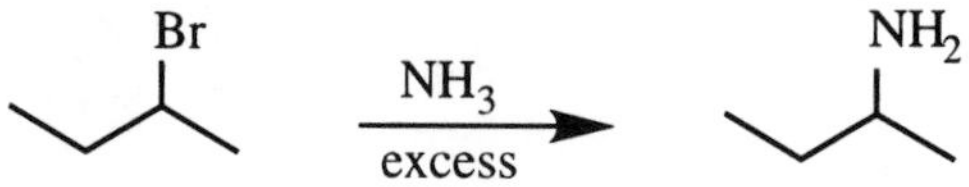

Br
NH3
excess
NH2

(c) $(CH_3)_2CHBr + (CH_3)_2NH \xrightarrow{-\,HBr} (CH_3)_2CHN(CH_3)_2$

12.9

(a) 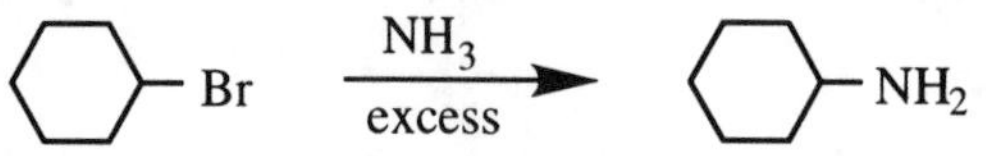

Br
NH3
excess
NH2

(b) 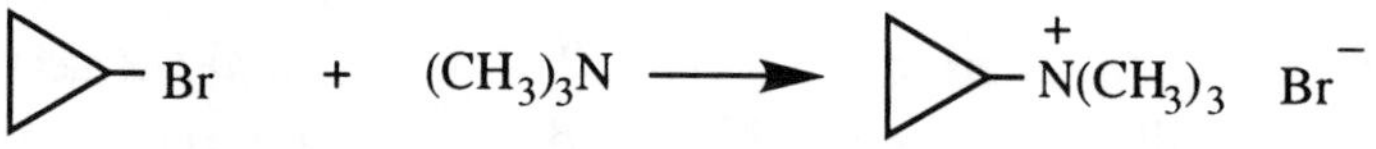

Br
+
(CH3)3N
+
N(CH3)3
Br−

12.10

(a) $(C_6H_5)_2NH + CH_3COCl \xrightarrow{NaOH} (C_6H_5)_2NCOCH_3$

(b) 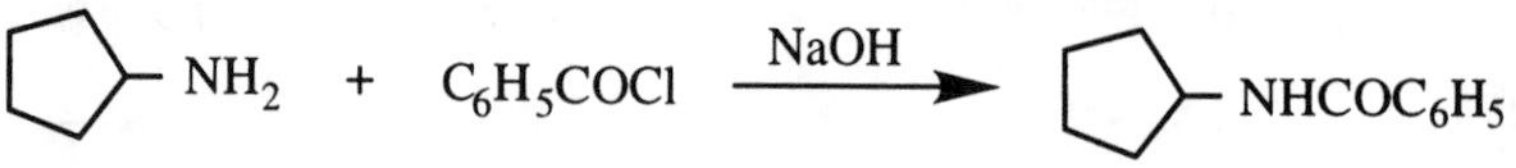

NH2
+
C6H5COCl
NaOH
NHCOC6H5

(c) $CH_3CH_2CH_2NH_2 + C_2H_5COCl \xrightarrow{NaOH} CH_3CH_2CH_2NHCOC_2H_5$

12.11

(a) $C_6H_5COCl + C_6H_5NH_2 \xrightarrow{\text{pyridine}} C_6H_5CONHC_6H_5$

(b) 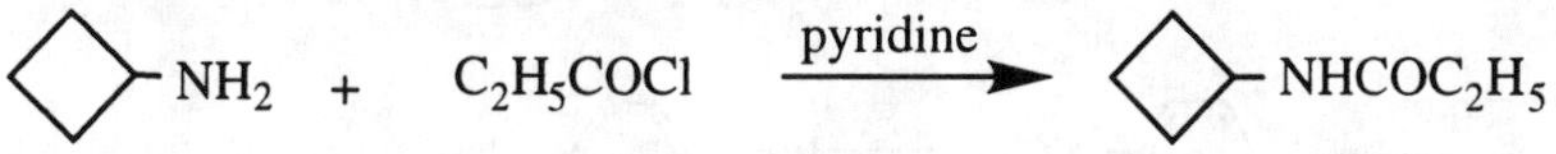

(c) 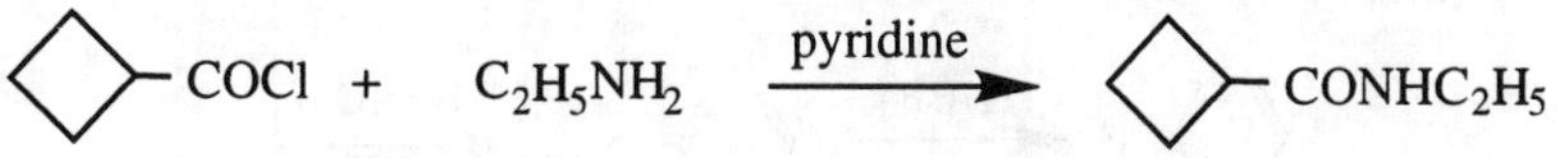

(d) $CH_3NH_2 + (CH_3)_2CHCOCl \xrightarrow{\text{pyridine}} CH_3NHCOCH(CH_3)_2$

12.12

(a), (b) 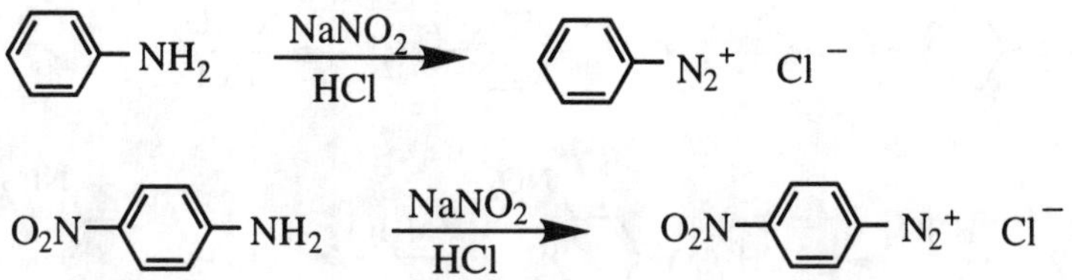

12.13 The primary amine would be converted to the diazonium ion the same as for an aromatic primary amine. However, the alkyl diazonium ion is not stabilized by resonance so quickly loses molecular nitrogen, forming a carbocation. From previous chapters we know that carbocations are very reactive. They react in an S_N1 reaction with nucleophiles which may be present, in this case water and chloride ion, and also can lose a proton to another nucleophile, leaving behind an alkene (this is an E1 elimination).

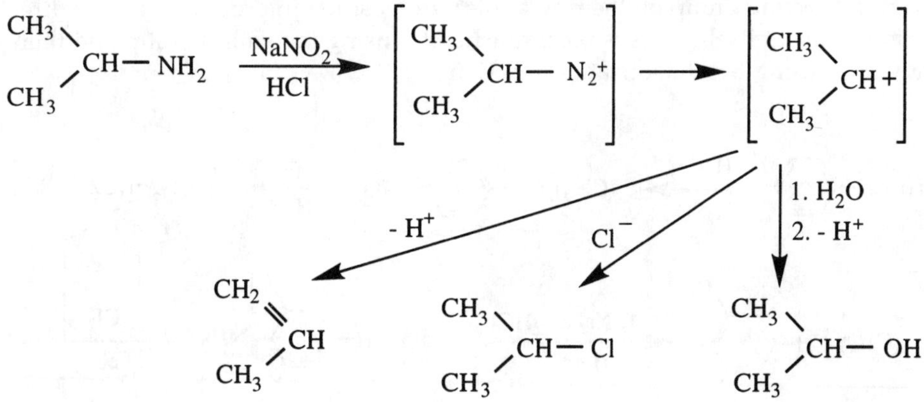

12.14

(a)

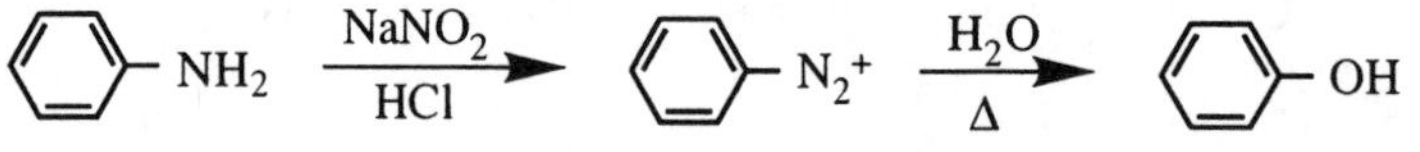

* (b)

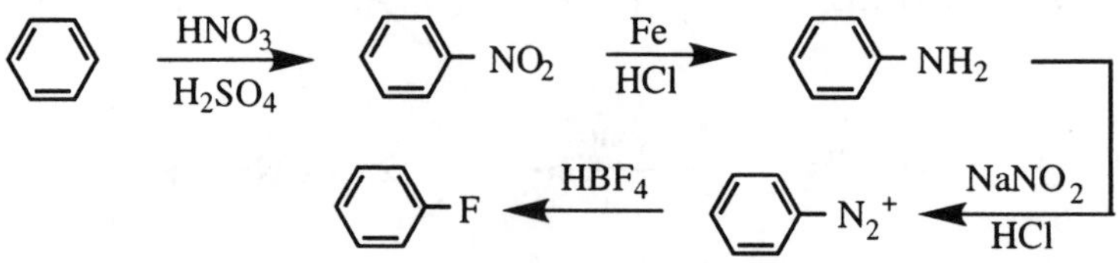

* (c)

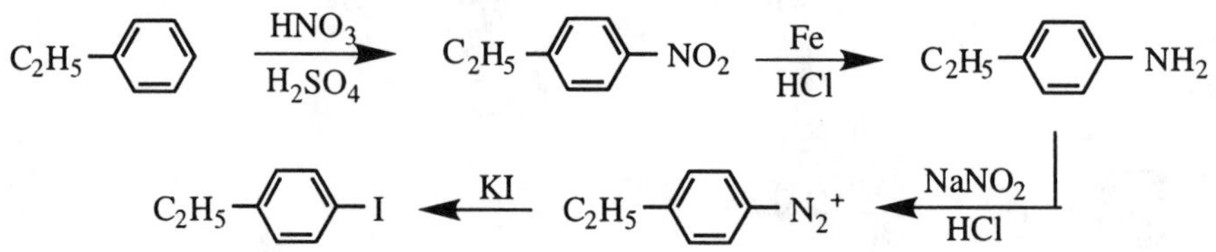

* (d)

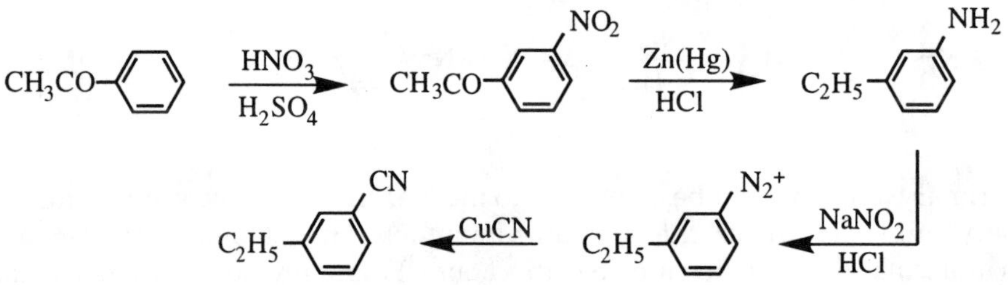

***12.15** The key to this synthesis is to note that the chlorines must be substituted *meta* to the isopropyl group. Since the isopropyl group is an *ortho/para* director this result cannot be accomplished by direct substitution. However, it can be accomplished by placing a more powerful directing group on the ring at the *para* position in order that it may direct incoming chlorines *ortho* to itself. This is accomplished by using the amino group and then later removing it using the diazotization reaction.

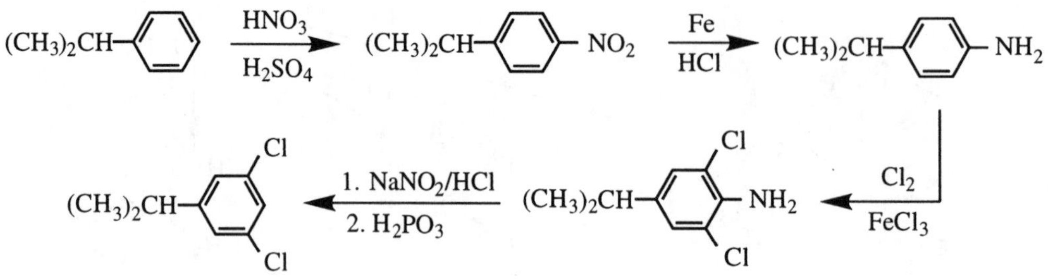

12.16

Starting materials **Products**

a) 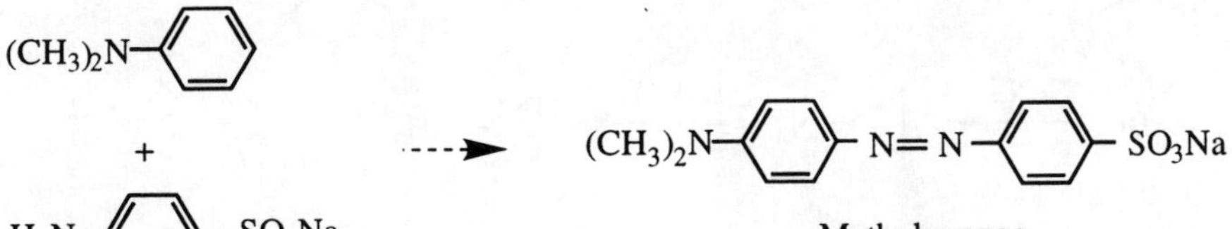
(CH3)2N
+
H2N
SO3Na
(CH3)2N
N=N
SO3Na

Methyl orange

b) 
(CH3)2N
+
H2N
(CH3)2N
N=N

Butter yellow

(c) 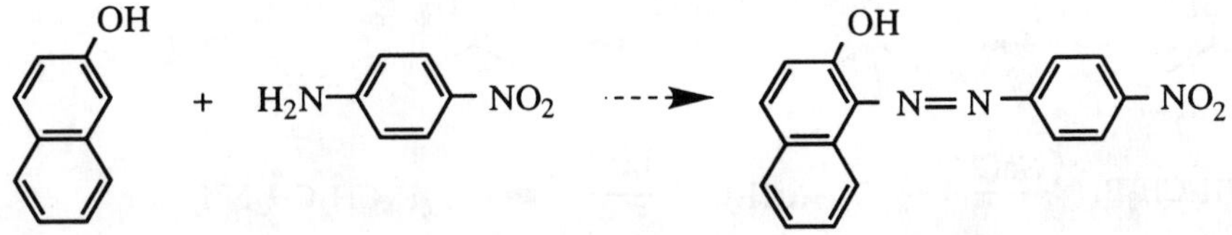
OH
+
H2N
NO2
OH
N=N
NO2

Para red

(d) 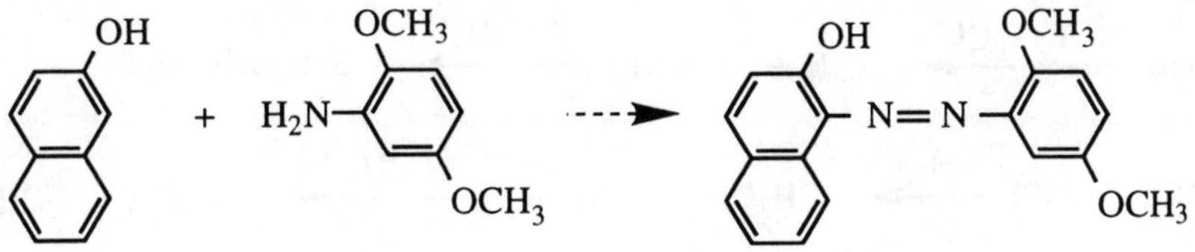
OH
+
OCH3
H2N
OCH3
OH
OCH3
N=N
OCH3

Citrus #2

12.17

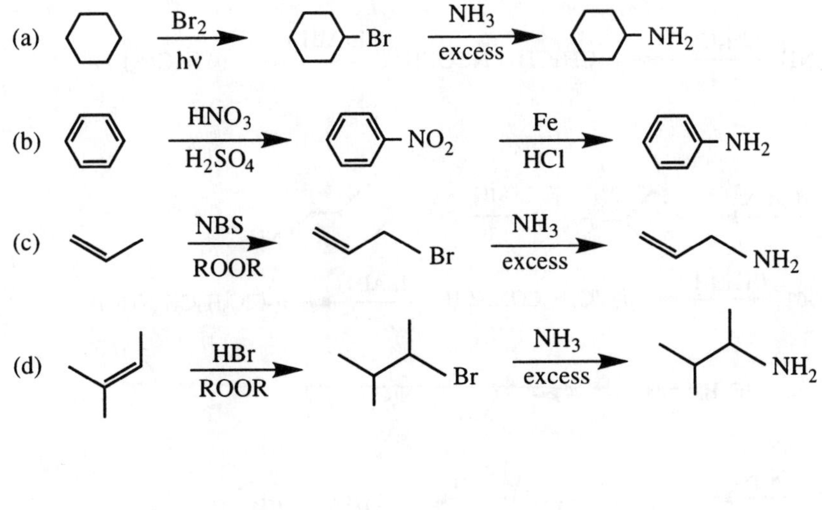
(a)
Br2
hν
Br
NH3
excess
NH2
(b)
HNO3
H2SO4
NO2
Fe
HCl
NH2
(c)
NBS
ROOR
Br
NH3
excess
NH2
(d)
HBr
ROOR
Br
NH3
excess
NH2

12.18

(a) 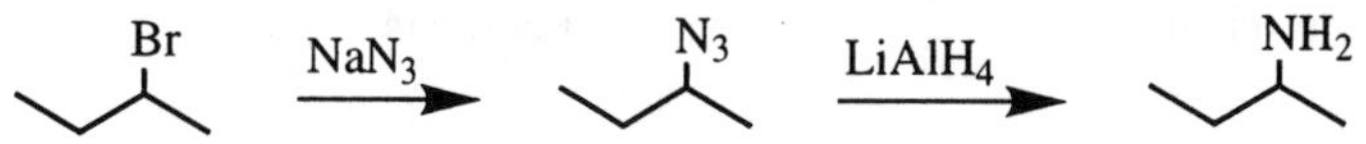

(b) 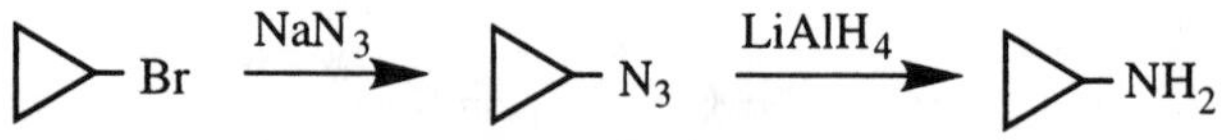

(c) 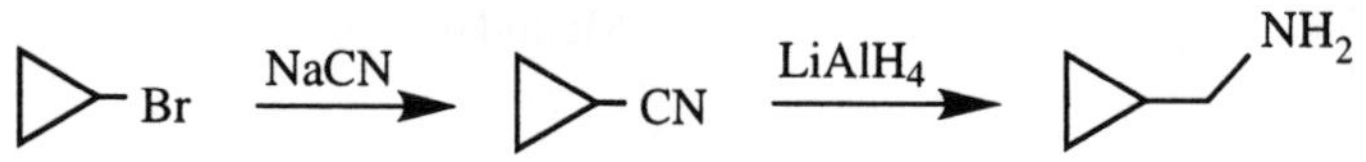

(d) 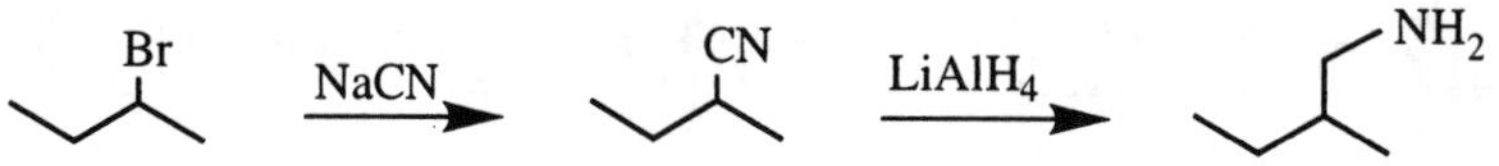

(e) 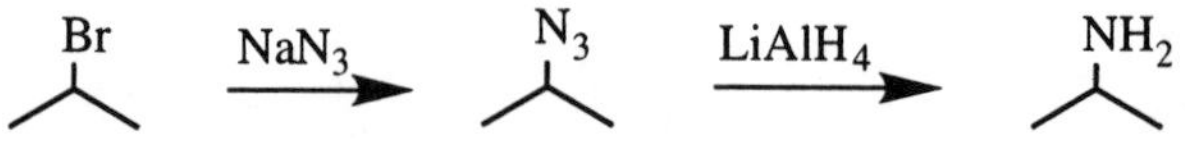

(f) $C_6H_5CH_2Br \xrightarrow{NaCN} C_6H_5CH_2CN \xrightarrow{LiAlH_4} C_6H_5CH_2CH_2NH_2$

12.19

(a) $C_6H_5NH_2 \xrightarrow{CH_3COCl} C_6H_5NHCOCH_3 \xrightarrow{LiAlH_4} C_6H_5NHC_2H_5$

(b) $CH_3CH_2CH_2COCl \xrightarrow{NH_3} CH_3CH_2CH_2CONH_2 \xrightarrow{LiAlH_4} CH_3CH_2CH_2CH_2NH_2$

(c) $C_3H_7NH_2 \xrightarrow{CH_3CH_2COCl} C_3H_7NHCOCH_2CH_3 \xrightarrow{LiAlH_4} (CH_3CH_2CH_2)_2NH$

(d) $(CH_3CH_2)_2NH \xrightarrow{CH_3COCl} (CH_3CH_2)_2NCOCH_3 \xrightarrow{LiAlH_4} (CH_3CH_2)_3N$

12.20

(a) 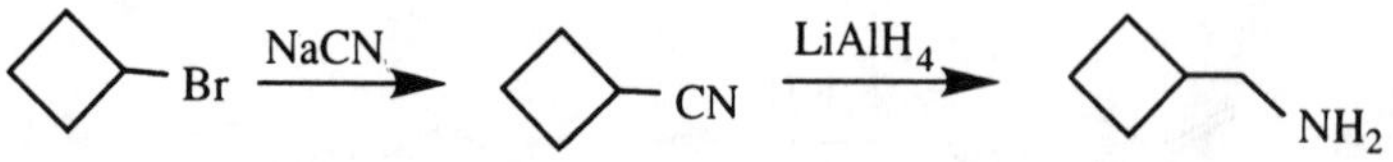

(b) $p\text{-}ClC_6H_4COCl \xrightarrow{CH_3NH_2} p\text{-}ClC_6H_4CONHCH_3 \xrightarrow{LiAlH_4} p\text{-}ClC_6H_4CH_2NHCH_3$

(c) 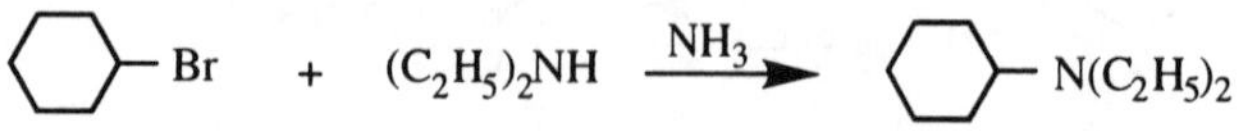

(d) $C_6H_5CH_2Br \xrightarrow{NaN_3} C_6H_5CH_2N_3 \xrightarrow{LiAlH_4} C_6H_5CH_2NH_2$

12.21

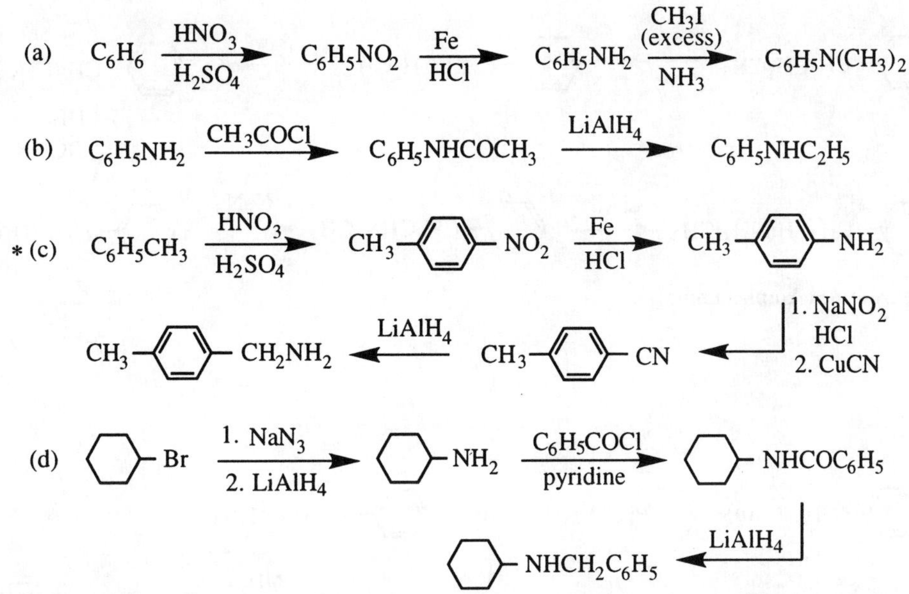
(a) $C_6H_6 \xrightarrow[H_2SO_4]{HNO_3} C_6H_5NO_2 \xrightarrow[HCl]{Fe} C_6H_5NH_2 \xrightarrow[NH_3]{CH_3I\ (excess)} C_6H_5N(CH_3)_2$
(b) $C_6H_5NH_2 \xrightarrow{CH_3COCl} C_6H_5NHCOCH_3 \xrightarrow{LiAlH_4} C_6H_5NHC_2H_5$
* (c) $C_6H_5CH_3$
HNO_3
H_2SO_4
CH_3
NO_2
Fe
HCl
CH_3
NH_2
1. $NaNO_2$
HCl
2. CuCN
CH_3
CN
$LiAlH_4$
CH_3
CH_2NH_2
(d)
Br
1. NaN_3
2. $LiAlH_4$
NH_2
C_6H_5COCl
pyridine
$NHCOC_6H_5$
$LiAlH_4$
$NHCH_2C_6H_5$

***12.22** Retrosynthesis, a mental process of thinking backwards from the desired product to a starting material mainly in terms of the carbon skeleton required, leads to the analysis and synthesis shown below:

Retrosynthetic analysis

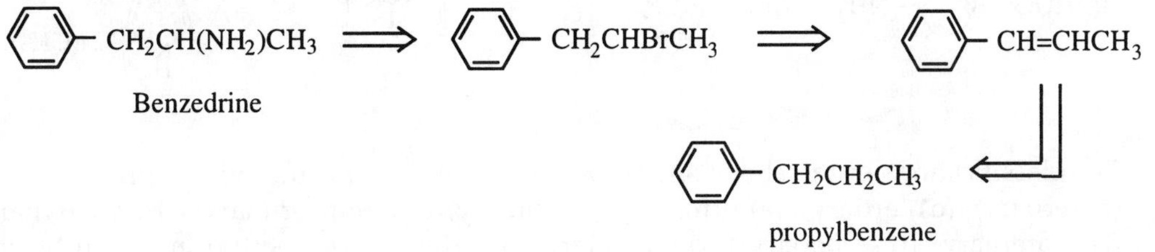
$CH_2CH(NH_2)CH_3$
Benzedrine
$CH_2CHBrCH_3$
$CH{=}CHCH_3$
$CH_2CH_2CH_3$
propylbenzene

The first key is realize that it is easiest to obtain this particular amine from a precursor bromide. The problem then shifts to "how to get the bromide?" Recognize that a bromide cannot simply be substituted on 1-phenylpropane in the 2-position but that it can be substituted on the 1-position because of the stability of the benzylic radical. Moving the bromide from position one to position two is possible using an elimination reaction and the anti-Markovnikov addition characteristic of radical addition of HBr to the alkenylbenzene. With this broad outline then it is possible to design the specific synthetic steps with the necessary reagents

Synthesis

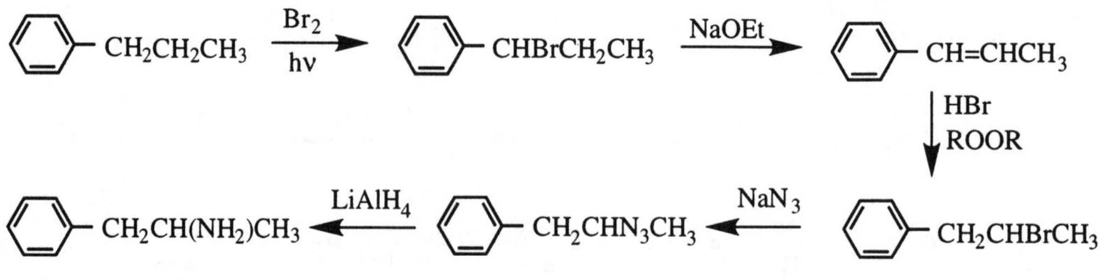

Benzedrine (Amphetamine)

12.23

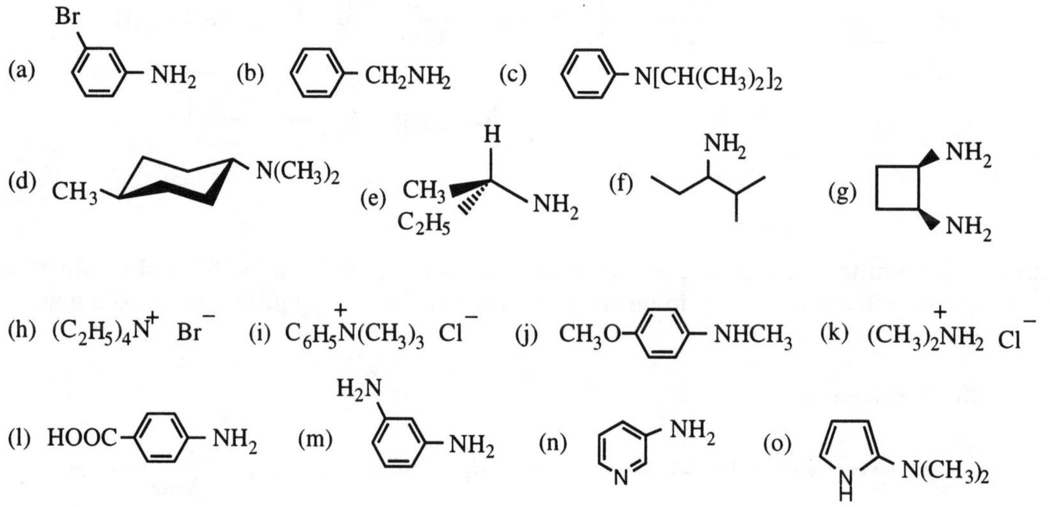

12.24 The classifications of the above amines are as follows: (a) primary; (b) primary; (c) tertiary; (d) tertiary; (e) primary; (f) primary; (g) both primary; (h) quaternary; (i) quaternary; (j) secondary; (k) secondary; (l) primary; (m) both primary; (n) primary; (o) tertiary and secondary.

12.25 (a) 1,6-hexanediamine (also frequently called by its common name, hexamethylenediamine); (b) *trans*-4-(*N,N*-dimethylamino)cyclohexanol; (c) Trimethylanilinium chloride (also trimethylphenylammonium chloride); (d) *p*-isopropylaniline; (e) ethylisobutylamine (also *N*-ethyl-2-methylpropanamine); (f) diethylamine; (g) *trans*-2-methoxycyclobutanamine; (h) *p*-toluenediazonium chloride; (i) 4-cyclopropylpyridine; (j) 2-buten-1-amine; (k) tetrapropylammonium iodide; (l) (*S*)-3-buten-2-amine.

12.26

(a) 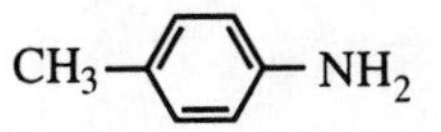

p-toluidine, primary

(b) 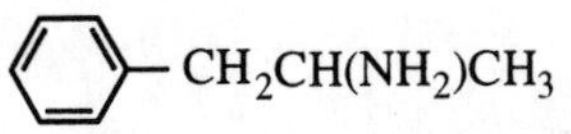

amphetamine, primary

(c) 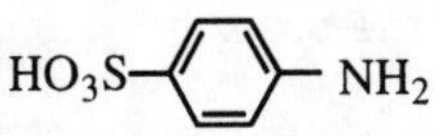

sulfanilic acid, primary

(d) 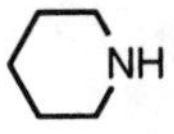 (also occasionally written $(CH_2)_5NH$)

piperidine, secondary

(e) 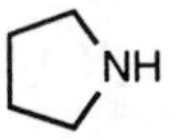 (also written $(CH_2)_4NH$)

pyrrolidine, secondary

(f) 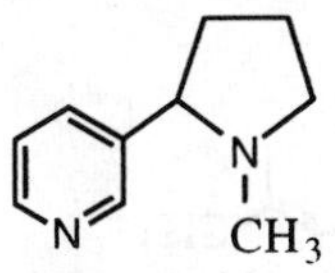

nicotine, tertiary

12.27 Any hydrochloride salt of an amine will contain a proton attached to the amine nitrogen (but not the amide nitrogen), forming an ammonium salt with its chloride anion.

Lidocaine hydrochloride 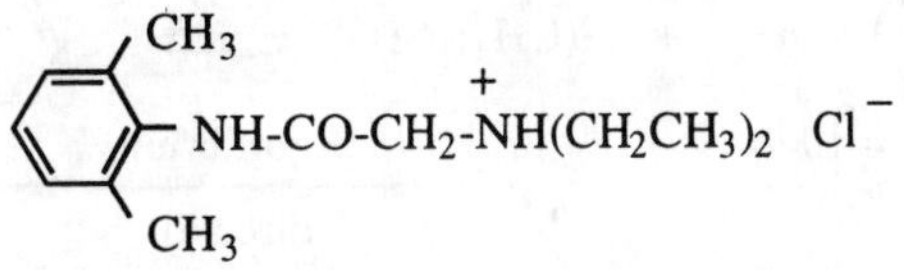

12.28 1-Butanamine ($CH_3CH_2CH_2CH_2NH_2$) is water soluble because it can hydrogen bond with water. It can be both an electron donor (using the electron pair on nitrogen) as well as an electron acceptor (using its N-hydrogens). Pentane cannot participate in hydrogen bonding.

12.29 The trend in boiling points matches the trend in hydrogen bonding capability. The more readily one molecule hydrogen bonds with other molecules the more energy is required to break these bonds and effect vaporization. Butane does not hydrogen bond at all so is the lowest boiling. 1-Propanol very effectively hydrogen bonds, more so than 1-propanamine due to the higher electronegativity of oxygen and the corresponding higher polarity of the compound.

12.30

(a) $C_6H_5NH_2 + HCl \longrightarrow C_6H_5\overset{+}{N}H_3\ Cl^-$

(b) $(C_2H_5)_2NH + H_2SO_4 \longrightarrow (C_2H_5)_2\overset{+}{N}H_2\ HSO_4^-$

(c) $C_6H_5N(CH_3)_2 + CH_3I \longrightarrow C_6H_5\overset{+}{N}(CH_3)_3\ I^-$

(d) $(CH_3)_2\overset{+}{N}H_2\ Cl^- + NaOH \longrightarrow (CH_3)_2NH + H_2O + NaCl$

(e) $(C_2H_5)_3N + C_2H_5I \longrightarrow (C_2H_5)_4\overset{+}{N}\ I^-$

12.31 The equilibria lie in the direction in which the strongest acid (lowest pKa) loses its proton to the base.

(a)

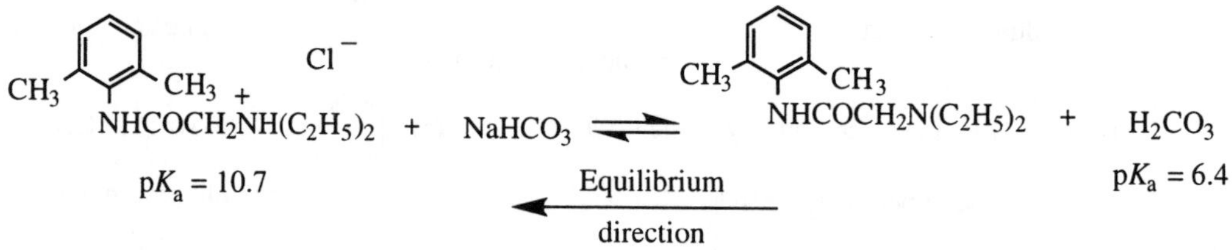

Cl^-
CH_3
CH_3 +
$NHCOCH_2NH(C_2H_5)_2$ + $NaHCO_3$
CH_3
CH_3
$NHCOCH_2N(C_2H_5)_2$ + H_2CO_3
$pK_a = 10.7$
Equilibrium
direction
$pK_a = 6.4$

(b)

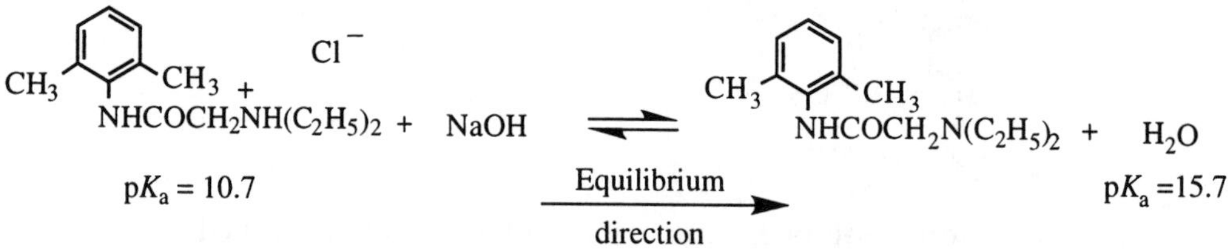

Cl^-
CH_3
CH_3 +
$NHCOCH_2NH(C_2H_5)_2$ + NaOH
CH_3
CH_3
$NHCOCH_2N(C_2H_5)_2$ + H_2O
$pK_a = 10.7$
Equilibrium
direction
$pK_a = 15.7$

(c)

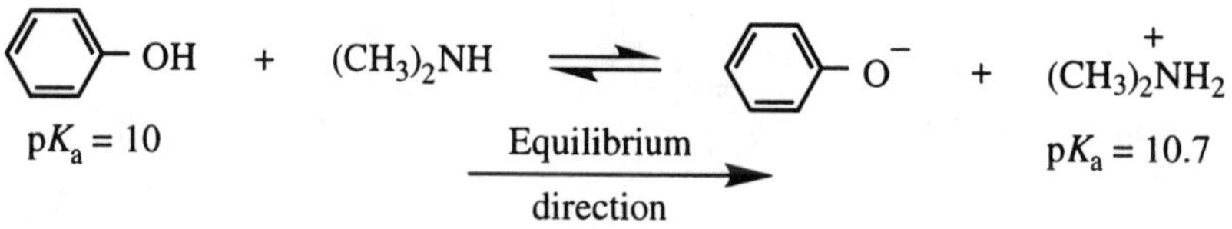

OH + $(CH_3)_2NH$
O^- + $(CH_3)_2NH_2^+$
$pK_a = 10$
Equilibrium
direction
$pK_a = 10.7$

(d)

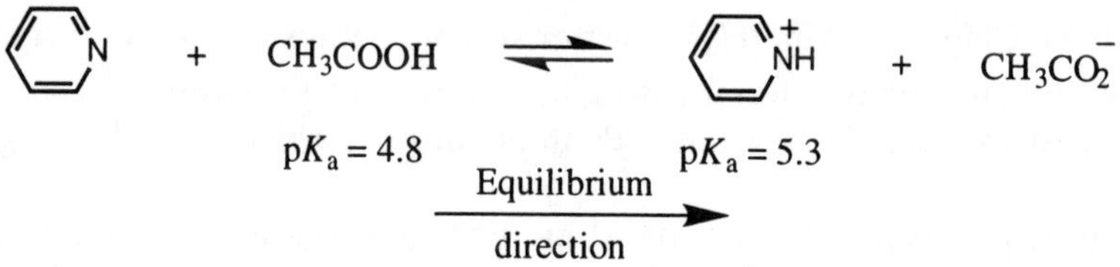

N + CH_3COOH
NH^+ + $CH_3CO_2^-$
$pK_a = 4.8$
Equilibrium
direction
$pK_a = 5.3$

12.32 (a) dimethylamine is more basic than methylamine because of the presence of two, rather than just one, methyl groups which are relatively electron donating (toward nitrogen).

$(CH_3)_2NH$ > CH_3NH_2

dimethylamine methylamine

(b) aniline is more basic than p-fluoroaniline because in the latter compound the fluoro group attracts electron density away from the nitrogen due to its electronegativity, reducing the compounds basicity relative to aniline.

NH_2
>
F
NH_2

aniline *p*-fluoroaniline

(c) aniline is more basic than diphenylamine because phenyl groups are relatively electron withdrawing from nitrogen, and two such groups reduces the electron density on nitrogen more than one.

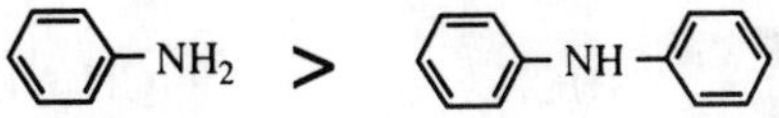
NH2
>
NH

aniline diphenylamine

(d) pyrrolidine is more basic than pyrrole. The former is a typical secondary amine whereas the latter is an aromatic system involving the lone pair on nitrogen, making it essentially non-basic.

N
H
>
N
H

pyrrolidine pyrrole

(e) aniline is basic whereas acetanilide is neutral. The acetyl group in the latter is a strong electron withdrawing group, delocalizing the nitrogen electrons such that they are essentially unavailable for protonation.

NH2
>
NHCOCH3

aniline acetanilide

12.33 The withdrawl of electron density from the amine nitrogen through resonance with the nitro group decreases the electron density on the amine nitrogen and therefore makes the *p*-nitroaniline less basic than aniline.

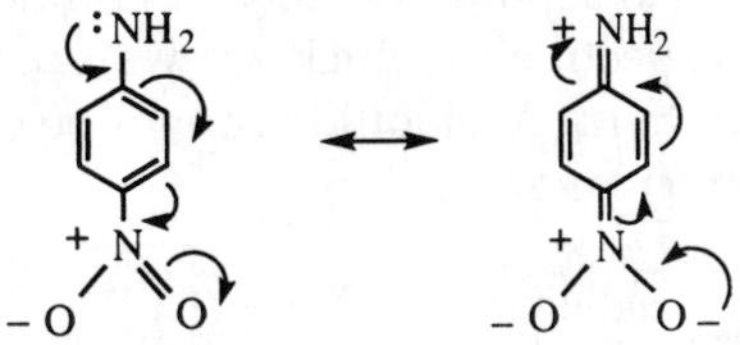
:NH2
+ N
- O
O
+ NH2
+ N
- O
O -

12.34 The key in the separation is to take advantage of the ability to convert water-insoluble N,N-dimethylaniline to its water-soluble hydrochloride salt, and then separate it from the water-insoluble benzene.

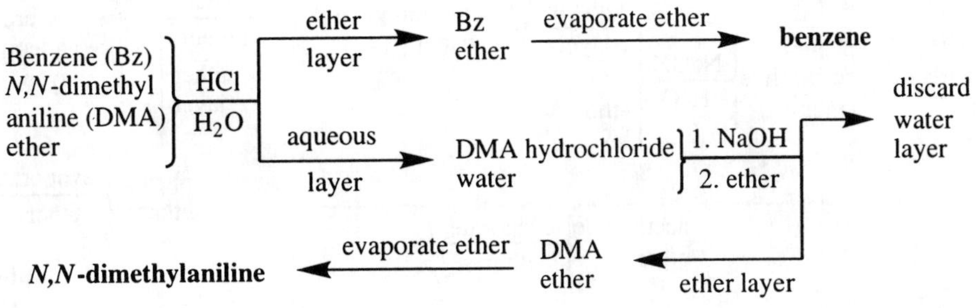
Benzene (Bz)
N,N-dimethyl
aniline (DMA)
ether
HCl
H2O
ether
layer
Bz
ether
evaporate ether
benzene
aqueous
layer
DMA hydrochloride
water
1. NaOH
2. ether
discard
water
layer
ether layer
DMA
ether
evaporate ether
N,N-dimethylaniline

12.35

(*R*)-*N*-methyl-2-pentanamine (*S*)-*N*-methyl-2-pentanamine

12.36 Two isomeric ammonium salts are formed in this S_N2 reaction because the benzyl group can be attached to nitrogen with an axial or the equatorial orientation. In the ammonium salt the nitrogen atom is isoelectronic with carbon, and the geometry about nitrogen is the same as in carbon (sp^3 hybridization). Therefore, a *cis*- and a *trans*-isomer can be formed.

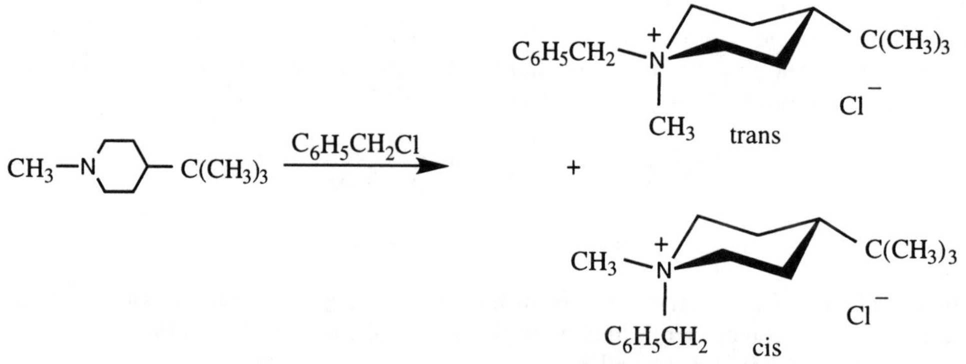
CH3—N
C(CH3)3
C6H5CH2Cl
C6H5CH2—N
CH3
trans
Cl−
CH3—N
C6H5CH2
cis

12.37 The key to this separation is to separately convert aniline and phenol to salts (by addition and removal of a proton, respectively) which are water soluble and are thereby separable from the organic (ether) solution. Acetanilide cannot be converted to a salt so always remains in the organic (ether) layer.

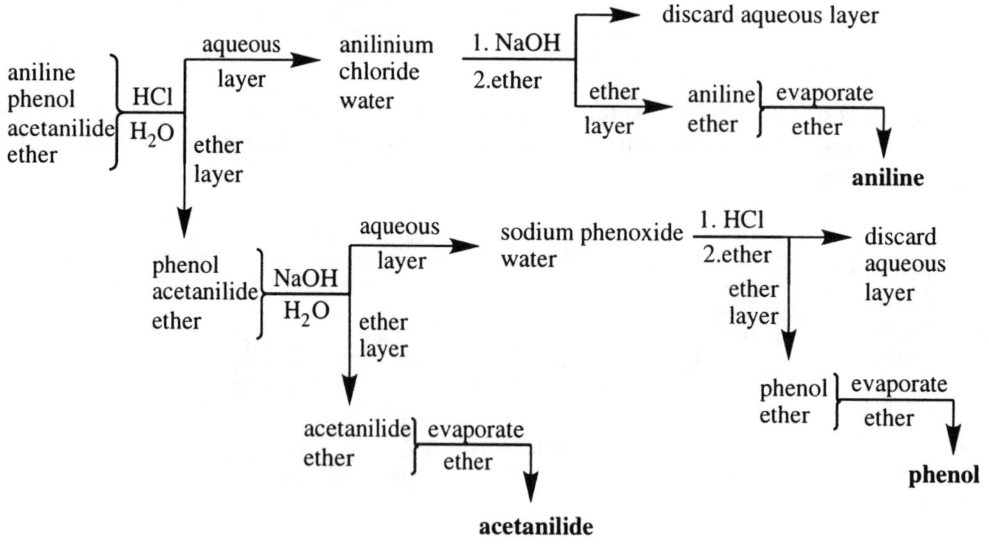
aniline
phenol
acetanilide
ether
HCl
H2O
aqueous layer
anilinium chloride water
1. NaOH
2.ether
discard aqueous layer
ether layer
aniline ether
evaporate ether
aniline
ether layer
phenol
acetanilide
ether
NaOH
H2O
aqueous layer
sodium phenoxide water
1. HCl
2.ether
discard aqueous layer
ether layer
phenol ether
evaporate ether
phenol
ether layer
acetanilide ether
evaporate ether
acetanilide

12.38

(a) $C_6H_5NH_2 + CH_3I \text{ (excess)} \longrightarrow C_6H_5\overset{+}{N}(CH_3)_3\ \ \overset{-}{I}$

(b) $C_6H_5CH_2Br + NH_3 \text{ (excess)} \longrightarrow C_6H_5CH_2NH_2$

(c)

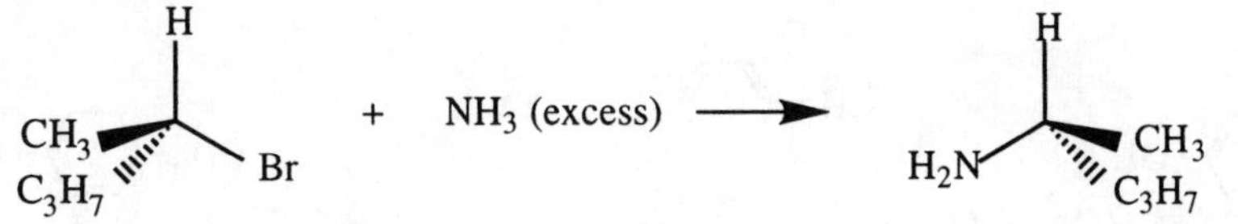
H
CH3
C3H7
Br
+ NH3 (excess)
H
H2N
CH3
C3H7

(R)-2-bromopentane — (S)-2-aminopentane

(d)

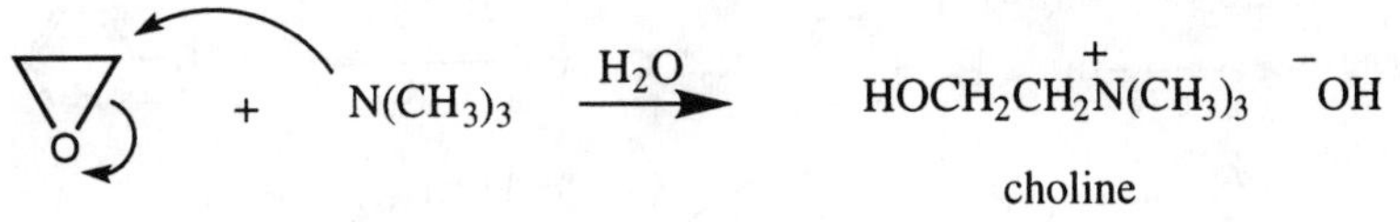
O
+ N(CH3)3
H2O
HOCH2CH2N(CH3)3 OH
choline

12.39

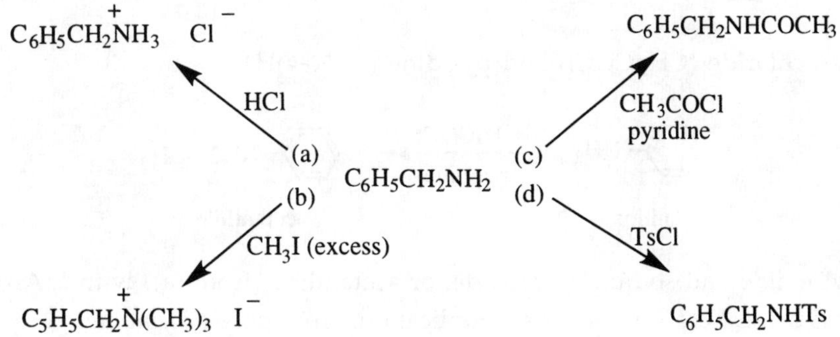
C6H5CH2NH3 Cl
HCl
(a)
C6H5CH2NHCOCH3
CH3COCl
pyridine
(c)
C6H5CH2NH2
(b)
(d)
CH3I (excess)
TsCl
C5H5CH2N(CH3)3 I
C6H5CH2NHTs

12.40

(a) $C_6H_5NH_2 + CH_3COCl \xrightarrow{NaOH} C_6H_5NHCOCH_3$

(b) $C_6H_5NHCOCH_3 \xrightarrow{LiAlH_4} C_6H_5NHCH_2CH_3$

(c)

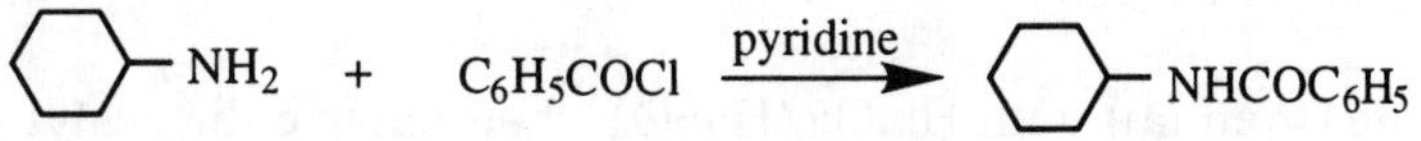
NH2
+ C6H5COCl
pyridine
NHCOC6H5

(d)

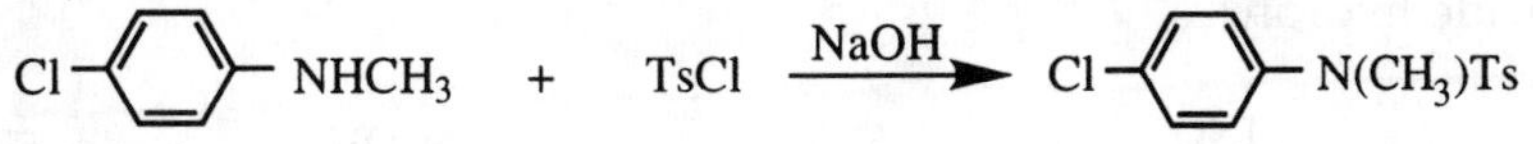
Cl
NHCH3
+ TsCl
NaOH
Cl
N(CH3)Ts

12.41

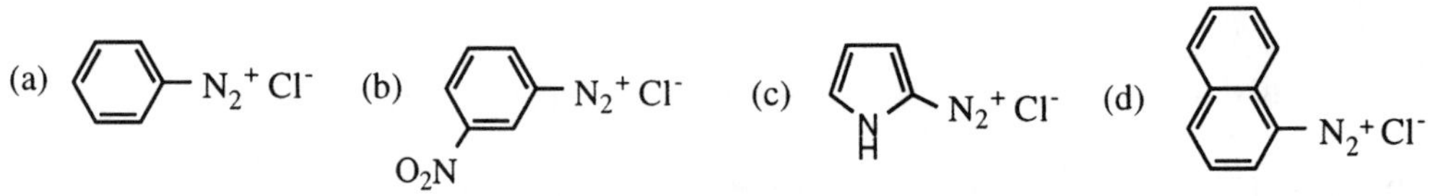
(a)
N2+ Cl-
(b)
N2+ Cl-
O2N
(c)
N
H
N2+ Cl-
(d)
N2+ Cl-

12.42

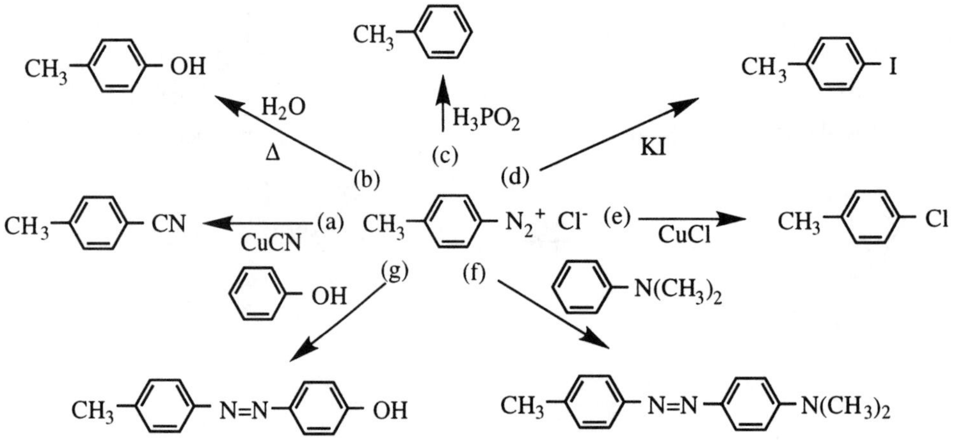
CH3
OH
H2O
Δ
(b)
H3PO2
(c)
(d)
KI
I
CN
CuCN
(a)
N2+ Cl-
(e)
CuCl
Cl
(g)
(f)
OH
N(CH3)2
N=N
OH
N=N
N(CH3)2

12.43 (a) acetyl chloride (CH_3COCl) and pyridine (or NaOH)

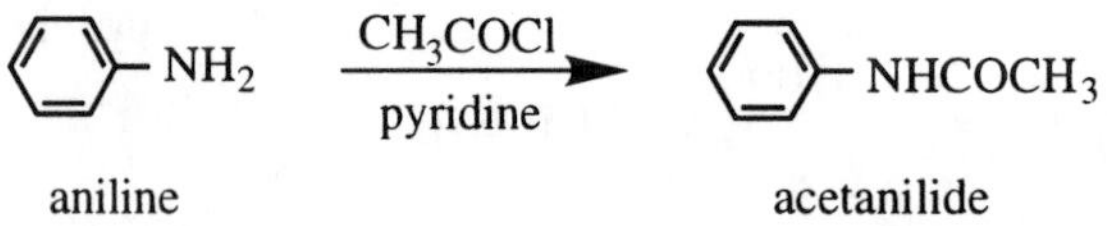
NH2
CH3COCl
pyridine
NHCOCH3
aniline
acetanilide

(b) ethyl iodide and sodium hydroxide, or acetanilide (from (a)) with $LiAlH_4$. The latter process is better because it avoids complications from poly-alkylation

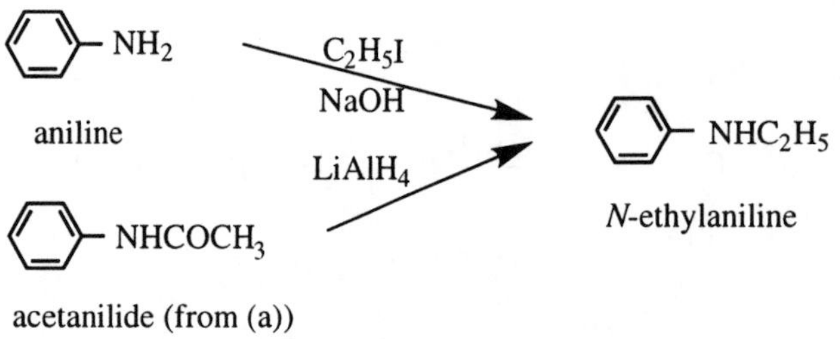
NH2
aniline
C2H5I
NaOH
LiAlH4
NHC2H5
N-ethylaniline
NHCOCH3
acetanilide (from (a))

(c) nitrate acetanilide (from (a)) with HNO_3/H_2SO_4, then remove the acetyl group with sodium hydroxide hydrolysis

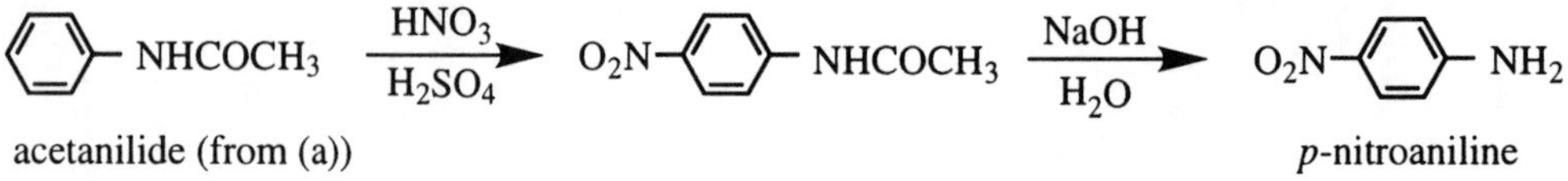
NHCOCH3
HNO3
H2SO4
O2N
NHCOCH3
NaOH
H2O
O2N
NH2
acetanilide (from (a))
p-nitroaniline

(d) diazotize with $NaNO_2$ and HCl, then treat with KI

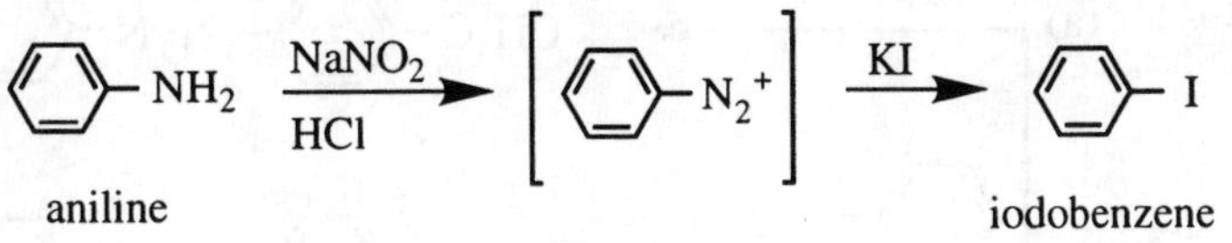
NH2
NaNO2
HCl
N2+
KI
I
aniline
iodobenzene

(e) diazotize with $NaNO_2$ and HCl, then warm the aqueous solution

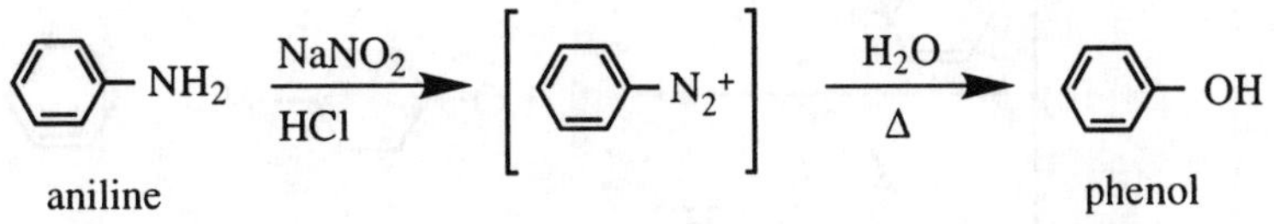
NH2
NaNO2
HCl
N2+
H2O
Δ
OH
aniline
phenol

(f) diazotize with $NaNO_2$ and HCl, then treat with CuCN

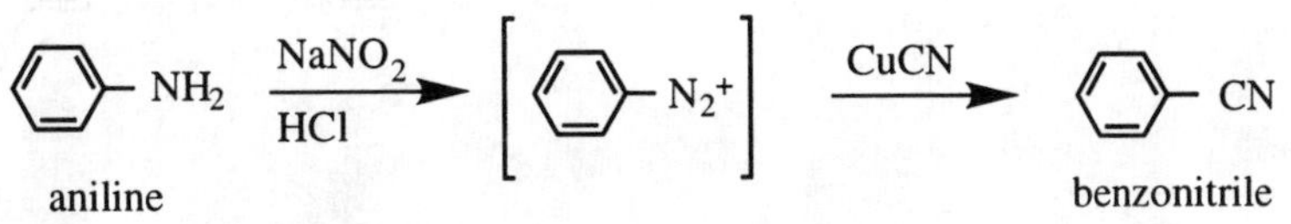
NH2
NaNO2
HCl
N2+
CuCN
CN
aniline
benzonitrile

(g) diazotize with $NaNO_2$ and HCl, then reduce with H_3PO_2

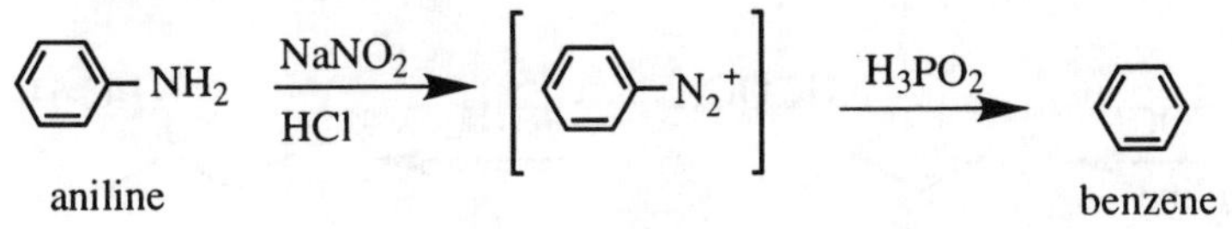
NH2
NaNO2
HCl
N2+
H3PO2
aniline
benzene

(h) diazotize with $NaNO_2$ and HCl, then treat with HBF_4

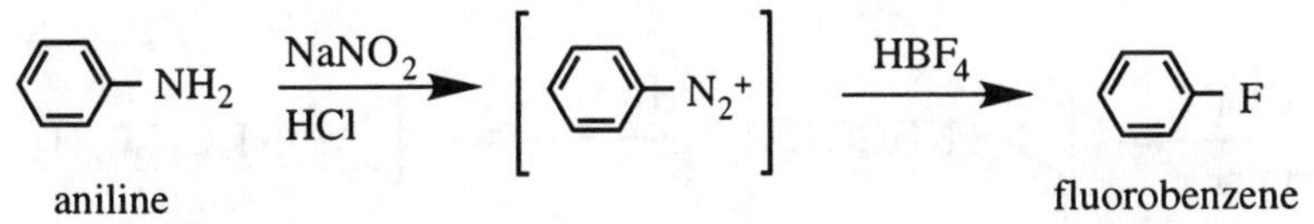
NH2
NaNO2
HCl
N2+
HBF4
F
aniline
fluorobenzene

(i) react with *p*-chlorobenzoyl chloride (ClC_6H_4COCl) to form the amide, then reduce the amide with $LiAlH_4$

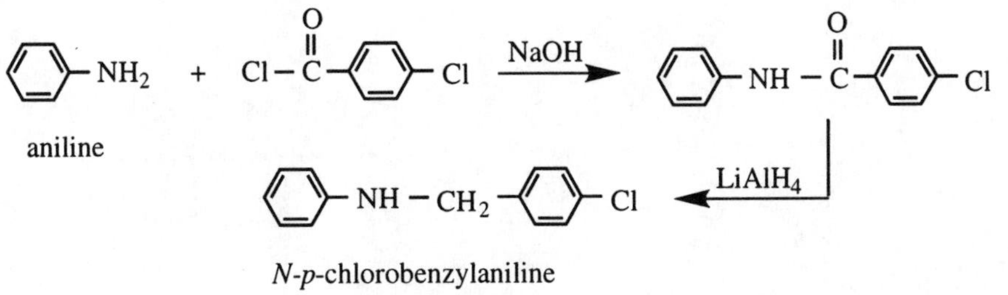
NH2
+
Cl−C
O
Cl
NaOH
NH − C
O
Cl
aniline
LiAlH4
NH − CH2
Cl
N-p-chlorobenzylaniline

12.44

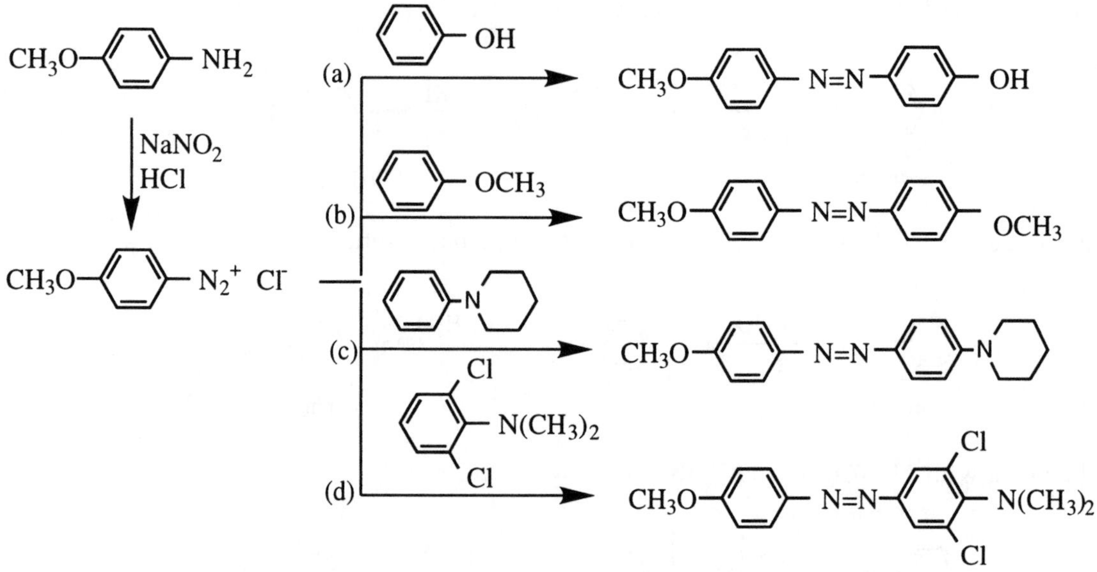

12.45

(a)

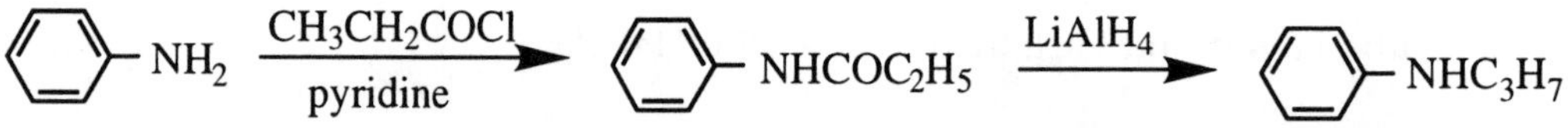

(b)

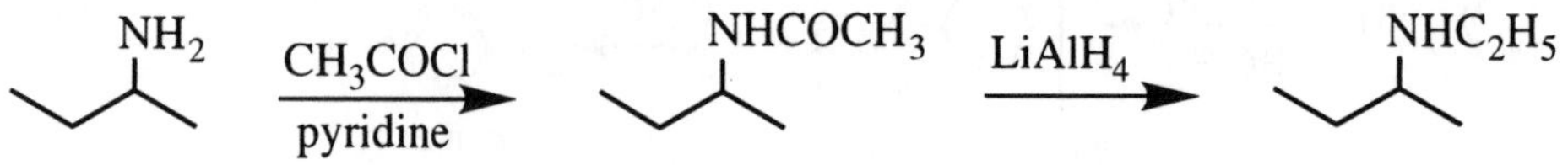

(c) $CH_3CH_2CHBrC_6H_5 \xrightarrow{NaN_3} CH_3CH_2CHN_3C_6H_5 \xrightarrow{LiAlH_4} CH_3CH_2CHNH_2C_6H_5$

(d)

(e)

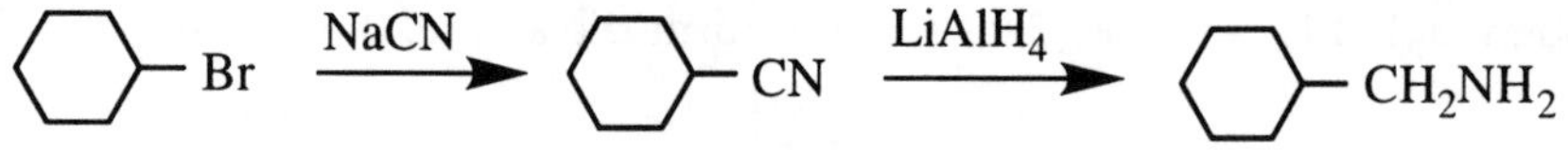

12.46

(a) 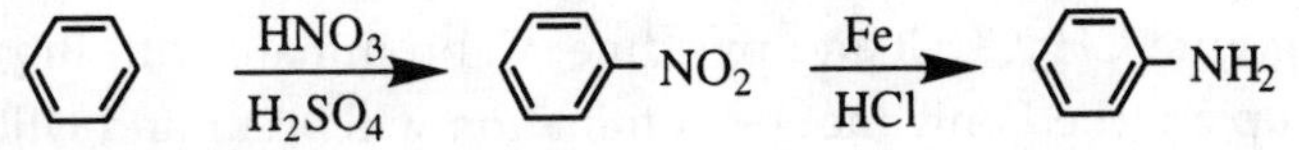

(b) 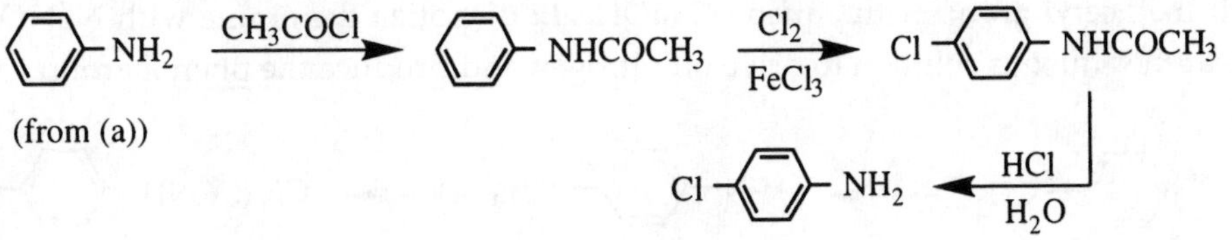

(from (a))

(c) 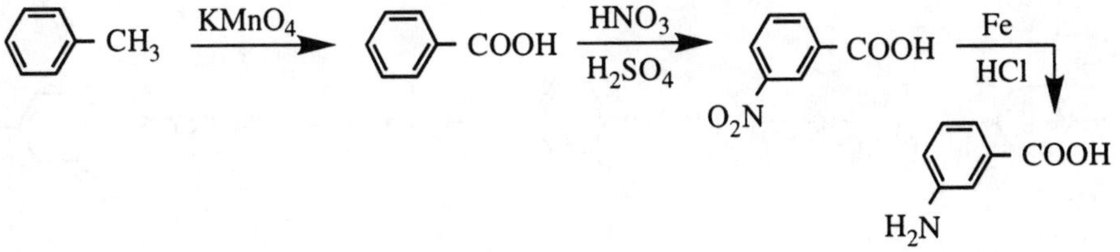

(d) 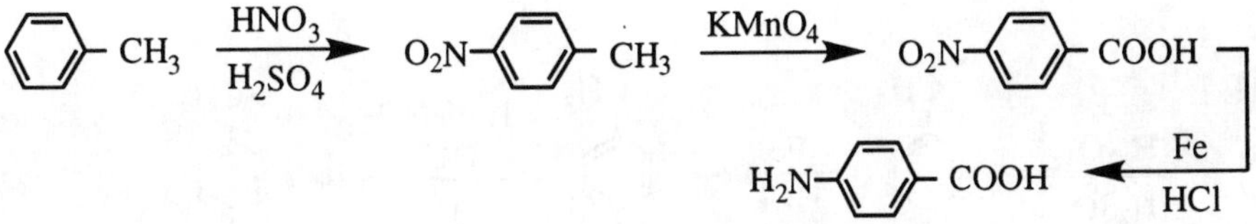

(e) 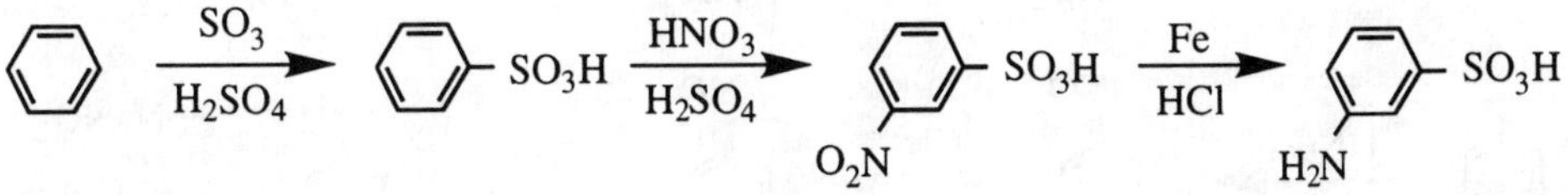

* (f) 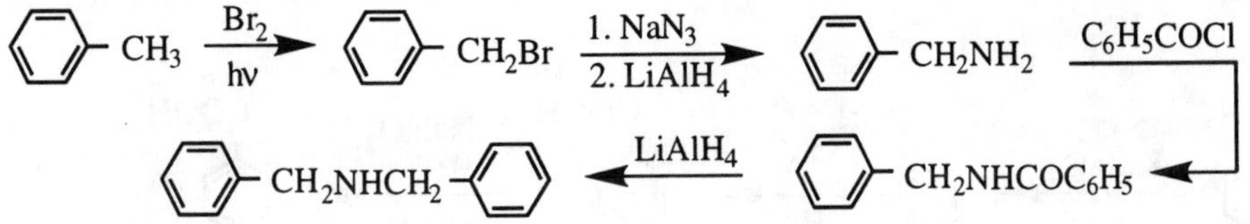

12.47

(a) NH_3 (excess) $\xrightarrow{CH_3CH_2CH_2CH_2CH_2Br}$ $C_5H_{11}NH_2$

(b) $CH_3CH_2CH_2CH_2CONH_2 \xrightarrow{LiAlH_4} C_5H_{11}NH_2$

(c) $CH_3CH_2CH_2CH_2Br \xrightarrow{NaCN} CH_3CH_2CH_2CH_2CN \xrightarrow{LiAlH_4} C_5H_{11}NH_2$

(d) $C_5H_{11}Br \xrightarrow{NaN_3} C_5H_{11}N_3 \xrightarrow{LiAlH_4} C_5H_{11}NH_2$

12.48 **A:** nitrate with HNO_3/H_2SO_4, then reduce the nitro group with Fe/HCl; **B:** de-activate the amine by acetylating with CH_3COCl and pyridine; **C:** brominate with $Br_2/FeBr_3$ (with the acetamido group attached only mono-bromination will occur and will be ortho to the acetamido group, which is a stronger activator than the methyl group); **D:** hydrolyze off the acetyl group with aqueous NaOH; **E:** diazotize the amine with $NaNO_2$/HCl then heat the aqueous solution to drive off nitrogen and produce the phenol group.

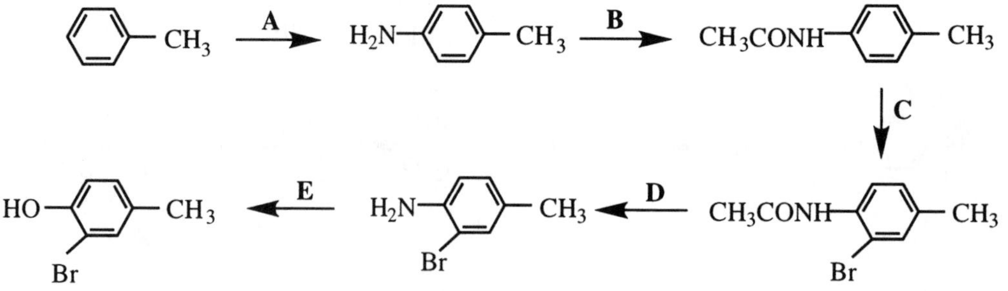

12.49

(a) 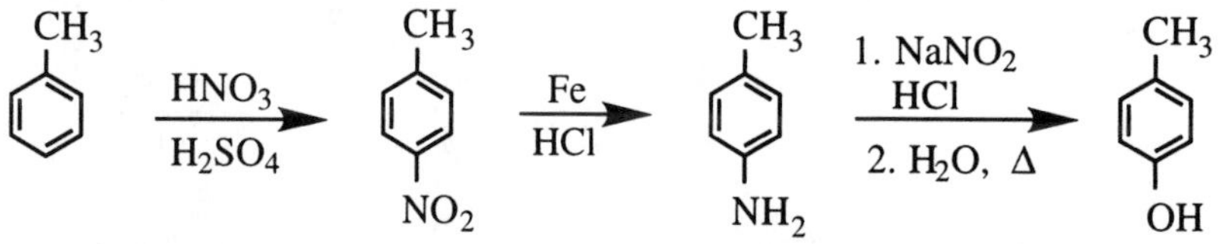

* (b) 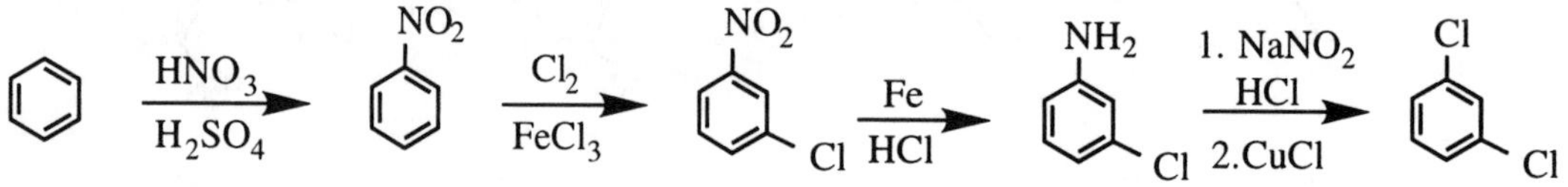

(c) 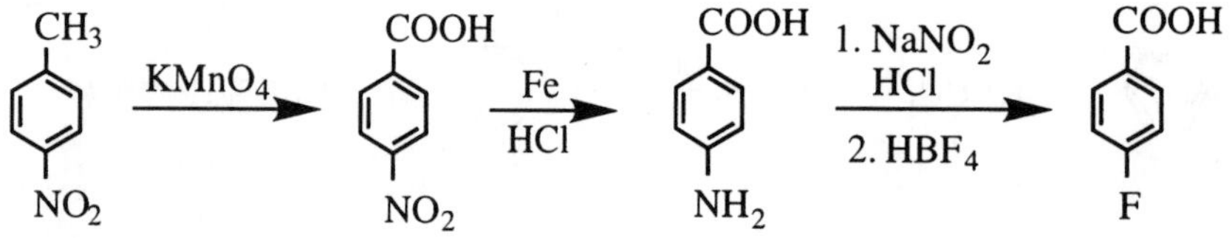

(from (a))

(d) 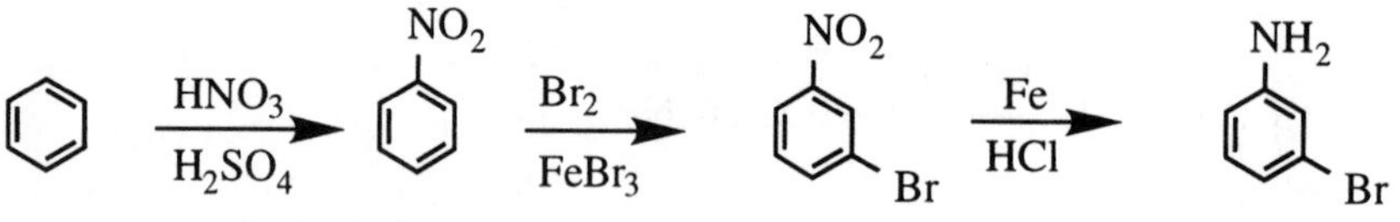

12.50 (a) benzene and pyridine both are insoluble in water but pyridine will dissolve when dilute HCl is added because of protonation to form a water-soluble pyridinium salt;

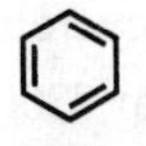

benzene

pyridine

(b) the *primary* amine *p*-toluidine will react with acetyl chloride to form an amide which will precipitate, whereas the *tertiary* amine *N,N*-dimethyl-*p*-toluidine will not react since there are no hydrogens on nitrogen which can be replaced by the acetyl group;

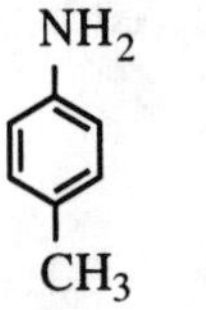

p-toluidine

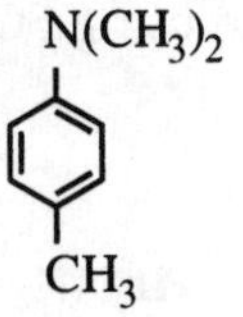

N,N-dimethyl-
p-toluidine

(c) benzylamine will dissolve in dilute hydrochloric acid due to protonation and salt formation, whereas benzamide is not basic to dilute HCl and therefore will not be protonated or dissolve;

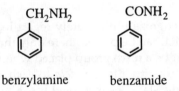

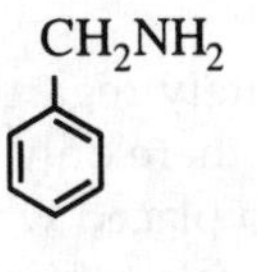

benzylamine

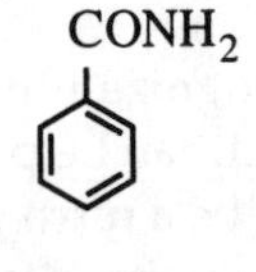

benzamide

(d) both 1,3-dimethylcyclohexane and 2,6-dimethylpiperidine are insoluble in water, but the latter will dissolve when dilute HCl is added because of protonation and salt formation.

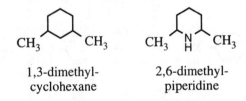

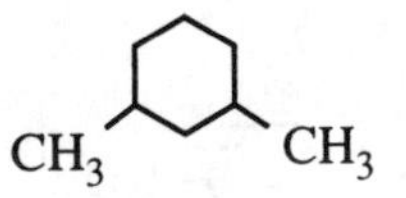

1,3-dimethyl-
cyclohexane

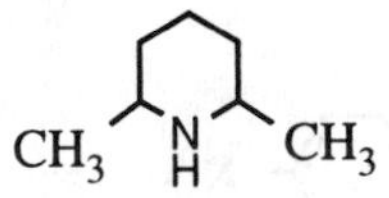

2,6-dimethyl-
piperidine

12.51 (a) ^{13}C-NMR spectra would distinguish benzene and pyridine because of a single peak for benzene but three peaks for pyridine; MS also would distinguish the two with benzene having a molecular ion at m/z 78 and pyridine having a molecular ion at m/z 79;

(b) IR spectra would distinguish *p*-toluidine from *N,N*-dimethyl-*p*-toluidine because the former would show two NH stretching peaks near 3300 cm^{-1} and the latter would show no absorption in that region;

(c) IR spectra would distinguish benzylamine and benzoyl amide because the latter would show a carbonyl peak near 1700 cm^{-1};

(d) IR spectra would distinguish 1,3-dimethylcyclohexane and 2,6-dimethylpiperidine because the latter would show the NH peak near 3300 cm^{-1}; ^1H-NMR spectra also would distinguish the two using the NH absorption.

12.52 **A:** HNO_3/H_2SO_4 to nitrate followed by reduction with Fe/HCl; **B:** acetylation with CH_3COCl and pyridine; **C:** sulfonation with SO_3/H_2SO_4; **D:** conversion of the sulfonic acid to the sulfonyl chloride using $SOCl_2$, followed by the amide-forming reaction with pyrrolidine [$(CH_2)_4NH$].

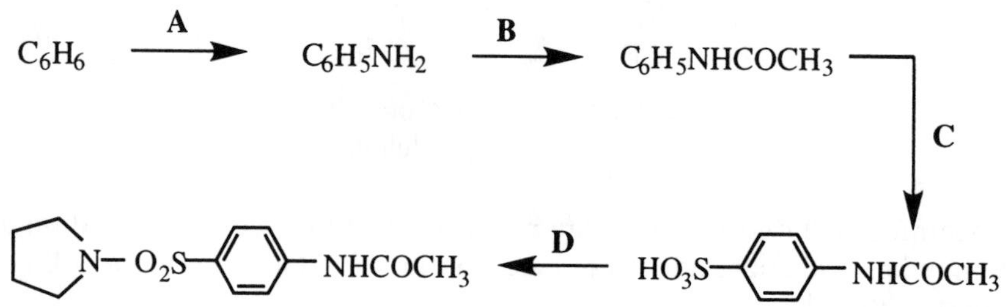

A
B
C
D
C6H6
C6H5NH2
C6H5NHCOCH3
N–O2S
NHCOCH3
HO3S
NHCOCH3

***12.53** There are two things to recognize immediately regarding this synthesis. First, there is an iodo group on the ring which can be placed there only through the diazonium ion route. That means there must first be a nitro group placed where the iodo group is to be located. Second, the two halogen substituents are *meta* to each other, yet both are *ortho/para* directors. Therefore, at some stage a substituent must be placed on the ring which will direct an incoming electrophile to the *meta* position. The nitro group is the obvious candidate for this role as well. Therefore, in the synthesis the nitro group should be attached first and then the chlorine should be attached. Finally, the nitro can be converted to an iodo group.

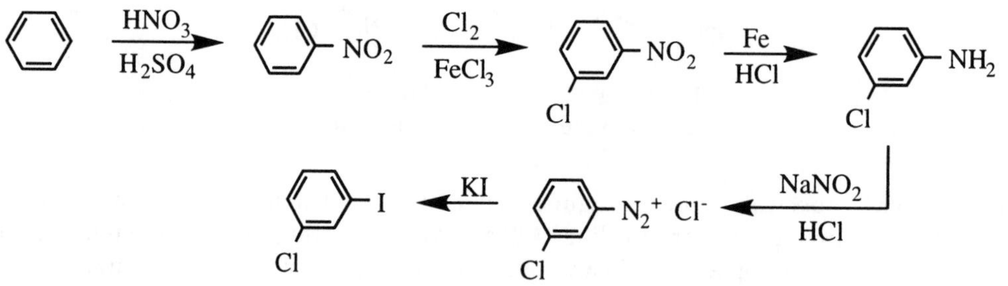

HNO3
H2SO4
NO2
Cl2
FeCl3
NO2
Cl
Fe
HCl
NH2
Cl
NaNO2
HCl
N2+ Cl-
Cl
KI
I
Cl

12.54

(a) 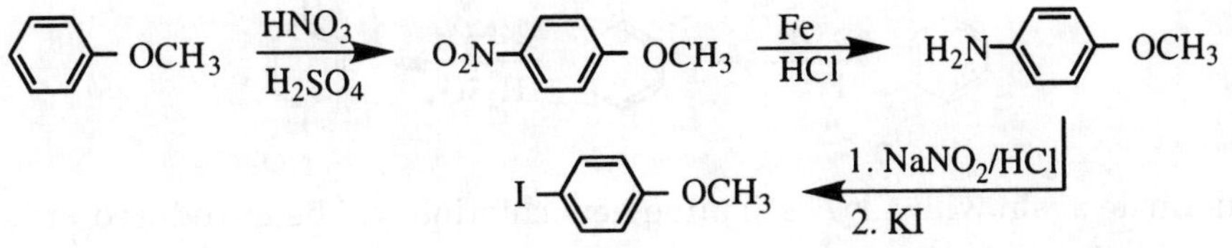

(b) $C_4H_9Br \xrightarrow[2.\ LiAlH_4]{1.\ NaN_3} C_4H_9NH_2 \xrightarrow[\text{pyridine}]{CH_3COCl} C_4H_9NHCOCH_3 \xrightarrow{LiAlH_4} C_4H_9NHC_2H_5$

(c) $C_6H_5CH_3 \xrightarrow[h\nu]{Br_2} C_6H_5CH_2Br \xrightarrow{NaN_3} C_6H_5CH_2N_3 \xrightarrow{LiAlH_4} C_6H_5CH_2NH_2$

(d) 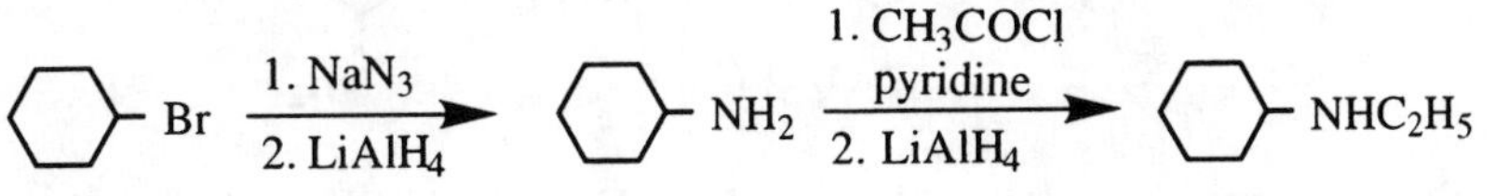

(e) 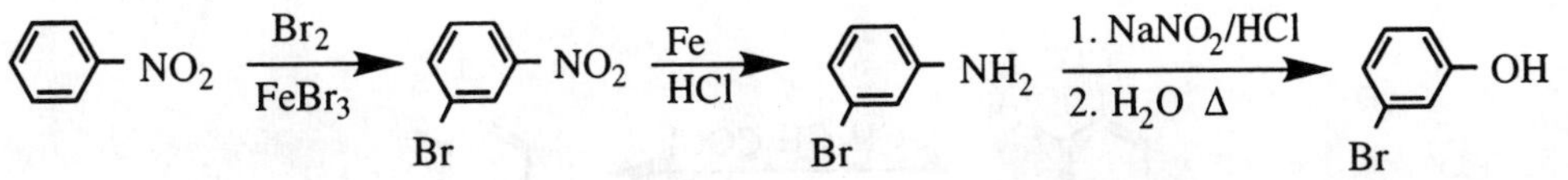

* (f) 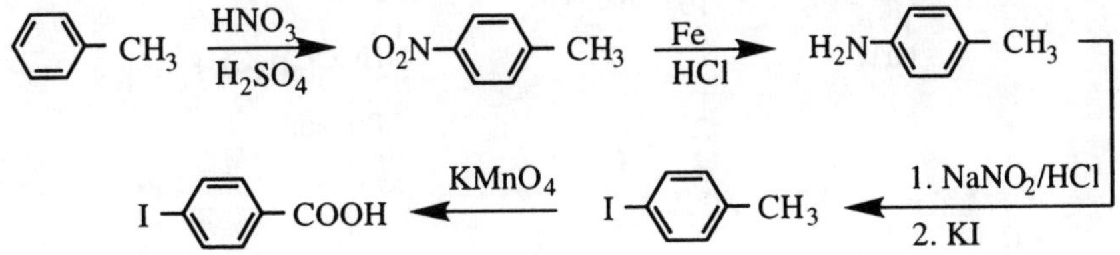

12.55

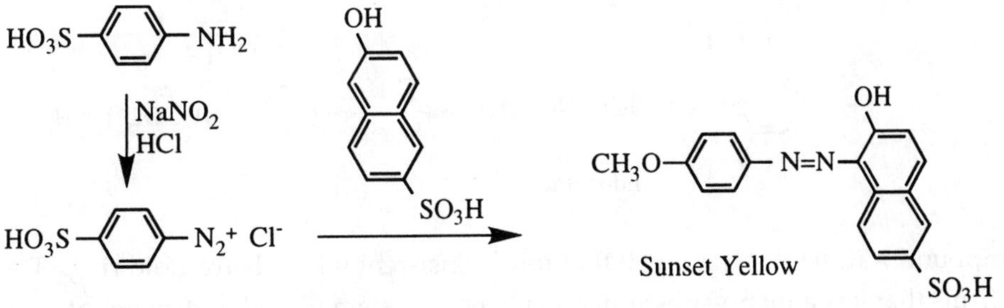

12.56 **A:** Chlorinate with $Cl_2/FeCl_3$ then nitrate with HNO_3/H_2SO_4

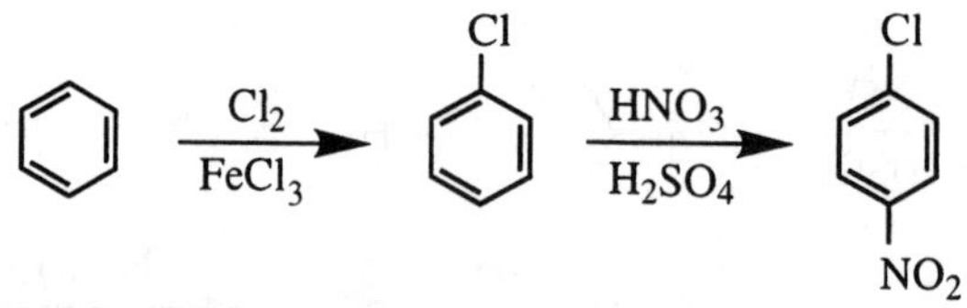

B: Chlorinate again with $Cl_2/FeCl_3$ (the new chlorine will be introduced ortho to the existing chlorine and meta to the nitro group) then reduce the nitro group to an amine group with Fe/HCl

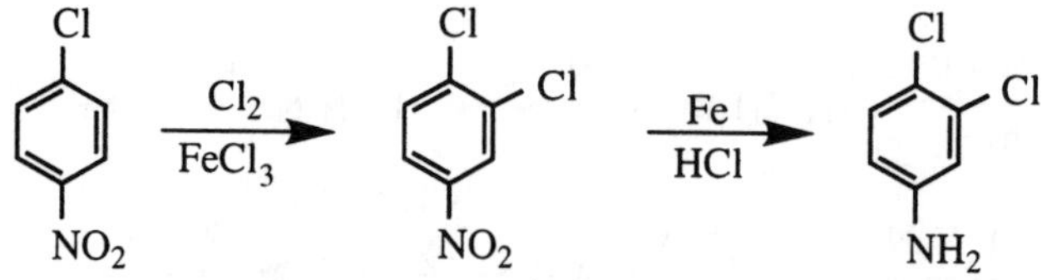

C: acylate the amine with propanoyl chloride (CH_3CH_2COCl) and pyridine.

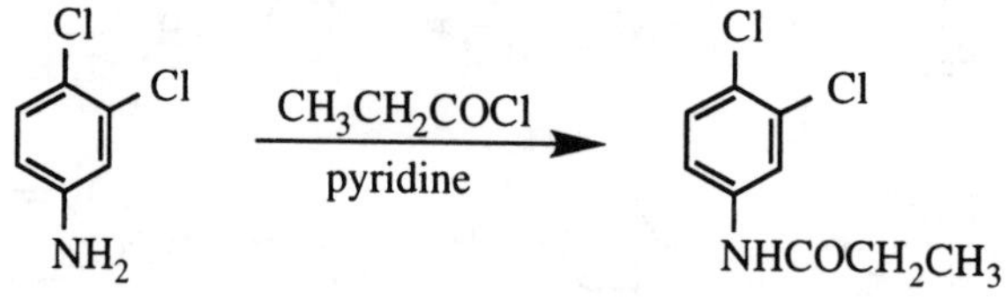

Propanil

12.57

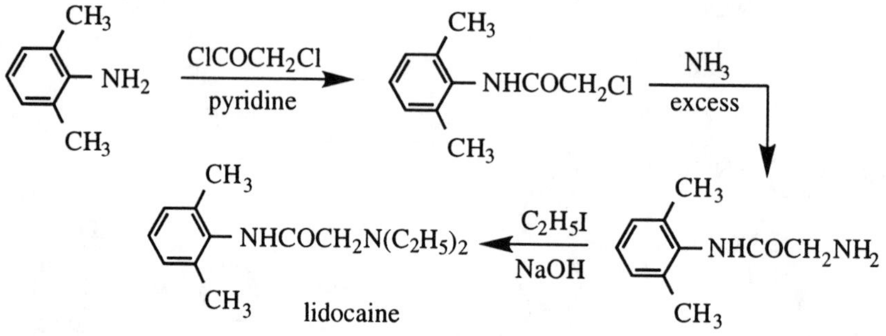
lidocaine

12.58 Compound **X** (C_7H_7Br) has an HDI of four, consistent with a benzenoid ring. The ^1H-NMR confirms that it is a mono-substituted benzenoid system (5 aryl hydrogens at 7.3 ppm) and the singlet of area = 2 at 4.2 ppm means the structure probably is $C_6H_5CH_2Br$. Reaction with sodium cyanide affords $C_6H_5CH_2CN$ (C_8H_7N) and the IR peak at 2250 cm^{-1} for **Y** confirms the triple bond of the cyanide group. Reduction of the nitrile affords $C_6H_5CH_2CH_2NH_2$ (**Z**) which is insoluble in water and soluble in dilute acid. The ^1H-NMR shown is consistent with this structure for **Z** showing five aryl protons at 7.0 ppm, a doublet at 2.6 ppm for the CH_2 adjacent to the ring, a doublet at 2.7 ppm for the CH_2 next to the nitrogen, and a singlet at 0.9 ppm for the NH_2 protons. The IR peaks at 3350 cm^{-1} are consistent with hydrogens on a primary amine (**Z**).

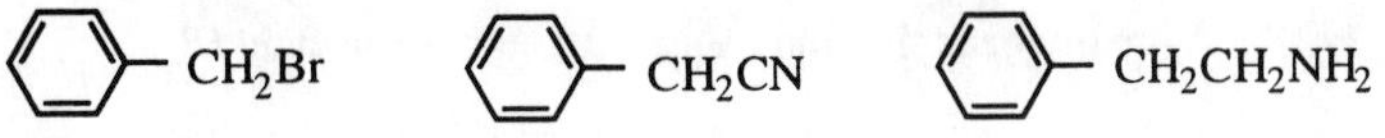

CH_2Br
CH_2CN
$CH_2CH_2NH_2$

X **Y** **Z**

12.59

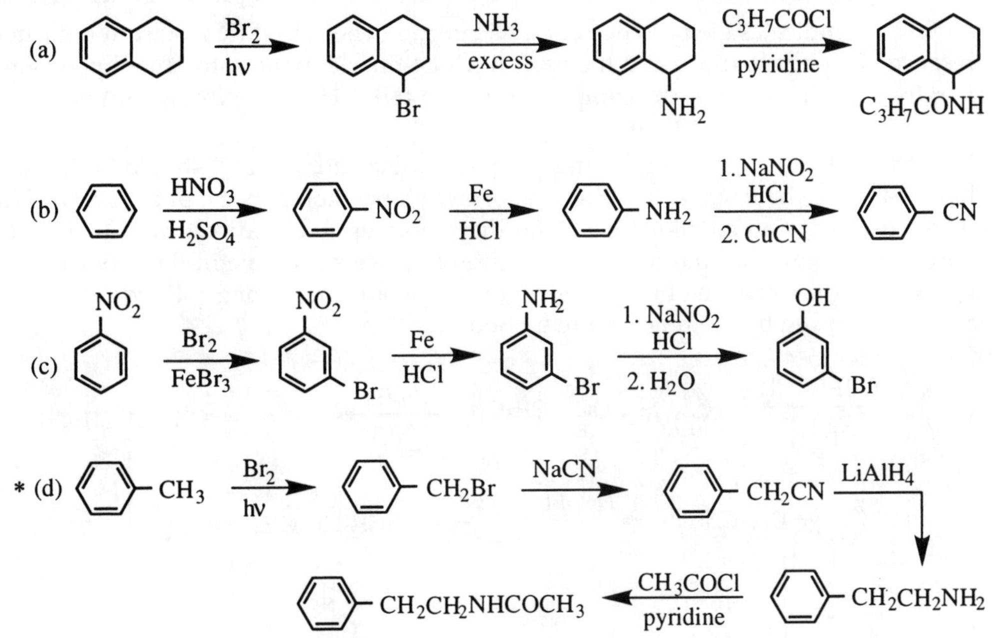

(a)
Br_2
hν
Br
NH_3
excess
NH_2
C_3H_7COCl
pyridine
C_3H_7CONH
(b)
HNO_3
H_2SO_4
NO_2
Fe
HCl
NH_2
1. $NaNO_2$
HCl
2. CuCN
CN
(c)
NO_2
Br_2
$FeBr_3$
Br
NH_2
1. $NaNO_2$
HCl
2. H_2O
OH
* (d)
CH_3
CH_2Br
NaCN
CH_2CN
$LiAlH_4$
$CH_2CH_2NH_2$
CH_3COCl
$CH_2CH_2NHCOCH_3$

12.60 The molecular ion of 121 for **A** leads to suspicion of an amine because of the odd number, and the 106 and 77 peaks lead to suspicion of the presence of a methyl group and a phenyl group. Solubility in HCl confirms **A** as an amine. The ^{1}H-NMR indicates eleven hydrogens (11), which together with six carbons (72) for a benzenoid ring and a nitrogen atom (14) accounts for 97 units of the formula weight, meaning that the remaining 24 units probably represents two additional carbons, making the molecular formula $C_8H_{11}N$. The NMR indicates the compound contains a mono-substituted benzene ring (C_6H_5), the remainder of the molecule therefore being C_2H_6N. The UV spectrum peak at 264 nm is consistent with a substituted benzene ring, but not with a ring having a trivalent nitrogen directly attached. The fact that the NMR has singlets indicates that the two carbons cannot be attached to each other (i.e., not a $CH_2CH_2NH_2$ or a $NHCH_2CH_3$ group). Therefore, the only other possibility is a -CH_2NHCH_3 group which fits the NMR spectrum (singlet CH_2, singlet CH_3, and singlet NH). Thus, **A** appears to be $C_6H_5CH_2NHCH_3$. The IR of **A** shows a singlet NH at 3300 cm^{-1} as expected and the reaction with tosyl chloride adds confirmation. Oxidation with $KMnO4$ produces benzoic acid (C_6H_5COOH) as expected and the NMR is in agreement with that structure for **B**. Therefore, **A** is *N*-methylbenzylamine and **B** is benzoic acid.

N-methylbenzylamine (**A**) benzoic acid (*B*)

12.61 $C_8H_{11}N$ in this question also is an amine as indicated by its solubility in dilute HCl. The MS peaks at m/z 106 and 92 indicate the fragmentation of a methyl and ethyl group, respectively, and the peak at m/z 77 indicates the presence of a phenyl group. The IR peak at 3400 cm^{-1} indicates the presence of an NH group. The ^{1}H-NMR spectrum indicates the presence of a phenyl group and the typical triplet-quartet pattern for an ethyl group. Therefore, the structure of the compound is $C_6H_5NHCH_2CH_3$, *N*-ethylaniline.

***12.62** The retrosynthesis approach indicates the pyrrolidine-carbon bond should be formed last. That means the challenge is to place a halogen in a position β to the phenyl ring. However, it is the α-position in an alkyl side chain that is susceptible to direct radical substitution. Therefore, employ anti-Markovnikov addition to place a bromine in the β-position. Finally, recognize that the butyl side-chain can be attached using a Friedel-Crafts acylation followed by Clemmensen reduction.

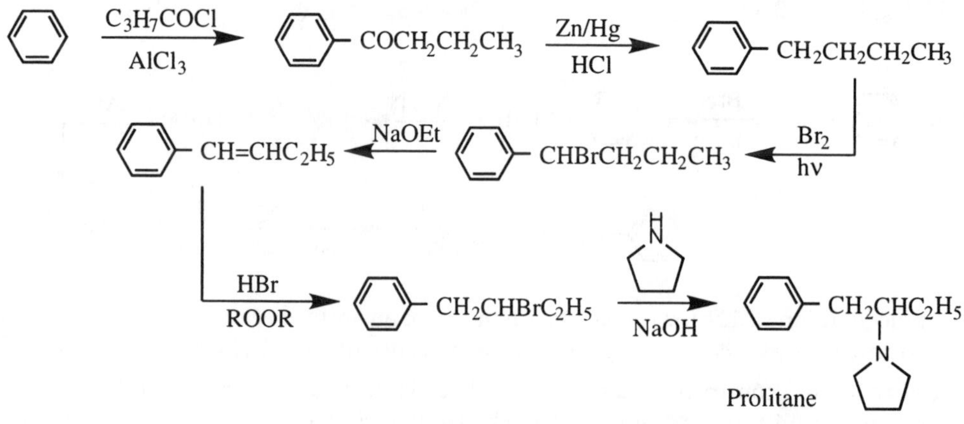

C3H7COCl
AlCl3
COCH2CH2CH3
Zn/Hg
HCl
CH2CH2CH2CH3
Br2
hν
CHBrCH2CH2CH3
NaOEt
CH=CHC2H5
HBr
ROOR
CH2CHBrC2H5
NaOH
CH2CHC2H5
Prolitane

12.63 The molecular ion at m/z 87 indicates it is an amine and the NMR singlet disappearing with D_2O confirms this suspicion. The IR doublet peak at 3300 cm^{-1} confirms the presence of an NH_2 group as does the relative area of 2 for the ^{1}H-NMR singlet at 1.0 ppm. The NH_2 group of formula weight 16 means the hydrocarbon portion of the compound has a formula weight of 71 (87-16=71), consistent only with a formula C_5H_{11} for an alkyl group. The NMR singlet at 0.9 ppm of area = 9 indicates the presence of a $(CH_3)_3C$- fragment and the remaining singlet of area = 2 at 2.4 ppm can only represent a CH_2 group attached to the electronegative nitrogen. Therefore, the compound is 2,2-dimethyl-1-propanamine, $(CH_3)_3CCH_2NH_2$.

***12.64** Two separate transformation sequences are required, one to produce the amide and the second to produce the ethoxy group. Retrosynthetic analysis suggests the ethoxy group is obtainable from a phenol which in turn can arise from an amino group through the diazotization sequence. The amide group is obtainable by simply acetylating the starting amine. Consideration of the relative reactivity of substituents on an aromatic ring leads to the conclusion to develop the amide group first and then do a nitration which leads eventually to the phenolic group, to which can be applied a Williamson ether synthesis.

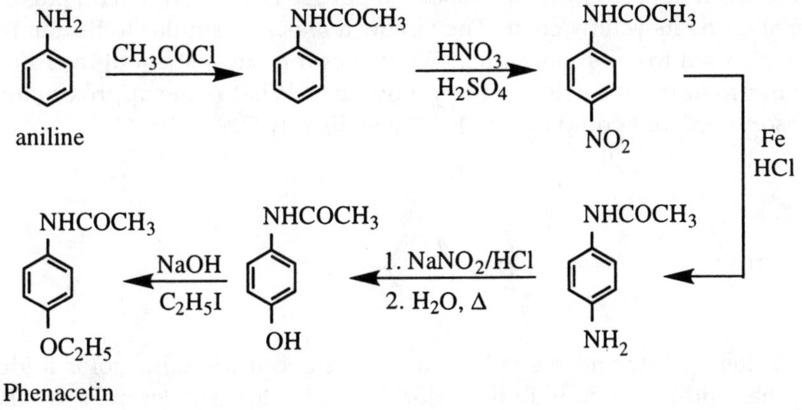
NH2
CH3COCl
NHCOCH3
HNO3
H2SO4
NHCOCH3
aniline
NO2
Fe
HCl
NHCOCH3
NaOH
C2H5I
NHCOCH3
1. NaNO2/HCl
2. H2O, Δ
NHCOCH3
OC2H5
OH
NH2
Phenacetin

VII. Conceptual Problem

Shades of Yellow

A textile designer was experimenting with different dyes. He found a substance that had a yellow color he liked, but the compound turned red in acid. Household ammonia restored the original yellow. The structure of the compound is shown in the here:

- What is the molecular formula of this compound?
  - Ans: $C_{14}H_{14}N_3NaO_3S$
- Classify the amine group present in this compound.
  - Ans: It is tertiary.
- What feature of this compound causes it to be colored?
  - Ans: Its long conjugated system of pi bonds and the nonbonding electrons on the tertiary amine group.

■ What is the structure of this substance when dissolved in acidic solution?

• Ans:

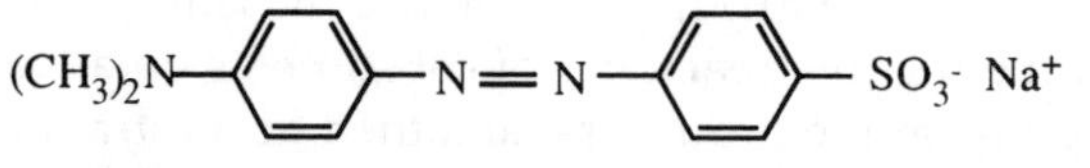

■ The compound shown here is similar to one called Sunset Yellow (shown on page 369) that is now used to give margarine its yellow color. The yellow dye is also similar to Butter Yellow shown on page 425, formerly used to color margarine. What does this suggest about the impotance of the -SO_3Na group in providing the color to the yellow dye? What is the approximate wavelength of the UV-VIS absorption you would expect for the yellow dye?

• Ans:

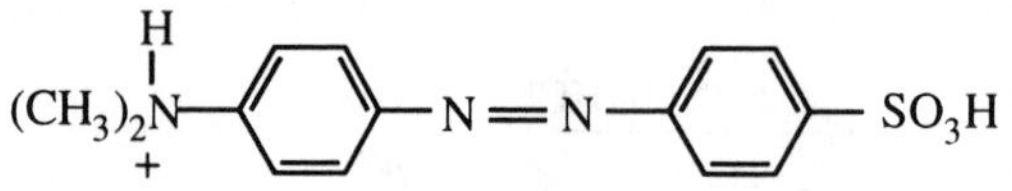

The fact that Butter Yellow and the yellow dye have about the same color inidcates that the -SO_3Na group has nothing to do with the color. Using the table of complementary colors (text, page 367) indicates that a yellow dye should absorb at about 400 nm wavelength.

CHAPTER 13

Carbonyl Compounds (Aldehydes and Ketones)

I. Textbook Chapter Contents

This chapter introduces the family of compounds which contain the carbonyl (C=O) group, known collectively as carbonyl compounds. Aldehydes (which contain at least one hydrogen attached to the carbonyl carbon) and ketones (which contain no hydrogens attached to carbonyl carbon) are two sub-sets of carbonyl compounds. They are considered together because most of their reactions are identical and are a result of the presence of the carbonyl group. This chapter also introduces the third reactive intermediate of organic chemistry—carbanions.

II. Learning Objectives

- Be able to name aldehydes and ketones using the IUPAC system.
- Know the common names of simple and frequently encountered aldehydes and ketones.
- Know the electronic structure of the carbonyl group and use this information to understand the general chemical behavior of the group: (a) its susceptibility to nucleophilic attack at the carbonyl carbon; (b) protonation of the carbonyl oxygen; (c) the acidity of an α-hydrogen and the stabilization of the resulting enolate anion.
- Write the enol form of aldehydes and ketones and by equations show the phenomenon of tautomerism.
- Write equations for the oxidation of aldehydes to carboxylic acids. Be able to use this reaction, as well as spectroscopic information, to distinguish between aldehydes and ketones.
- Understand the mechanism for nucleophilic addition reactions to carbonyl groups.
- Write equations for the reduction of aldehydes and ketones to primary and secondary alcohols, respectively.
- Write equations for the reactions of carbonyl compounds with amines to form imines, and the hydrolysis of the latter back to starting materials.
- Write equations for, and know the mechanism for, the acid-catalyzed reactions of carbonyl compounds with alcohols to form unstable hemiacetals, and continued reaction to form stable acetals. Know the use of acetals to protect the carbonyl group, and subsequent de-protection using dilute acid.
- Write equations for the reaction of carbonyl compounds with organolithium compounds and Grignard reagents to form alcohols. Be able to use this reaction in designing syntheses of alcohols.

- Write equations for the reaction of carbonyl compounds with phosphonium ylides to form alkenes (Wittig reaction).
- Write equations for the preparation of aldehydes by the PCC oxidation of primary alcohols.
- Write equations for the preparation of aldehydes by the reduction of acid chlorides.
- Write equations for the preparation of ketones by the oxidation of secondary alcohols.
- Write equations for the preparation of ketones by the reaction of organocuprate reagents with acid chlorides.
- Be able to determine the structure of unknown aldehydes and ketones based on chemical and spectroscopic information.
- Be able to devise multi-step syntheses of organic compounds involving carbonyl compounds as reactants or products.

III. Glossary

acetal a compound of general formula $R_2C(OR')_2$ formed from a carbonyl compound ($R_2C{=}O$) and an alcohol (R'OH) under acid catalysis. Acetals also can be formed from hemiacetals

acyl group the RCO- or ArCO- group

aldehyde a sub-family of carbonyl compounds in which at least one hydrogen is attached to the carbonyl group. The general structures are RCHO and ArCHO

alkanal the IUPAC general name for aliphatic aldehydes

alkanone the IUPAC general name for aliphatic ketones

carbonyl compounds a family of organic compounds which contain the carbonyl group in two sub-families, aldehydes or ketones

carbonyl group the C=O group which appears in carbonyl compounds, carboxylic acids, and derivatives of carboxylic acids

cyanohydrin a compound of general structure $R_2C(OH)CN$ which results from the addition of HCN across a carbonyl group

2,4-dinitrophenylhydrazone a kind of imine [$R_2C{=}NNHC_6H_3(NO_2)_2$] formed by reaction of a carbonyl compound with 2,4-dinitrophenylhydrazine [$H_2NNHC_6H_3(NO_2)_2$], abbreviated 2,4-DNPH

dithioacetal an acetal in which sulfur has replaced oxygen, usually formed from a carbonyl compound and a thiol

enol a compound with an -OH group attached to a carbon which is part of a carbon-carbon double bond [-C=C(OH)-]

enolate anion the resonance stabilized anion which results from removal of a proton from an enol

enolization the conversion of an aldehyde or ketone into its enol through a tautomeric shift of a hydrogen

formyl group the -CHO group

hemiacetal a compound with the general formula $R_2C(OR')OH$ formed from an alcohol (R'OH) and a carbonyl compound ($R_2C=O$) under acid catalysis

hydrogenolysis the cleavage of a bond with molecular hydrogen, a hydrogen atom being added to each fragment in place of the bond

imine a compound with a $R_2C=N-R'$ group usually formed from reacting a carbonyl compound ($R_2C=O$) with a primary amine ($R'NH_2$)

ketone a sub-family of carbonyl compounds in which two carbon atoms are attached to the carbonyl group. The general structures are R_2CO, RCOAr, and Ar_2CO

ketonization the conversion of an enol to an aldehyde or ketone through a tautomeric shift of a hydrogen

nucleophilic addition the addition of a nucleophile to a multiple bond, usually a carbonyl group

oxime a kind of imine ($R_2C=NOH$) resulting from reaction of a carbonyl compound with hydroxylamine (H_2NOH)

semicarbazone a kind of imine ($R_2C=NNHCONH_2$) resulting from reaction of a carbonyl compound with semicarbazide ($H_2NNHCONH_2$)

tautomerism the mobile equilibrium between enol and carbonyl forms of an aldehyde or ketone

tautomers an enol and a keto form of a compound, which are constitutional isomers

thioacetal the sulfur analog of an acetal [$R_2C(SR')_2$]

transamination the conversion of an imine into a carbonyl compound with concomitant transfer of the released amine to form a new imine in reaction with another carbonyl compound. In other words, the exchange reaction between an imine and a carbonyl compound

Wittig reaction the reaction between a phosphonium ylide and a carbonyl compound to form an alkene

ylide a class of compounds used in Wittig reactions with carbonyl compounds. The major group of ylides are phosphonium ylides of general structure $(C_6H_5)_3P=CR_2$

IV. Summary of Reactions of Carbonyl Compounds

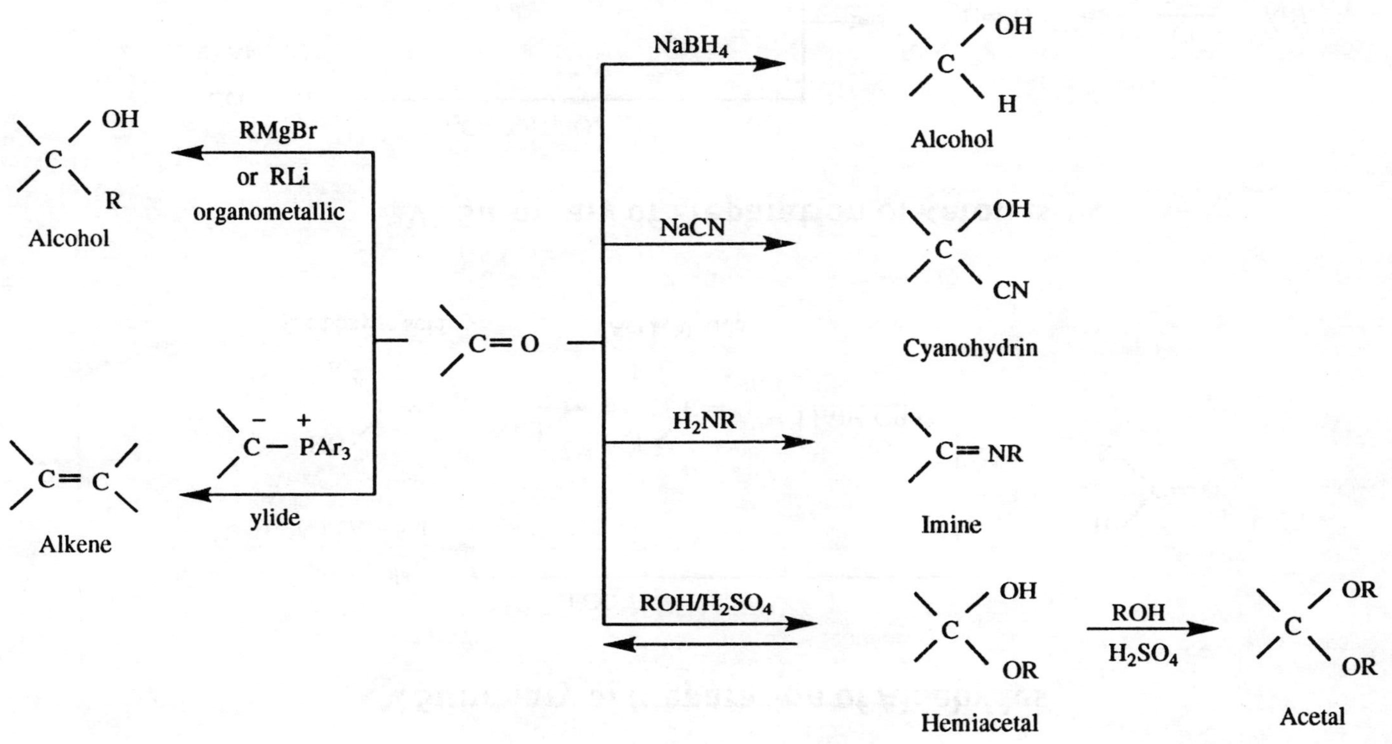
NaBH4
OH
H
Alcohol
RMgBr
or RLi
organometallic
OH
R
Alcohol
NaCN
OH
CN
Cyanohydrin
C=O
H2NR
C= NR
Imine
C — PAr3
ylide
C= C
Alkene
ROH/H2SO4
OH
OR
Hemiacetal
ROH
H2SO4
OR
OR
Acetal

V. Summary of Preparation of Aldehydes

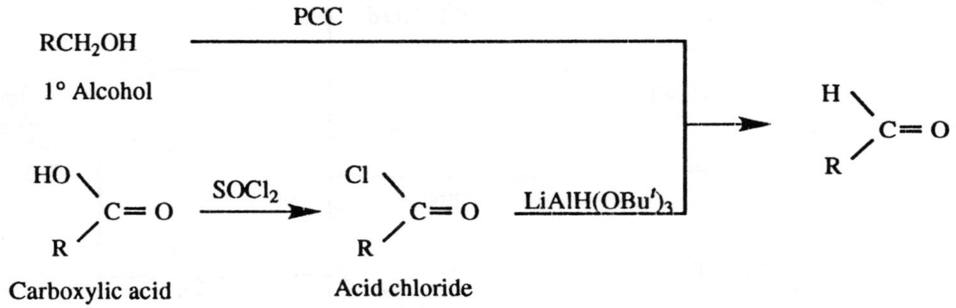
PCC
RCH2OH
1° Alcohol
HO
C= O
R
Carboxylic acid
SOCl2
Cl
C= O
R
Acid chloride
LiAlH(OBut)3
H
C= O
R

VI. Summary of Preparation of Ketones

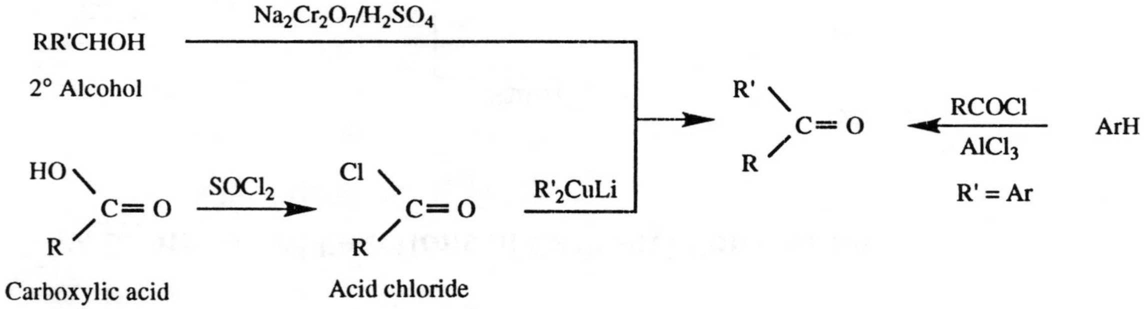
Na2Cr2O7/H2SO4
RR'CHOH
2° Alcohol
HO
C= O
R
Carboxylic acid
SOCl2
Cl
C= O
R
Acid chloride
R'2CuLi
R'
C= O
R
RCOCl
AlCl3
R' = Ar
ArH

VII. Solutions to Problems

For "**How to Solve a Problem,**" review pages 450, 457, 468, 474, and 481.

13.1

(a) $CH_3CH_2CH(CH_3)CHO$ or 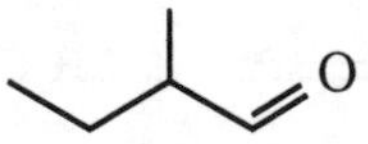 (b) 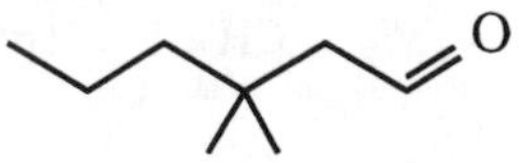

(c) 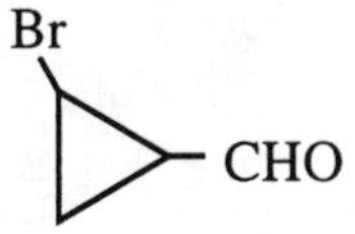 (d) 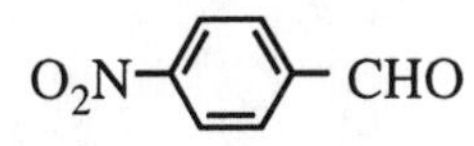 (e) $CH_3CH_2C{\equiv}CCHO$

13.2 (a) 2-methylpropanal; (b) 4-methylcyclohexanecarbaldehyde; (c) *trans*-5-methyl-2,4-hexadienal or 5-methyl-2*E*,4-hexadienal; (d) 3-methoxybutanal; (e) *m*-ethoxybenzaldehyde; (f) 2-cyclopentenecarbaldehyde.

13.3

(a) $CH_3CH_2COCH_2CH_3$ or 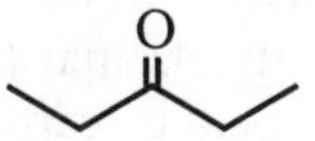 (b) 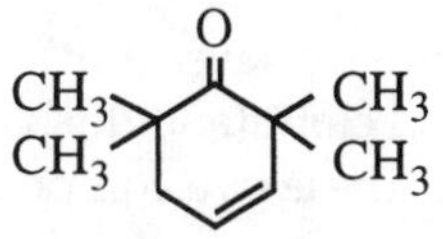

(c) 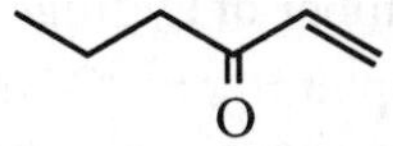

13.4 (a) 3-phenyl-2-butanone; (b) 1,4-pentadien-3-one; (c) 3-fluorocyclohex-2-enone; (d) 7-(*N*-methylamino)-5-octyn-2-one.

13.5

(a) 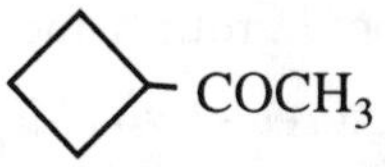 (b) 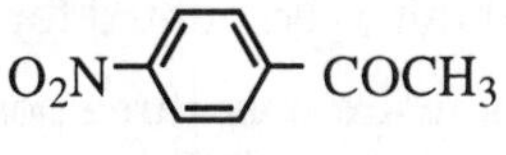 (c) 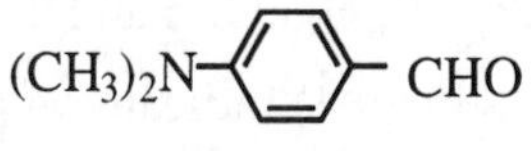

(d) 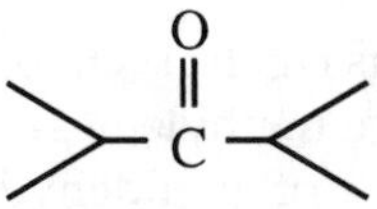 (e) 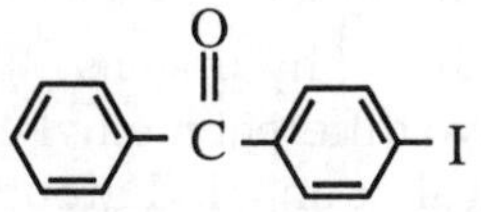 (f) $CH_3CH_2COCH_2CH_3$

13.6

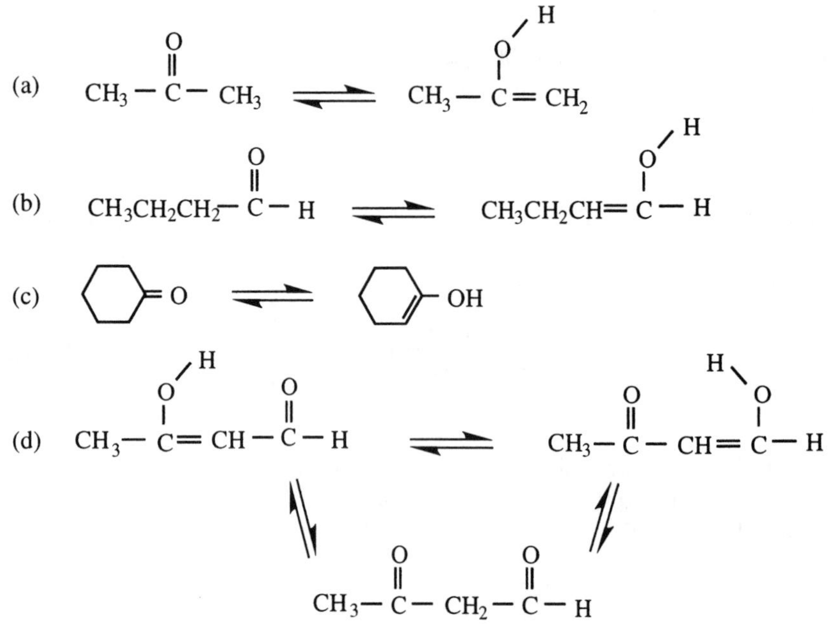

13.7 There are several other aldehydes which fit the experimental observations. Two of those are cyclobutane derivatives, cyclobutylethanal (**A**) and 2-methylcyclobutanecarbaldehyde (**B**). These two compounds and cyclopentanecarbaldehyde (**C**) could be distinguished using ^{1}H-NMR spectroscopy (key distinguishing features are the number of hydrogens α to the carbonyl group (**B** & **C** vs **A**) and the presence of a methyl group in **B**) or ^{13}C-NMR spectroscopy (**A** has five different carbons, **B** has six different carbons, and **C** has four different carbons).

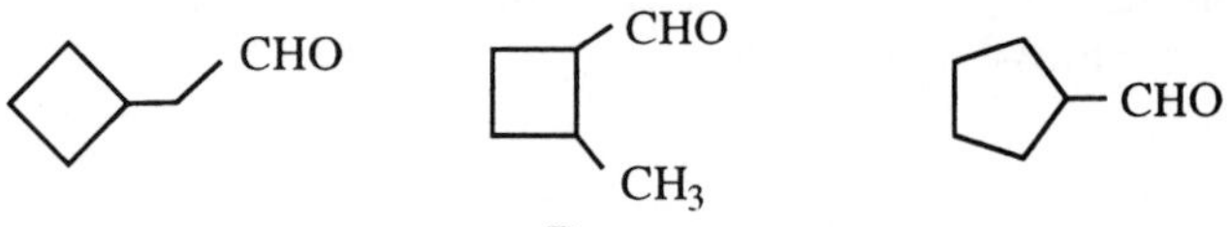
CHO
CHO
CH3
CHO

A **B** **C**

13.8 C_4H_8O has an HDI of one and this is accounted for by a carbonyl group which the IR (1700 cm^{-1}) indicates is present. There are only three possible structures - two aldehydes (butanal and 2-methylpropanal) and one ketone (2-butanone). Consideration of the area ratios in the ^{1}H-NMR and the known number of hydrogens (8) the peak areas can be seen to represent 3, 2 and 3 hydrogens, typical of two different methyl groups and one methylene group. The triplet-quartet pattern is typical of an ethyl group. The absence of an aldehyde hydrogen rules out the two possible aldehydes. Therefore, the ^{1}H-NMR is consistent with the unknown structure being 2-butanone ($CH_3COCH_2CH_3$).

13.9 This isomer of C_4H_8O must be one of the aldehydes mentioned above (1-butanal or 2-methylpropanal) in view of the ^{1}H-NMR peak at 9.5 ppm. The doublet for the two methyl groups clearly indicates the presence of an isopropyl group [$(CH_3)_2CH$-], the methyl peak being split by the methinyl hydrogen. Therefore, the structure of this isomer is 2-methylpropanal, $(CH_3)_2CHCHO$.

13.10

(a) 

(b) 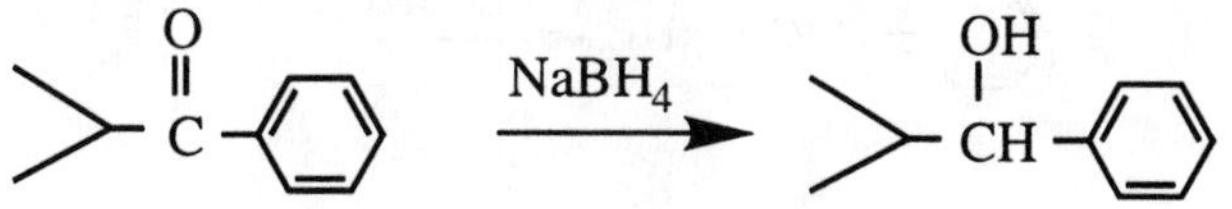

(c) 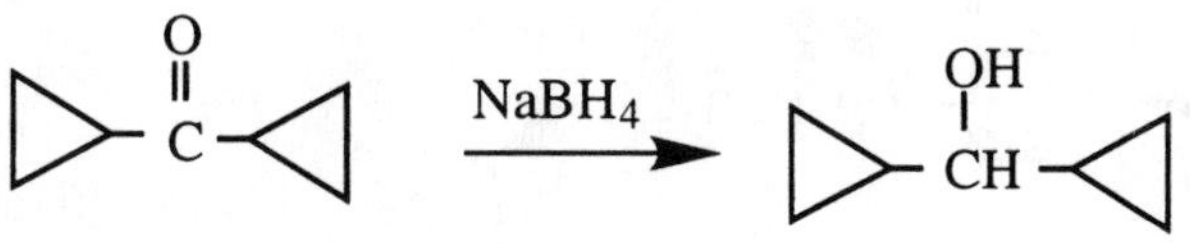

13.11

(a) 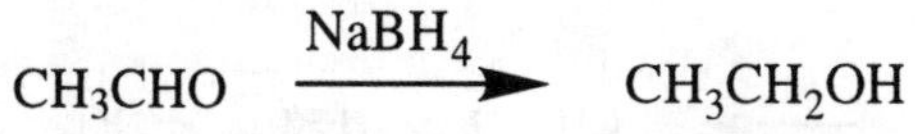

ethanol

(b) 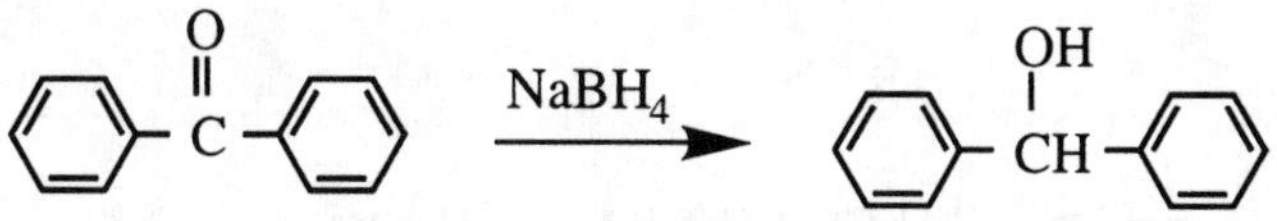

diphenylmethanol

(c) 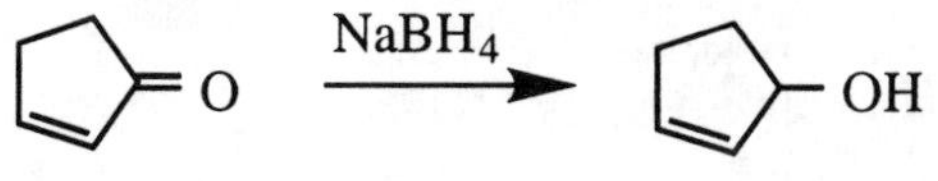

2-cyclopentenol

13.12

(a) 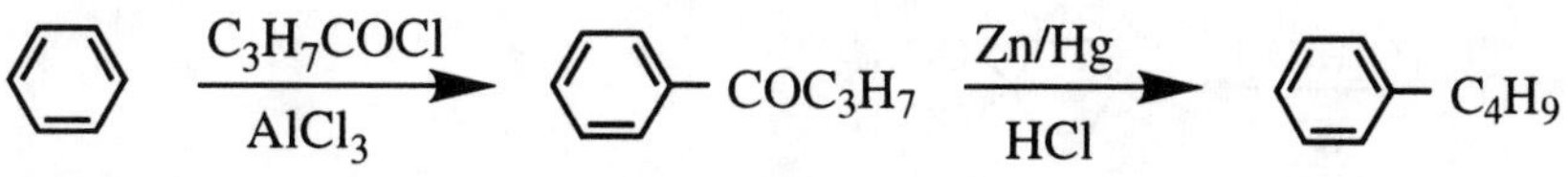

(b) 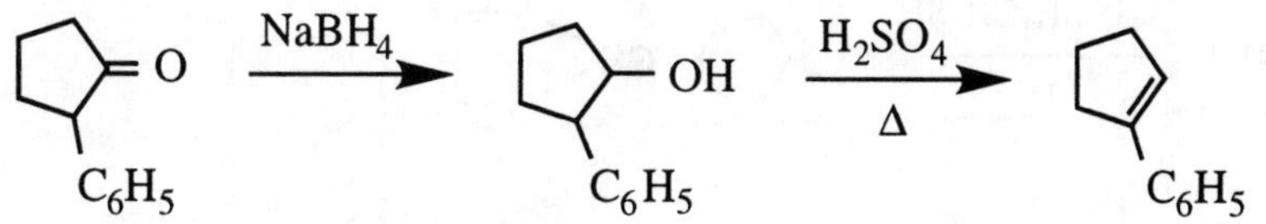

13.13

(a) 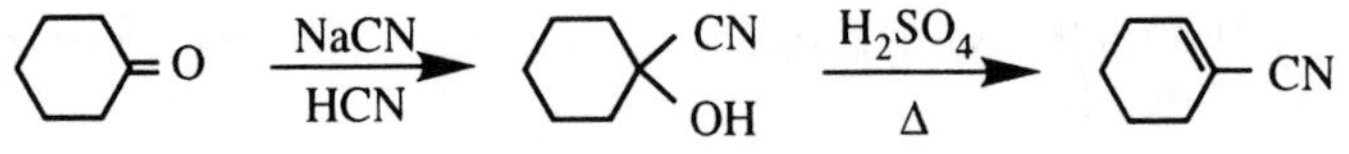

(b) 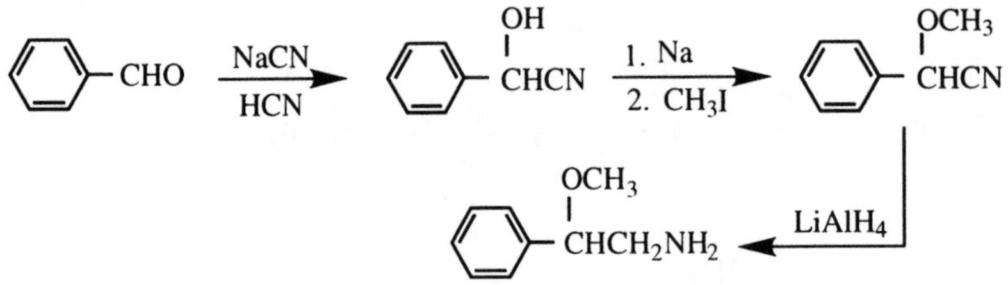

13.14

(a) 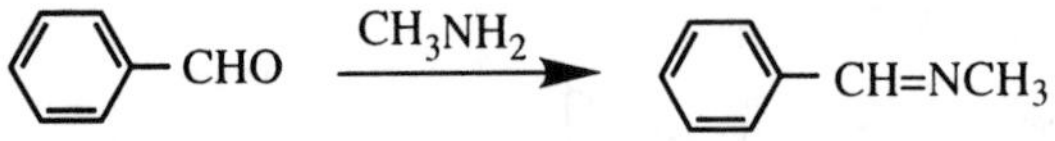

(b) 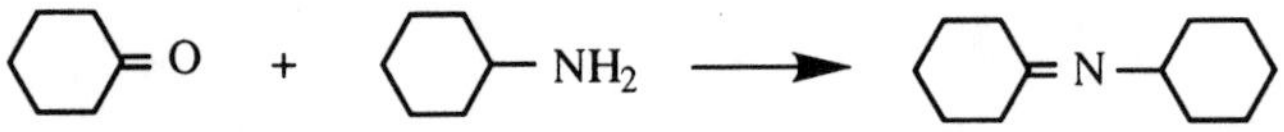

(c) 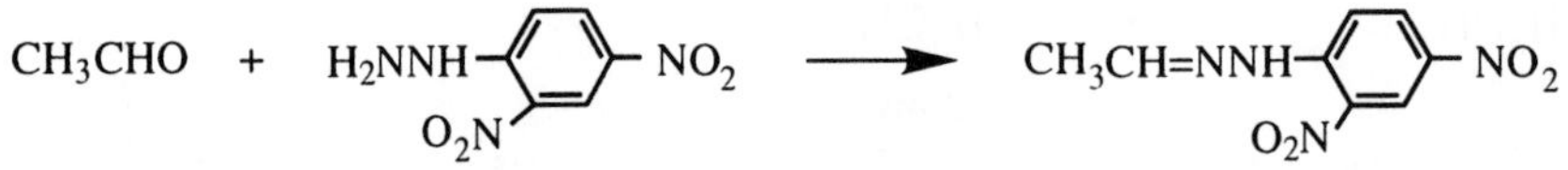

13.15

(a) $C_6H_5CH_2CH{=}NC_6H_5 \xrightarrow[H_2O]{H^+} C_6H_5CH_2CHO + C_6H_5NH_2$

(b) 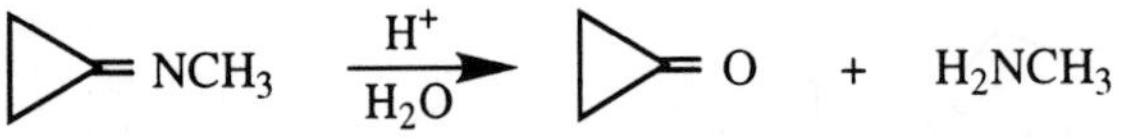

(c) 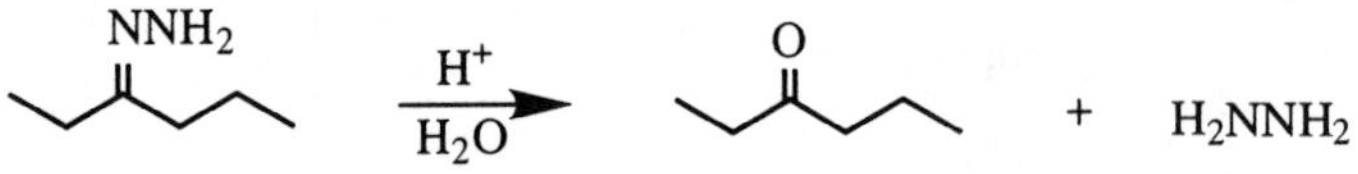

13.16

(a) 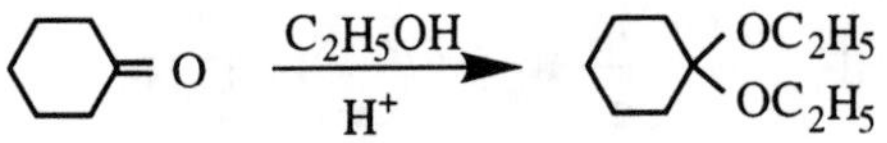

(b) 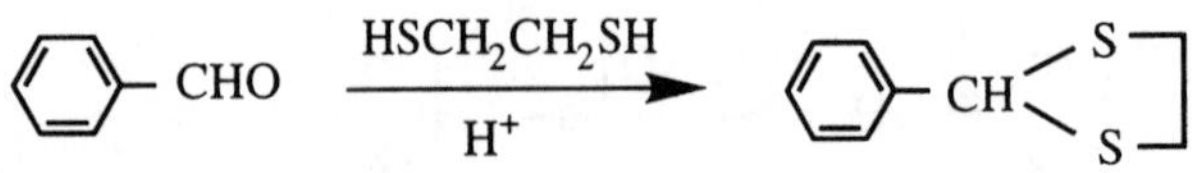

(c) 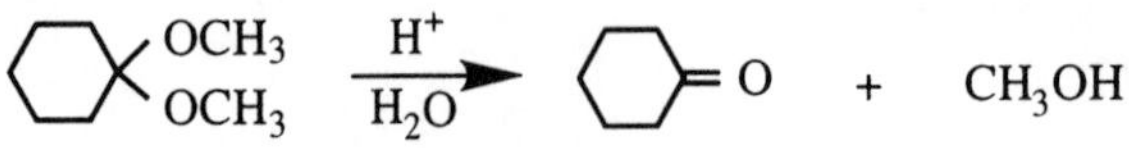

13.17

(a)

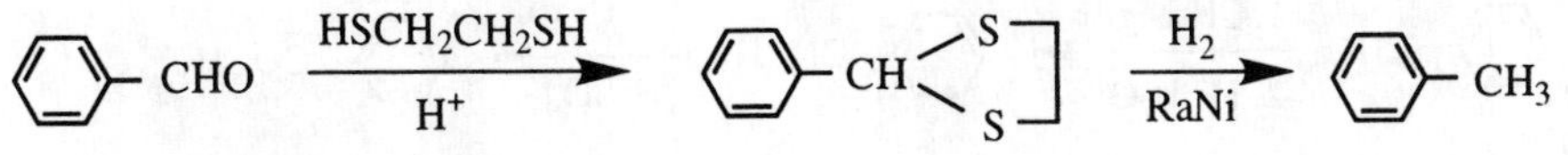
CHO
HSCH2CH2SH
H+
CH
S
S
H2
RaNi
CH3

(b)

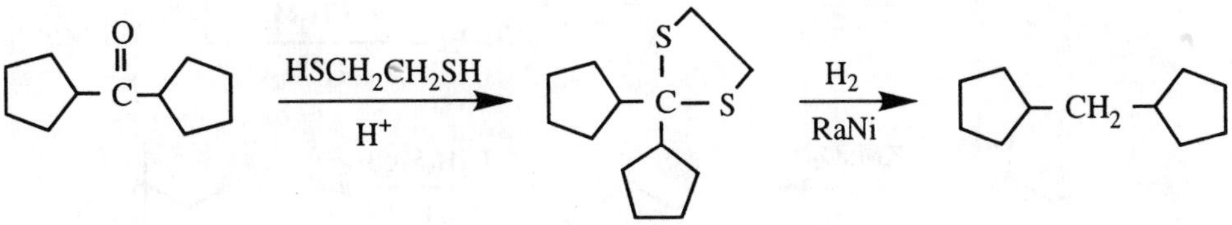
O
C
HSCH2CH2SH
H+
S
C
S
H2
RaNi
CH2

13.18 Retrosynthetic analysis of the desired product, 2-phenyl-2-butanol indicates that there are three possible combinations of ketones and Grignard reagents from which it could be obtained. The second and third shown below are the two methods in addition to that shown in the example problem.

$$CH_3CH_2C(C_6H_5)(OH)CH_3 \Rightarrow CH_3CH_2COCH_3 + C_6H_5MgBr$$

$$CH_3CH_2C(C_6H_5)(OH)CH_3 \Rightarrow CH_3CH_2COC_6H_5 + CH_3Li$$

$$CH_3CH_2C(C_6H_5)(OH)CH_3 \Rightarrow C_6H_5COCH_3 + CH_3CH_2Li$$

13.19

(a) $C_6H_5COCH_3 \xrightarrow[2.\ H^+/H_2O]{1.\ CH_3CH_2CH_2MgBr} CH_3C(C_6H_5)(OH)CH_2CH_2CH_3$

2-phenyl-2-pentanol

(b)

O
1. CH3MgBr
2. H+/H2O
OH
CH3
H2SO4
Δ
CH3

1-methylcyclobutene

(c) CH_3CHO

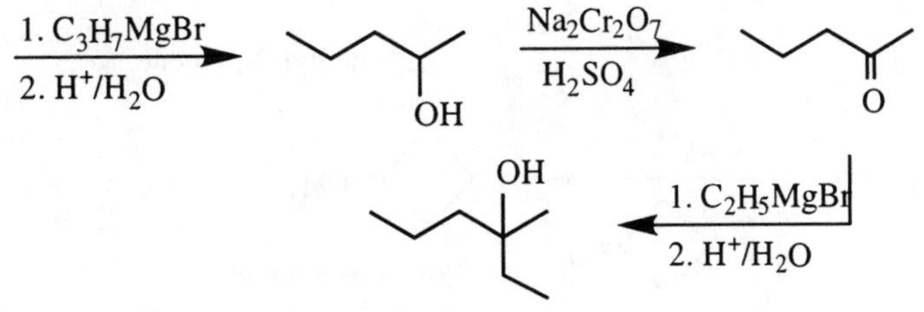
1. C3H7MgBr
2. H+/H2O
OH
Na2Cr2O7
H2SO4
O
OH
1. C2H5MgBr
2. H+/H2O

3-methyl-3-hexanol

13.20

(a) 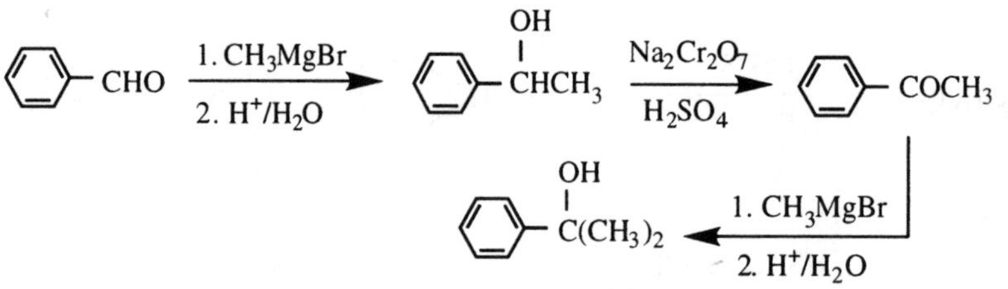

(b) 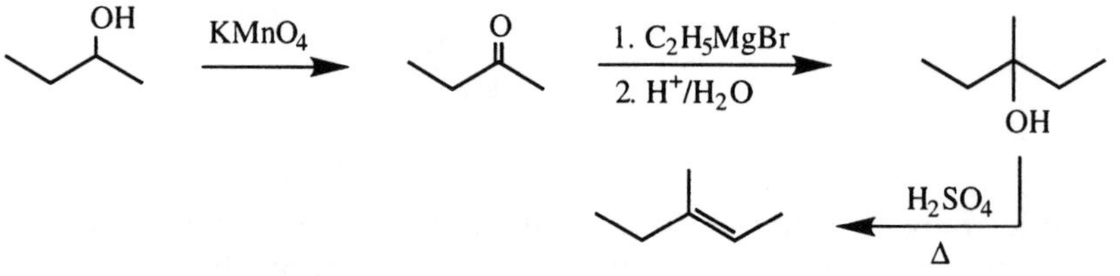

*(c) 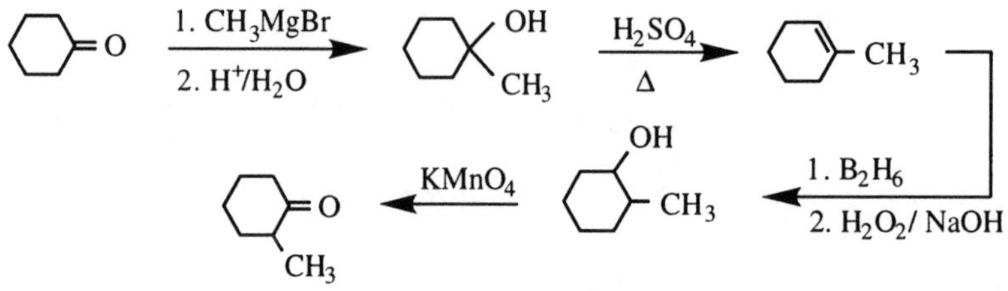

13.21

(a) $(C_6H_5)_3\overset{+}{P}\text{-}CH_2C_6H_5 \xrightarrow{C_4H_9Li} (C_6H_5)_3\overset{+}{P}\text{-}\overset{-}{C}HC_6H_5 \xrightarrow{C_6H_5CHO} C_6H_5CH{=}CHC_6H_5$

(b) 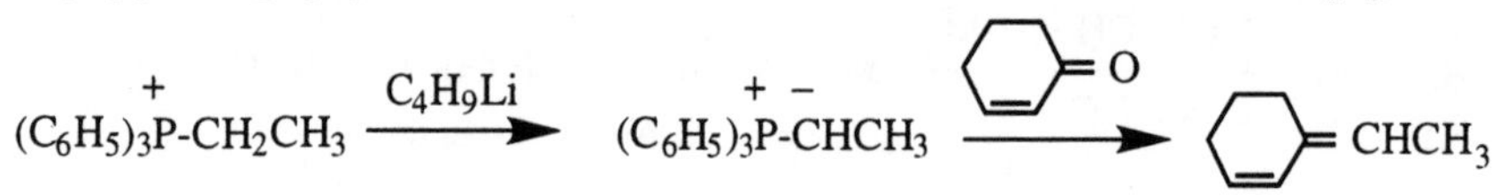

13.22

(a) 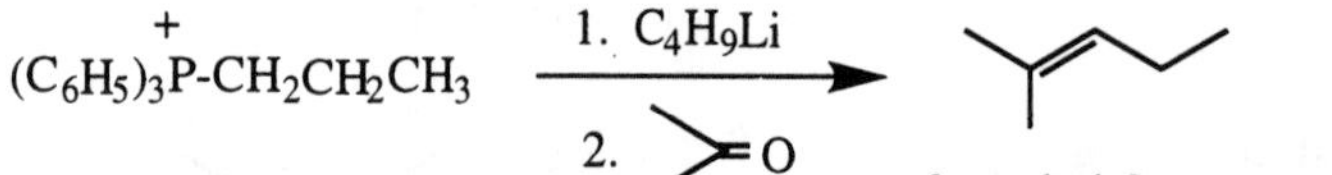

2-methyl-2-pentene

(b) 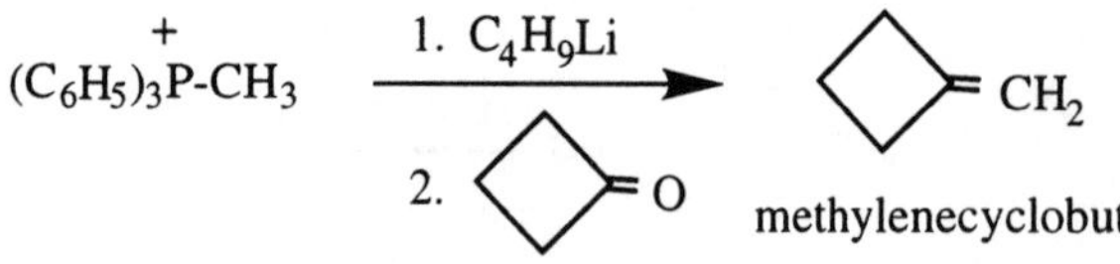

methylenecyclobutane

(c) $(C_6H_5)_3\overset{+}{P}\text{-}CH_2CH{=}CH_2 \xrightarrow[2.\ C_6H_5CHO]{1.\ C_4H_9Li} C_6H_5CH{=}CH\text{-}CH{=}CH_2$

1-phenyl-1,3-butadiene

13.23

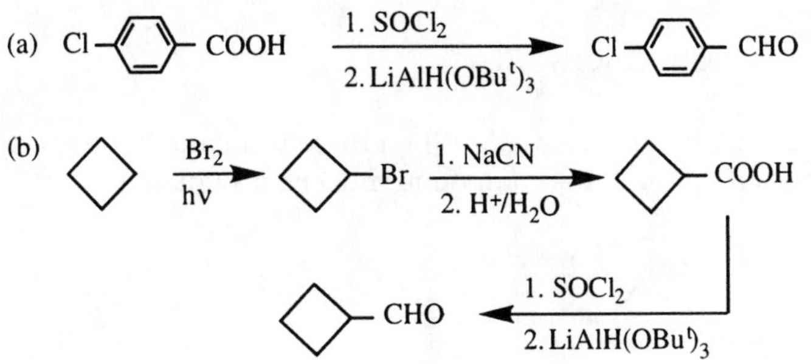
(a)
Cl
COOH
1. SOCl2
2. LiAlH(OBut)3
Cl
CHO
(b)
Br2
hν
Br
1. NaCN
2. H+/H2O
COOH
CHO
1. SOCl2
2. LiAlH(OBut)3

13.24

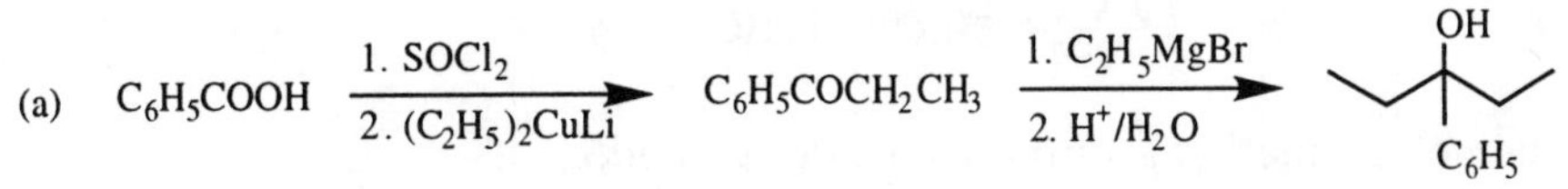
(a)
C6H5COOH
1. SOCl2
2. (C2H5)2CuLi
C6H5COCH2CH3
1. C2H5MgBr
2. H+/H2O
OH
C6H5

(b) $C_6H_5CH_3 \xrightarrow[\Delta]{KMnO_4} C_6H_5COOH \xrightarrow[2.\ (CH_3)_2CuLi]{1.\ SOCl_2} C_6H_5COCH_3$

(c) $CH_3CH_2CHO \xrightarrow{HNO_3} CH_3CH_2COOH \xrightarrow[2.\ (C_2H_5)_2CuLi]{1.\ SOCl_2} (CH_3CH_2)_2CO$

13.25

(a) $CH_3CH_2CH_2COCH_3$ (b) 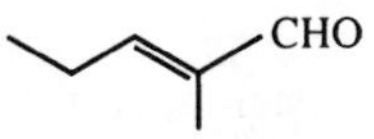
CHO
(c) 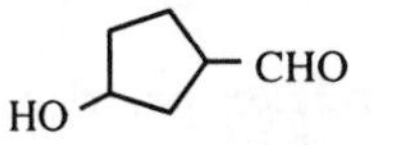
HO
CHO

(d) 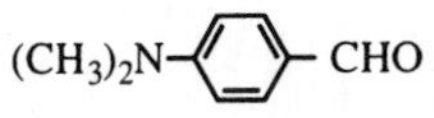
(CH3)2N
CHO
(e) 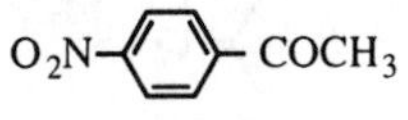
O2N
COCH3
(f) 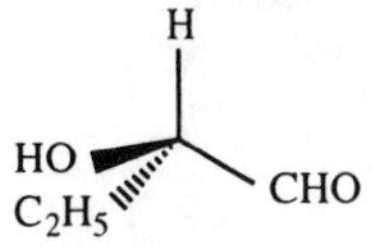
H
HO
C2H5
CHO

(g) CH_3COCH_3 (h) $CH_3CH_2COCH(CH_3)_2$ (i) $C_6H_5COC_6H_5$ (j) $C_6H_5CH_2COC_6H_5$

13.26 (a) *p*-nitrobenzophenone; (b) ethyl isopropyl ketone or 2-methyl-3-pentanone; (c) cyclohexa-2,5-dienone or 2,5-cyclohexadienone; (d) 5-hydroxypent-3-enal or 5-hydroxy-3-pentenal; (e) dicyclopropyl ketone; (f) *Z*-3-methyl-2,4-pentadienal; (g) *m*-*t*-butylbenzaldehyde; (h) 2-ethylpentanal; (i) *cis*-3,4-dihydroxycyclopentanone.

13.27

(a) $CH_2{=}CHCH_2COCH_3$ — 4-penten-2-one

(b) $C_6H_5CH_2COCH_2C_6H_5$ — 1,3-diphenylpropanone

(c) $C_6H_5CH_2CHO$ — phenylethanal

(d) $(CH_3)_3CCOCH_2CH_3$ — 2,2-dimethyl-3-pentanone

(e) $CH_2{=}CHCOCH{=}CH_2$ — 1,4-pentadien-3-one

13.28 (a) there cannot be a ketone at carbon number one - the compound would be an aldehyde. The correct name is butanal.

$$CH_3CH_2CH_2CHO$$

(b) cyclopentanal implies a five-carbon compound. When there is an aldehyde group on a cyclopentane ring (a six-carbon compound) the compound must be designated as cyclopentanecarbaldehyde;

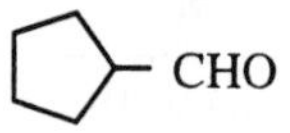
CHO

(c) propionaldehyde is not a IUPAC name. The correct name is 2-phenylpropanal.

$$CH_3CH(C_6H_5)CHO$$

(d) the position of the methyl group must be designated.

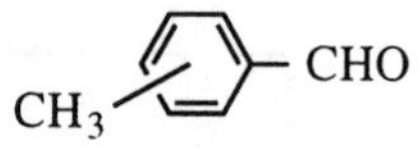
CHO
CH3

(e) there are no *cis-trans* isomers in propenal because of the two hydrogens on the terminal methylene group. The correct name is propenal.

$$CH_2{=}CHCHO$$

(f) the keto group takes priority in the numbering, so the correct name is 3-hydroxycyclohexanone;

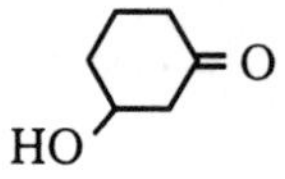
O
HO

(g) the ketone group has not been assigned the lowest possible number. The correct name is 5,5-dimethyl-3-hexanone.

$$(CH_3)_3CCH_2COCH_2CH_3$$

13.29 The boiling points increase in the order pentane < butanal < 1-butanol which is the order of the amount of energy required for dissociation before vaporization. There is no hydrogen bonding in pentane, there is slight dipole-dipole association in butanal, while there is strong hydrogen bonding in 1-butanol.

13.30

(a) $CH_3CH(OCH_3)_2$ — an acetal

(b) $CH_3CH{=}C(OH)CH_3$ — an enol

(c) $CH_3CH(OH)OCH_3$ — a hemiacetal

(d) 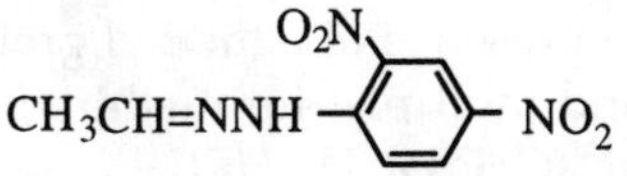
O2N
CH3CH=NNH
NO2
a 2,4-dinitrophenylhydrazone

(e) $CH_3CH{=}NCH_3$ — an imine

(f) $CH_3CH(OH)CN$ — a cyanohydrin

13.31 The α-hydrogen of propanal is slightly acidic because the resulting anion, which is a resonance stabilized enolate anion, is relatively stable. The adjacent carbonyl group provides opportunity for delocalization of the negative charge onto the oxygen, an atom which is electronegative and is "comfortable" being an anion (recall alkoxides).

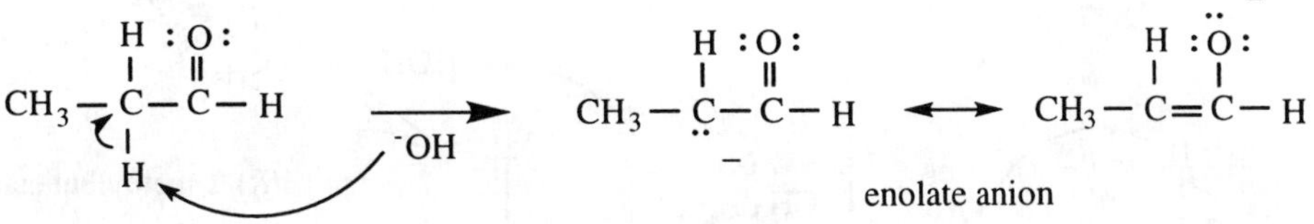
H :O:
CH3 C C H
H
⁻OH
H :O:
CH3 C C H
H :O:
CH3 C=C H
enolate anion

13.32 The most stable enolate will be that which has the most stabilized double bond. Recall that the higher the substitution on a double bond the more stable it is (see Section 6.2.3). Therefore **A** is more stable than **B**, and **C** is more stable than **D**.

(a) 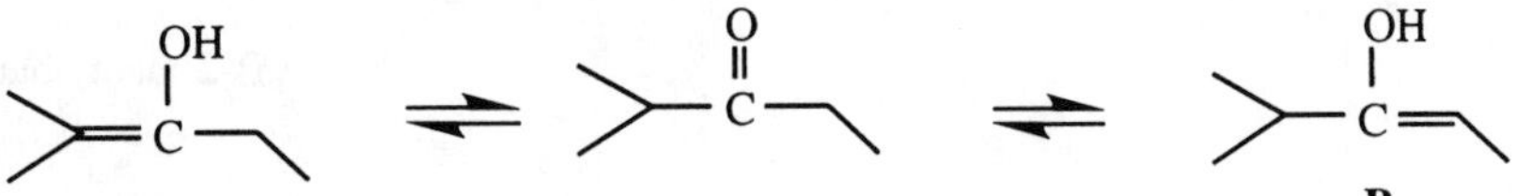
OH
C
O
C
OH
C
A **B**

(b) 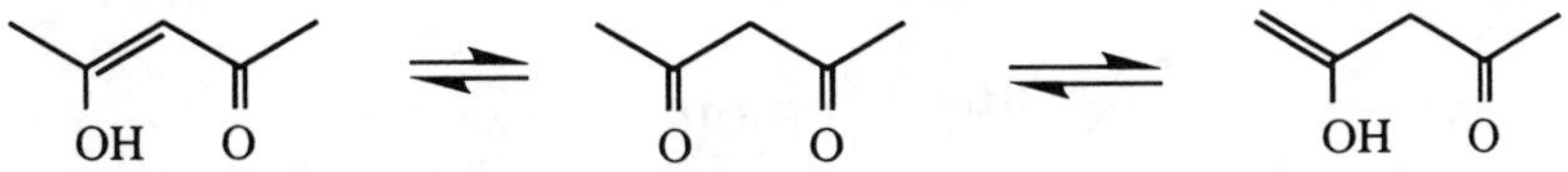
OH
O
O
O
OH
O
C **D**

13.33 The Tollen's silver mirror test (oxidation with ammoniacal silver nitrate) would be positive with an aldehyde but negative with a ketone. The use of ^{1}H-NMR also would be conclusive because of the unique appearance of an aldehyde proton near 9.5 ppm.

13.34 The IR indicates the compound has a carbonyl group which has a formula weight of 12 + 16 = 28. Therefore, the remainder of the molecule must have a formula weight of 72 - 28 = 44 which is satisfied only by C_3H_8 and the molecular formula therefore must be C_4H_8O.

Since the ^{1}H-NMR shows a peak at 9.5 ppm the compound must be an aldehyde, meaning there are only two possible structures, $CH_3CH_2CH_2CHO$ and $(CH_3)_2CHCHO$. The MS data is consistent with both structures, indicating the presence of a methyl group. The area ratios of 6:1 and the splittings (doublet for methyl and multiplet for methinyl hydrogens) clearly indicates the compound is 2-methylpropanal, $(CH_3)_2CHCHO$.

13.35 The removal of the α -proton from (*R*)-2-methylbutanal, (which is chiral) forms an enolate anion which has a plane of symmetry and therefore is not chiral. When the planar enolate anion is re-protonated in the equilibrium the proton may return to the top or bottom side of the planar enolate anion. Thus, there is equal probability of forming the *R*- or *S*-2-methylbutanal and the resulting 50/50 mixture is a racemate.

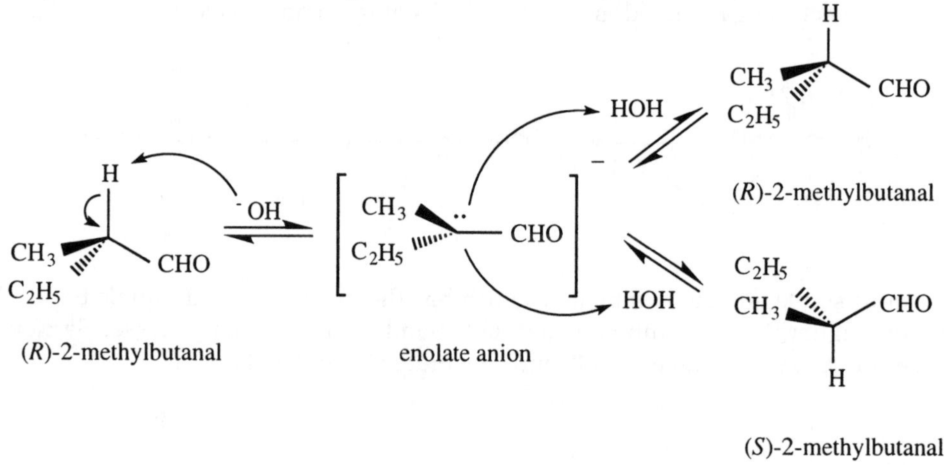
H
CH3
C2H5
CHO
⁻OH
(R)-2-methylbutanal
CH3
C2H5
CHO
enolate anion
HOH
HOH
CH3
C2H5
CHO
(R)-2-methylbutanal
C2H5
CH3
CHO
(S)-2-methylbutanal

13.36

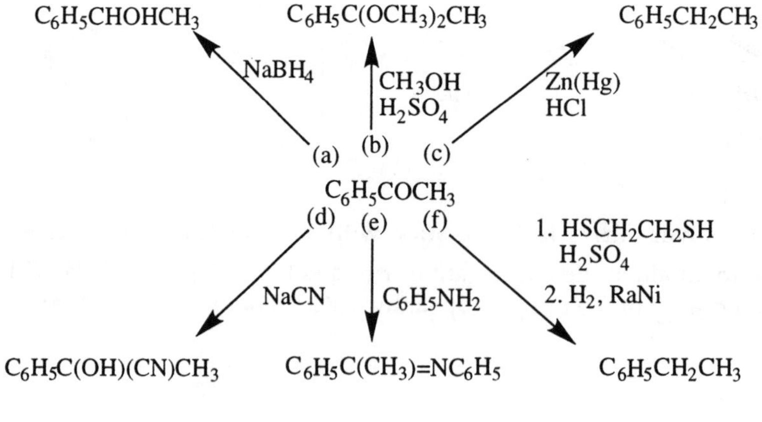
C6H5CHOHCH3
C6H5C(OCH3)2CH3
C6H5CH2CH3
NaBH4
CH3OH
H2SO4
Zn(Hg)
HCl
(a)
(b)
(c)
C6H5COCH3
(d)
(e)
(f)
1. HSCH2CH2SH
H2SO4
2. H2, RaNi
NaCN
C6H5NH2
C6H5C(OH)(CN)CH3
C6H5C(CH3)=NC6H5
C6H5CH2CH3

13.37

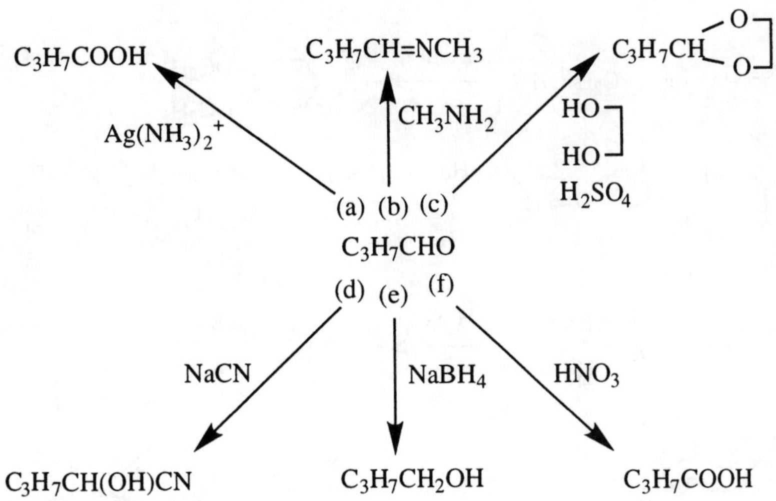
C3H7COOH
C3H7CH=NCH3
C3H7CH
O
O
Ag(NH3)2+
CH3NH2
HO
HO
H2SO4
(a) (b) (c)
C3H7CHO
(d) (e) (f)
NaCN
NaBH4
HNO3
C3H7CH(OH)CN
C3H7CH2OH
C3H7COOH

***13.38** In a homologation reaction a carbon must be added and use of the cyanohydrin addition accomplishes that goal. What remains is manipulation of the functional groups: (a) hydrolysis of the cyano group to a carboxyl group, (b) removal of the hydroxyl group (dehydrate to an alkene then hydrogenate to an alkane unit), and (c) reduction of the carboxyl group to an aldehyde group.

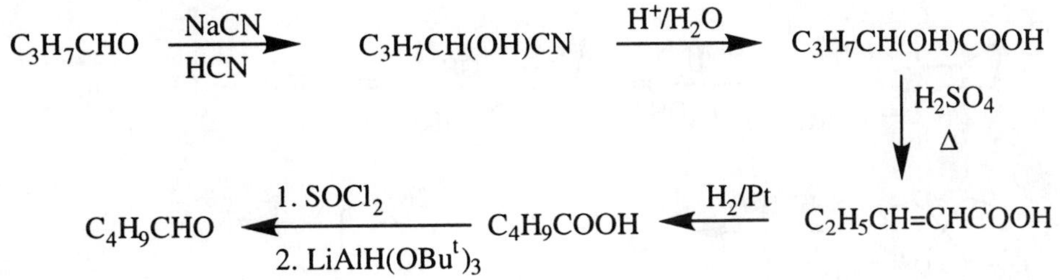
C3H7CHO
NaCN
HCN
C3H7CH(OH)CN
H+/H2O
C3H7CH(OH)COOH
H2SO4
Δ
C2H5CH=CHCOOH
H2/Pt
C4H9COOH
1. SOCl2
2. LiAlH(OBut)3
C4H9CHO

13.39 The transformation requires only replacement of the carbonyl group by a methylene group (replace a formyl group by a methyl group). This is accomplished by thioacetal formation and hydrogenolysis.

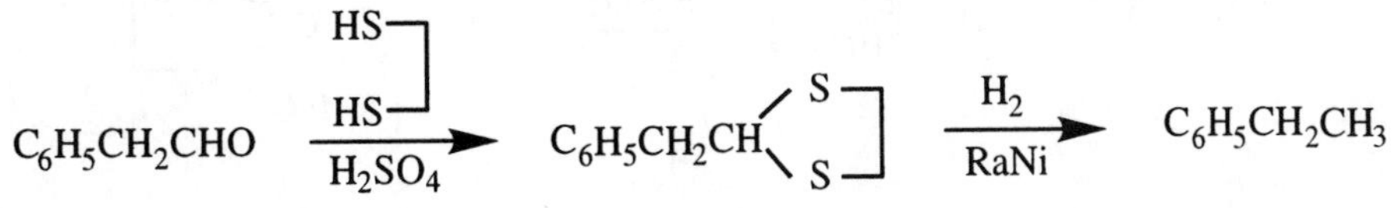
C6H5CH2CHO
HS
HS
H2SO4
C6H5CH2CH
S
S
H2
RaNi
C6H5CH2CH3

13.40

(a) 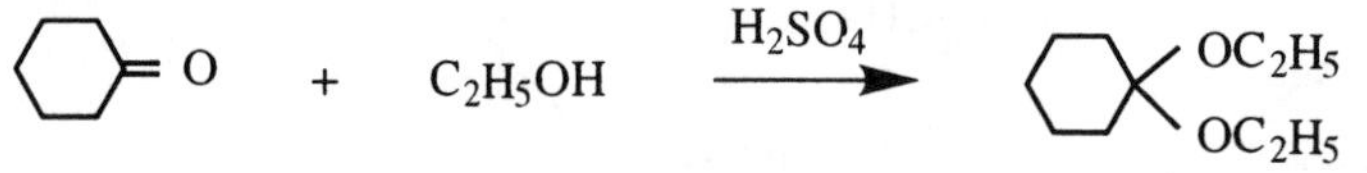
O
+
C_2H_5OH
H_2SO_4
OC_2H_5
OC_2H_5

(b) 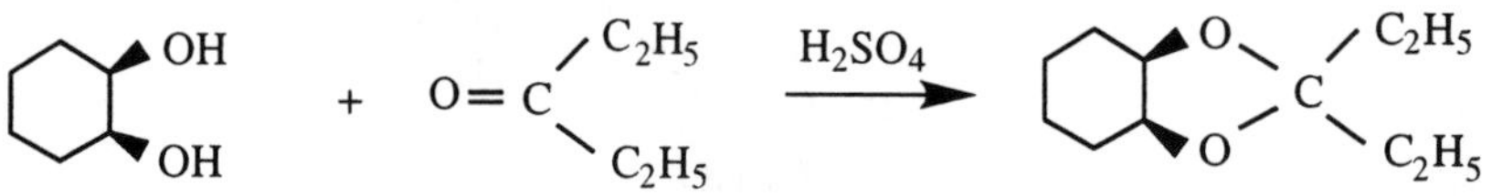
OH
OH
+
O= C
C_2H_5
C_2H_5
H_2SO_4
O
C
O
C_2H_5
C_2H_5

(c) 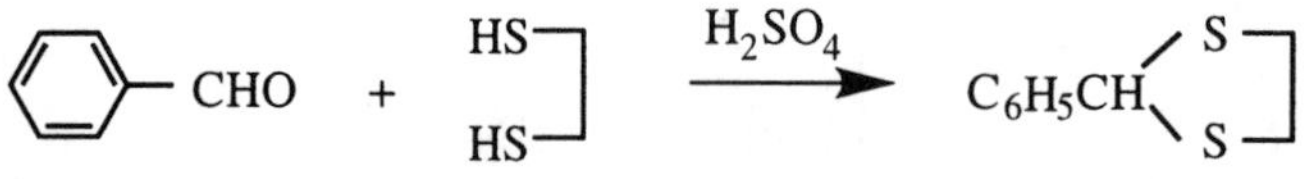
CHO
+
HS
HS
H_2SO_4
C_6H_5CH
S
S

(d) 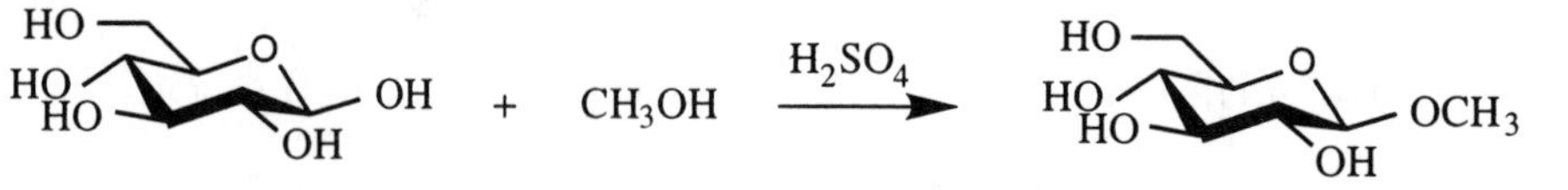
HO
HO
HO
O
OH
OH
+
CH_3OH
H_2SO_4
HO
HO
HO
O
OCH_3
OH

β-gluco-D-pyranose
(a hemiacetal)

methyl β-D-glucopyranoside
(an acetal)

13.41

(a) 
CH_3O OCH_3
H^+/H_2O
O
+ CH_3OH

(b) 
O
OCH_3
H^+/H_2O
$- CH_3OH$
OH
CHO
= $HO(CH_2)_4CHO$

(c) 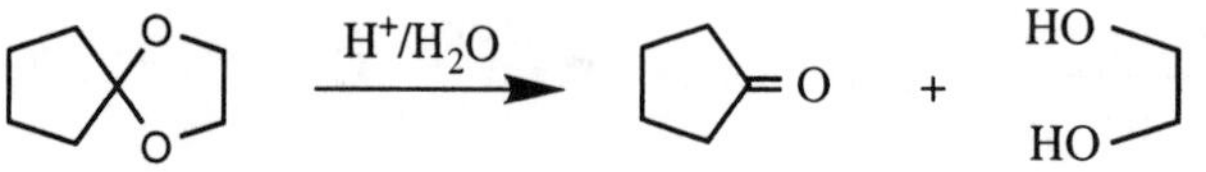
O
O
H^+/H_2O
O
+
HO
HO

13.42 The aldehyde group of propenal must be protected during the oxidation of the alkene group to a diol. This is accomplished by formation of an acetal. De-protection is accomplished using acid catalysis.

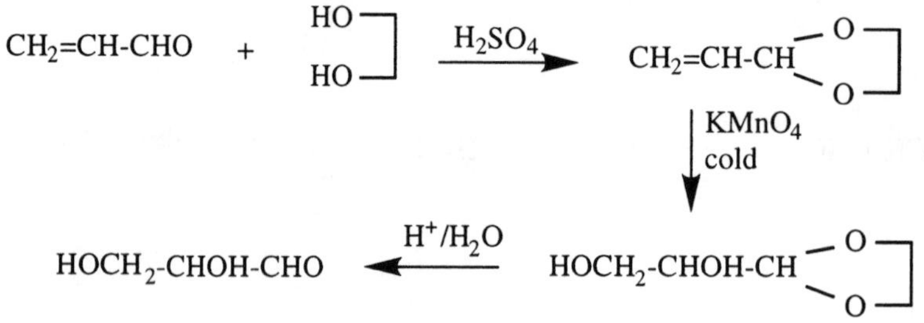
CH_2=CH-CHO
+
HO
HO
H_2SO_4
CH_2=CH-CH
O
O
$KMnO_4$
cold
H^+/H_2O
$HOCH_2$-CHOH-CHO
$HOCH_2$-CHOH-CH
O
O

13.43 (a) The Tollen's test with ammoniacal silver nitrate will be positive with benzaldehyde but not benzyl alcohol, forming a silver mirror.

$$C_6H_5CHO + Ag(NH_3)_2^+ \longrightarrow C_6H_5COOH + Ag^o\downarrow$$

(b) 2-Hexanone will react with 2,4-dinitrophenylhydrazine to form an orange 2,4-dinitrophenylhydrazone which precipitates.

$$\begin{matrix} CH_3(CH_2)_3 \\ CH_3 \end{matrix}\!\!>C=O \xrightarrow{H_2NNHC_6H_3(NO_2)_2} \begin{matrix} CH_3(CH_2)_3 \\ CH_3 \end{matrix}\!\!>C=NNHC_6H_3(NO_2)_2\downarrow$$

(c) Methyl vinyl ketone will react with Br_2/CCl_4, leading to decoloration of the reagent, whereas cyclobutanone will not react.

$$CH_2{=}CH\text{-}COCH_3 \xrightarrow{Br_2/CCl_4} BrCH_2CHBrCOCH_3$$

(d) Pentanal will react with the Tollen's reagent to form a silver mirror but 3-pentanone will not.

$$CH_3CH_2CH_2CH_2CHO \xrightarrow{Ag(NH_3)_2^+} CH_3CH_2CH_2CH_2COOH + Ag^o\downarrow$$

13.44 With carbonyl reagents glucose will react in its aldehyde form which is in equilibrium with the cyclic hemiacetal forms (α- and β-glucose).

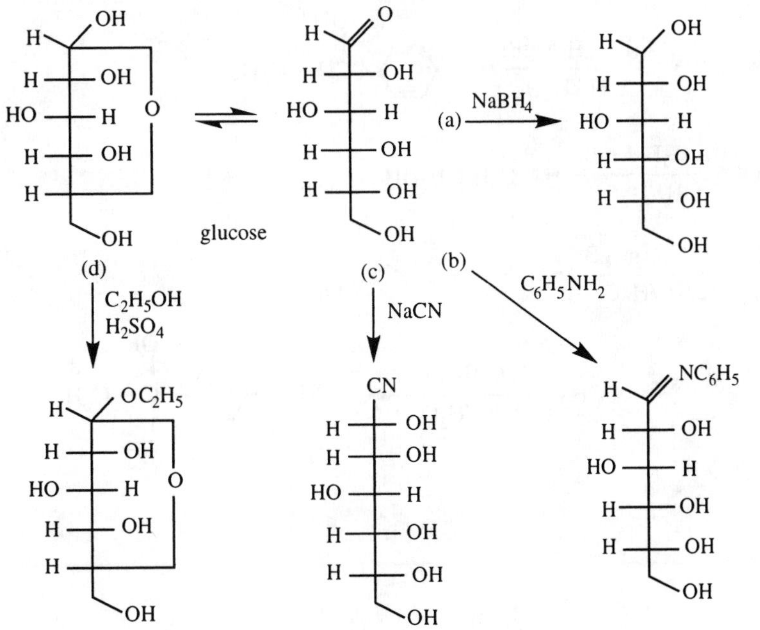

glucose
NaBH4
(a)
(b)
C6H5NH2
(c)
NaCN
(d)
C2H5OH
H2SO4
OC2H5
CN
NC6H5

13.45 4-Hydroxypentanal has the hydroxyl group located in a position favorable for formation of a five-membered hemiacetal ring. Therefore, in preference to forming an ordinary acetal this compound forms the relatively stable five-membered cyclic hemi-acetal which then reacts with methanol to form an acetal.

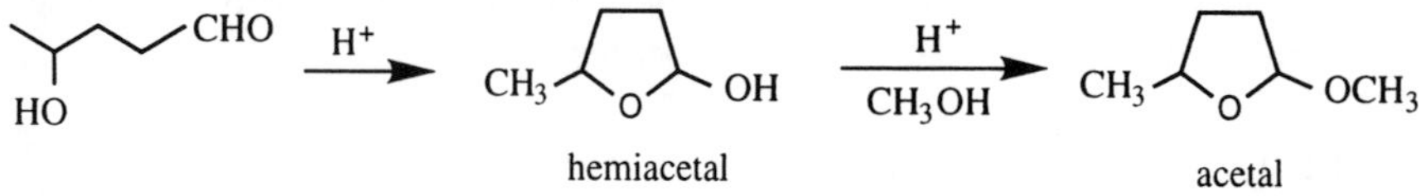
CHO
HO
H+
CH3
O
OH
hemiacetal
H+
CH3OH
CH3
O
OCH3
acetal

13.46

(a) 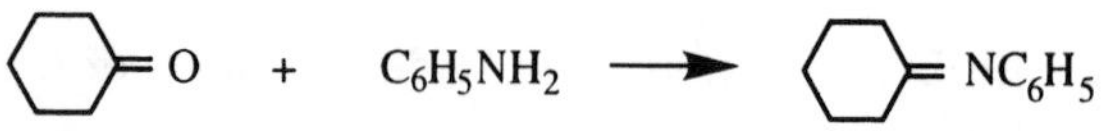
O
+
C6H5NH2
NC6H5

(b) 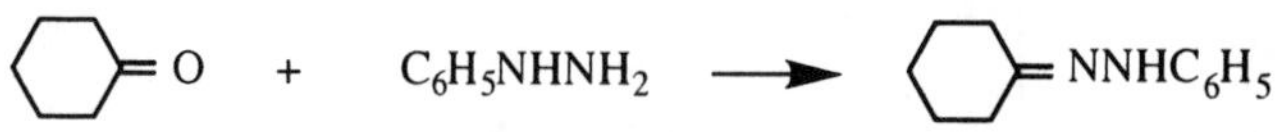
O
+
C6H5NHNH2
NNHC6H5

(c) 
O
+
H2NOH
NOH

(d) 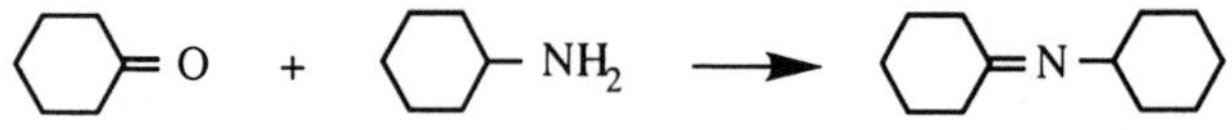
O
+
NH2
N

13.47

(a) 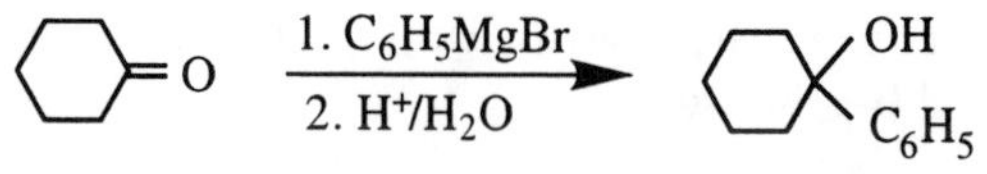
O
1. C6H5MgBr
2. H+/H2O
OH
C6H5

(b) 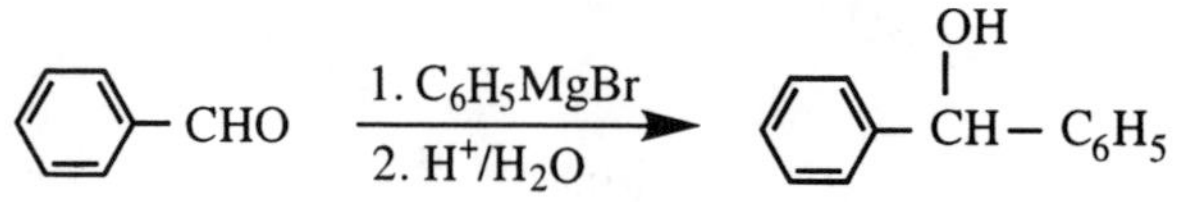
CHO
1. C6H5MgBr
2. H+/H2O
OH
CH– C6H5

(c) $H_2CO \xrightarrow[2.\ H^+/H_2O]{1.\ C_6H_5MgBr} C_6H_5CH_2OH$

(d) 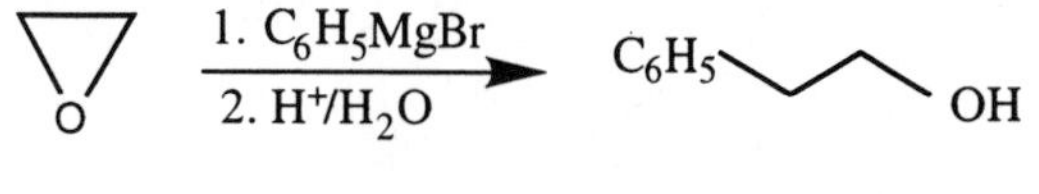
O
1. C6H5MgBr
2. H+/H2O
C6H5
OH

(e) 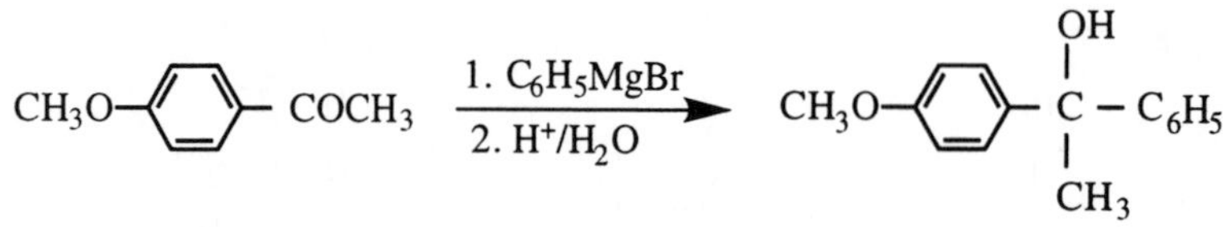
CH3O
COCH3
1. C6H5MgBr
2. H+/H2O
CH3O
OH
C – C6H5
CH3

13.48

(a) $CH_3CH_2Br + (C_6H_5)_3P \longrightarrow (C_6H_5)_3\overset{+}{P}\text{-}CH_2CH_3\ \ \overset{-}{Br}$

(b) $(C_6H_5)_3\overset{+}{P}\text{-}CH_2CH_3\ \ \overset{-}{Br} \xrightarrow{BuLi} (C_6H_5)_3\overset{+}{P}\text{-}\overset{-}{C}HCH_3$

(c) 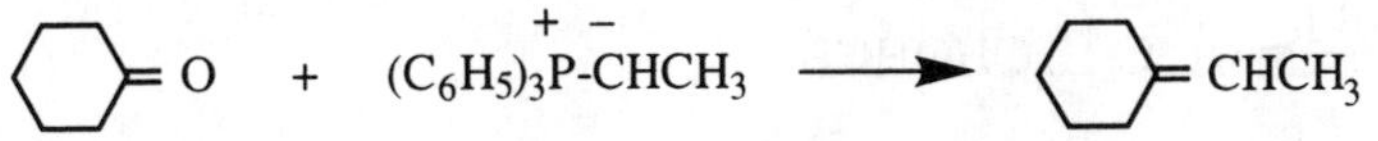

13.49

(a) $C_6H_5CHO + (C_6H_5)_3\overset{+}{P}\text{-}\overset{-}{C}H_2 \longrightarrow C_6H_5CH{=}CH_2$

$H_2CO + (C_6H_5)_3\overset{+}{P}\text{-}\overset{-}{C}HC_6H_5 \longrightarrow C_6H_5CH{=}CH_2$

(b) $CH_3CH_2CHO + (C_6H_5)_3\overset{+}{P}\text{-}\overset{-}{C}HCH_3 \longrightarrow CH_3CH_2CH{=}CHCH_3$

$CH_3CHO + (C_6H_5)_3\overset{+}{P}\text{-}\overset{-}{C}HCH_2CH_3 \longrightarrow CH_3CH_2CH{=}CHCH_3$

(c) $CH_3CH_2CH_2COCH_3 + (C_6H_5)_3\overset{+}{P}\text{-}\overset{-}{C}(CH_3)_2 \longrightarrow$

$CH_3COCH_3 + (C_6H_5)_3\overset{+}{P}\text{-}\overset{-}{C}(CH_3)CH_2CH_2CH_3 \longrightarrow$

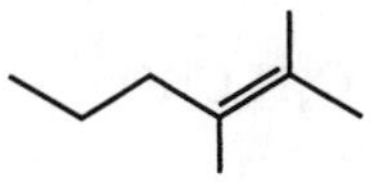

(d) 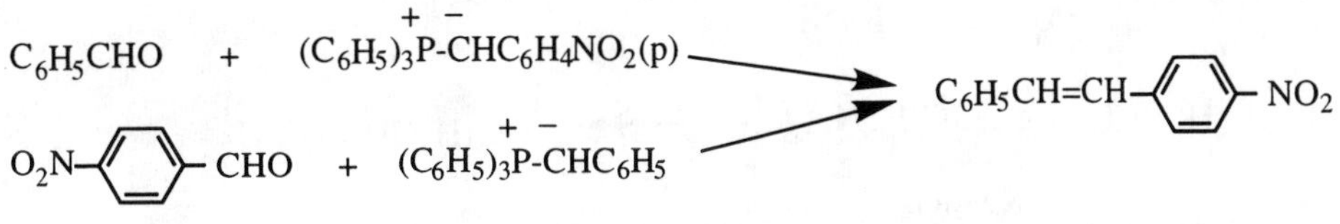

13.50

(a) 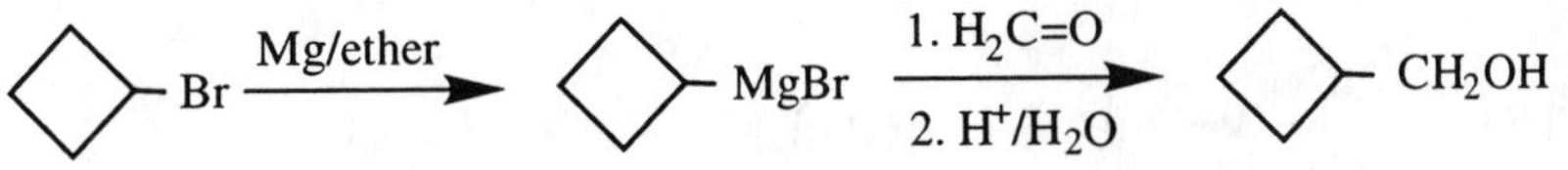

(b) $CH_3MgBr + CH_3COCH_3 \xrightarrow[2.\ H^+/H_2O]{1.\ ether} (CH_3)_3COH$

(c) $CH_3CH_2COCH_3 + C_6H_5MgBr \xrightarrow[2.\ H^+/H_2O]{1.\ ether} CH_3CH_2C(C_6H_5)(OH)CH_3$

13.51 (Note: In the following equations the group C_4H_9- represents the *n*-butyl group, $CH_3CH_2CH_2CH_2$-)

a) C_4H_9CHO + H_2NNH—⟨O_2N ... NO_2⟩ ⟶ $C_4H_9CH=NNH$—⟨O_2N ... NO_2⟩ 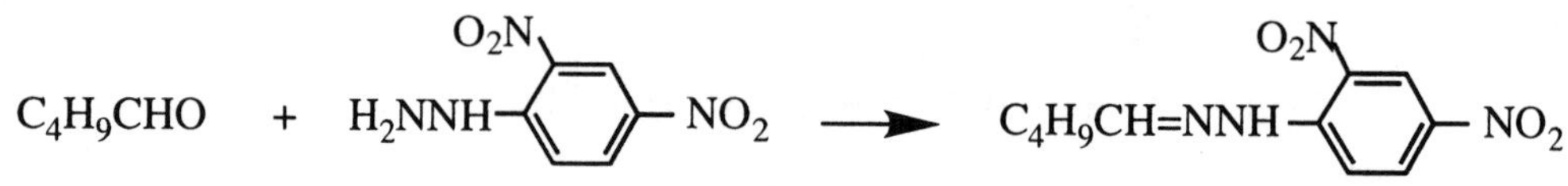

b) C_4H_9CHO $\xrightarrow{NaBH_4}$ $CH_3(CH_2)_4OH$

c) C_4H_9CHO $\xrightarrow{CH_3Li}$ $C_4H_9CHOHCH_3$

d) C_4H_9CHO $\xrightarrow{HNO_3}$ C_4H_9COOH $\xrightarrow{(e)\ SOCl_2}$ C_4H_9COCl

f) C_4H_9COCl + C_6H_6 $\xrightarrow{AlCl_3}$ $C_4H_9COC_6H_5$

g) C_4H_9COCl + $(C_2H_5)_2CuLi$ ⟶ $C_4H_9COC_2H_5$

h) C_4H_9CHO + C_6H_5MgBr ⟶ $C_4H_9CHOHC_6H_5$

i) $(C_6H_5)_3\overset{+}{P}\text{-}CH_3$ Br^- $\xrightarrow[\text{2. } C_4H_9CHO]{\text{1. BuLi}}$ $C_4H_9CH=CH_2$

j) C_4H_9CHO + $\begin{matrix} HS \\ HS \end{matrix}$ $\xrightarrow{H_2SO_4}$ $C_4H_9CH\begin{matrix} -S \\ -S \end{matrix}$ 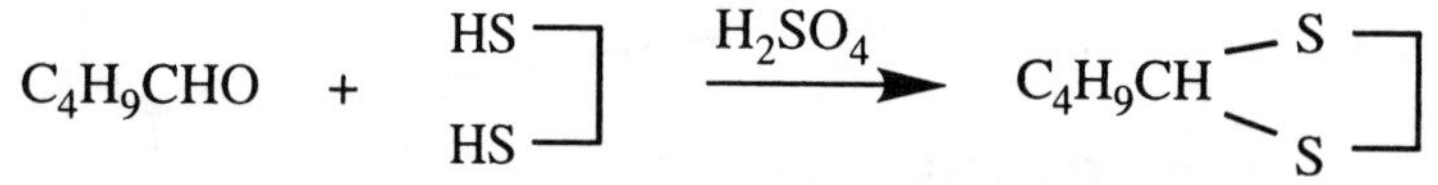

k) $C_4H_9CH\begin{matrix} -S \\ -S \end{matrix}$ $\xrightarrow[RaNi]{H_2}$ $CH_3(CH_2)_3CH_3$ 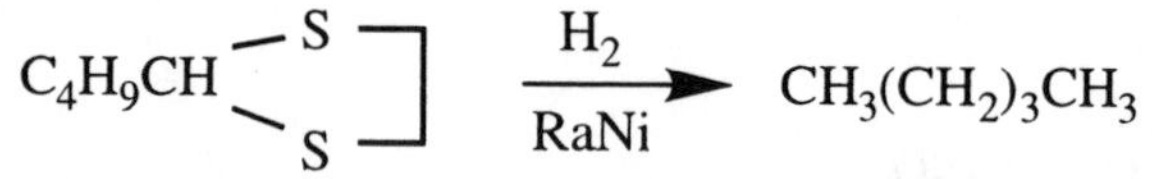

l) C_4H_9CHO + $C_6H_5NH_2$ ⟶ $C_4H_9CH=NC_6H_5$

m) C_4H_9CHO $\xrightarrow{KMnO_4}$ C_4H_9COOH

n) C_4H_9CHO + H_2NOH ⟶ $C_4H_9CH=NOH$

o) C_4H_9CHO $\xrightarrow[HCN]{NaCN}$ $C_4H_9CH(OH)CN$

p) C_4H_9CHO $\xrightarrow[H_2SO_4]{Na_2Cr_2O_7}$ C_4H_9COOH

13.52

a) $CH_3CHOHCH_3 \xrightarrow[H_2SO_4]{Na_2Cr_2O_7} CH_3COCH_3$

b) $CH_3CHOHCH_3 \xrightarrow[H_2SO_4]{Na_2Cr_2O_7} CH_3COCH_3 \xrightarrow{(C_6H_5)_3\overset{+}{P}\text{-}\overset{-}{C}HCH_3} CH_3C(CH_3){=}CHCH_3$

c) $C_6H_5CHO \xrightarrow{HNO_3} C_6H_5COOH \xrightarrow[2.\ (CH_3)_2CuLi]{1.\ SOCl_2} C_6H_5COCH_3$

d) 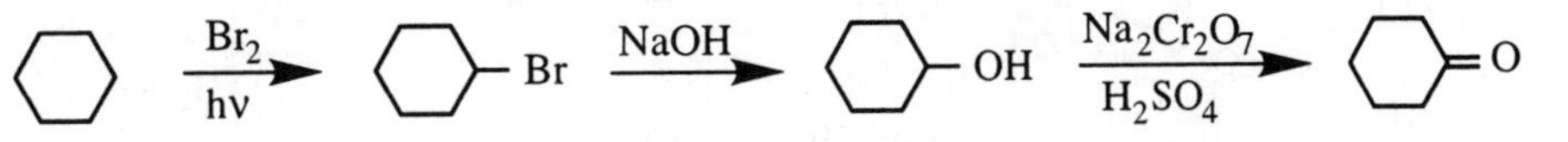

e) 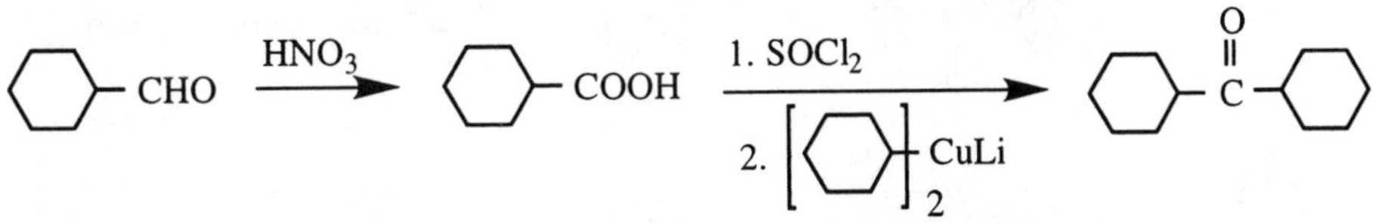

f) $C_3H_7OH \xrightarrow{PBr_3} C_3H_7Br \xrightarrow[2.\ CuI]{1.\ Li} (C_3H_7)_2CuLi \xrightarrow{C_2H_5COCl} C_3H_7COC_2H_5$

g) 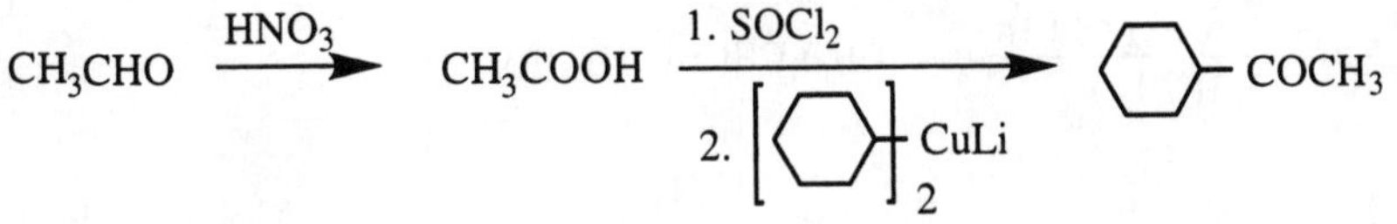

h) $C_6H_6 \xrightarrow[AlCl_3]{C_6H_5COCl} C_6H_5\text{-}CO\text{-}C_6H_5$

i) $CH_3CH_2CH_2OH \xrightarrow{PCC} C_2H_5CHO \xrightarrow[2.\ H^+/H_2O]{1.\ C_3H_7MgBr} C_2H_5CHOHC_3H_7$

***13.53** This is a typical synthetic problem that appears to involve moving a functional group, in this instance a carbonyl group. Of course, there is no means of accomplishing this directly. This change almost invariably means considering Markovnikov vs anti-Markovnikov addition to an alkene for the solution.

The carbonyl group can be reduced to an alcohol which can be dehydrated to an alkene. Re-addition of water with the opposite regiochemistry produces an isomeric alcohol which then can be oxidized to the desired carbonyl compound.

$$\underset{\text{propiophenone}}{C_6H_5COCH_2CH_3} \xrightarrow{NaBH_4} C_6H_5CHOHCH_2CH_3 \xrightarrow[\Delta]{H_2SO_4} C_6H_5CH{=}CHCH_3$$

$$C_6H_5CH{=}CHCH_3 \xrightarrow[2.\ H_2O_2,\ NaOH]{1.\ B_2H_6} C_6H_5CH_2CHOHCH_3 \xrightarrow[H_2SO_4]{Na_2Cr_2O_7} \underset{\text{1-phenyl-2-propanone}}{C_6H_5CH_2COCH_3}$$

13.54

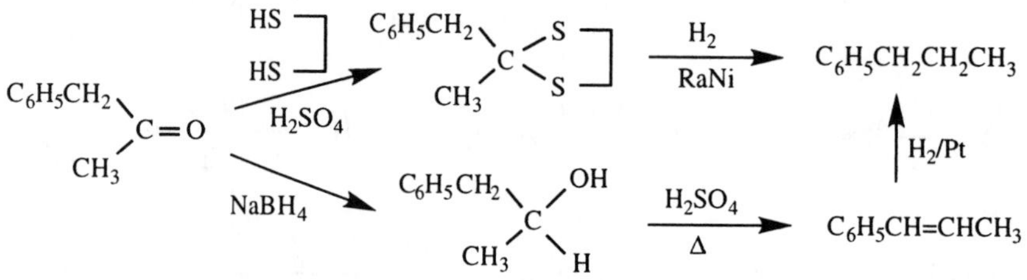

13.55

(a) $CH_3CH_2OH \xrightarrow[H_2SO_4]{CH_3CHO} CH_3CH(OC_2H_5)_2$

(b) $C_6H_5CH_2Br \xrightarrow[3.\ H^+/H_2O]{1.\ Mg/ether;\ 2.(CH_3)_2CHCHO} (CH_3)_2CHCH(OH)CH_2C_6H_5$

(c)

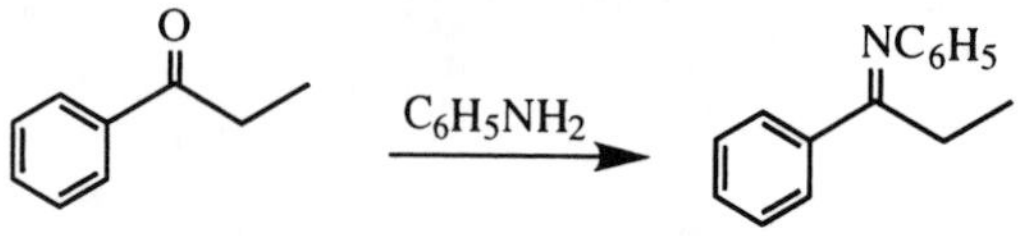

(d)

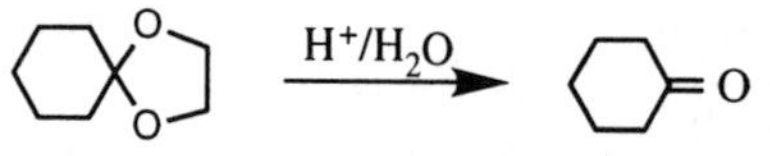

13.56

(a) $CH_3COCH_3 + (C_6H_5)_3\overset{+}{P}\text{-}\overset{-}{C}HC_6H_5 \longrightarrow C_6H_5CH{=}C(CH_3)_2$

(b)

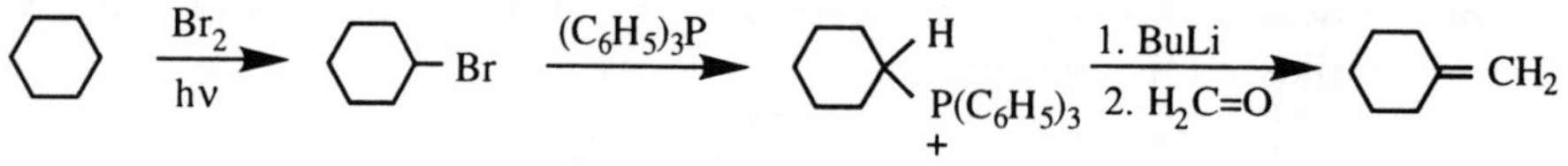

(c) $(CH_3)_3CH \xrightarrow[hv]{Br_2} (CH_3)_3CBr \xrightarrow[2.\ H_2C{=}O;\ 3.\ H^+/H_2O]{1.\ Mg/ether} (CH_3)_3CCH_2OH$

(d)

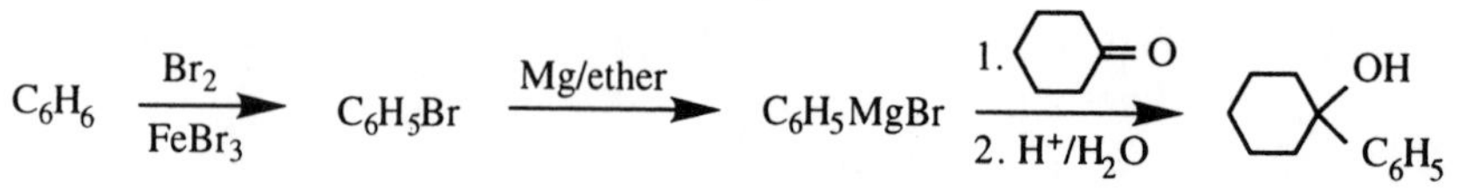

13.57

$(C_6H_5)_3\overset{+}{P}\text{-}CH_2\text{-}CH{=}CH_2\ Br^-$ $\xrightarrow[\text{2. } C_6H_5CHO]{\text{1. BuLi}}$ $C_6H_5CH{=}CH\text{-}CH{=}CH_2$

$(C_6H_5)_3\overset{+}{P}\text{-}CH_2C_6H_5\ Br^-$ $\xrightarrow[\text{2. } CH_2{=}CH\text{-}CHO]{\text{1. BuLi}}$ $C_6H_5CH{=}CH\text{-}CH{=}CH_2$

13.58

(a) $CH_3MgBr + (CH_3)_2CHCHO \longrightarrow (CH_3)_2CHCHOHCH_3$

$(CH_3)_2CHMgBr + CH_3CHO \longrightarrow (CH_3)_2CHCHOHCH_3$

(b) $(CH_3)_3CMgBr + H_2CO \longrightarrow (CH_3)_3CCH_2OH$

(c)

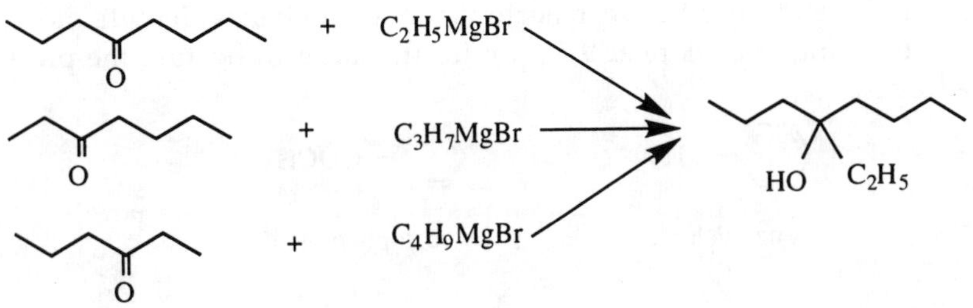

O
+
C2H5MgBr
O
+
C3H7MgBr
O
+
C4H9MgBr
HO
C2H5

13.59

(a) $CH_3COCH(CH_3)_2 \xrightarrow{NaBH_4} CH_3CHOHCH(CH_3)_2$

(b) $(CH_3)_3CCHO \xrightarrow{NaBH_4} (CH_3)_3CCH_2OH$

(c) This tertiary alcohol cannot be made by a reduction reaction. Only primary and secondary alcohols can be made by reduction of carbonyl compounds because, by definition, only such alcohols have at least one hydrogen (which is provided by the reducing agent) on the alcohol carbon.

13.60

$CH_3CH_2OH \xrightarrow{HBr} CH_3CH_2Br \xrightarrow{(C_6H_5)_3P} (C_6H_5)_3\overset{+}{P}\text{-}CH_2CH_3\ Br^-$

$\xrightarrow{BuLi} (C_6H_5)_3\overset{+}{P}\text{-}\overset{-}{C}HCH_3$

$(C_6H_5)_3\overset{+}{P}\text{-}\overset{-}{C}HCH_3 + C_6H_5COCH_3 \longrightarrow CH_3C(C_6H_5){=}CHCH_3$

2-phenyl-2-butene

13.61

(a) the Tollen's test with ammoniacal silver nitrate will distinguish between acetophenone and benzaldehyde by oxidizing the latter to benzoic acid and precipitating the reduced silver as a mirror.

(b) sodium metal will distinguish between cyclopentanone and cyclopentanol by producing bubbles of hydrogen from reaction with the hydroxyl group of the latter.

(c) Br_2/CCl_4 will distinguish between cyclopentanone and cyclopentene by adding to the double bond of the latter, causing the color of bromine to disappear.

(d) the Tollen's test with ammoniacal silver nitrate will distinguish between 3-pentanone and pentanal by oxidizing the latter to pentanoic acid and precipitating the reduced silver as a mirror.

13.62

(a) ^{1}H-NMR would distinguish between acetophenone and benzaldehyde most simply by the observation of a singlet peak near 9.5 ppm for the latter indicating the presence of an aldehyde hydrogen.

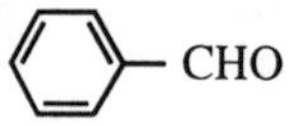
CHO

benzaldehyde

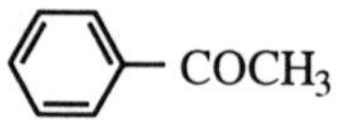
COCH3

acetophenone

(b) IR would distinguish between cyclopentanone and cyclopentanol by the presence of a carbonyl peak near 1700 cm^{-1} for the former and the presence of a hydroxyl peak near 3300 cm^{-1} for the latter.

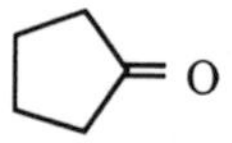
O

cyclopentanone

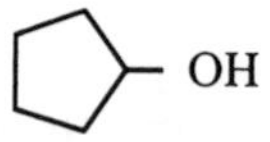
OH

cyclopentanol

(c) IR would distinguish between cyclopentanone and cyclopentene by the presence of a carbonyl peak near 1700 cm^{-1} for the former and the presence of an alkene peak near 1625 cm^{-1} for the latter.

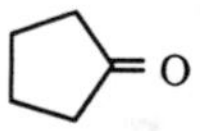
O

cyclopentanone

cyclopentene

(d) ^{1}H-NMR would distinguish between 3-pentanone and pentanal most simply by the observation of a singlet peak near 9.5 ppm for the latter indicating the presence of an aldehyde hydrogen.

$CH_3CH_2COCH_2CH_3$ — 3-pentanone

$CH_3CH_2CH_2CH_2CHO$ — pentanal

13.63

(a) $C_3H_7Br \xrightarrow{\text{Mg/ether}} C_3H_7MgBr \xrightarrow[\text{2. } H^+/H_2O]{\text{1. } C_6H_5CHO} C_6H_5CHOHCH_2CH_2CH_3$

(b) $C_3H_7Br \xrightarrow{\text{Mg/ether}} C_3H_7MgBr \xrightarrow[\text{2. } H^+/H_2O]{\text{1. } CH_2O} CH_3CH_2CH_2CH_2OH$

(c) $C_3H_7Br \xrightarrow{\text{NaOH}} C_3H_7OH \xrightarrow{\text{PCC}} C_2H_5CHO \xrightarrow[\text{2. } H^+/H_2O]{\text{1. } CH_3MgBr} CH_3CH_2CHOHCH_3$

(d) $C_3H_7Br \xrightarrow{\text{Mg/ether}} C_3H_7MgBr \xrightarrow[\text{2. } H^+/H_2O]{\text{1. } CH_3CHO} CH_3CH_2CH_2CHOHCH_3$

13.64

$(C_6H_5)_3\overset{+}{P}\text{-}(CH_2)_{10}CH_3 \xrightarrow{\text{BuLi}} (C_6H_5)_3\overset{+}{P}\text{-}\overset{-}{C}H(CH_2)_9CH_3$

$\downarrow (CH_3)_2CH(CH_2)_4CHO$

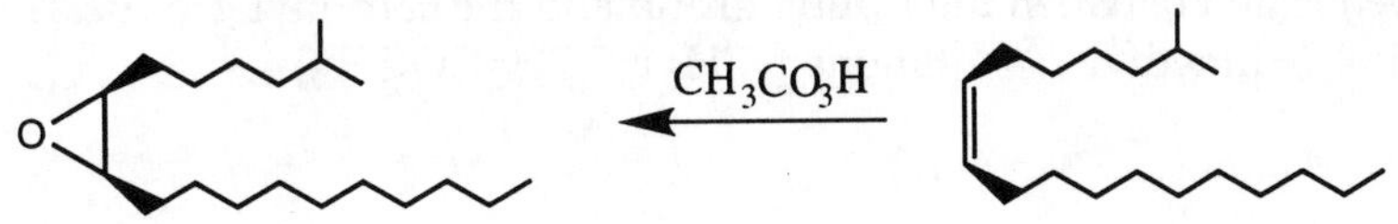
CH3CO3H
O

Disparlure

13.65 **A:** place a nitro group on the ring using HNO_3/H_2SO_4; **B:** reduce the nitro group using Fe/HCl; **C:** deactivate the amine by acetylating with CH_3COCl in the presence of pyridine; **D:** mono-chlorinate the ring in the *para* position using $Cl_2/FeCl_3$; **E:** conduct a Friedel-Crafts acylation using C_6H_5COCl (note the acylium ion will attack ortho to the acetamido group, the strongest activator on the ring); **F:** de-protect the amine by hydrolyzing the acetyl group using $NaOH/H_2O$: **G:** make the oxime derivative (an imine) of the ketone group using H_2NOH.

In a following step an amide is formed by reaction with α-chloroacetyl chloride. Upon warming the nucleophilic nitrogen of the oxime effects an internal S_N2 reaction to form a new ring and produce Valium, a widely sold relaxant.

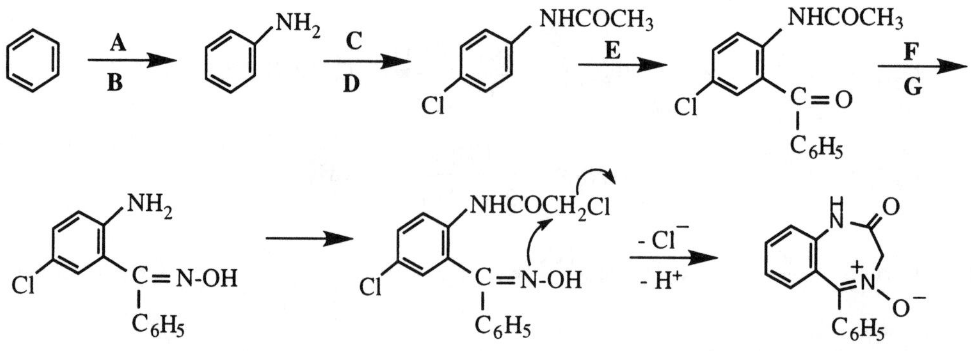
A
B
NH_2
C
D
$NHCOCH_3$
Cl
E
$NHCOCH_3$
Cl
C=O
C_6H_5
F
G
NH_2
Cl
C=N-OH
C_6H_5
$NHCOCH_2Cl$
Cl
C=N-OH
C_6H_5
- Cl^-
- H^+
H
N
O
N
O
C_6H_5

Valium

13.66 $C_7H_{14}O$ has an HDI of one so there is a ring or a double bond. The IR peak at 1720 cm^{-1} indicates a carbonyl group. The absence of a peak near 9.5 ppm in the NMR indicates the compound is not an aldehyde, so must be a ketone. The singlet at 2.5 ppm is typical of a methyl group next to a ketone (CH_3CO-). The singlet at 1.0 ppm is typical of three methyl groups on the same carbon (($(CH_3)_3C$-). This leaves only one carbon unaccounted for, and since it is a singlet of area = 2 (that is, there are no adjacent hydrogens to split this signal) it can only be located between the *t*-butyl group and the carbonyl group. Therefore, the compound is 4,4-dimethyl-2-pentanone [$(CH_3)_3CCH_2COCH_3$].

13.67

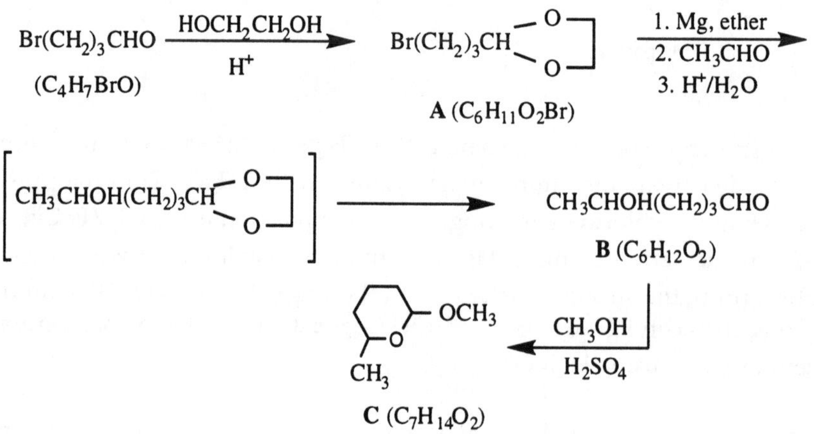
$Br(CH_2)_3CHO$
(C_4H_7BrO)
$HOCH_2CH_2OH$
H^+
$Br(CH_2)_3CH$
O
O
A ($C_6H_{11}O_2Br$)
1. Mg, ether
2. CH_3CHO
3. H^+/H_2O
$CH_3CHOH(CH_2)_3CH$
$CH_3CHOH(CH_2)_3CHO$
B ($C_6H_{12}O_2$)
CH_3OH
H_2SO_4
OCH_3
O
CH_3
C ($C_7H_{14}O_2$)

13.68 **A:** PCC; **B:** CH_3OH/H_2SO_4; **C:** cold $KMnO_4$; **D:** H^+/H_2O

$$CH_2{=}CH\text{-}CH_2OH \xrightarrow{A} CH_2{=}CH\text{-}CHO \xrightarrow{B} CH_2{=}CH\text{-}CH(OCH_3)_2 \xrightarrow{C}$$

$$HOCH_2CHOHCH(OCH_3)_2 \xrightarrow{D} HOCH_2CHOHCHO$$

Glyceraldehyde

13.69 **A:** NaOH to form the phenoxide then reaction with CH_3I to form the methyl ether (to protect the OH group); **B:** $NaBH_4$ to reduce the aldehyde to an alcohol; **C:** PBr_3 to produce the alkyl bromide; **D:** Mg/ether to form the Grignard reagent; **E:** CH_3CHO for the Grignard reaction followed by H^+/H_2O work-up; **F:** dehydration with H_2SO_4 to form the conjugated alkene; **G:** anti-Markovnikov re-hydration with B_2H_6 then H_2O_2/NaOH to form the alcohol; **H:** oxidation with $Na_2Cr_2O_7/H_2SO_4$ to form the ketone; **I:** HI to cleave the ether and de-protect the phenolic hydroxyl group.

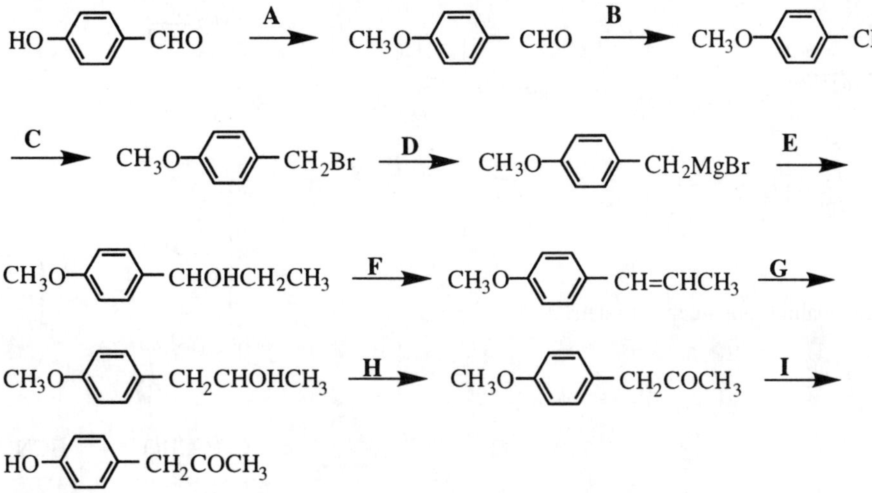
HO–C6H4–CHO
A
CH3O–C6H4–CHO
B
CH3O–C6H4–CH2OH
C
CH3O–C6H4–CH2Br
D
CH3O–C6H4–CH2MgBr
E
CH3O–C6H4–CHOHCH2CH3
F
CH3O–C6H4–CH=CHCH3
G
CH3O–C6H4–CH2CHOHCH3
H
CH3O–C6H4–CH2COCH3
I
HO–C6H4–CH2COCH3

13.70 The formula $C_{10}H_{12}O$ indicates an HDI of five. The IR spectrum indicates the presence of a carbonyl group (C=O) and the absence of NMR peaks near 9.5 indicates they are not aldehydes. The NMR peaks of area 5 near 7.0 ppm in both compounds indicate the presence of a phenyl ring (C_6H_5). Thus, all of the unsaturation is accounted for (carbonyl = 1 and phenyl = 4) and the atoms unaccounted for are C_3H_7. Therefore, the compounds must be phenyl derivatives of 2-butanone ($CH_3COCH_2CH_3$) with the difference being the position of attachment of the phenyl group, for which there are only three alternatives (C_1, C_3, and C_4 as shown in structures **A**, **C** and **B**, respectively).

The presence of a singlet methyl at 1.9 ppm in the spectrum of **B** indicates a $COCH_3$ group is present. The presence of a typical ethyl triplet/quartet pattern centered at 1.0 and 2.2 ppm in **A** indicates its structure can only be 1-phenyl-2-butanone. The two triplets in the spectrum of **B** indicate its structure is 4-phenyl-2-butanone, rather than the only other possibility of 3-phenyl-2-butanone (**C**) which would have a doublet (CH_3) and quartet (CH).

$CH_3CH_2COCH_2C_6H_5$	$C_6H_5CH_2CH_2COCH_3$	$CH_3CH(C_6H_5)COCH_3$
A	**B**	**C**

13.71 (a) The absolute configuration of amygdalin at the cyanohydrin carbon is *R*. (b) Acid-catalyzed hydrolysis will break the acetal linkage to form the free cyanohydrin of benzaldehyde and the hemiacetal of the disaccharide. The disaccharide (which is maltose) itself has an acetal linking the two glucose units. This linkage also will be hydrolyzed to form two equivalents of glucose. The cyanohydrin formation will be reversed upon hydrolysis to produce benzaldehyde and HCN.

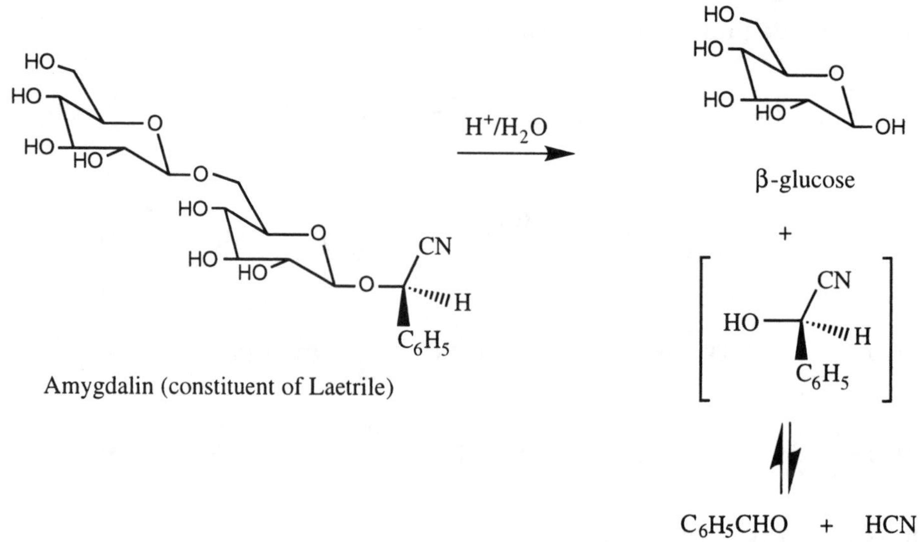
HO
HO
HO
HO
O
O
HO
HO
HO
O
O
CN
H
C_6H_5
H^+/H_2O
β-glucose
+
HO
CN
H
C_6H_5
C_6H_5CHO + HCN
Amygdalin (constituent of Laetrile)

VIII. Solutions to Problems

Dollars and Scents

The cosmetics company you work for is interested in developing a line of perfumes. Some in the company think that perfumes made strictly from all-natural sources might add special appeal to the product line and thereby give the company an advantage in a fiercely competitive market. Others wonder if the added cost of "all natural" would be too prohibitive. It's your job to gather samples to assess quality of scent and compare costs of natural versus synthetic.

You start with the fragrance of jasmine. One of your regular suppliers has some, but "jasmin absolut," the essential oil extracted from jamine flowers, is extremely expensive Three other suppliers offer you jasmine at just a fraction of what your original supplier wanted, but you wonder if what they are selling is really natural jasmine oil. You bring the four samples to a chemist you know and ask for analysis of the samples.

The IR spectra of all four of the samples show a peak near 1690 cm^{-1}. After obtaining ^{1}H-NMR and mass spectra, the chemist identifies some of the compounds present in the four samples. Sample #1 consists of Compound A and is fairly pure. Sample #2 is a mixture of compound A and its trans isomer. Sample #3 is Compound B. Sample #4 is a complex mixture that includes compound A as a major component.

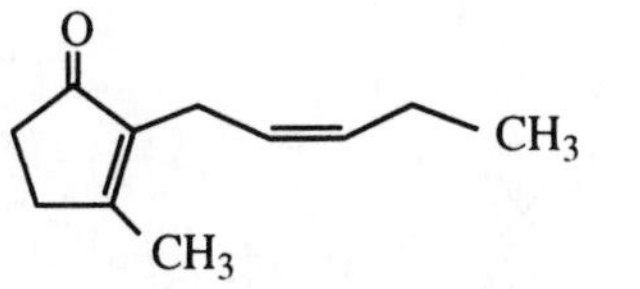
O
CH3
CH3

Compound A (jasmone)

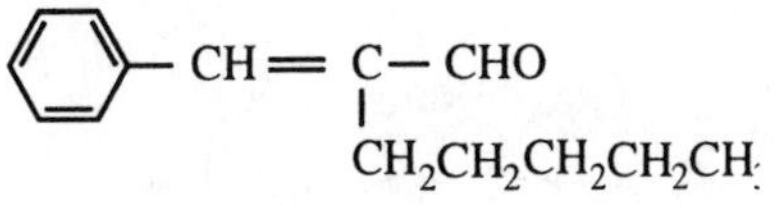
CH= C— CHO
CH2CH2CH2CH2CH

Compound B

■ What are the molecular formulas of the compounds shown?

- Ans: A is $C_{11}H_{16}O$; B is $C_{14}H_{18}O$

■ What does the presence of an IR peak at approximately 1690 cm^{-1} tell you about the structure of the compounds in each sample?

- Ans: A carbonyl group is present in each.

■ The chemist had a vague memory that the active ingredient in jasmine oil is a compound called jasmone. If this is true, which of the four samples is definitely a synthetic?

- Ans: The structure of compound B is an aldehyde, and the name jasmone suggests that this active ingredient is a ketone (-one suffix). This would eliminate sample #3 as being jasmone.

■ Propose a synthesis of compound A from the starting material C shown below.

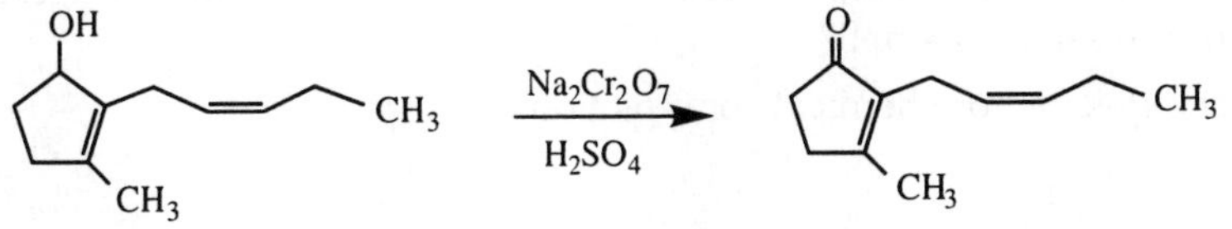
OH
CH3
CH3
Na2Cr2O7
H2SO4
O
CH3
CH3

Compound C

Compound A (jasmone)

- Ans: Oxidize the compound shown with Na_2Cr_2O7 in the presence of H_2SO_4

■ Propose a synthesis of compound A and its trans isomer, as in Sample #2, from the starting material D. (Hint: Wittig.)

• Ans: React the starting material with $(C_6H_5)_3P{=}CHCH_2CH_3$ (Wittig reaction). Then hydrolyze the result in the presence of acid to remove the acetal protecting group. The product of the reaction is a mixture of cis and trans isomers; the Witting reaction gives both under normal circumstances.

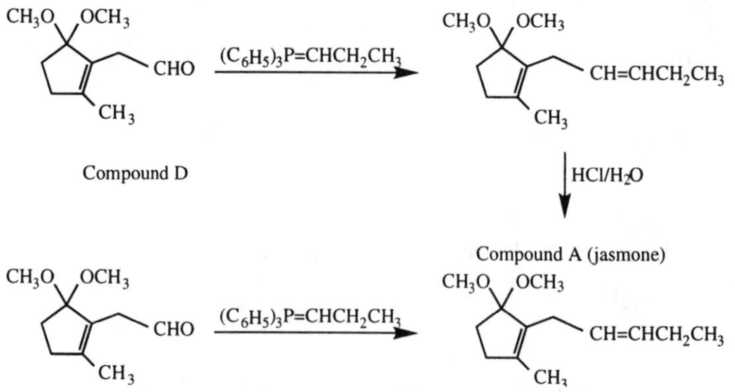
CH3O OCH3
CHO
CH3
Compound D
(C6H5)3P=CHCH2CH3
CH3O OCH3
CH=CHCH2CH3
CH3
HCl/H2O
Compound A (jasmone)
CH3O OCH3
CHO
CH3
(C6H5)3P=CHCH2CH3
CH3O OCH3
CH=CHCH2CH3
CH3

■ The chemist also remembers that jasmine oil does not include any jasmone isomers. Which of the samples does this eliminate?

• Ans: sample #2, which consists of cis and trans isomers.

■ Which sample is the natural sample?

• Ans: Sample #4 is a mixture of a large number of compounds. Natural fragrance samples are like that.

■ You recognize that Compounds A and B above have essentially identical fragrances. What does this tell you about the sense of smell?

• Ans: It is not very specific for chemical composition.

CHAPTER 14

Carboxylic Acids

I. Textbook Chapter Contents

This chapter introduces the family of compounds known as carboxylic acids, characterized by the presence of the carboxyl (-COOH) group. These are the common acids of organic chemistry. They represent the highest state of oxidation for carbon while still attached to an organic group.

II. Learning Objectives

- Be able to name carboxylic acids using the IUPAC system.
- Know the common of names of simple and frequently encountered carboxylic acids.
- Know the names of the first three dicarboxylic acids (C_2, C_3, and C_4).
- Understand the electronic structure of the carboxyl group as a basis for explaining its polarity, hydrogen bonding, and acidity.
- Understand the formation and resonance stabilization of the carboxylate anion and the influence of substituents on its stability. Be able to explain the changes in pK_as of substituted carboxylic acids.
- Write equations for the reduction of carboxylic acids to primary alcohols.
- Write equations for the α-bromination of carboxylic acids. Be able to use this reaction to introduce functionality into the α- position of aliphatic carboxylic acids.
- Write equations for the preparation of carboxylic acids by carbonation of the Grignard or organolithium reagent formed from an alkyl or aromatic bromide.
- Know the preparation of carboxylic acids by the hydrolysis of nitriles. Be able to write equations for the formation of nitriles from alkyl halides, aromatic amines, and carbonyl compounds.
- Write equations for the formation of carboxylic acids by the oxidation of alkyl aromatics and primary alcohols.
- Be able to devise a separation scheme of a mixture of organic compounds which includes a carboxylic acid.
- Be able to carry out multi-step syntheses of carboxylic acids from other organic compounds.
- Be able to determine the structure of an unknown carboxylic acid using chemical and spectroscopic information.

III. Glossary

alkanedioic acid a compound with an alkane parent structure but containing two carboxyl groups

alkanoic acid a carboxylic acid in which the carboxyl group is attached to an alkane or cycloalkane fragment

α-bromination a reaction in which a bromine is introduced to the alpha position of a carboxylic acid or carbonyl compound. When applied to alkanoic acids it is called the Hell-Volhard-Zelinsky reaction

carbonyl group a C=O group

carboxyl group a -COOH group

carboxylate group a -COO- anion

carboxylation a reaction in which an organometallic reagent (organolithium or Grignard reagent) adds across a carbonyl group of carbon dioxide to ultimately produce a carboxylic acid

cyano a -CN group

decarboxylation a reaction to eject carbon dioxide from a carboxylic acid

fatty acid a long straight chain alkanoic acid containing an even number of carbon atoms. Fatty acids may contain a saturated alkane chain or may contain one or more double bonds in the chain (unsaturated fatty acids)

Hell-Volhard-Zelinsky reaction a reaction to attach a bromine atom to the α-carbon of an alkanoic acid

hydrophilic the property of being soluble in aqueous media

hydrophobic the property of being insoluble in aqueous media

lipophilic the property of being soluble in an organic solvent

nitrile a compound containing the -CN group

pheromone a compound, frequently from the insect world, which is the basis of chemical communication between members usually of the same species. Examples are alarm pheromones and sex pheromones.

reduction a process of lowering the oxidation state of a compound. The carboxyl group (-COOH) is reduced by $LiAlH_4$ to a primary alcohol ($-CH_2OH$) group

saponification the term means "soap-making" and was originally applied to the process of making soaps from fats by heating with lye. It more generally describes the process of hydrolyzing an ester under basic conditions to form a carboxylate anion and an alcohol.

soap usually the sodium salt of a fatty acid (a sodium carboxylate)

surfactant a truncation of the description "surface-active agent" which is a compound that has a hydrophilic end and a lipophilic end, thereby dissolving in both phases at an organic-aqueous interface

IV. Summary of Reactions of Carboxylic Acids

V. Summary of Preparation of Carboxylic Acids

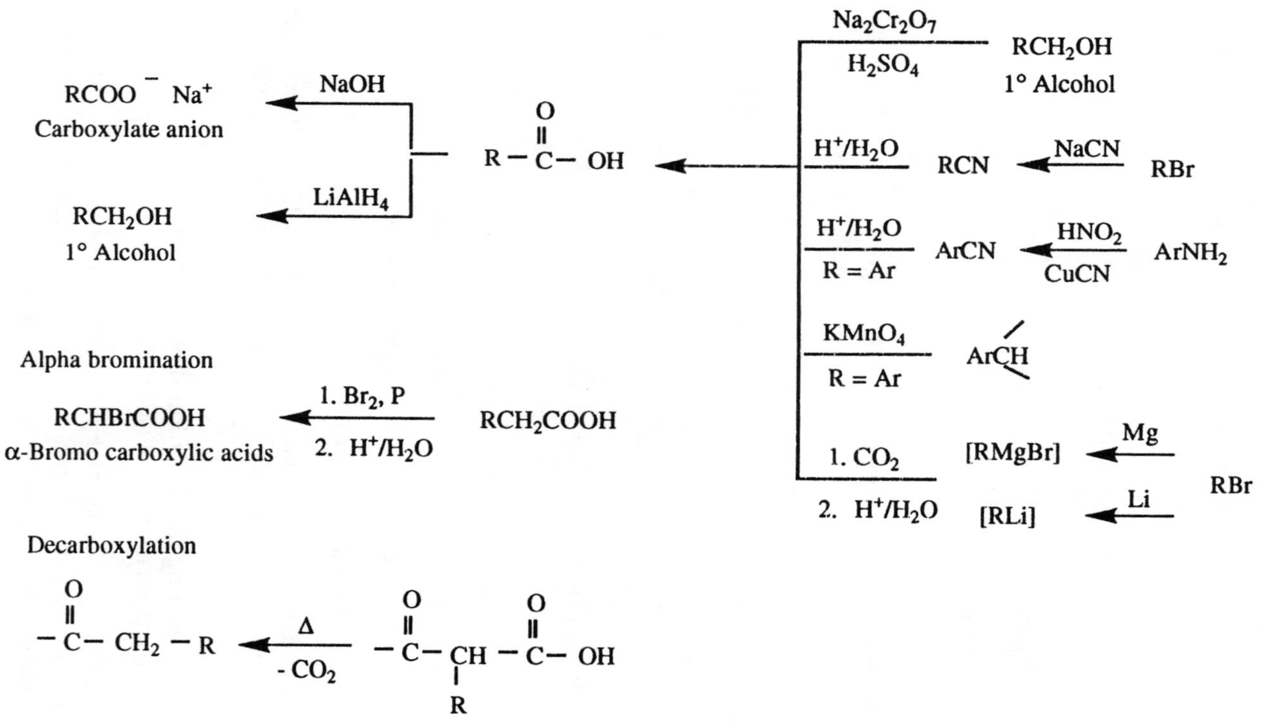
RCOO⁻ Na⁺
Carboxylate anion
NaOH
LiAlH4
RCH2OH
1° Alcohol
R–C(=O)–OH
Alpha bromination
RCHBrCOOH
α-Bromo carboxylic acids
1. Br2, P
2. H⁺/H2O
RCH2COOH
Decarboxylation
Δ
- CO2
Na2Cr2O7
H2SO4
RCH2OH
1° Alcohol
H⁺/H2O
RCN
NaCN
RBr
H⁺/H2O
R = Ar
ArCN
HNO2
CuCN
ArNH2
KMnO4
R = Ar
ArCH
1. CO2
2. H⁺/H2O
[RMgBr]
Mg
[RLi]
Li
RBr

VI. Solutions to Problems

For "**How to Solve a Problem,**" review pages 497, 504, 509, 514, and 516.

14.1

(a) $(CH_3)_2CHCOOH$ (b) $CH_3CH{=}CHCOOH$ (c) 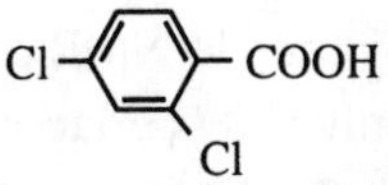
Cl
COOH
Cl

(d) $CH_3CHOHCOOH$ (e) 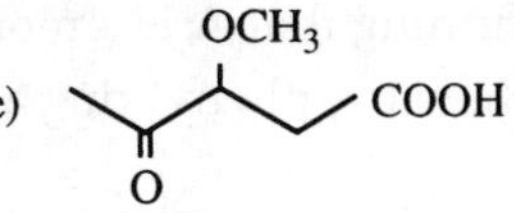
OCH3
COOH
O
(f) CH_3COCH_2COOH

14.2 (a) 3-methylbutanoic acid; (b) (*E*)-7-oxo-3-octenoic acid; (c) cyclopentanecarboxylic acid; (d) 3-butynoic acid; (e) undecanoic acid; (f) 2,6-diethoxybenzoic acid.

14.3 The order of acidity for the carboxylic acids is as follows:

(a) 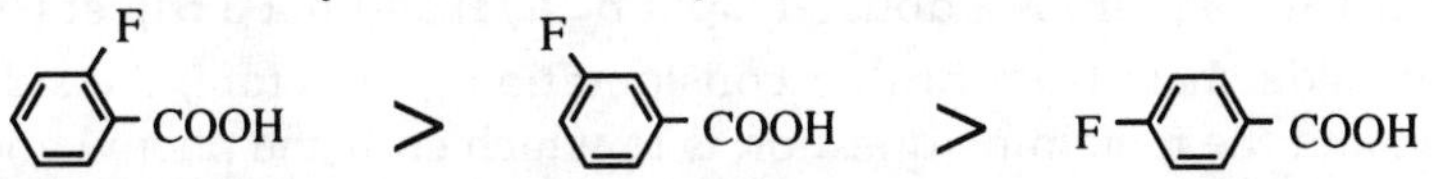
F
COOH
>
F
COOH
>
F
COOH

(b) 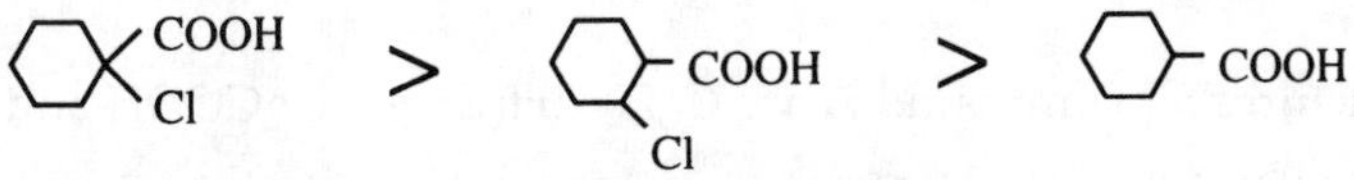
COOH
Cl
>
COOH
Cl
>
COOH

(c) 
O2N
COOH
>
H2N
COOH

(d) CH_3CBr_2COOH > CH_3CH_2COOH

14.4

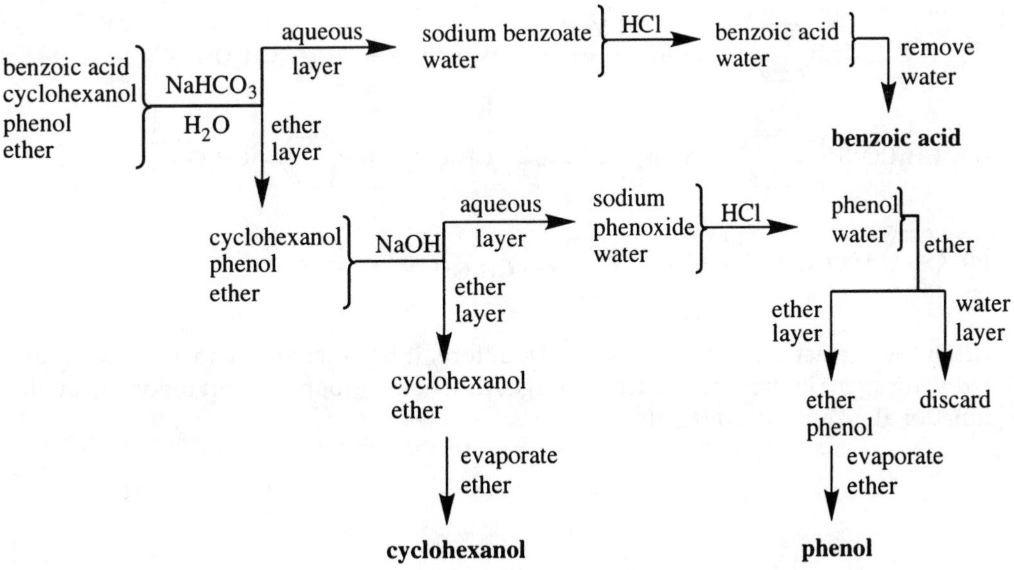
benzoic acid
cyclohexanol
phenol
ether
NaHCO3
H2O
aqueous
layer
ether
layer
sodium benzoate
water
HCl
benzoic acid
water
remove
water
benzoic acid
cyclohexanol
phenol
ether
NaOH
aqueous
layer
ether
layer
sodium
phenoxide
water
HCl
phenol
water
ether
ether
layer
water
layer
cyclohexanol
ether
evaporate
ether
cyclohexanol
ether
phenol
discard
evaporate
ether
phenol

14.5 Compound **A** ($C_{10}H_{12}O_2$) is a carboxylic acid by virtue of its solubility in sodium bicarbonate, and the carboxyl group (CO_2H) accounts for all the oxygens in the compound. The IR confirms that **A** is a carboxylic acid (carbonyl peak at 1710 and hydroxyl peak at 3400 cm^{-1}) and indicates the presence of unsaturation (peak at 1625 cm^{-1}). The HDI of **A** is five, this being accounted for by the C=O portion of the carboxyl group and a phenyl ring confirmed by the ^{1}H-NMR peak at 7.2 ppm. Thus, C_6H_5 + COOH accounts for $C_7H_6O_2$ of **A**, leaving only C_3H_6 unaccounted for. The oxidation of **A** produces **B** which appears to be benzoic acid ($C_7H_6O_2$, mw 122), confirming that **A** is a mono-substituted derivative of benzene with a C_3 group located between the phenyl ring and the terminal carboxyl group.

Only three structures are possible for the C_3 group: a linear chain ($-CH_2CH_2CH_2-$), a branched chain with a methyl side chain ($-CH_2CH(CH_3)-$, or a branched chain with an ethyl side chain ($-CH(C_2H_5)-$. The area ratios of 2:1:3 for the remaining hydrogens in the ^{1}H-NMR eliminates the linear chain from further consideration. The fact that the methyl group (peak of area 3 at 1.0 ppm) is a doublet (split by CH) and not a triplet (split by CH_2) eliminates the ethyl side chain from further consideration. Therefore, the side chain is $-CH_2CH(CH_3)-$, and the remaining question is to which ends the phenyl and carboxyl groups are attached.

The two possible structures for compound **A** are $C_6H_5CH(CH_3)CH_2COOH$ and $C_6H_5CH_2CH(CH_3)COOH$. The ^{1}H-NMR cannot absolutely distinguish between these two structures because the hydrogens on carbon next to the phenyl ring should be deshielded about the same as those on carbon next to the carboxyl group. The remaining step would be to compare the IR spectrum of **A** with the known spectra of the two candidate carboxylic acids and determine identity of spectra and, therefore, of structure.

14.6

(a) 
(CH3)2CH
COOH
LiAlH4
(CH3)2CH
CH2OH

(b) 
CH3CONH
COOH
LiAlH4
CH3CH2NH
CH2OH

(c) 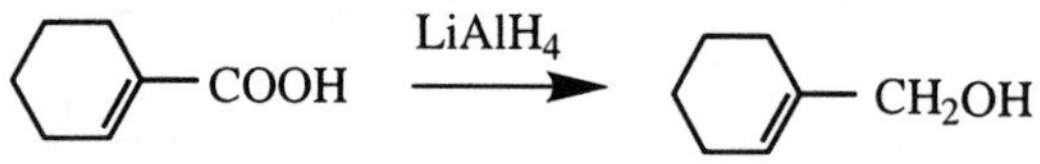
COOH
LiAlH4
CH2OH

14.7 All of these reactions are reductions. Therefore, it is a matter of choosing the appropriate reducing agent in order to reduce the target functional group without reducing another functional group inadvertently.

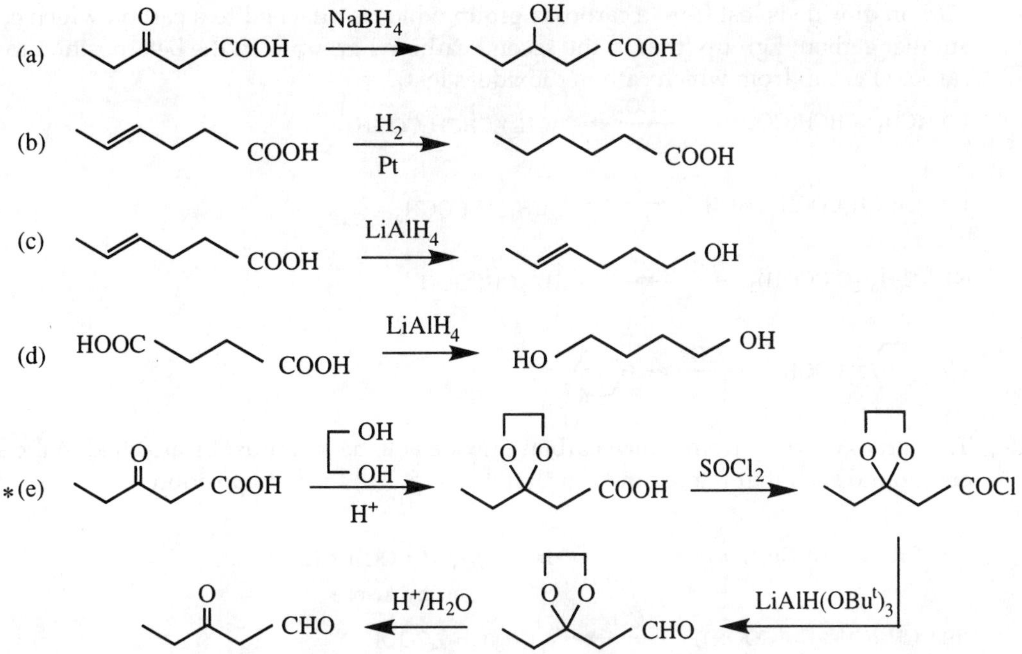

Note that in part (e) the challenge is to accomplish reduction of the carboxyl group in the presence of the more easily reduced ketone group. There is only one solution to that kind of challenge - protect the ketone group, and it can be done by temporary conversion to an acetal.

14.8

(a) $C_6H_5CH_2COOH \xrightarrow[\text{2. } H^+/H_2O]{\text{1. } Br_2/P} C_6H_5CHBrCOOH \xrightarrow{NaOH} C_6H_5CHOHCOOH$

(b) $C_6H_5CH_2COOH \xrightarrow[\text{2. } H^+/H_2O]{\text{1. } Br_2/P} C_6H_5CHBrCOOH \xrightarrow{NH_3} C_6H_5CHNH_2COOH$

∗(c) $C_6H_5CH_2CHO \xrightarrow[HCN]{NaCN} C_6H_5CH_2CHOHCN \xrightarrow{H+/H_2O} C_6H_5CH_2CHOHCOOH$

$C_6H_5CH_2CHOHCOOH \xrightarrow{PBr_3} C_6H_5CH_2CHBrCOOH \xrightarrow{NH_3} C_6H_5CH_2CHNH_2COOH$

(d) $C_6H_5CH_2CH_2COOH \xrightarrow[\text{2. } H^+/H_2O]{\text{1. } Br_2/P} C_6H_5CH_2CHBrCOOH \xrightarrow{NH_3} C_6H_5CH_2CHNH_2COOH$

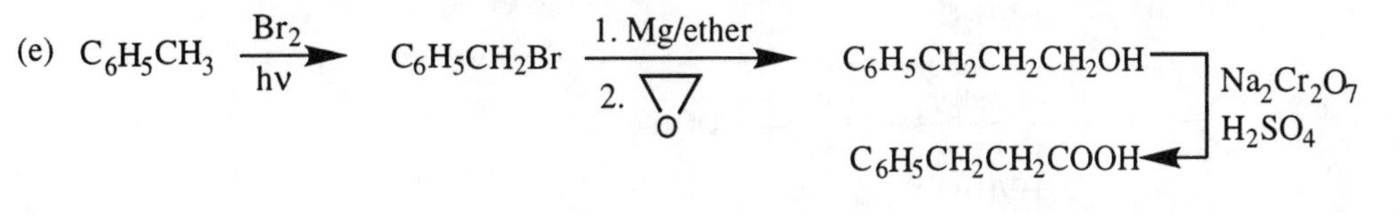

14.9 Carbon dioxide is lost from a carboxyl group which is attached to a carbon which contains another carbonyl group (that is, the second carbonyl group is in the beta position to the carboxyl group from which carbon dioxide is lost).

(a) $(CH_3)_2CHCH(COOH)_2 \xrightarrow[\Delta]{-CO_2} (CH_3)_2CHCH_2COOH$

(b) $CH_3CH_2COCH_2COOH \xrightarrow[\Delta]{-CO_2} CH_3CH_2COCH_3$

(c) $(C_6H_5)_2C(COOH)_2 \xrightarrow[\Delta]{-CO_2} (C_6H_5)_2CHCOOH$

(d) 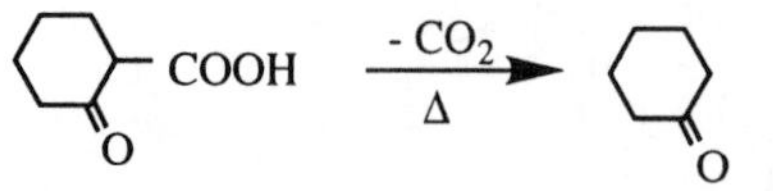

14.10 The carboxyl group from which carbon dioxide is to be lost must be attached to the starting compound such that the retained carbonyl group is in the beta position.

(a) $CH_3CH_2COCH(COOH)CH_3 \xrightarrow[\Delta]{-CO_2} CH_3CH_2COCH_2CH_3$
diethyl ketone

(b) $CH_3(CH_2)_3CH(COOH)_2 \xrightarrow[\Delta]{-CO_2} CH_3(CH_2)_4COOH$
hexanoic acid

(c) $C_6H_5CH(COOH)_2 \xrightarrow[\Delta]{-CO_2} C_6H_5CH_2COOH$
phenylacetic acid

(d) 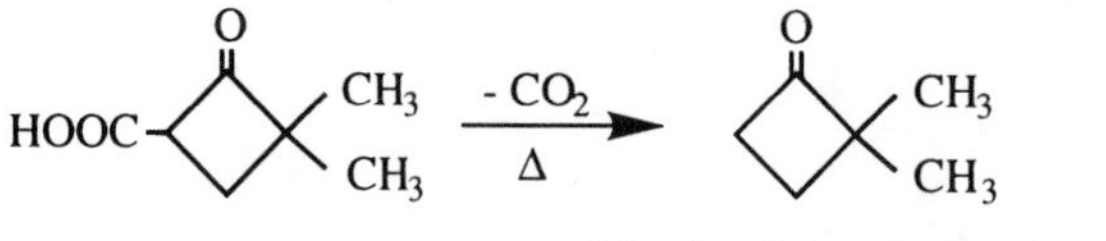

2,2-dimethylcyclobutanone

14.11

14.12

(a) 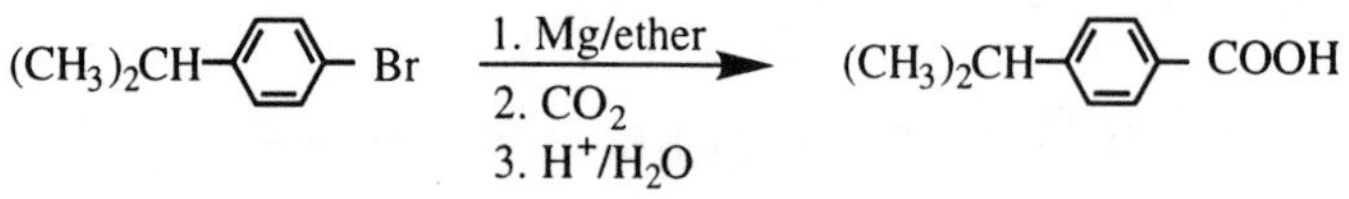

(b) $(CH_3)_3CBr \xrightarrow[\text{2. } CO_2 \text{; 3. } H^+/H_2O]{\text{1. Mg/ether}} (CH_3)_3CCOOH$

(c) 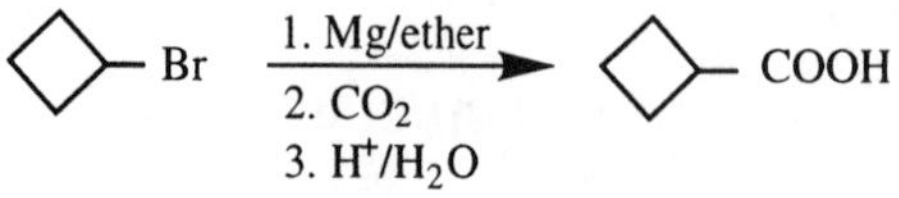

14.13 Retrosynthetic analysis indicates the carboxyl group can be attached where a bromine was located, so the problem becomes one of placing a bromine atom selectively at C_1 and C_2 of the starting material (1-butene). This is accomplished by normal HBr addition (Markovnikov addition) of HBr to form 2-bromobutane and radical addition of HBr (anti-Markovnikov addition) to form 1-bromobutane. The two alkyl bromides then are converted to Grignard reagents and carboxylated.

$$\text{(a) } CH_3CH_2CH_2CH_2COOH \Longrightarrow CH_3CH_2CH_2CH_2Br \Longrightarrow CH_3CH_2CH{=}CH_2$$

$$\text{(b) } CH_3CH_2CH(CH_3)COOH \Longrightarrow CH_3CH_2CHBrCH_3 \Longrightarrow CH_3CH_2CH{=}CH_2 \text{ (1-butene)}$$

$$\text{(a) } CH_3CH_2CH{=}CH_2 \xrightarrow[\text{ROOR}]{\text{HBr}} CH_3CH_2CH_2CH_2Br \xrightarrow[\text{2. } CO_2\text{; 3. } H^+/H_2O]{\text{1. Mg/ether}} \underset{\text{pentanoic acid}}{CH_3CH_2CH_2CH_2COOH}$$

$$\text{(b) } CH_3CH_2CH{=}CH_2 \xrightarrow{\text{HBr}} CH_3CH_2CHBrCH_3 \xrightarrow[\text{2. } CO_2\text{; 3. } H^+/H_2O]{\text{1. Mg/ether}} \underset{\text{2-methylbutanoic acid}}{CH_3CH_2CH(CH_3)COOH}$$

14.14

$$\text{(a) } C_6H_5CH_2Br \xrightarrow{\text{NaCN}} C_6H_5CH_2CN \xrightarrow{H+/H_2O} C_6H_5CH_2COOH$$

$$\text{(b) } CH_3CH_2CH_2Br \xrightarrow[\text{2. } H^+/H_2O]{\text{1. NaCN}} CH_3CH_2CH_2COOH$$

14.15

(a)

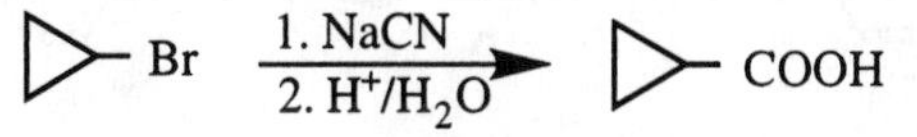
Br
1. NaCN
2. H+/H2O
COOH

$$\text{* (b) } C_6H_5CH_2CHO \xrightarrow[\text{HCN}]{\text{NaCN}} C_6H_5CH_2CH(OH)CN \xrightarrow{H^+/H_2O} C_6H_5CH_2CH(OH)COOH \xrightarrow[\Delta]{H_2SO_4} C_6H_5CH{=}CHCOOH \xrightarrow{H_2/Pt} C_6H_5CH_2CH_2COOH$$

$$\text{(c) } C_6H_5CH_2CH_3 \xrightarrow[h\nu]{Br_2} C_6H_5CHBrCH_3 \xrightarrow[\text{2. } H^+/H_2O]{\text{1. NaCN}} CH_3CH(C_6H_5)COOH$$

* (d)

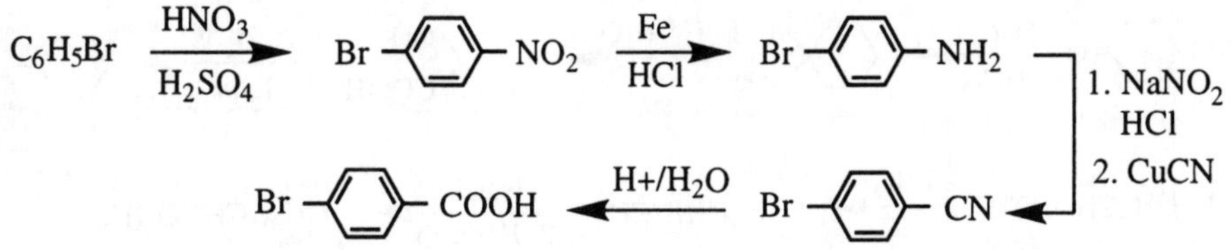
C6H5Br
HNO3
H2SO4
Br
NO2
Fe
HCl
Br
NH2
1. NaNO2
HCl
2. CuCN
Br
CN
H+/H2O
Br
COOH

14.16

(a) 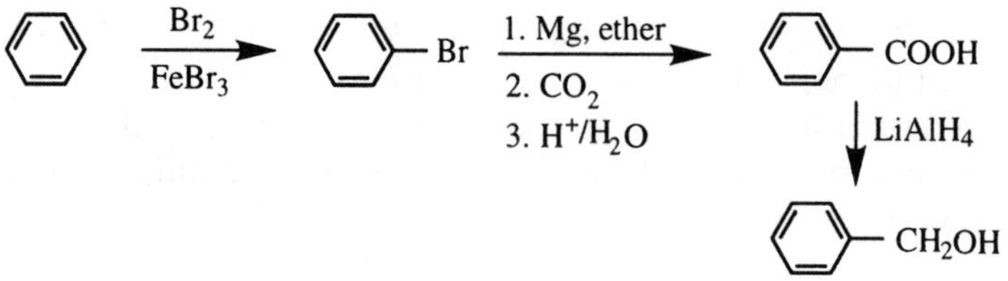

(b) 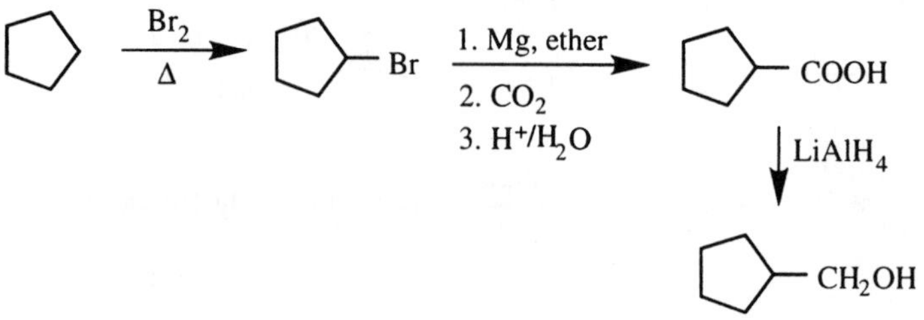

14.17

(a) $C_6H_5CH_2OH \xrightarrow{PBr_3} C_6H_5CH_2Br \xrightarrow[2.\ H^+/H_2O]{1.\ NaCN} C_6H_5CH_2COOH$

* (b) $C_6H_5CH_2CH_3 \xrightarrow[h\nu]{Br_2} C_6H_5CHBrCH_3 \xrightarrow{NaOC_2H_5} C_6H_5CH{=}CH_2$

$C_6H_5CH{=}CH_2 \xrightarrow[ROOR]{HBr} C_6H_5CH_2CH_2Br \xrightarrow[2.\ H^+/H_2O]{1.\ NaCN} C_6H_5CH_2CH_2COOH$

(c) 

14.18

(a) 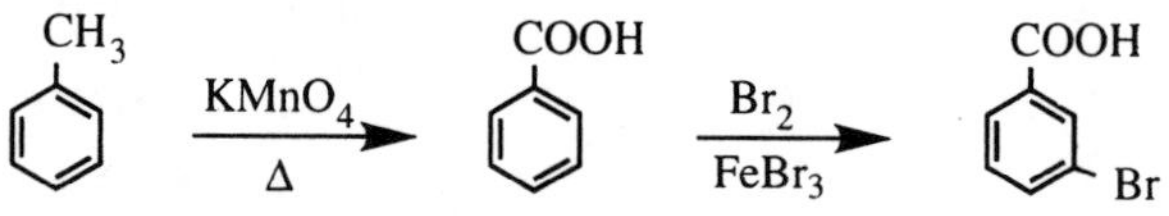

(b) 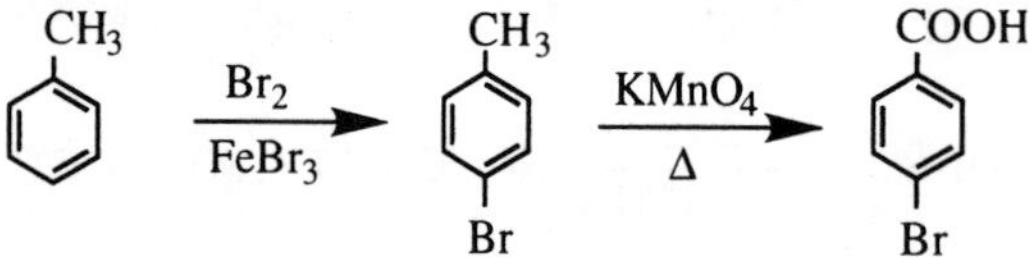

*(c) 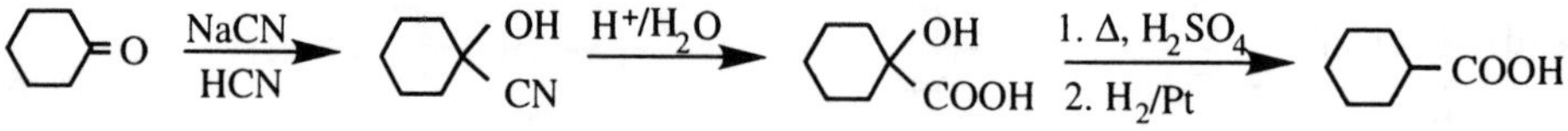

(d) $CH_3CHOHCH_3 \xrightarrow{PBr_3} CH_3CHBrCH_3 \xrightarrow[2.\ H^+/H_2O]{1.\ NaCN} (CH_3)_2CHCOOH$

14.19

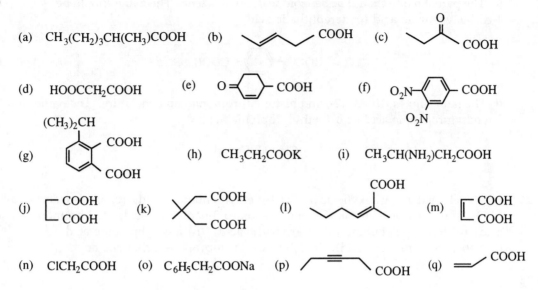

(a) $CH_3(CH_2)_3CH(CH_3)COOH$ (b)  (c) 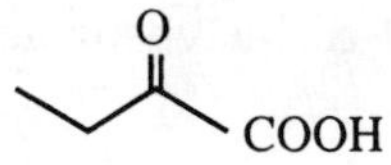

(d) $HOOCCH_2COOH$ (e) 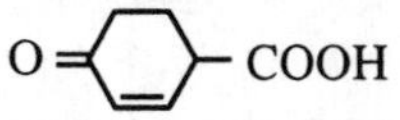 (f) 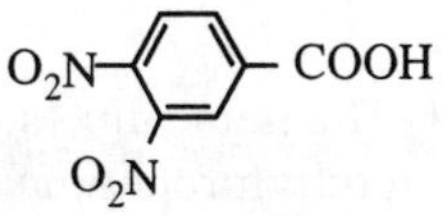

(g) 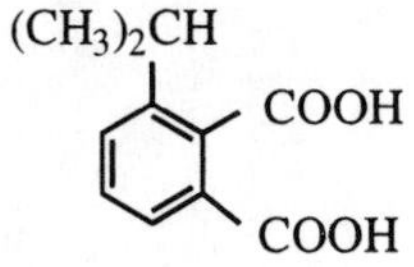 (h) CH_3CH_2COOK (i) $CH_3CH(NH_2)CH_2COOH$

(j) 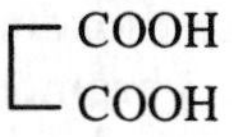 (k) 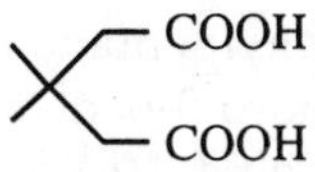 (l) 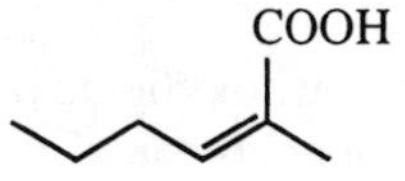 (m) 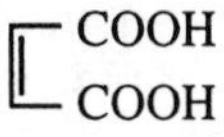

(n) $ClCH_2COOH$ (o) $C_6H_5CH_2COONa$ (p) 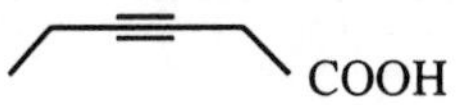 (q) 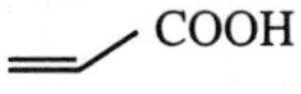

14.20 (a) The compound should be named as a carboxylic acid, not as a ketone. The name should be 3-oxobutanoic acid.

CH_3COCH_2COOH

(b) The name mixes historic (β) and IUPAC (butanoic) terminology. The name should be either 3-methylbutanoic acid or β-methylbutyric acid.

$(CH_3)_2CHCH_2COOH$

(c) The substituents should appear in alphabetic order. The name should be 4-bromo-3-chlorobenzoic acid.

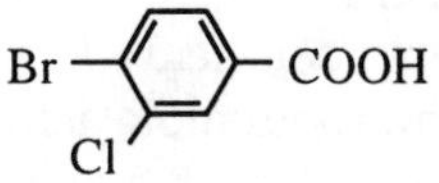

(d) The compound should be named as a carboxylic acid, not as an alcohol. The name should be 3-hydroxycyclohexanecarboxylic acid.

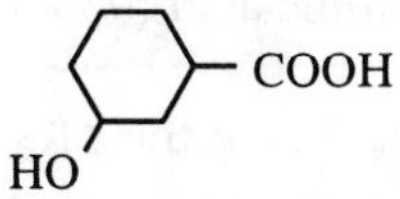

(e) The parent name should be benzoic acid, not benzene. The name should be 4-carboxybenzoic acid (or terephthalic acid).

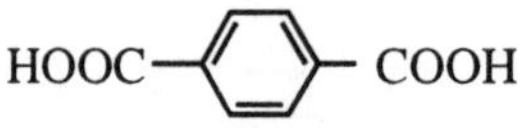

(f) The name mixes IUPAC (2-) and historic (propionic) nomenclature. The name should be 2-methylpropanoic acid or α-methylpropionic acid.

$(CH_3)_2CHCOOH$

14.21 (a) 1-cyclopentenecarboxylic acid; (b) 4-methylpentanoic acid; (c) 3,5-dioxohexanoic acid; (d) 3-fluoro-5-iodobenzoic acid; (e) (Z)-3-chloro-3-pentenoic acid; (f) 3-bromobutanoic acid; (g) *trans*-cyclobutane-1,3-dicarboxylic acid; (h) methylmalonic acid (2-methylpropanedioic acid); (i) 1-hydroxycyclopropanecarboxylic acid.

14.22

(a) 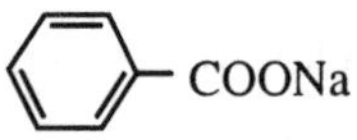

sodium benzoate

(b) $(CH_3CH_2COO)_2Ca$

calcium propanoate

(c) $CH_3CH{=}CH{-}CH{=}CH{-}COOK$

potassium sorbate

14.23 The orders of acidity are as follows:
(a) *p*-nitrobenzoic acid > benzoic acid
(b) 2,2-difluoropropanoic acid > 2-fluoropropanoic acid > propanoic acid
(c) acetic acid > ethanol > ethane
(d) benzoic acid > phenol > benzyl alcohol
(e) 2-chlorobutanoic acid > 3-chlorobutanoic acid

14.24 The order of decreasing pK_a values are as follows:
(a) benzoic acid > *p*-nitrobenzoic acid
(b) propanoic acid > 2-fluoropropanoic acid > 2,2-difluoropropanoic acid
(c) ethane > ethanol > acetic acid
(d) benzyl alcohol > phenol > benzoic acid
(e) 3-chlorobutanoic acid > 2-chlorobutanoic acid

14.25 The pK_a values are as follows:
(a) acetic acid (4.8), *p*-chlorobenzoic acid (4.0)
(b) propanoic acid (4.9), 3-chloropropanoic acid (4.0)
(c) *p*-nitrobenzoic acid (3.4), *p*-nitrophenol (7.2)
(d) benzoic acid (4.2), benzenesulfonic acid (0.7)

14.26 This problem is analyzed by considering the pK_a of the acid on each side of the equilibrium. Recall that the strongest acid (smallest pK_a) will give up its proton to the base.

14.27 The separation scheme depends on being able to separately convert each compound into an ionic form (a salt) which will be extracted into an aqueous layer which can be separateed from the organic (ether) layer.

(a) $CH_3COOH + NaHCO_3 \rightleftharpoons CH_3COONa + H_2O + CO_2$
(4.8) (6.4)

(b) $C_6H_5COOH + (CH_3)_2NH \rightleftharpoons C_6H_5COO^- + H_2\overset{+}{N}(CH_3)_2$
(4.2) (10.7)

(c) $CH_3CH_2CH_2COO^- \; Na^+ + HCl \rightleftharpoons CH_3CH_2CH_2COOH + NaCl$
(~1) (~4.8)

(d) $CH_3CH_2COOH + CH_3CH_2MgBr \rightleftharpoons CH_3CH_2COOMgBr + CH_3CH_3$
(~4.8) (~50)

(e)
HO
COOH
+ NaHCO3
HO
COONa
+ H2O + CO2
(~10 and 4.2)
(6.4)

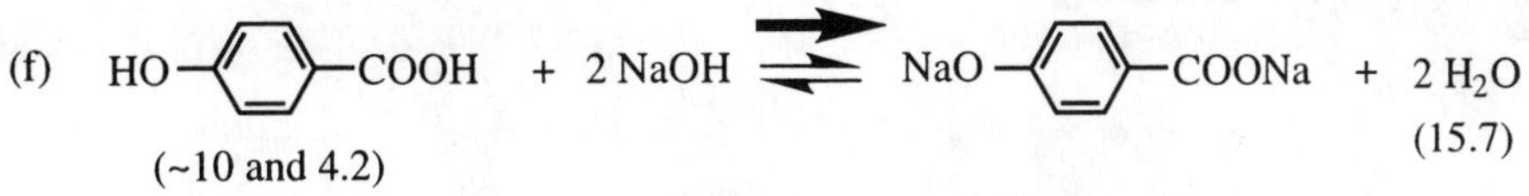
(f)
HO
COOH
+ 2 NaOH
NaO
COONa
+ 2 H2O
(~10 and 4.2)
(15.7)

(g) $C_6H_5Li + CH_3CH_2OH \rightleftharpoons C_6H_6 + CH_3CH_2OLi$
(16) (~40)

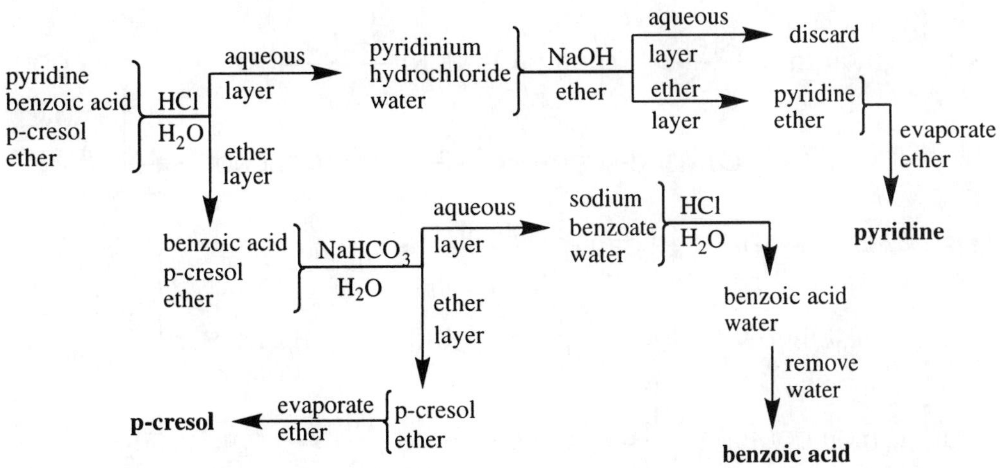
pyridine
benzoic acid
p-cresol
ether
HCl
H2O
aqueous
layer
pyridinium
hydrochloride
water
NaOH
ether
aqueous
layer
discard
ether
layer
pyridine
ether
evaporate
ether
pyridine
ether
layer
benzoic acid
p-cresol
ether
NaHCO3
H2O
aqueous
layer
sodium
benzoate
water
HCl
H2O
benzoic acid
water
remove
water
benzoic acid
ether
layer
p-cresol
ether
evaporate
ether
p-cresol

14.28 The IR peaks at 3100 (-OH) and 1690 cm^{-1} (C=O) indicate $C_6H_{12}O_2$ is a carboxylic acid. The carboxyl group is confirmed by the singlet peak at 11.2 ppm in the NMR spectrum. There are no splittings in the NMR indicating there are no adjacent hydrogens. The singlet peak at 1.1 ppm must represent methyl groups and the area of ~9 probably indicates a *t*-butyl group ($(CH_3)_3C$-). Thus, $C_5H_{10}O_2$ has been accounted for. The remaining unaccounted for carbon must be a CH_2 group which connects the *t*-butyl group to the carboxyl group and it's presence is indicated by an unsplit singlet at 2.2 ppm. Therefore, the compound is 3,3-dimethylbutanoic acid $(CH_3)_3CCH_2COOH$.

14.29

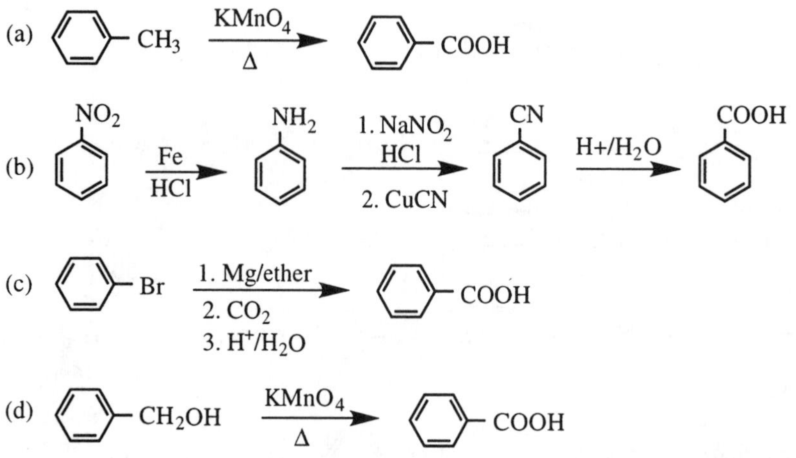

14.30

(a) $C_6H_5CH{=}CH_2 \xrightarrow[\text{ROOR}]{\text{HBr}} C_6H_5CH_2CH_2Br \xrightarrow[\text{2. } H^+/H_2O]{\text{1. NaCN}} C_6H_5CH_2CH_2COOH$

* (b) $C_6H_5CH_2CHO \xrightarrow[\text{HCN}]{\text{NaCN}} C_6H_5CH_2CHOHCN \xrightarrow{H+/H_2O} C_6H_5CH_2CHOHCOOH \xrightarrow[\Delta]{H_2SO_4} C_6H_5CH{=}CHCOOH \xrightarrow{H_2/Pt} C_6H_5CH_2CH_2COOH$

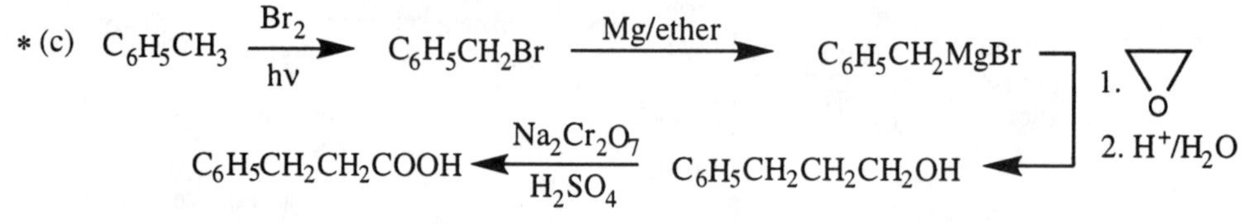

(d) $C_6H_5CH_2COOH \xrightarrow{\text{LiAlH}_4} C_6H_5CH_2CH_2OH \xrightarrow{\text{PBr}_3} C_6H_5CH_2CH_2Br \xrightarrow[\text{2. } CO_2\text{; 3. } H^+/H_2O]{\text{1. Mg/ether}} C_6H_5CH_2CH_2COOH$

14.31

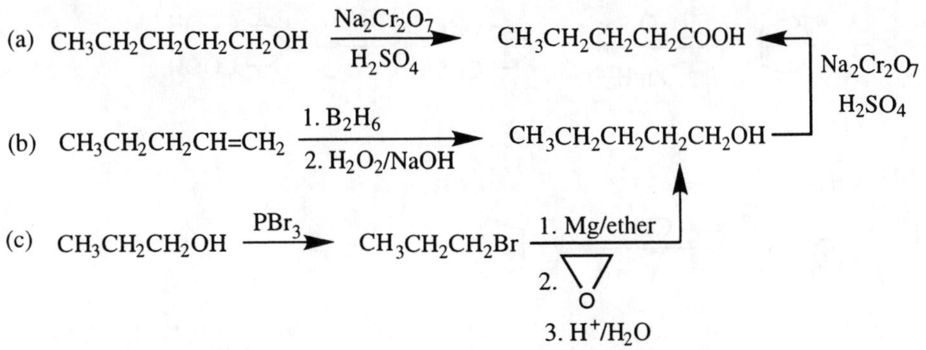
(a) $CH_3CH_2CH_2CH_2CH_2OH$
$Na_2Cr_2O_7$
H_2SO_4
$CH_3CH_2CH_2CH_2COOH$
$Na_2Cr_2O_7$
H_2SO_4
(b) $CH_3CH_2CH_2CH{=}CH_2$
1. B_2H_6
2. H_2O_2/NaOH
$CH_3CH_2CH_2CH_2CH_2OH$
(c) $CH_3CH_2CH_2OH$
PBr_3
$CH_3CH_2CH_2Br$
1. Mg/ether
2.
3. H^+/H_2O

14.32 The ethyl group must become the eventual carboxyl group, and this can only happen via an oxidation. The remaining question is when to attach the bromine through bromination. Since the bromine must be in the *meta* position the bromination must occur after the carboxyl group is formed (the ethyl group would direct bromine to the *ortho* and *para* positions).

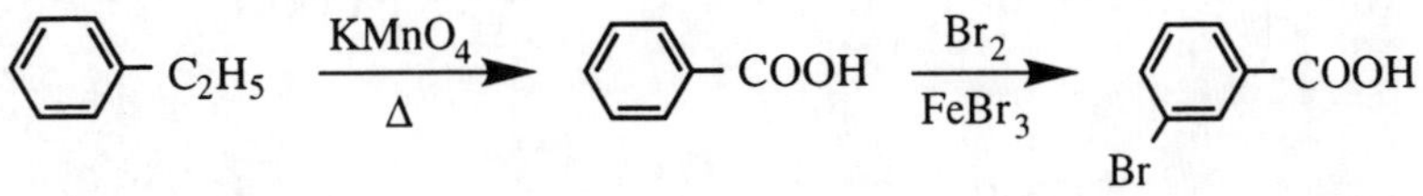
C_2H_5
$KMnO_4$
Δ
COOH
Br_2
$FeBr_3$
COOH
Br

14.33

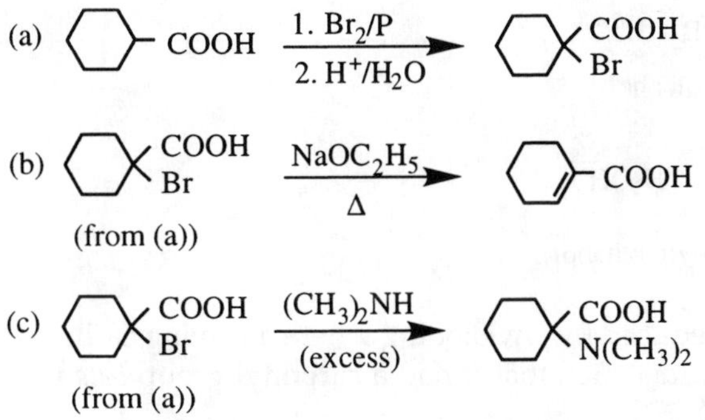
(a)
COOH
1. Br_2/P
2. H^+/H_2O
COOH
Br
NaOH
COOH
OH
(b)
COOH
Br
$NaOC_2H_5$
Δ
COOH
(from (a))
(c)
COOH
Br
$(CH_3)_2NH$
(excess)
COOH
$N(CH_3)_2$
(from (a))

14.34 The introduction of a double bond most often occurs via an elimination reaction. Therefore, the initial task is to attach to pentanoic acid a group that can be eliminated, and that is accomplished by α-bromination of pentanoic acid.

$$CH_3CH_2CH_2CH_2COOH \xrightarrow[2.\ H^+/H_2O]{1.\ Br_2/P} CH_3CH_2CH_2CHBrCOOH$$

$$CH_3CH_2CH_2CHBrCOOH \xrightarrow[\Delta]{NaOC_2H_5} CH_3CH_2CH{=}CHCOOH$$

2-pentenoic acid

14.35

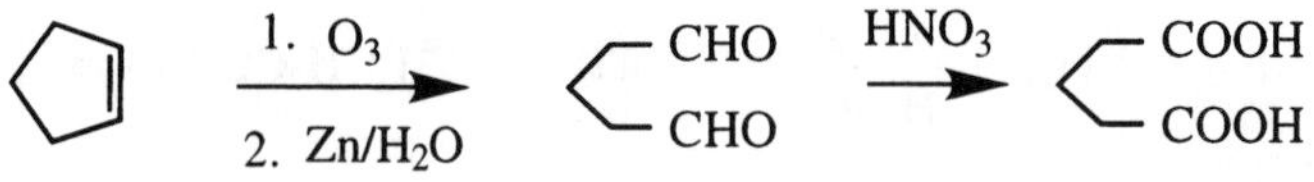

14.36

(a) 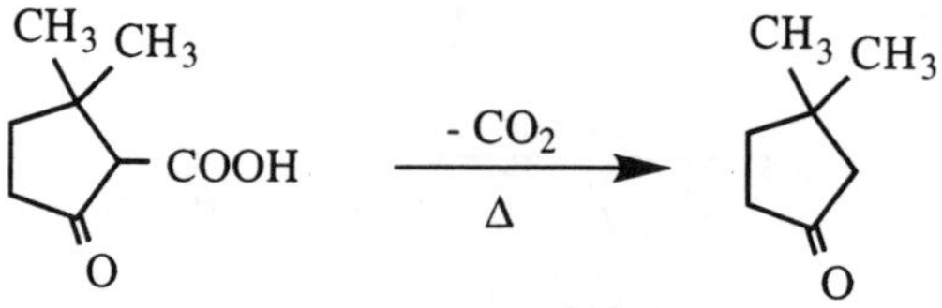

(b) 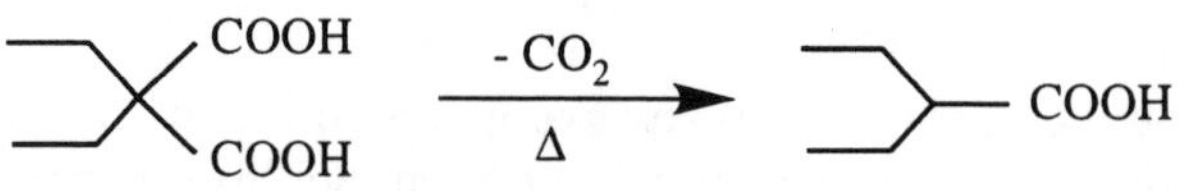

(c) 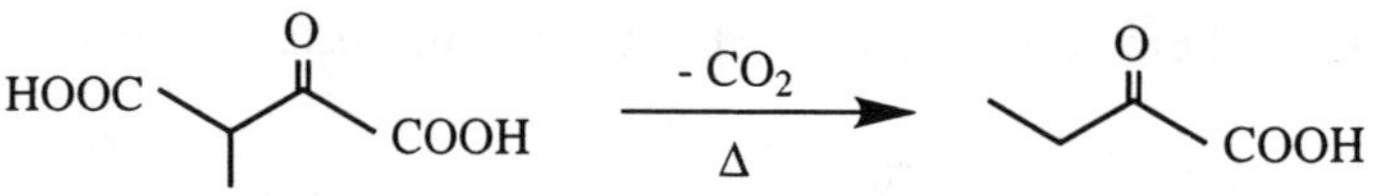

14.37

(a) $CH_3CH_2CH_2COOH \xrightarrow{LiAlH_4} CH_3CH_2CH_2CH_2OH$

1-butanol

(b) $C_6H_5COOH \xrightarrow{LiAlH_4} C_6H_5CH_2OH$

benzyl alcohol

(c) 

cyclopropylmethanol

14.38 The answers to these problems are deduced by envisioning where a leaving carboxyl group could be attached to the desired product such that it had a carbonyl group *beta* to it in the starting compound.

(a) $(C_6H_5)_2C(COOH)_2 \xrightarrow[\Delta]{-CO_2} (C_6H_5)_2CHCOOH$

(b) 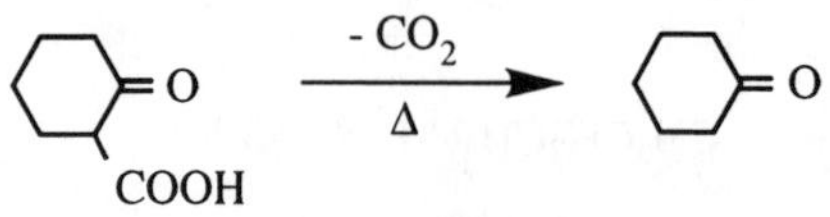

(c) $CH_3COCH_2COOH \xrightarrow[\Delta]{-CO_2} CH_3COCH_3$

(d) $CH_3CH_2CH_2C(CH_3)(COOH)_2 \xrightarrow[\Delta]{-CO_2} CH_3CH_2CH_2CH(CH_3)COOH$

14.39

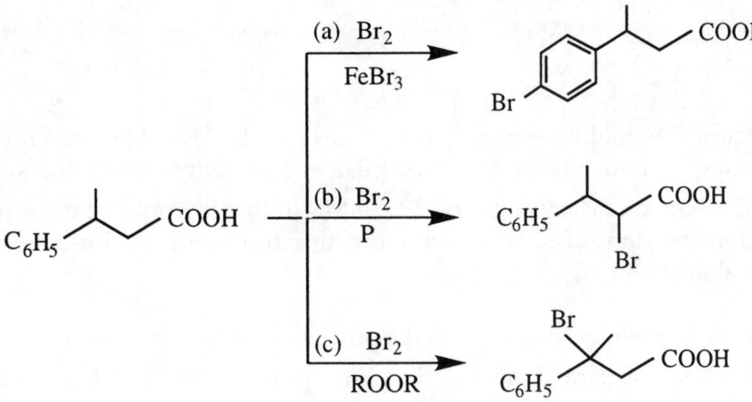
(a) Br_2
$FeBr_3$
(b) Br_2
P
(c) Br_2
ROOR
COOH
C_6H_5
Br

14.40

(a)
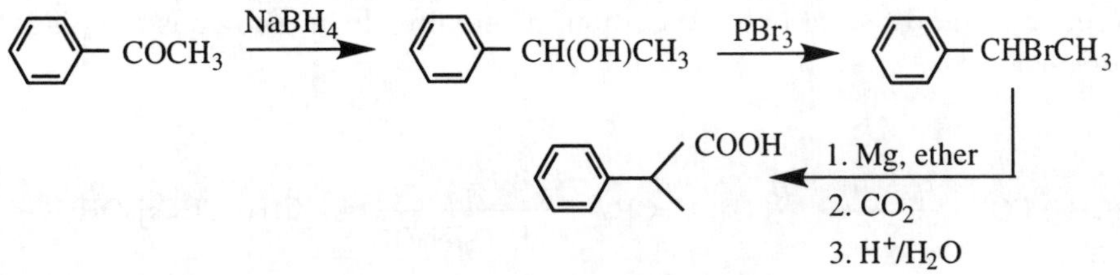
$COCH_3$
$NaBH_4$
$CH(OH)CH_3$
PBr_3
$CHBrCH_3$
COOH
1. Mg, ether
2. CO_2
3. H^+/H_2O

(b)
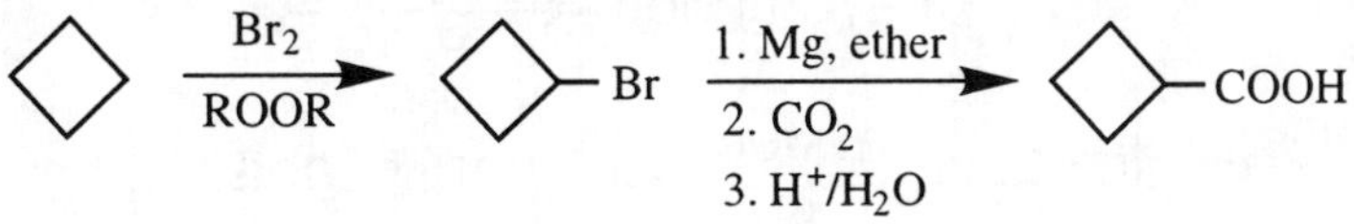
Br_2
ROOR
Br
1. Mg, ether
2. CO_2
3. H^+/H_2O
COOH

(c)
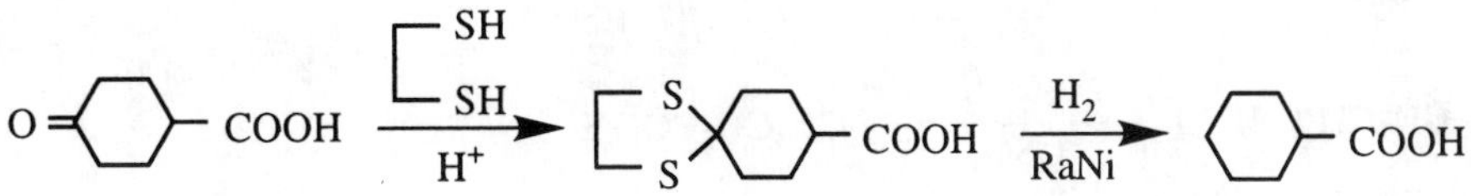
O
COOH
SH
SH
H^+
S
S
H_2
RaNi

(d)
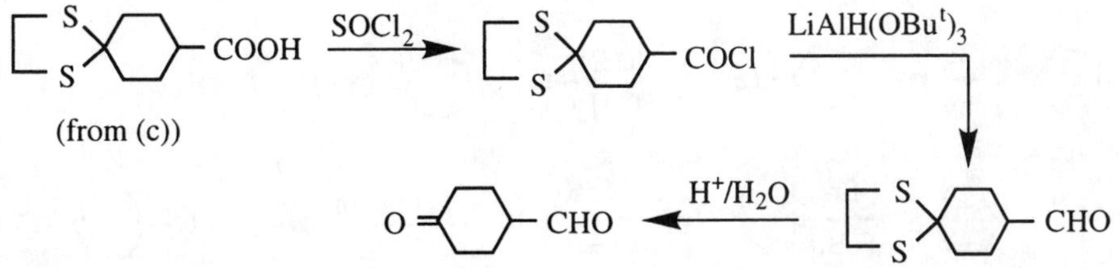
S
S
COOH
(from (c))
$SOCl_2$
COCl
$LiAlH(OBu^t)_3$
CHO
H^+/H_2O
O

14.41 $C_5H_8O_4$ must be a dicarboxylic acid because the 12.8 ppm peak in the ^{1}H-NMR indicates a carboxyl hydrogen, and the area ratio must be 2:6 to account for the eight hydrogens in the formula. Therefore, only C_3H_6 remains unaccounted for. Only three structural possibilities exist for these three carbons as represented in structures **A**, **B** and **C** shown below.

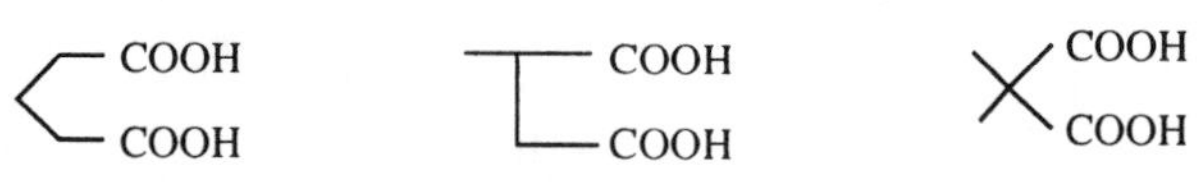

A **B** **C**

Only structure **C** would have a single alkyl peak in the ^{1}H-NMR, that for two identical methyl groups, and this fits the observed peak at 1.29 ppm representing six hydrogens. Structure **C** also is consistent with the ^{13}C-NMR in that it would be expected to show peaks for three different kinds of carbon. Therefore, the structure of the unknown is dimethylmalonic acid (**C**).

14.42 The isomer of compound **C** described in the previous question must be compound **B** on the basis of both NMR spectra. **B** should have four peaks in the ^{1}H-NMR representing singlet carboxyl (12.7 ppm), methyl doublet (0.9 ppm), methine multiplet (2.6 ppm), and methylene doublet (2.4 ppm). The ^{13}C-NMR of **B** would be expected to show four peaks representing four different kinds of carbon. Therefore, the unknown isomer is methyl succinic acid (**B**).

14.43

(a) $(CH_3)_3COH \xrightarrow[\Delta]{H_2SO_4} (CH_3)_2C{=}CH_2 \xrightarrow[2.\ H_2O_2/NaOH]{1.\ B_2H_6} (CH_3)_2CHCH_2OH \xrightarrow[H_2SO_4]{Na_2Cr_2O_7} (CH_3)_2CHCOOH$

(b) $(CH_3)_2C{=}CH_2$ (from (a)) $\xrightarrow{HBr} (CH_3)_3CBr \xrightarrow[2.\ CO_2;\ 3.\ H^+/H_2O]{1.\ Mg/ether} (CH_3)_3CCOOH$

(c) $CH_3CH_2CH_2OH \xrightarrow[H_2SO_4]{Na_2Cr_2O_7} CH_3CH_2COOH$

(d) $CH_3CH_2CH_2OH \xrightarrow{HBr} CH_3CH_2CH_2Br \xrightarrow[2.\ CO_2;\ 3.\ H^+/H_2O]{1.\ Mg/ether} CH_3CH_2CH_2COOH$

(e) 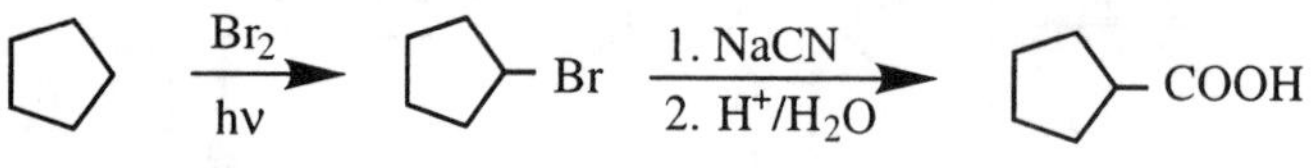

(f) 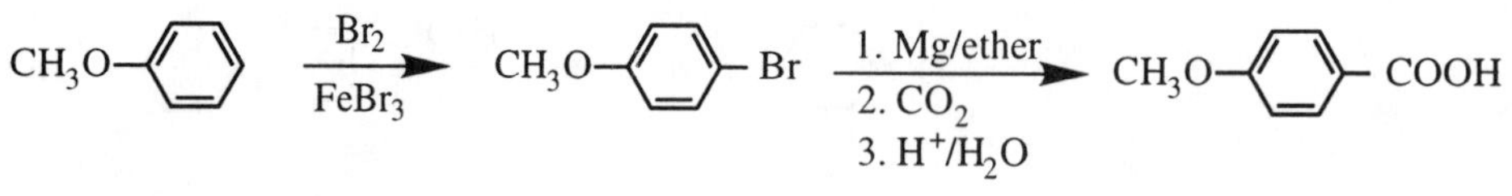

(g) $CH_2{=}CHCH{=}CH_2 \xrightarrow{HBr} CH_3CH{=}CHCH_2Br \xrightarrow[2.\ H^+/H_2O]{1.\ NaCN} CH_3CH{=}CHCH_2COOH$

(h) 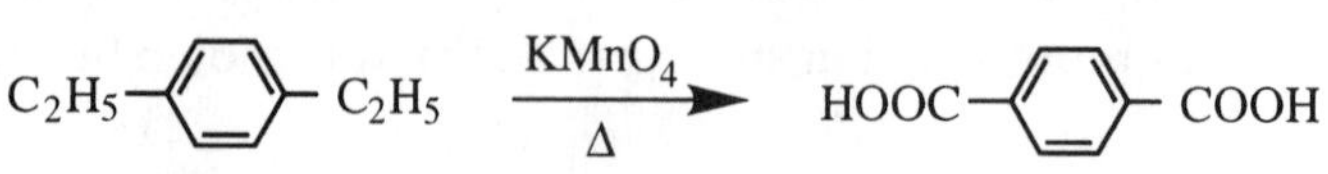

***14.44**

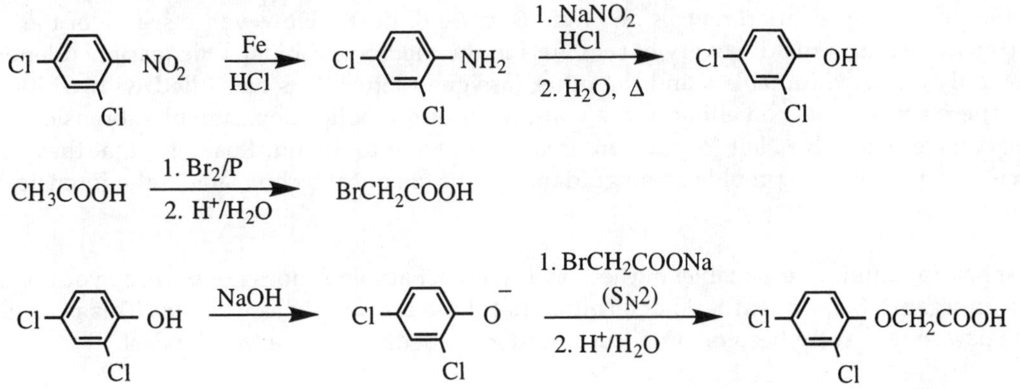
Cl
NO2
Cl
Fe
HCl
Cl
NH2
Cl
1. NaNO2
HCl
2. H2O, Δ
Cl
OH
Cl
CH3COOH
1. Br2/P
2. H+/H2O
BrCH2COOH
Cl
OH
Cl
NaOH
Cl
O−
Cl
1. BrCH2COONa
(SN2)
2. H+/H2O
Cl
OCH2COOH
Cl

2,4-D (2,4-dichlorophenoxyacetic acid)

14.45 $C_8H_8O_3$ has an HDI of five. Since it dissolves in sodium bicarbonate it must be a carboxylic acid and the IR confirms the presence of the -COOH group. The carbonyl group therein plus a phenyl ring, indicated by the ^{1}H-NMR peak at 7.3 ppm, accounts for the HDI. The compound is a di-substituted benzene derivative as indicated by the NMR peak at 7.3 ppm having area = 4. To this point C_6H_4 + COOH = $C_7H_6O_2$ has been accounted for, leaving CH_3O to be specified. The NMR indicates a likely methoxy group (-OCH_3) which must be on the ring to account for di-substitution on the benzene ring. The decoupled ^{13}C-NMR spectrum indicates the presence of six different kinds of carbon which can only be satisfied by having the methoxy group *para* to the carboxyl group (the *ortho* and *meta* isomers have eight different kinds of carbon). Therefore, the compound is *p*-methoxybenzoic acid.

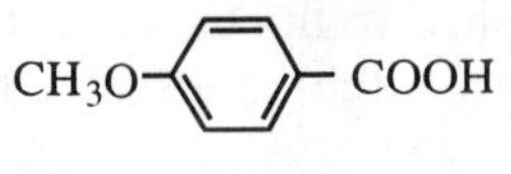
CH3O
COOH

VII. Conceptual Problem

Getting Oriented

You are aboard the world renowned train the Orient Express, en route to a conference of forensic pathologists in Budapest. As it pulls into the station in Vienna, some of your fellow passengers disembark, at the end of their journey. As the conductor makes an accounting of the disembarking passengers, she realizes she has one too few—someone who should have left the train has remained behind. A search of each compartment in your car brings the discovery of the body of a dead passenger. Austrian police are summoned, the car is detached from the train to remain in Vienna with you aboard, and the rest of the train then continues its run to Budapest. The initial police investigation reveals no obvious cause of death. However, a search of the compartment results in the discovery of two vials in the medicine cabinet. One (assigned letter A) contains only a few white tablets and the other (assigned letter B) is half filled with white tablets. There are no labels on either of the vials. Most of the police department's forensic specialists have themselves left for the conference you were to attend. Realizing that they are short-handed, you offer to provide some guidance to the chemical technicians in the forensic laboratory.

You first have a sample of each tablet burned on a spatula. Sample A does not burn, so you conclude that it is inorganic. Subsequent tests determine that these are simply salt tablets. This is consistent with the passenger having been on a rigorous outdoor expedition in the Middle East.

Sample B burns completely, so you conclude it is organic. The tablets have a capital letter "E" stamped on them so you suspect that they are Excedrin, a commercial analgesic. Referring to the Merck Index you find that Excedrin contains acetominophen, acetylsalicylic acid, and caffeine.

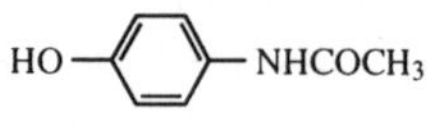
HO
NHCOCH3
Acetaminophen

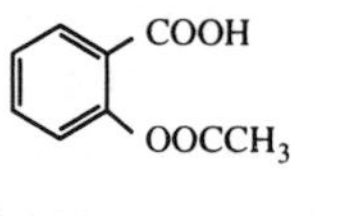
COOH
OOCCH3
Acetylsalicylic acid

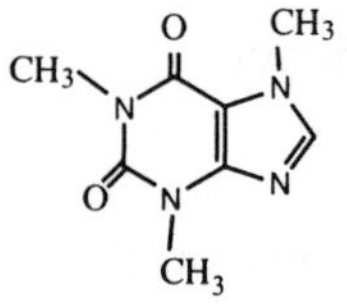
O
CH3
CH3
N
N
N
N
O
CH3
Caffeine

The police want to confirm your suspicion and ask you to design a scheme whereby the separate components of Excedrin can be isolated. They can then be identified by comparison of their physical properties with literature information, including spectra. Your task, therefore, is to:

■ Design a separation scheme to be applied to the Excedrin tablets, assuming they are first ground to a fine powder and all but the filler (starch) is dissolved in ethyl ether solvent.

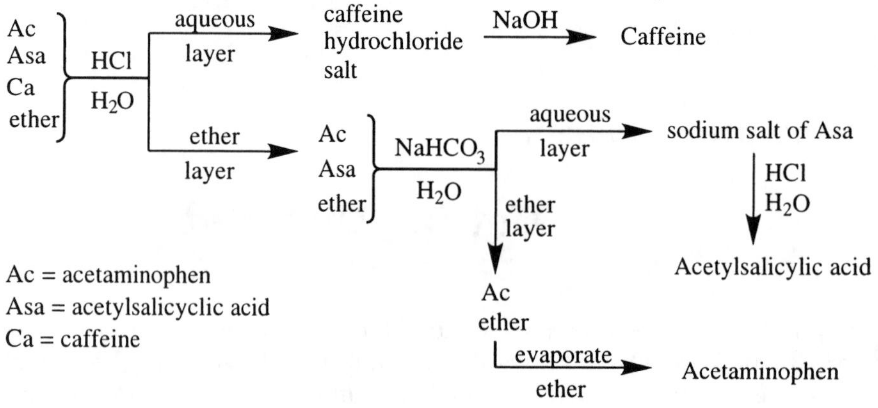
Ac
Asa
Ca
ether
HCl
H2O
aqueous
layer
caffeine
hydrochloride
salt
NaOH
Caffeine
ether
layer
Ac
Asa
ether
NaHCO3
H2O
aqueous
layer
sodium salt of Asa
HCl
H2O
Acetylsalicylic acid
ether
layer
Ac
ether
evaporate
ether
Acetaminophen
Ac = acetaminophen
Asa = acetylsalicyclic acid
Ca = caffeine

■ Indicate some important spectral peaks the technicians can look for in the IR and ^{1}H-NMR spectra of each of the pure compounds, once obtained and purified.

- Ans:Acetaminophen should show IR peaks at about 3300 cm^{-1} for OH and NH (perhaps both as one peak) and near 1700 cm^{-1} (amide group). Acetylsalicylic acid should show a very broad peak near 3300 cm^{-1} (OH), a two sharp peaks near 1680 cm^{-1} (carboxyl and ester groups). Caffeine should show a single peak near 1700 cm^{-1} (two amide groups).

  In the NMR the peaks should be located approximately as follows (number of hydrogens followed by peak position in brackets):

  acetaminophen: aryl multiplet (4, 7.5 ppm), methyl singlet (3, 2.5 ppm), HO and NH (1 each as singlets, probably near 5 ppm)

  acetylsalicylic acid: aryl multiplet (4, 7.5 ppm), carboxyl singlet (1, 11.5 ppm), methyl singlet (2.5 ppm)

  caffeine: aryl singlet (1, 7.5 ppm), methyl singlet (3, 2.4 ppm), methyl singlet (6, 3.0 ppm)

Alas, you rush off to Budapest and never learn the results of the investigation.

15 Derivatives of Carboxylic Acids

I. Textbook Chapter Contents

This chapter discusses the chemistry of four derivatives of carboxylic acids—acid chlorides, acid anhydrides, esters, and amides. All can be produced from carboxylic acids and can be re-converted to carboxylic acids by hydrolysis.

II. Learning Objectives

- Know the general structures for acid chlorides, acid anhydrides, esters, and amides.
- Be able to name acid chlorides based on the IUPAC names for the parent carboxylic acids.
- Write equations for the conversion of carboxylic acids into their acid chlorides.
- Know the general mechanism for acyl nucleophilic substitution.
- Write equations for the hydrolysis, alcoholysis, and ammonolysis of acid chlorides.
- Know the structures and names of simple acid anhydrides and the common cyclic anhydrides.
- Write equations for the formation of the common cyclic anhydrides by heating the parent dicarboxylic acids.
- Write equations for the hydrolysis, alcoholysis, and ammonolysis of acid anhydrides.
- Know the IUPAC names for esters.
- Write equations for the formation of esters from acid chlorides and acid anhydrides (alcoholysis reactions).
- Know the mechanism of the formation of esters by Fischer esterification.
- Write equations for the hydrolysis and ammonolysis of esters.
- Write equations for the Claisen condensation of esters to form β-keto esters.
- Know the general structure of fatty acids and fats.
- Write equations for the saponification (base-catalyzed hydrolysis) of fats.
- Know the IUPAC names for amides.
- Write equations for the ammonolysis of acid chlorides, acid anhydrides, and esters to form amides.
- Write equations for the acid-catalyzed hydrolysis of amides to carboxylic acids.

- Be able to carry out multi-step syntheses using carboxylic acid derivatives as starting materials.
- Be able to carry out multi-step syntheses of carboxylic acid derivatives from simpler starting materials.
- Be able to deduce the structure of esters and amides from chemical and spectroscopic information.

III. Glossary

acid anhydride a compound of general structure RCO-O-OCR in which two acyl groups are attached to an oxygen atom

acid chloride a compound in which an acyl group is attached to a chlorine atom (RCO-Cl)

acyl group a RCO- or ArCO- group

acylating reagent a reagent such as an acid chloride or an acid anhydride which is reactive enough to transfer an acyl group to another compound

acylation the attachment of an acyl group to another compound, often by replacement of a hydrogen by the acyl group

alcoholysis reaction of an acylating reagent with an alcohol to form an ester

amide a compound with an acyl group attached to an amino or substituted amino group, such as $RCONH_2$, RCONHR′, or $RCONR'_2$

ammonolysis reaction of an acylating reagent with ammonia to form an amide

antibiotic a compound that kills bacteria or inhibits their growth, thus counteracting bacterial infections

chemical weapons chemicals used to kill, maim, or incapacitate humans

Claisen condensation the reaction between two molecules of the same ester resulting in displacement of an alkoxy group from one ester molecule by an enolate anion of a second ester molecule, resulting in formation of a β-keto ester

coenzyme A a key reactant in many enzyme-catalyzed reactions which serves as an acyl transfer agent. It contains an adenine nucleotide fragment, a pantothenic acid unit, and a 2-aminoethanol unit. It is abbreviated CoA-SH

ester a compound with an acyl group attached to an alkoxy or aryloxy group, such as RCOOR′ or RCOOAr

fat a tri-ester of glycerol

fatty acid a carboxylic acid which is found in fats. They are saturated or unsaturated long chain carboxylic acids containing an even number of carbon atoms (most often 12-18 carbons)

Fischer esterification the acid-catalyzed reaction between a carboxylic acid and an alcohol to form an ester through intermolecular dehydration

hydrolysis the reaction of a compound with water in which the compound usually splits into two fragments as the elements of water are added. Reaction of an acylating agent with water forms a carboxylic acid

lactam an cyclic amide

lactone a cyclic ester

macrolide a large-ring lactone, often with important biological activity

nerve gas a chemical weapon which attacks the nervous system, usually through reaction with choline, causing immobility or death

non-persistent pesticide a pesticide which undergoes relatively rapid decomposition when exposed to the elements, usually through hydrolysis

nucleophilic acyl substitution a reaction in which one nucleophile replaces another attached to an acyl group, but through a two-step addition-ejection (also called addition-elimination) mechanism

persistent pesticide a pesticide which is not readily decomposed upon exposure to the elements and therefore remains effective for considerable time

saponification the term means "soap-making" and was originally applied to the process of making soaps from fats. It more generally describes the process of hydrolyzing an ester under basic conditions to form a carboxylate anion and an alcohol.

triglyceride a tri-ester of glycerol (1,2,3-propanetriol), the acids usually being fatty acids

IV. Summary of Interconversions and Reactions of Carboxylic Acid Derivatives

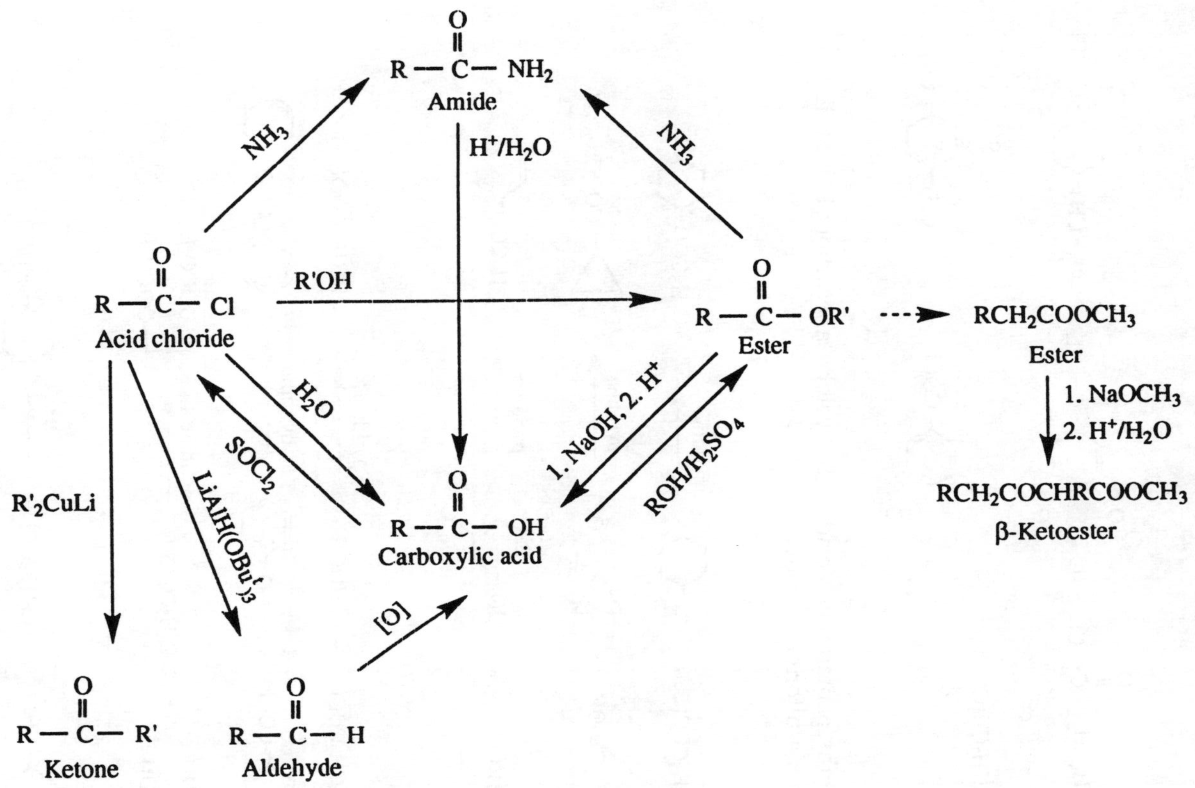

Amide
Acid chloride
Carboxylic acid
Ester
Ketone
Aldehyde
β-Ketoester
NH3
H+/H2O
R'OH
H2O
SOCl2
R'2CuLi
LiAlH(OBu^t)3
[O]
1. NaOH, 2. H+
ROH/H2SO4
RCH2COOCH3
1. NaOCH3
2. H+/H2O
RCH2COCHRCOOCH3

V. Solutions to Problems

For "**How to Solve a Problem,**" review pages 552, 555, 566, and 570.

15.1

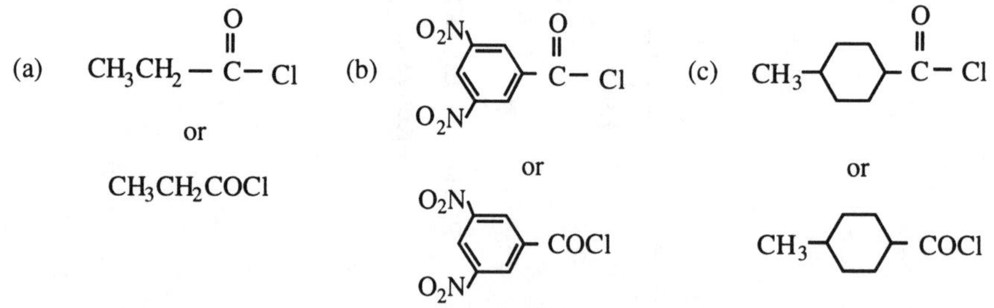

15.2 (a) 4-methylpentanoyl chloride; (b) cyclobutanecarbonyl chloride; (c) benzenesulfonyl chloride.

15.3

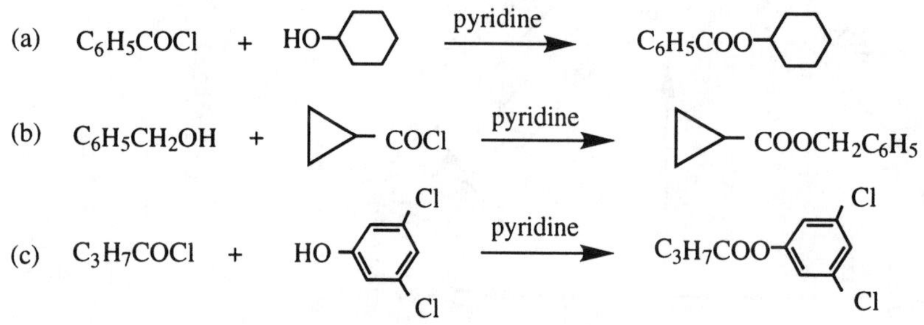

15.4

(a) $CH_3CH_2COCl + HOC_2H_5 \xrightarrow{\text{pyridine}} CH_3CH_2COOC_2H_5$

(b)

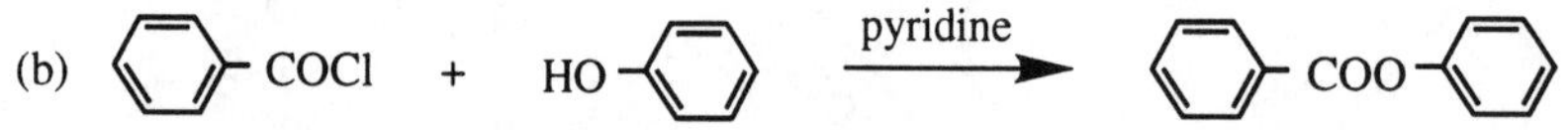

(c)

15.5

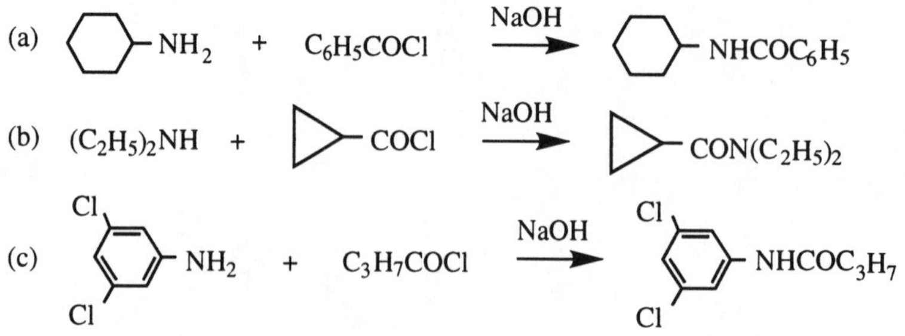

15.6

(a) CH_3CH_2COCl + $H_2NC_2H_5$ $\xrightarrow{NaOH}$ $CH_3CH_2CON(C_2H_5)_2$

(b) 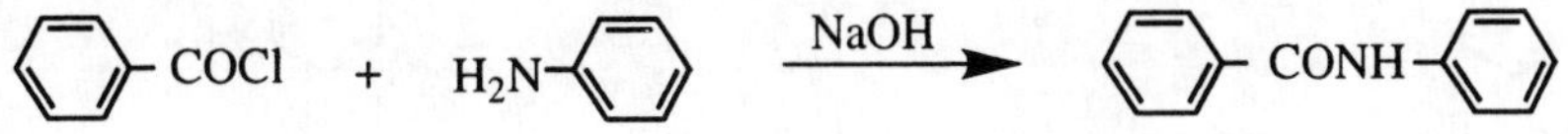

(c) 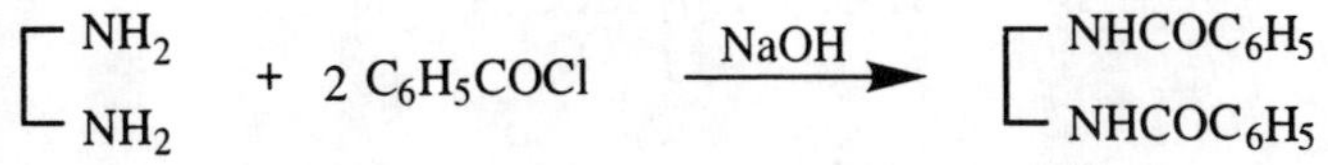

15.7

(a) C_2H_5COCl + $(C_2H_5)_2CuLi$ $\longrightarrow$ $C_2H_5COC_2H_5$

(b) 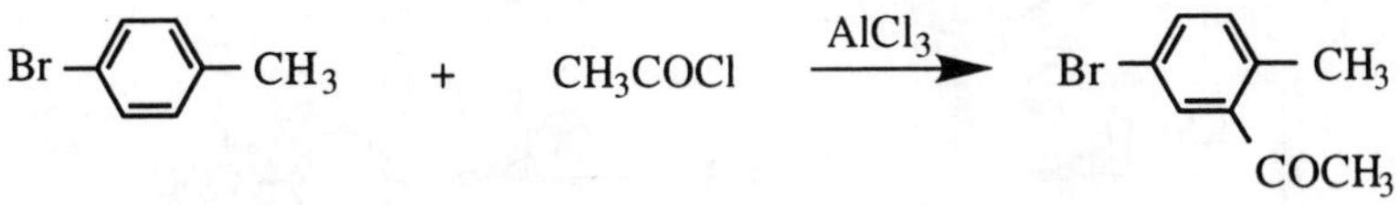

(c) C_6H_5COCl + $LiAlH(OBu^t)_3$ $\longrightarrow$ C_6H_5CHO

15.8

(a) C_6H_5COCl + $((CH_3)_2CHCH_2)_2CuLi$ $\longrightarrow$ $C_6H_5COCH_2CH(CH_3)_2$

(b) $CH_3CH_2CH_2Br$ $\xrightarrow[2.\ CuI]{1.\ Li}$ $(CH_3CH_2CH_2)_2CuLi$ $\xrightarrow{CH_3COCl}$ $CH_3CH_2CH_2COCH_3$

(c) C_2H_5COCl $\xrightarrow[AlCl_3]{C_6H_6}$ $C_2H_5COC_6H_5$

15.9 Acid chlorides, like acetyl chloride, undergo hydrolysis rapidly in water, the reaction producing acetic acid and hydrochloric acid. When inhaled acetyl chloride is converted to these acids by moisture in the lungs and the acids then destroy lung tissue.

$$CH_3COCl + H_2O \longrightarrow CH_3COOH + HCl$$

15.10

(a) 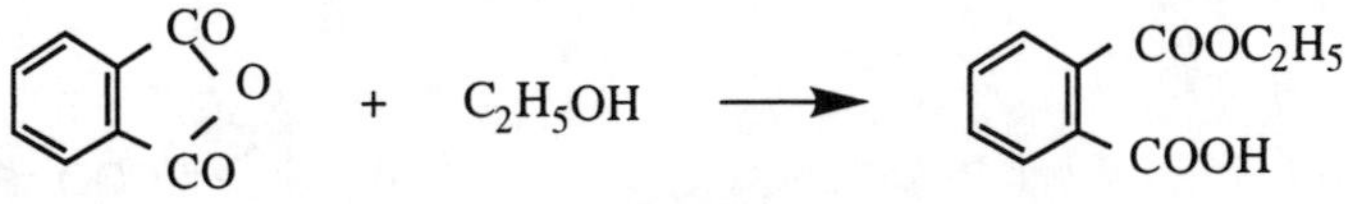

(b) $(CH_3CO)_2O$ + $(C_6H_5)_2NH$ $\longrightarrow$ $(C_6H_5)_2NCOCH_3$ + CH_3COOH

(c) 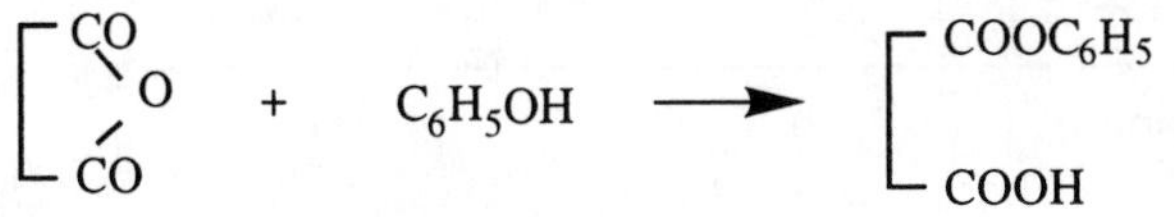

15.11

(a)

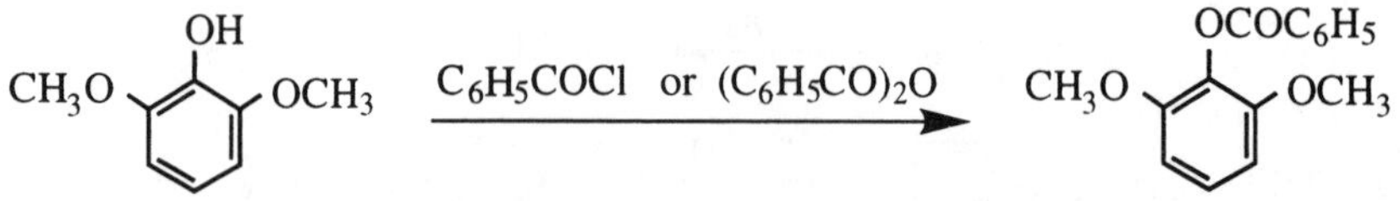
OH
CH₃O
OCH₃
C₆H₅COCl or (C₆H₅CO)₂O
OCOC₆H₅
CH₃O
OCH₃

(b) $(CH_3CH_2CH_2)_2NH \xrightarrow{(CH_3CO)_2O} (CH_3CH_2CH_2)_2NCOCH_3$

15.12

(a)

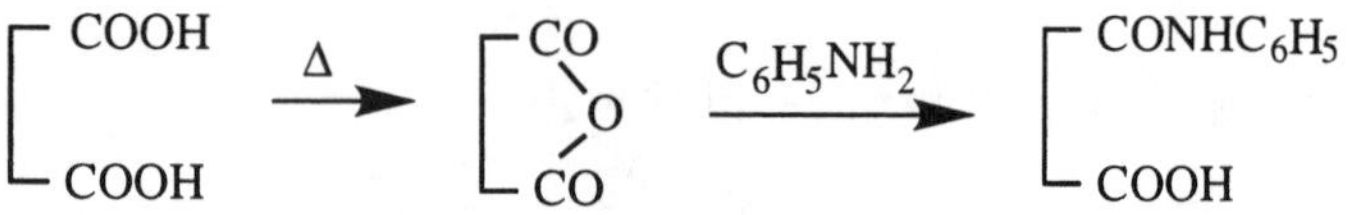
COOH
COOH
Δ
CO
O
CO
C₆H₅NH₂
CONHC₆H₅
COOH

(b)

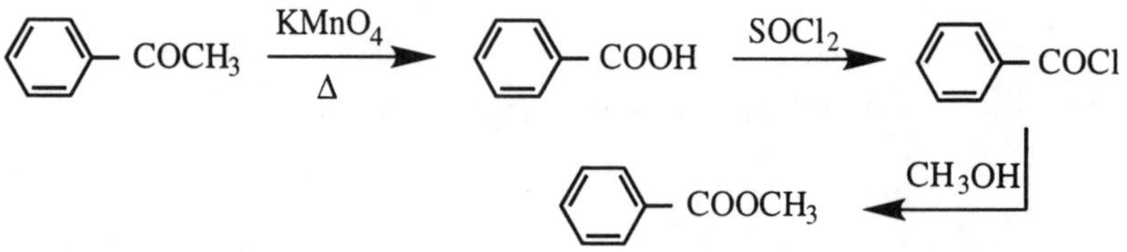
COCH₃
KMnO₄
Δ
COOH
SOCl₂
COCl
CH₃OH
COOCH₃

(c)

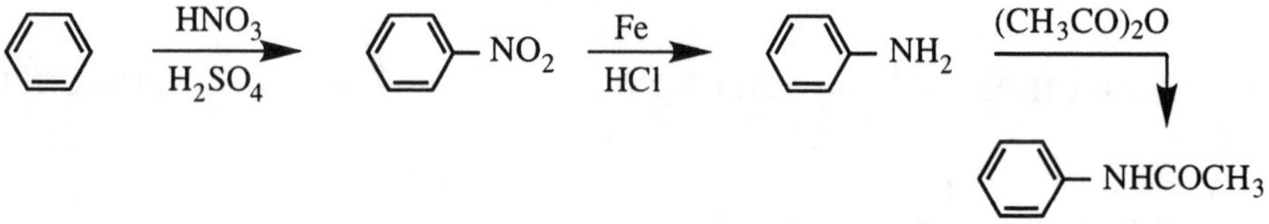
HNO₃
H₂SO₄
NO₂
Fe
HCl
NH₂
(CH₃CO)₂O
NHCOCH₃

(d)

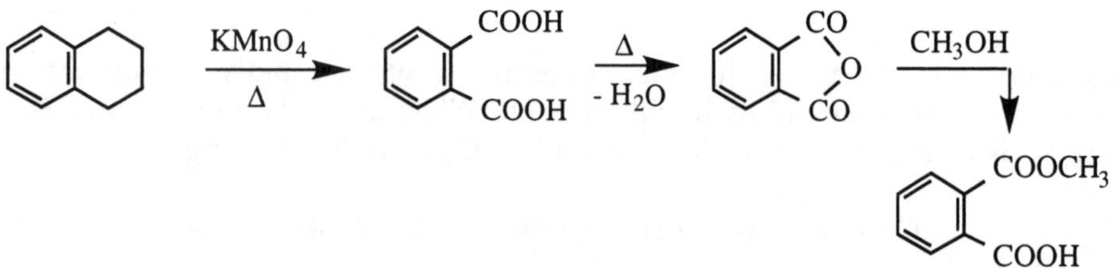
KMnO₄
Δ
COOH
COOH
Δ
- H₂O
CO
O
CO
CH₃OH
COOCH₃
COOH

15.13

(a)

COOCH(CH₃)₂

(b)

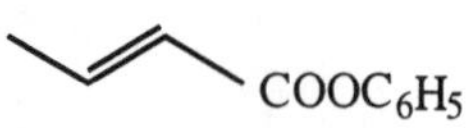
COOC₆H₅

(c)

COO

15.14 (a) cyclopentyl propanoate
(b) propyl butanoate
(c) 2,5-cyclohexadienyl ethanoate
(d) methyl 3-oxobutanoate

15.15

(a) $C_6H_5COOCH(CH_3)_2 \xrightarrow[H_2O]{NaOH} C_6H_5COONa + (CH_3)_2CHOH$

(b) $(CH_3)_2CHCOOC_6H_5 \xrightarrow[H_2O]{NaOH} (CH_3)_2CHCOONa + C_6H_5ONa$

(c)

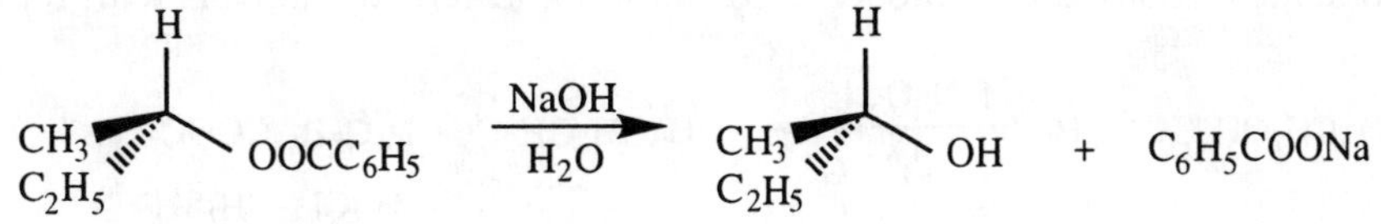
H
CH3
C2H5
OOCC6H5
NaOH
H2O
H
CH3
C2H5
OH
+ C6H5COONa

15.16

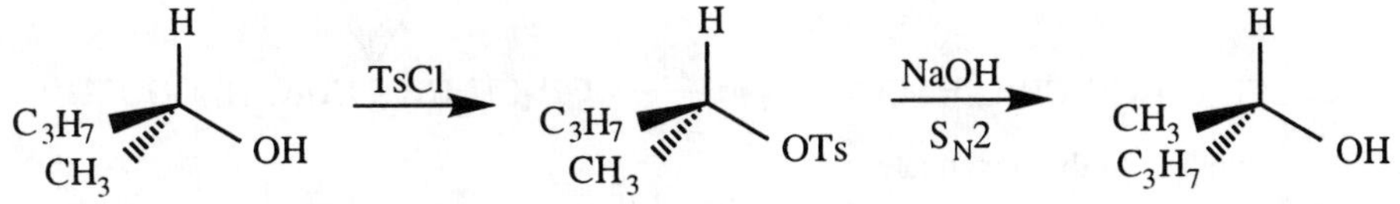
H
C3H7
CH3
OH
TsCl
H
C3H7
CH3
OTs
NaOH
SN2
H
CH3
C3H7
OH

(*S*)-2-pentanol (*R*)-2-pentanol

15.17

(a) $C_6H_5COOC_6H_5 + NH_3 \longrightarrow C_6H_5CONH_2 + C_6H_5OH$

(b)

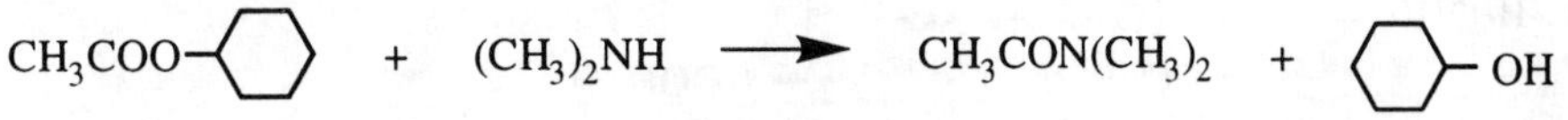
CH3COO–
+ (CH3)2NH
CH3CON(CH3)2 +
OH

(c)

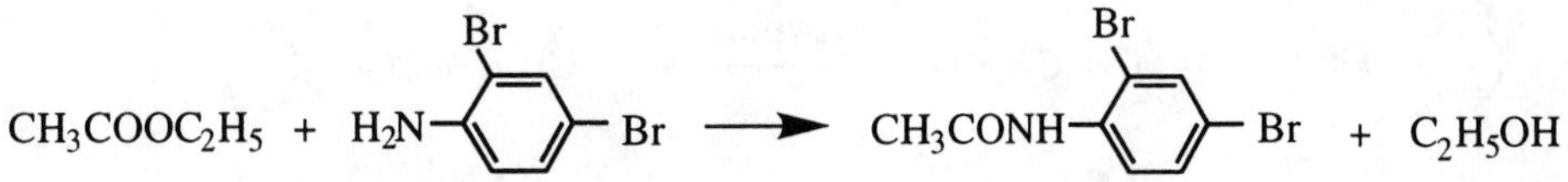
CH3COOC2H5 + H2N–
Br
Br
CH3CONH–
Br
Br
+ C2H5OH

15.18 In the presence of sodium methoxide some of the ester, methyl phenylethanoate, will be converted to its enolate anion. The latter, as a nucleophile, will attack the carbonyl carbon of a second ester molecule, carrying out a nucleophilic acyl substitution. The resulting β-ketoester will be converted to its enolate until the reaction is worked up with dilute acid. The final product will be methyl 2,4-diphenyl-3-oxo-butanoate.

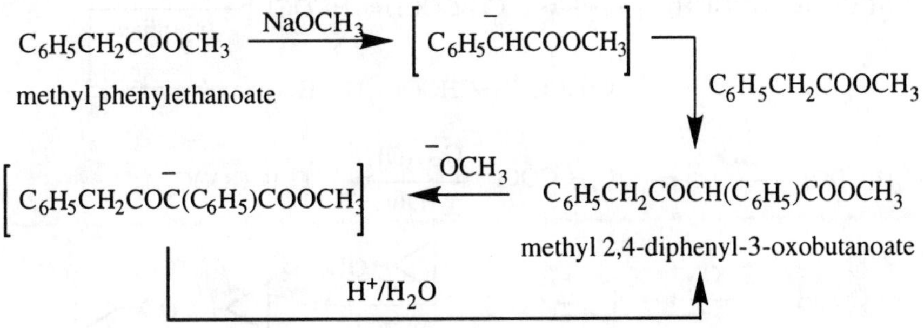
C6H5CH2COOCH3
NaOCH3
C6H5CHCOOCH3
methyl phenylethanoate
C6H5CH2COOCH3
OCH3
C6H5CH2COC(C6H5)COOCH3
C6H5CH2COCH(C6H5)COOCH3
methyl 2,4-diphenyl-3-oxobutanoate
H+/H2O

15.19 Since the synthesis must use the Claisen condensation, try to envision in the product at which bond the two ester molecules could have been joined, keeping in mind that an enolate anion (at an β-carbon) must have been involved. It is apparent that the bond between carbons 2 and 3 must have been formed in the Claisen condensation. This necessitates using the methyl ester of a C4 acid as the starting material, methyl butanoate. Since the normal product of a Claisen condensation is a β -keto ester, the ketone group must be removed. This can be done most easily using thioacetal formation and hydrogenolysis with Raney nickel.

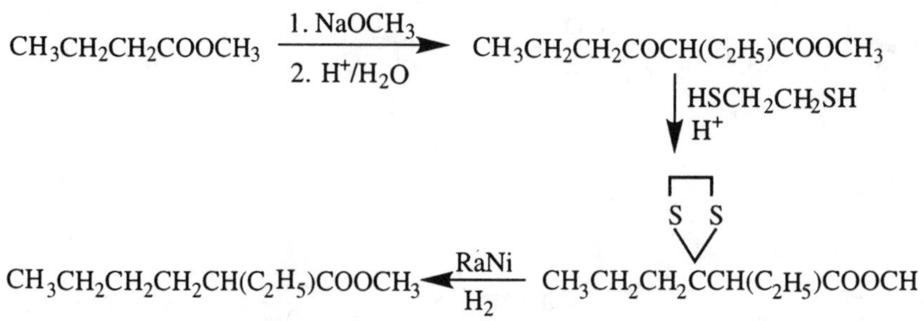
CH3CH2CH2COOCH3
1. NaOCH3
2. H+/H2O
CH3CH2CH2COCH(C2H5)COOCH3
HSCH2CH2SH
H+
S S
CH3CH2CH2CCH(C2H5)COOCH
RaNi
H2
CH3CH2CH2CH2CH(C2H5)COOCH3
methyl 2-ethylhexanoate

15.20

(a) $CH_3CH_2CH_2OH + (CH_3CO)_2O \xrightarrow{-\ CH_3COOH} CH_3COOCH_2CH_2CH_3$

(b) 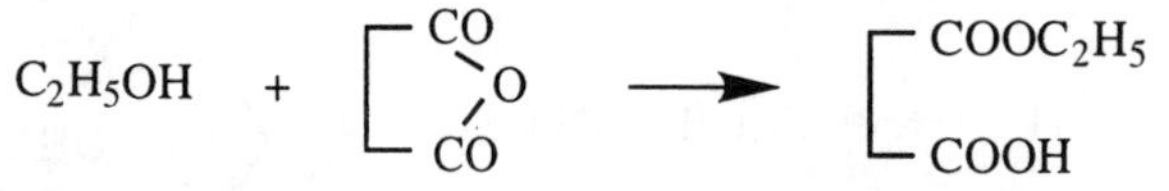
C2H5OH
+
CO
O
CO
COOC2H5
COOH

(c) 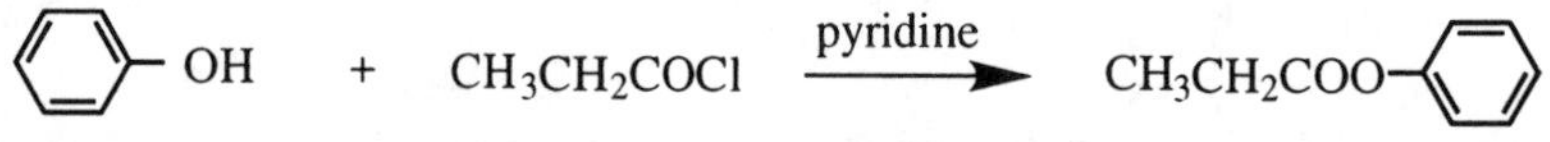
OH
+
CH3CH2COCl
pyridine
CH3CH2COO

(d) 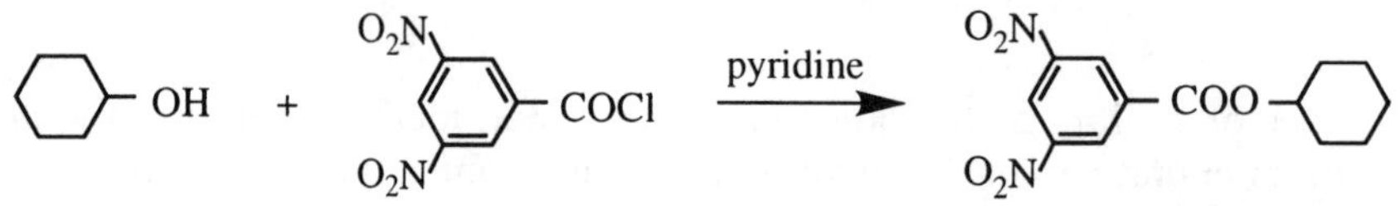
OH
+
O2N
O2N
COCl
pyridine
O2N
O2N
COO

15.21

(a) $CH_3COCH{=}CHCOOH \xrightarrow{SOCl_2} CH_3COCH{=}CHCOCl \xrightarrow[pyridine]{(CH_3)_2CHOH} CH_3COCH{=}CHCOOCH(CH_3)_2$

(b) $C_6H_5COOH \xrightarrow{SOCl_2} C_6H_5COCl \xrightarrow[pyridine]{C_6H_5OH} C_6H_5COOC_6H_5$

(c) 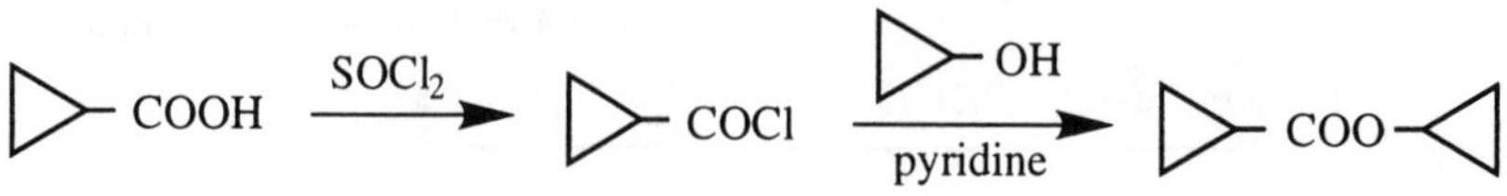
COOH
SOCl2
COCl
OH
pyridine
COO

15.22

(a) $C_2H_5OH + C_6H_5COOH \xrightarrow{H^+} C_6H_5COOC_2H_5$

(b)

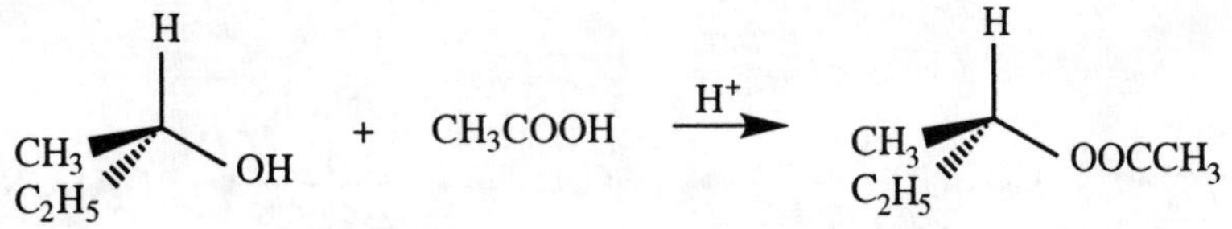

15.23

(a) $(CH_3)_2CHOH + CH_3COOH \xrightarrow{H^+} (CH_3)_2CHOOCCH_3$

(b)

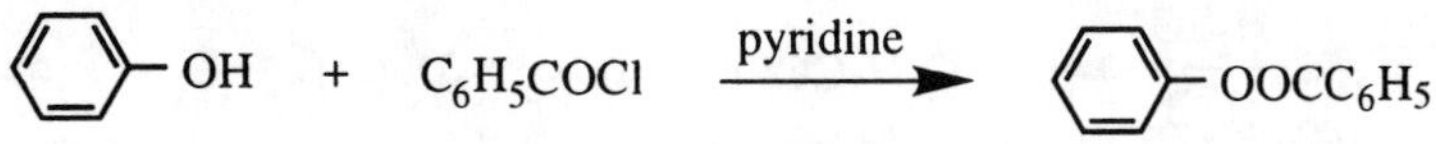

(c)

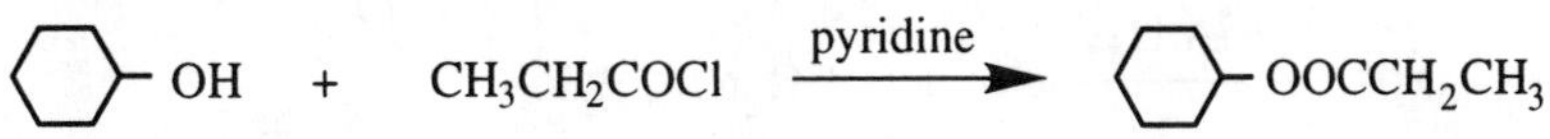

(d)

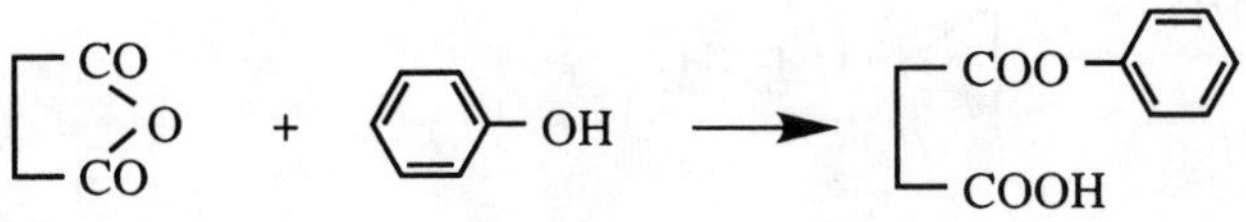

15.24

(a)

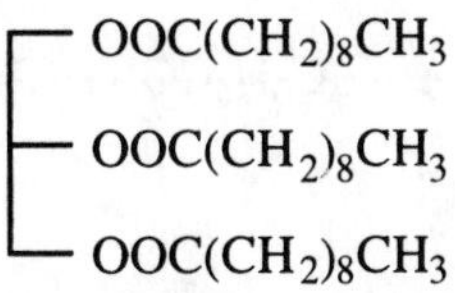

glyceryl tridecanoate

(b)

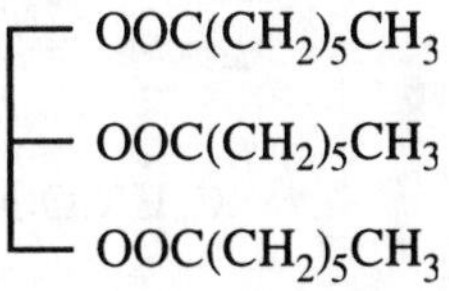

glyceryl triheptanoate

(c)

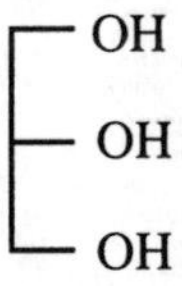

glycerol
(1,2,3-propanetriol)

and $CH_3(CH_2)_8COONa$

sodium decanoate

15.25

(a) $C_5H_{11}CONH_2$ (b)

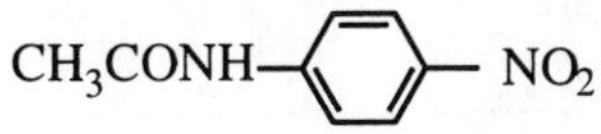

(c) $CH_3CH(OH)CH_2CONHCH_3$

(d)

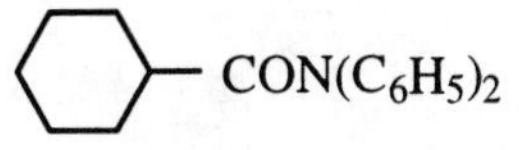

(e) $CH_3CH_2CH_2CH_2CONHCH_2C_6H_5$

15.26 (a) *N*-phenylbenzamide
(b) *N*-(*m*-methoxyphenyl)acetamide (*m*-methoxyacetanilide)
(c) *N,N*-dimethylpropanamide

***15.27**

$$C_6H_6 \xrightarrow[H_2SO_4]{HNO_3} C_6H_5NO_2 \xrightarrow[HCl]{Fe} C_6H_5NH_2 \xrightarrow[2.\ CuCN]{1.\ NaNO_2,\ HCl} C_6H_5CN \xrightarrow{LiAlH_4} C_6H_5CH_2NH_2$$

15.28

(a) $$C_6H_5CONHC_2H_5 \xrightarrow[H_2O]{H_2SO_4} C_6H_5COOH + C_2H_5NH_3^+$$

(b) $$CH_3CON(C_6H_5)_2 \xrightarrow{LiAlH_4} CH_3CH_2N(C_6H_5)_2$$

(c) 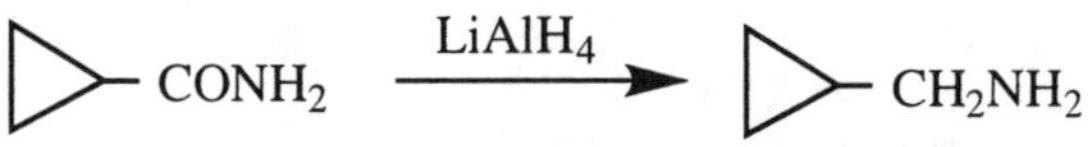

15.29

(a) $$C_6H_5COOH \xrightarrow{SOCl_2} C_6H_5COCl \xrightarrow{CH_3NH_2} C_6H_5CONHCH_3$$

$$C_6H_5COOCH_3 \xrightarrow{CH_3NH_2} C_6H_5CONHCH_3$$

(b) 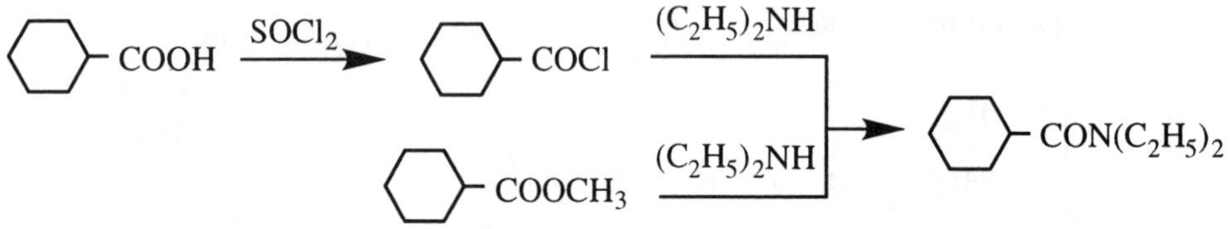

15.30 (a) methyl 3-hydroxyhexanoate
(b) *N*-methyl-2,6-dichlorobenzamide
(c) butyl heptanoate
(d) *m*-trifluoromethylbenzoyl chloride
(e) *N,N*-diethyl-4-oxohexanamide
(f) phenyl cyclohexanecarboxylate
(g) benzoic anhydride
(h) 2-aminopropanamide
(i) diethyl succinate

15.31

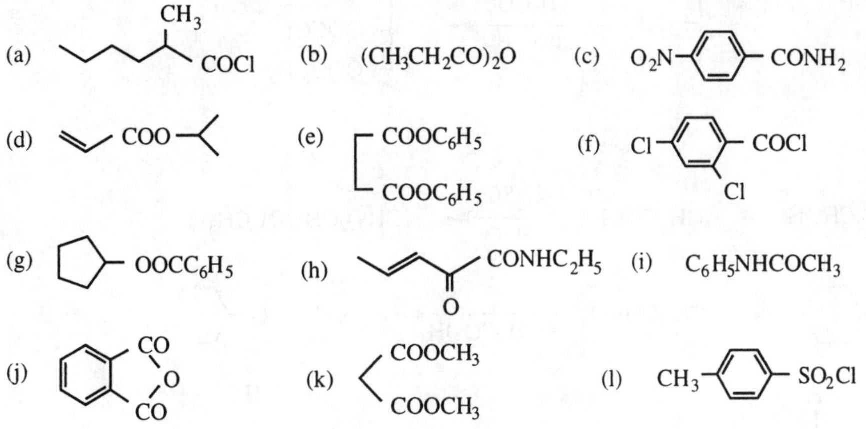
(a)
CH3
COCl
(b) (CH3CH2CO)2O
(c) O2N CONH2
(d) COO
(e) COOC6H5
COOC6H5
(f) Cl COCl
Cl
(g) OOCC6H5
(h) CONHC2H5
O
(i) C6H5NHCOCH3
(j) CO
O
CO
(k) COOCH3
COOCH3
(l) CH3 SO2Cl

15.32

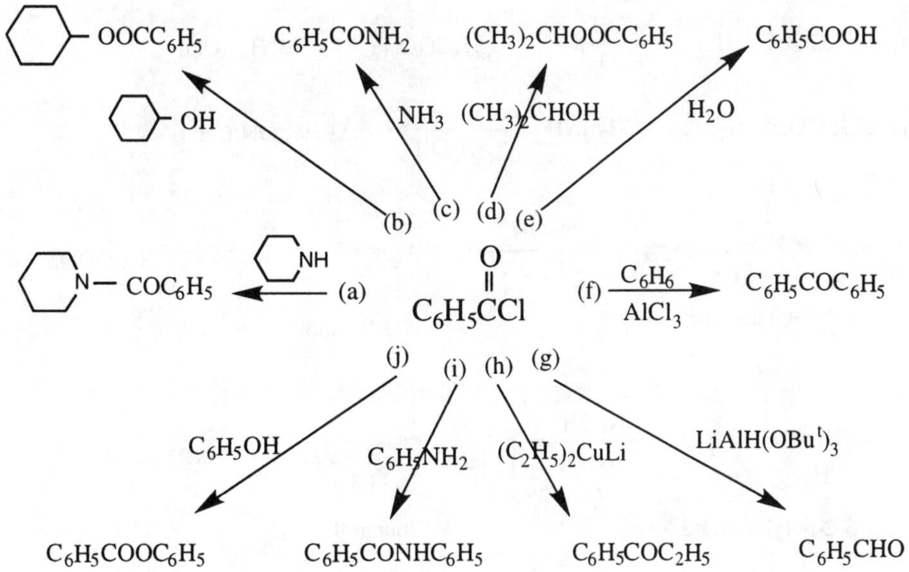
OOCC6H5
C6H5CONH2
(CH3)2CHOOCC6H5
C6H5COOH
OH
NH3
(CH3)2CHOH
H2O
(b) (c) (d) (e)
NH
N— COC6H5
(a)
C6H5CCl
(f)
C6H6
AlCl3
C6H5COC6H5
(j) (i) (h) (g)
C6H5OH
C6H5NH2
(C2H5)2CuLi
LiAlH(OBut)3
C6H5COOC6H5
C6H5CONHC6H5
C6H5COC2H5
C6H5CHO

15.33

(a) $C_6H_5CONH_2 \xrightarrow[\Delta]{H^+/H_2O} C_6H_5COOH + NH_4^+$

(b) $C_6H_5CONH_2 \xrightarrow{LiAlH_4} C_6H_5CH_2NH_2$

15.34

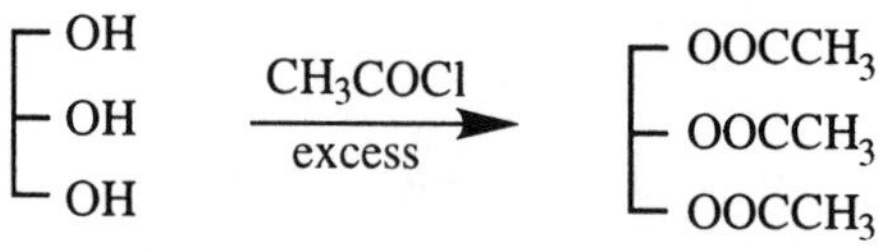

15.35

(a) $$(CH_3)_2CHOH + CH_3COOH \xrightarrow[-\,H_2O]{H_2SO_4} (CH_3)_2CHOOCCH_3$$

(b) 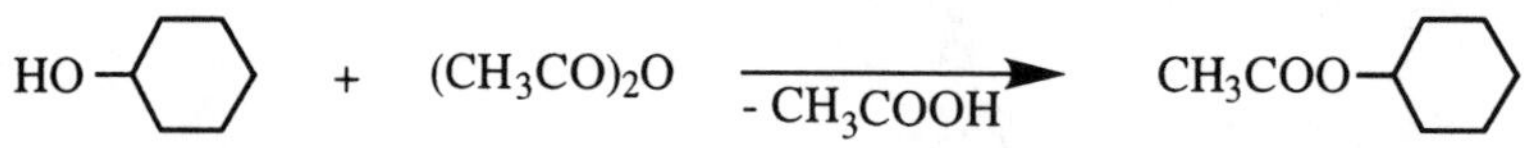

(c) 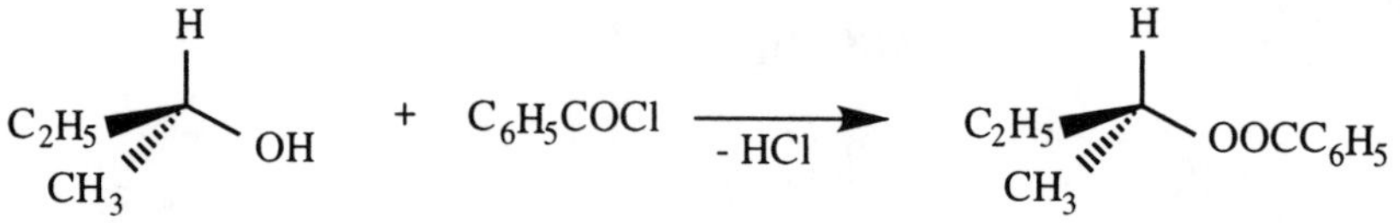

S-2-butanol *S*-2-butyl benzoate

(d) $$C_6H_5COOC(CH_3)_3 \xrightarrow[H_2O]{NaOH} C_6H_5COONa + (CH_3)_3COH$$

(e) $$C_6H_5COOC_2H_5 + (CH_3)_2NH \xrightarrow[-\,C_2H_5OH]{} C_6H_5CON(CH_3)_2$$

(f) 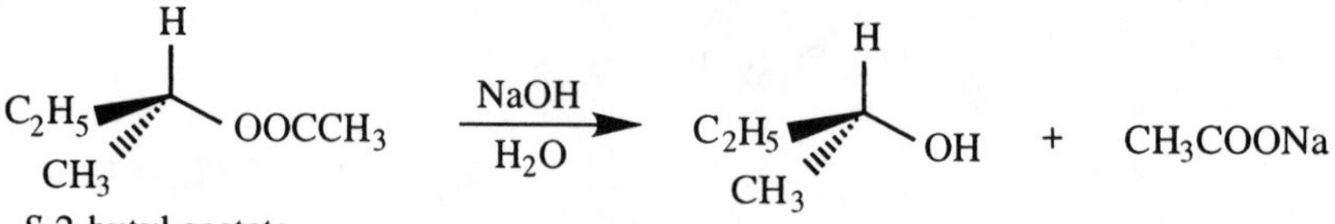

S-2-butyl acetate *S*-2-butanol

(g) 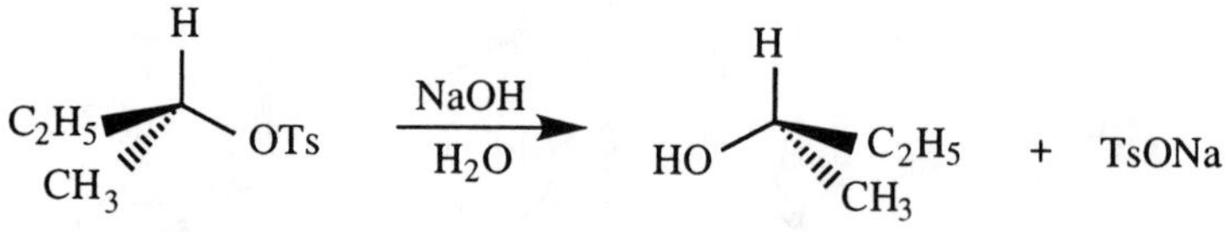

S-2-butyl tosylate *R*-2-butanol

(h) 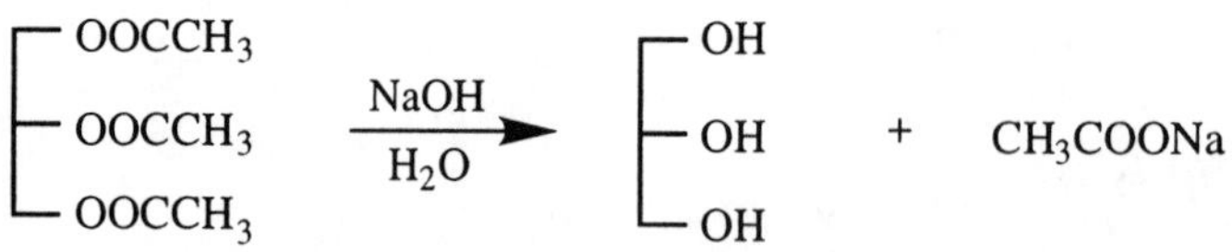

(i) $$CH_3COOC_2H_5 \xrightarrow[2.\ HCl/H_2O]{1.\ NaOC_2H_5} CH_3COCH_2COOC_2H_5$$

15.36

$$CH_3CH_2COOCH_3 \xrightarrow[(a)]{NaOCH_3} CH_3CH_2CO\overset{-}{C}(CH_3)COOCH_3 \quad Na^+$$

$$\xrightarrow{(b)\ HCl} CH_3CH_2COCH(CH_3)COOCH_3$$

$$\xrightarrow[H_2O]{(c)\ NaOH} CH_3CH_2COCH(CH_3)COONa$$

$$\xrightarrow{(d)\ HCl} CH_3CH_2COCH(CH_3)COOH \xrightarrow[-\ CO_2]{(e)\ \Delta} CH_3CH_2COCH_2CH_3$$

15.37

(a) $$CH_3COOC_2H_5 \xrightarrow[2.\ H^+/H_2O]{1.\ NaOC_2H_5} CH_3COCH_2COOC_2H_5$$

(b) $$CH_3CH_2COOC_2H_5 \xrightarrow[2.\ H^+/H_2O]{1.\ NaOC_2H_5} CH_3CH_2COCH(CH_3)COOC_2H_5$$

15.38

(a) $$CH_3COOC_2H_5 \xrightarrow[2.\ H^+/H_2O]{1.\ NaOC_2H_5} CH_3COCH_2COOC_2H_5 \xrightarrow[2.\ H^+]{1.\ NaOH} CH_3COCH_2COOH \xrightarrow[-\ CO_2]{\Delta} CH_3COCH_3$$

(b) $$CH_3CH_2CH_2COOCH_3 \xrightarrow[2.\ H^+/H_2O]{1.\ NaOCH_3} CH_3CH_2CH_2COCH(C_2H_5)COOCH_3$$

$$\xrightarrow[2.\ H^+]{1.\ NaOH} CH_3CH_2CH_2COCH(C_2H_5)COOH \xrightarrow[-\ CO_2]{\Delta} CH_3CH_2CH_2COCH_2CH_2CH_3$$

15.39 In all of these reactions one equivalent of benzoic acid is a by-product.

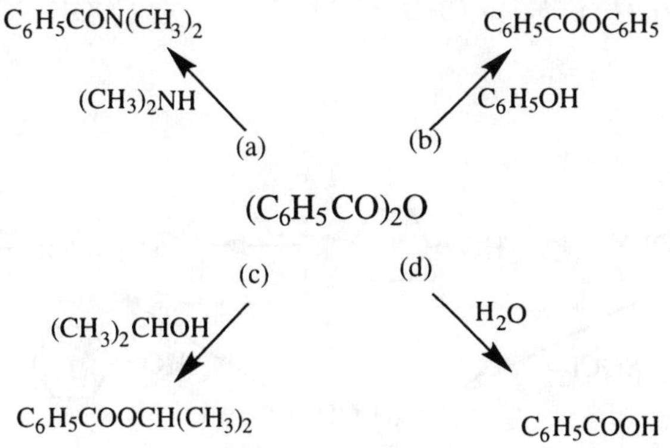
C6H5CON(CH3)2
(CH3)2NH
(a)
C6H5COOC6H5
C6H5OH
(b)
(C6H5CO)2O
(c)
(CH3)2CHOH
C6H5COOCH(CH3)2
(d)
H2O
C6H5COOH

15.40

(a) 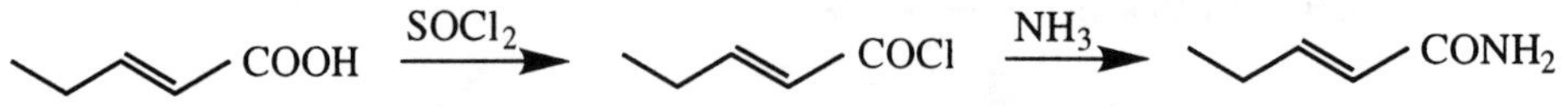
COOH
SOCl2
COCl
NH3
CONH2

(b) $C_6H_5COOH \xrightarrow{SOCl_2} C_6H_5COCl \xrightarrow[\text{pyridine}]{C_6H_5OH} C_6H_5COOC_6H_5$

(c) $CH_3CH_2COOH \xrightarrow[2.\ H_2O]{1.\ Br_2/P} CH_3CHBrCOOH \xrightarrow{SOCl_2} CH_3CHBrCOCl \xrightarrow[\text{excess}]{NH_3} CH_3CHNH_2CONH_2$

15.41

(a) $C_6H_6 \xrightarrow[FeBr_3]{Br_2} C_6H_5Br \xrightarrow[2.\ CO_2,\ 3.\ H^+/H_2O]{1.\ Mg/ether} C_6H_5COOH \xrightarrow[H^+]{C_2H_5OH} C_6H_5COOC_2H_5$

* (b) 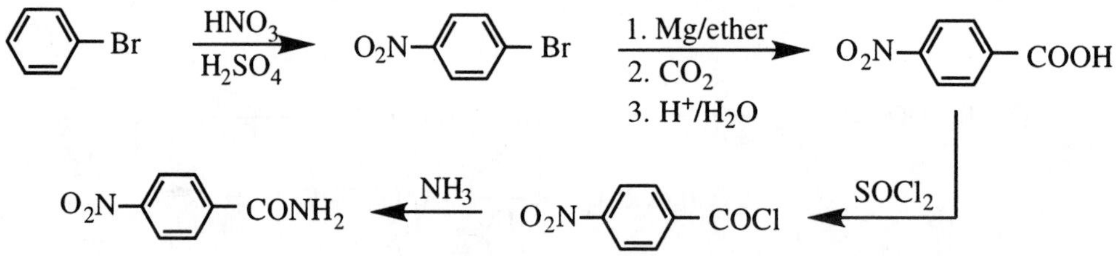
Br
HNO3
H2SO4
O2N
Br
1. Mg/ether
2. CO2
3. H+/H2O
O2N
COOH
SOCl2
O2N
COCl
NH3
O2N
CONH2

(c) 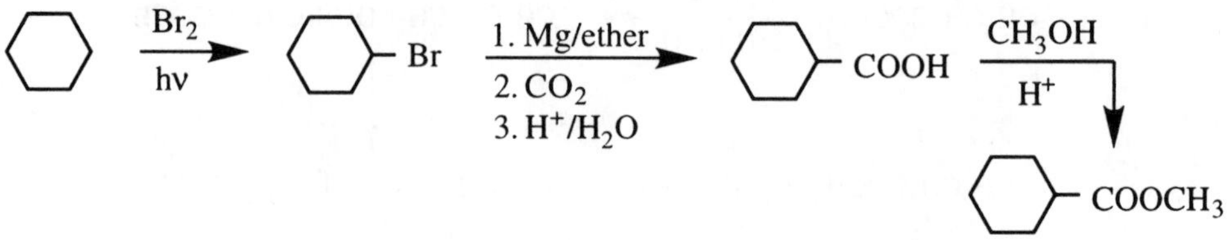
Br2
hν
Br
1. Mg/ether
2. CO2
3. H+/H2O
COOH
CH3OH
H+
COOCH3

(d) 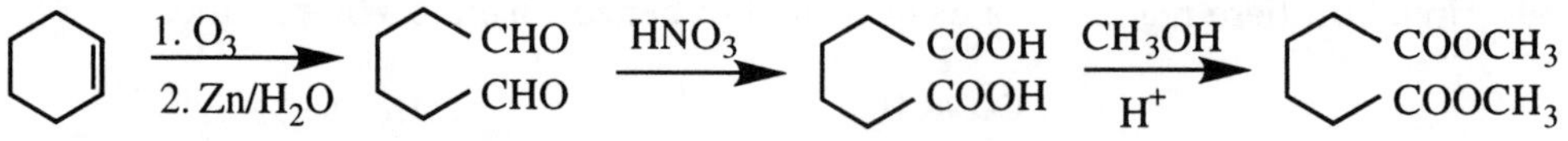
1. O3
2. Zn/H2O
CHO
CHO
HNO3
COOH
COOH
CH3OH
H+
COOCH3
COOCH3

15.42

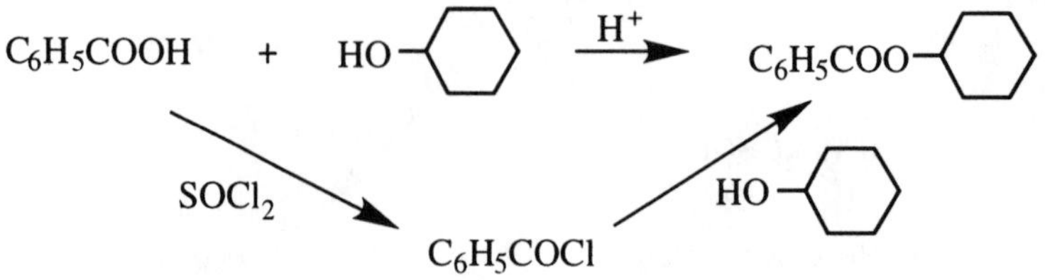
C6H5COOH
+
HO
H+
C6H5COO
SOCl2
C6H5COCl
HO

15.43 The key to using the Claisen condensation for synthesis is to first envision the β-ketoacid from which the product ketone could be obtained by decarboxylation—remember that carbon dioxide will be lost from a β-position. The result of this thinking is illustrated in the retrosyntheses outlined in parts (a) and (b). Then it should be clear where the new carbon-carbon bond should be formed in the Claisen condensation itself, as indicated in (a) by the location of the dotted line. Envisioning the two fragments separated by the dotted line will indicate the two esters which must be used in the Claisen condensation.

(a) $CH_3CH_2CH_2COCH_2CH_2CH_3 \Longrightarrow CH_3CH_2CH_2CO \,\vdots\, CH(COOH)CH_2CH_3$

$CH_3CH_2CH_2COOCH_3 \xrightarrow[\text{2. } H^+/H_2O]{\text{1. NaOCH}_3} C_3H_7COCH(COOCH_3)C_2H_5$

$C_3H_7COCH(COOCH_3)C_2H_5 \xrightarrow[\text{2. } H^+]{\text{1. NaOH}} C_3H_7COCH(COOH)C_2H_5 \xrightarrow[-\,CO_2]{\Delta} C_3H_7COC_3H_7$

(b) $C_6H_5CH_2COCH_2C_6H_5 \Longrightarrow C_6H_5CH_2COCH(COOH)C_6H_5 \Longrightarrow C_6H_5CH_2COOCH_3$

$C_6H_5CH_2COOCH_3 \xrightarrow[\text{2. } H^+/H_2O]{\text{1. NaOCH}_3} C_6H_5CH_2COCH(COOH)C_6H_5$

$C_6H_5CH_2COCH(COOH)C_6H_5 \xrightarrow[\text{2. H+/}H_2O]{\text{1. NaOH}} C_6H_5CH_2COCH(COOH)C_6H_5 \xrightarrow[-\,CO_2]{\Delta,} C_6H_5CH_2COCH_2C_6H_5$

15.44

COOH
OH
CH3COCl
pyridine
COOH
OOCCH3

salicylic acid — aspirin (acetylsalicylic acid)

15.45

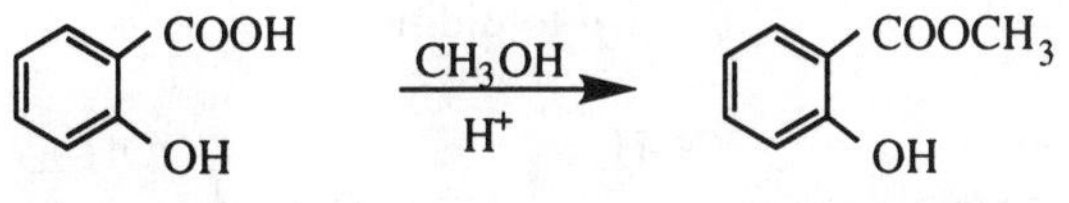
COOH
OH
CH3OH
H+
COOCH3
OH

salicylic acid — oil of wintergreen (methyl salicylate)

15.46

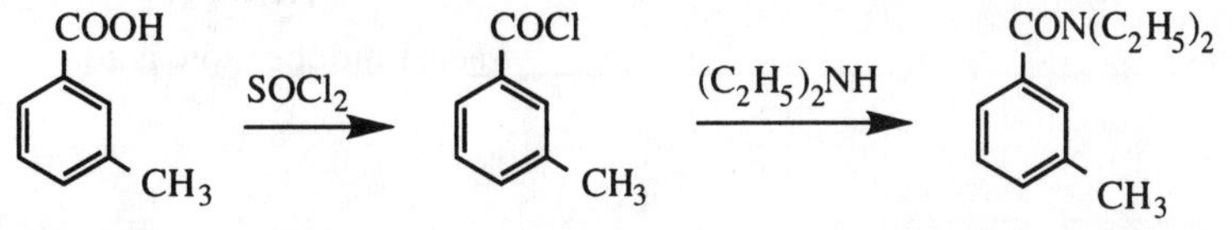
COOH
CH3
SOCl2
COCl
CH3
(C2H5)2NH
CON(C2H5)2
CH3

m-toluic acid — *N,N*-diethyl-*m*-toluamide ("Off")

***15.47**

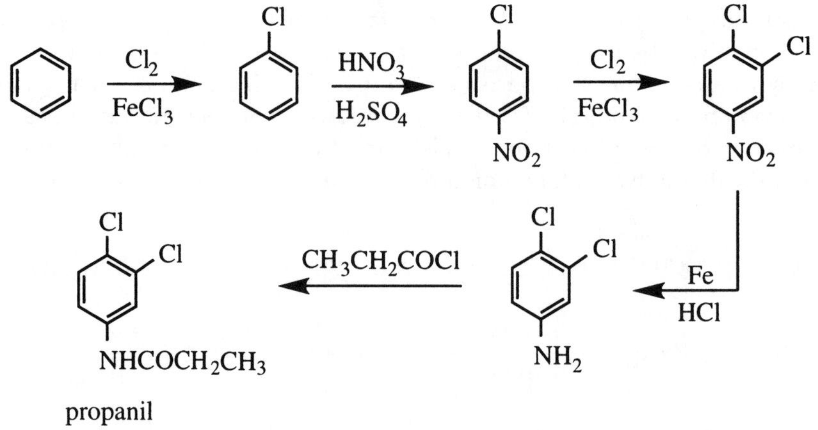
Cl
Cl_2
$FeCl_3$
HNO_3
H_2SO_4
NO_2
Fe
HCl
NH_2
CH_3CH_2COCl
$NHCOCH_2CH_3$
propanil

15.48 Aspartame has an ester group and an amide group that are both susceptible to hydrolysis.

$$C_6H_5CH_2CH(COOCH_3)NHCOCH(NH_2)CH_2COOH \quad \text{(Aspartame)}$$

$$\downarrow \; HCl, \; H_2O$$

$$C_6H_5CH_2CH(COOH)NH_2 \; + \; HOOCCH(NH_2)CH_2COOH \; + \; CH_3OH$$

phenylalanine — aspartic acid — methanol

***15.49**

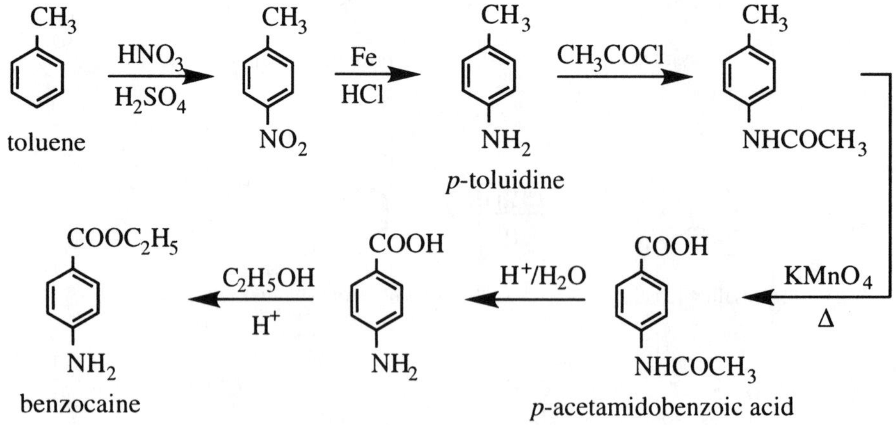
CH_3
toluene
HNO_3
H_2SO_4
NO_2
Fe
HCl
NH_2
p-toluidine
CH_3COCl
$NHCOCH_3$
$KMnO_4$
Δ
COOH
p-acetamidobenzoic acid
H^+/H_2O
C_2H_5OH
H^+
$COOC_2H_5$
benzocaine

***15.50**

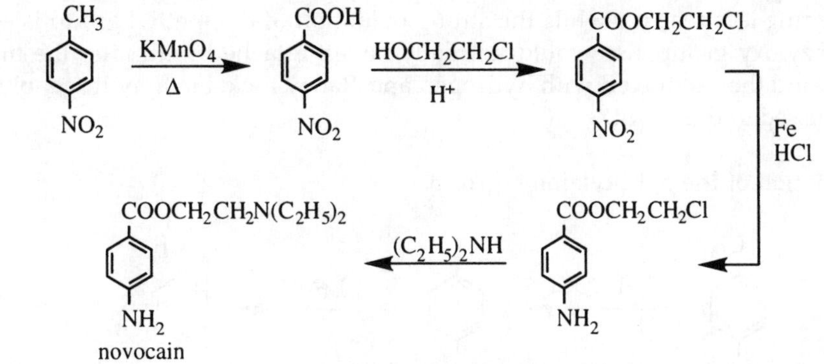
CH3
KMnO4
Δ
NO2
COOH
HOCH2CH2Cl
H+
NO2
COOCH2CH2Cl
NO2
Fe
HCl
COOCH2CH2N(C2H5)2
(C2H5)2NH
COOCH2CH2Cl
NH2
NH2
novocain

15.51 The concept of retrosynthesis can be applied to piecing together the structure of an unknown such as atropine. First write the structure you are given then to the right and using the retrosynthesis "arrow" write the structure from which the former must have been derived. A key concept is to realize that tropine must have a symmetrical structure (it is not an enantiomer —its mirror image is superimposable), and the hydroxyl can therefore only be in the position shown, not one position to the right or left. Because tropine is obtained by hydrolysis, and the other fragment was a carboxylic acid, atropine must be an ester.

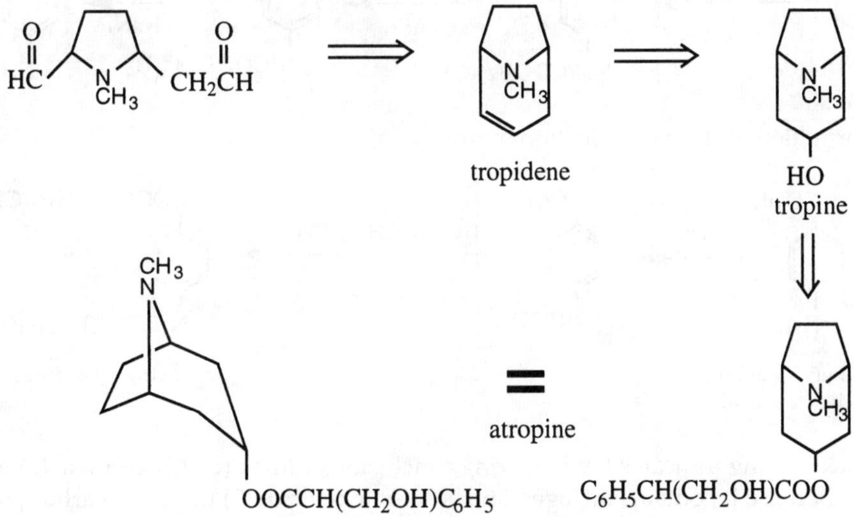
HC
CH3
CH2CH
tropidene
HO
tropine
atropine
OOCCH(CH2OH)C6H5
C6H5CH(CH2OH)COO

***15.52** Although there are many steps in the synthesis of tetracaine from *p*-toluidine the conceptual approach is succinct, involving only two major transformations: alkylate the amino group (sequence a), and convert the methyl group to a carboxyl group then to an ester (sequence c).

There is a third sequence required (labeled b) which must be employed to protect the amine group while the oxidation occurs, and then deprotect it. Unique is the application of the benzyloxy ester group ($C_6H_5CH_2OOC$-, abbreviated BzOOC-, and regularly used in peptide synthesis as demonstrated in Section 16.4) which is attached temporarily to the amine group to form an amide. The amide group protects the amine and also makes the benzene ring less reactive while the strong oxidation of the methyl group is accomplished. This benzyloxy group also would normally be left attached until after the final acylation reaction and then removed with hydrogen and Raney nickel in a hydrogenolysis reaction not discussed to this point.

(a) Formation of the *N*-butylamine group:

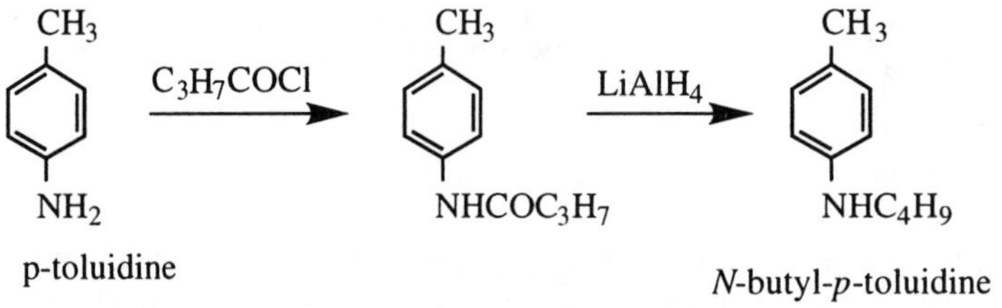
CH3
C3H7COCl
CH3
LiAlH4
CH3
NH2
NHCOC3H7
NHC4H9
p-toluidine
N-butyl-p-toluidine

(b) Protection and deprotection of the amine group during oxidation of the methyl group to a carboxyl group:

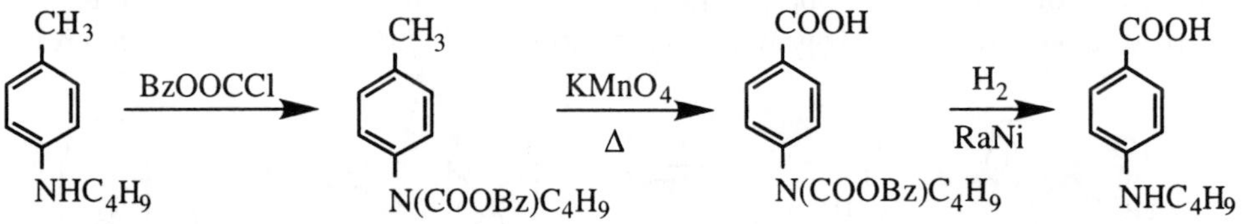
CH3
BzOOCCl
CH3
KMnO4
Δ
COOH
H2
RaNi
COOH
NHC4H9
N(COOBz)C4H9
N(COOBz)C4H9
NHC4H9

(c) Formation of the ester functional group:

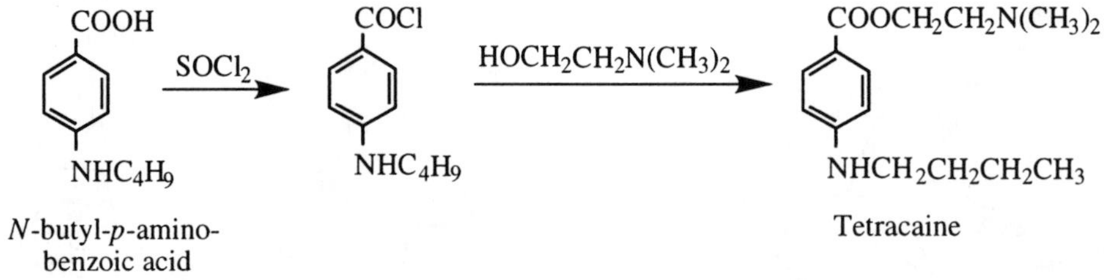
COOH
SOCl2
COCl
HOCH2CH2N(CH3)2
COOCH2CH2N(CH3)2
NHC4H9
NHC4H9
NHCH2CH2CH2CH3
N-butyl-p-amino-
benzoic acid
Tetracaine

15.53 A quick reading indicates the following conclusions can be readily drawn: (1) **A** must be an amine because it contains nitrogen and is soluble in acid; (2) there is a carbonyl group present as indicated by the IR peak at 1730 cm^{-1}; (3) **A** is a di-substituted aromatic because of the ^{1}H-NMR peak at 7.3 ppm, the area of which must represent four (not two) hydrogens (since the NMR integration accounts for ten hydrogens but there are actually twenty present in the formula); (4) the compound is an ester or an amide because hydrolysis produces a carboxylic acid (**C**) and an amino-alcohol (**B**).

The structure of **B** can be evolved quickly because it can be synthesized by reaction of diethylamine (a nucleophile) with ethylene oxide, a typical ring opening reaction which should produce 2-(*N,N*-diethylamino)ethanol. The IR and ^{1}H-NMR data are consistent with this structure for **B:** typical quartet and triplet for ethyl groups, triplets for the two methylene groups, and singlet for the hydroxyl group, also confirmed by the IR peak at 3300 cm^{-1}. In view of this structure, and the information that it was obtained by hydrolysis of **A**, the latter can only be an ester with a tertiary amine group present (not an amide, because an amine must be primary or secondary to participate in amide formation, and an amide would not be soluble in dilute acid).

(C2H5)2NH
+
O
(C2H5)2NCH2CH2OH

B

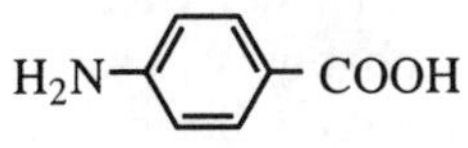
H2N
COOH

C

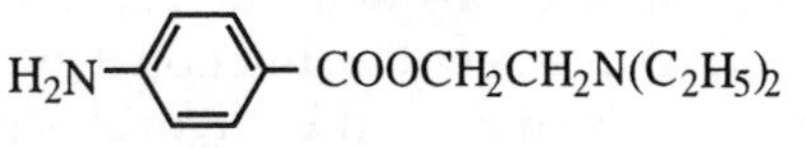
H2N
COOCH2CH2N(C2H5)2

A

Since **C** is soluble in both acid and base it must be amphoteric (i.e., have an acidic carboxyl group and a basic amine group). Consideration of the formula of **C** ($C_7H_7O_2N$), and recognition from the ^{1}H-NMR that **C** must be a disubstituted benzenoid compound, means that **C** can only be an aminobenzoic acid (the ^{1}H-NMR peaks and relative areas are consistent with this conclusion). The ^{13}C-NMR is consistent with the relative positions of the carboxyl and amino groups being *para*. Therefore, **C** is *p*-aminobenzoic acid.

Since **A** afforded **B** and **C** upon hydrolysis, and since **A** can only be an ester, application of retrosynthetic thinking indicates that the structure of **A** is as shown above. Re-checking the ^{1}H-NMR and IR data for **A** indicates it is consistent with this structure.

15.54 The HDI of the two $C_9H_{10}O_2$ isomers is five. These five "unsaturations" are accounted for by the presence of an aromatic ring (^{1}H-NMR peaks at 7.2-7.3 ppm; IR peak at 1600 cm^{-1}) and a carbonyl group (1675 cm^{-1}). These two groups account for seven of the nine carbons in each compound. The fact that both **X** and **Y** are hydrolyzed to afford a carboxylic acid and methanol indicates both are methyl esters. Therefore, only one other carbon atom can be present in each. The ^{1}H-NMR indicates **X** has a di-substituted phenyl ring (only four aromatic hydrogens) which must carry a methyl group and a carboxylate group. The ^{13}C-NMR data indicates **X** is *para* substituted and therefore must be methyl *p*-toluate. The ^{1}H-NMR of **Y** indicates five aromatic hydrogens so the additional carbon must be a methylene group between the carboxylate group and the phenyl ring. Therefore, **Y** must be methyl phenylacetate.

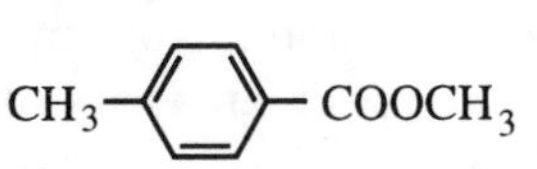
CH3
COOCH3

X

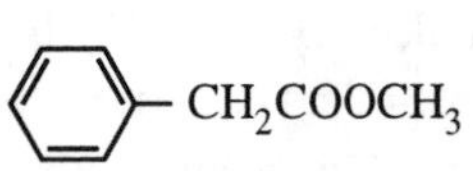
CH2COOCH3

Y

15.55 The HDI of $C_5H_8O_4$ is two, consistent with rings, alkenes, an alkyne, or carbonyl groups. The IR peak at 1740 cm^{-1} indicates a carbonyl group but no alkene or alkyne are detectable.

The ^{1}H-NMR integration of 1:3 indicates there must be two hydrogens of one kind and six of another kind, and the fact that all the peaks are singlets indicates there are no adjacent hydrogens. The downfield location of the two NMR peaks indicates both groups are attached to electron withdrawing groups, which, in view of the formula, could be oxygen or carbonyl groups. The number of oxygens in the compound argues for considering the presence of two ester groups, probably $-COOCH_3$ groups. Since the compound must be somewhat symmetrical (in view of the paucity of ^{1}H-NMR peaks for ten hydrogens) the only feasible structure is dimethyl malonate, $CH_2(COOCH_3)_2$.

15.56 The formula of compound **A** ($C_{11}H_{14}O_2$) indicates an HDI of five. The IR peak at 1690 cm^{-1} and the absence of reactions with the listed reagents (which detect hydroxyl, aldehyde, and ketone groups) indicates the functional group probably is an ester which accounts for both oxygens. This is confirmed by hydrolysis to a carboxylic acid (**B**) and an alcohol (**C**). **C** must be isopropyl alcohol ($(CH_3)_2CHOH$) in order to be oxidized to acetone (CH_3COCH_3). The ^{1}H-NMR peak of area = 5 indicates **B** is a mono-substituted benzene derivative which also is a carboxylic acid with one additional carbon unaccounted for. **C** can only be phenylacetic acid ($C_6H_5CH_2COOH$) which is consistent with the ^{1}H-NMR spectrum. Therefore, **A** is isopropyl phenylacetate, $C_6H_5CH_2COOCH(CH_3)_2$.

15.57 Compound **D**, an isomer of **A** in the preceding problem, also appears to be an ester in view of the absence of hydroxyl, aldehyde, ketone, and carboxylic acid functions. However, the ^{1}H-NMR peak of area 4 at 7.2 ppm indicates it contains a di-substituted benzene structure. Confirmation of the ester function comes from its hydrolysis to a carboxylic acid (**E**) and an alcohol (**F**). Since the alcohol (**F**) is a C_2 alcohol (determined by difference from **D** since **E** is a C_9 compound) it can only be ethanol and this is confirmed by the presence of a typical ethyl splitting pattern (quartet at 4.0 ppm and triplet at 1.1 ppm) in **D**. Since the strong oxidation of **E**, expected to remove any alkyl side chains, produces a C_8 di-acid, only a single carbon was lost and the product must be a benzene dicarboxylic acid (**G**). Thus, **E** can only be an ethyl benzoic acid ($C_2H_5C_6H_4COOH$) or a tolyacetic acid ($CH_3C_6H_4CH_2COOH$). The ^{1}H-NMR, in view of the two alkyl singlets with a ratio of 3:2, clearly indicates **E** is the latter. The relative position of the two carboxylic acid substituents on the benzene ring in **G** must be ortho as indicated by the ability of the compound to lose water upon heating, forming a cyclic anhydride (**H**). Therefore, **D** is ethyl *o*-tolyacetate.

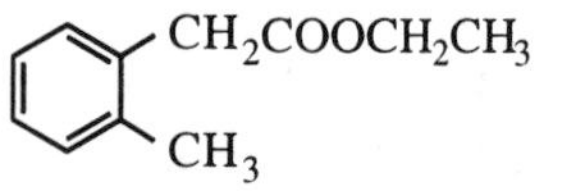
CH₂COOCH₂CH₃
CH₃

D

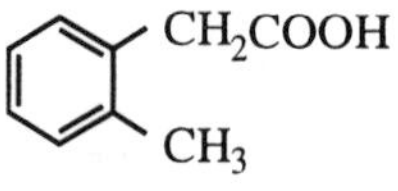
CH₂COOH
CH₃

E

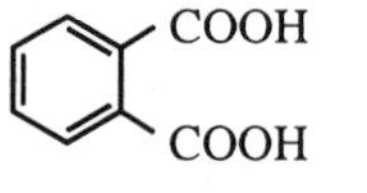
COOH
COOH

G

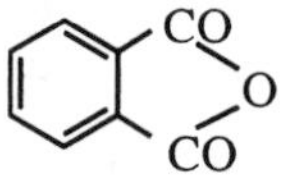
CO
O
CO

H

15.58 The ^{1}H-NMR peak at 0.9 ppm indicates there are nine unsplit methyl hydrogens, typical of a *t*-butyl group, $(CH_3)_3C-$ (note that the NMR peak areas are in the ratio 1:3, but since the compound has 12 hydrogens the ratio must be converted to 3:9). That leaves only two carbons unaccounted for, one of which is probably a carbonyl carbon ($C_6H_{12}O_2$ has an HDI of one). The remaining carbon must be a methyl group attached to an electronegative group (unsplit peak at 3.5 ppm). This is the pattern expected for a methyl ester. Therefore, the compound is methyl 2,2-dimethylpropanoate, $(CH_3)_3CCOOCH_3$.

VI. Conceptual Problem

Fat Free But Not Necessarily Calorie Free

The science reporter for the local newspaper is doing a story about the zero-calorie fat substitute Olestra. She wants to get some background information from a food scientist and so she calls you. You arrange to meet over lunch. She brings with her a chemist's report that shows three chemical structures:

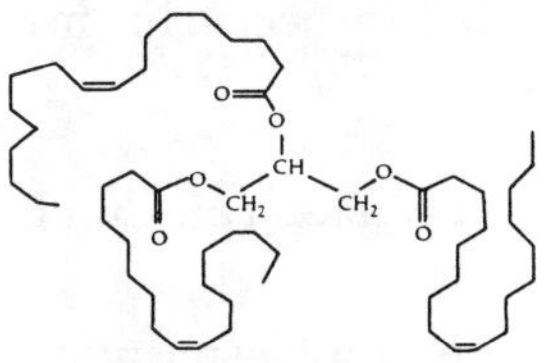

Molecule of olive oil

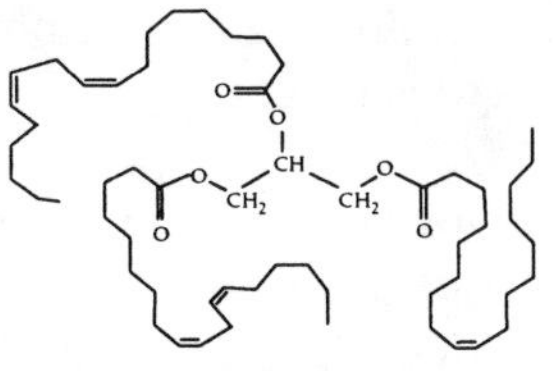

Molecule of corn oil

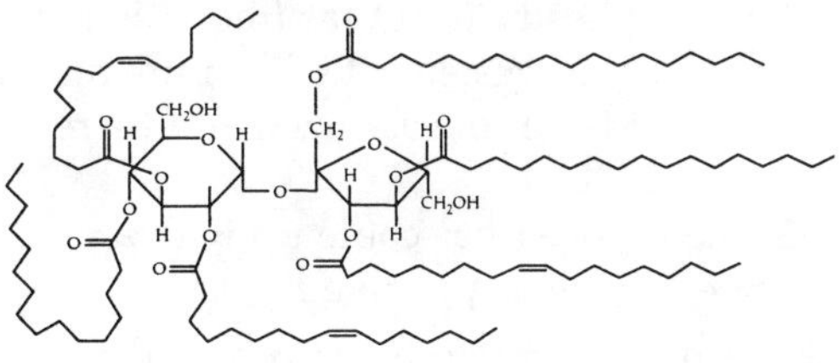

Molecule of Olestra

■ She can see the structural similarities between the molecules of olive oil and corn oil. And it's clear that the Olestra molecule is quite different. She asks you how a chemist would describe the differences.

- Ans: What is common to each is that they are esters (formed from reaction of an alcohol and a carboxylic acid), and the carboxylic acids in each are the long fatty acid "tails." You note that olive oil and corn oil have three such "tails" whereas the Olestra molecule shown has six. The important difference is in the "backbone" which holds the tails together - the glycerol of olive oil and corn oil versus the sugar (sucrose) of Olestra.

■ The reporter recalls some earlier reporting she did on the cancer-fighting drug paclitaxel. In that case, at least, the sheer size and complexity of the molecule made it very difficult to synthesize. She knows already that a molecule of olestra is about the same size, yet Proctor & Gamble can make olestra by the ton. What's the difference?

- Ans: Every part of the structure of paclitaxel is different from every other part, making the molecule very difficult to assemble from its many building blocks. Olestra has only two building blocks, sucrose and fatty acids, both of which are inexpensive and widely available. In addition, it is chemically easy to react the two together to make olestra.

■ Digestive enzymes break up fats into glycerol and fatty acids easily enough, but they don't break up olestra into sucrose and fatty acids, even though they're both esters. That seems odd. Why should it happen that way?

- Ans: Enzymes are very specific in that they will react with specific kinds of compounds, sometimes even specific to a single molecule. Small differences in molecular size or shape can slow or prevent enzyme-catalysis of a reaction. The size and shape of olestra is so different from other fats that the hydrolytic enzymes cannot break the ester linkages. You will see further examples in the next chapter, which discusses proteins (including enzymes).

■ Olestra products are required to be fortified with Vitamins A, D, E, and K because Olestra makes it hard for the body to absorb these fat-soluble vitamins. Obviously ordinary fats don't cause the same problem. Why is that?

- Ans: Digestive enzymes in the intestine will break up the triglyceride molecules of corn oil or olive oil. In the process, any dissolved fat-soluble vitamins are released and so absorbed independently. Olestra molecules remain intact as they pass through the digestive system, and that means lipophilic vitamin molecules can remain dissolved in the fat and not be released.

■ It seems contradictory to say that Olestra is fat free and and has no calories when in fact it is made from sugar and fat. How do you explain this?

- Ans: Olestra is not fat-free; it is a fat. It is calorie-free because the Olestra passes through the body undigested - it's like mineral oil and cellulose (dietary fiber) in that respect. This means that it is not metabolized and therefore provides no energy.

■ The reporter has come up with a catchy title for her piece, "Olestra: A Polyester You Can Eat." She asks how you like it?

- Ans: Olestra, technically speaking, is not a polyester as usually described (polyester often meaning a polymer which is a polyester). Olestra is a mixture of hexa-, hepta-, and predominantly octa-esters. The language of chemistry is important, certainly when chemists are communicating with other chemists.

■ Is it important here?

- Ans: Yes. The reporter has the responsibility to get it right since most people will assume that the information in the article is correct.

CHAPTER 16

Proteins

I. Textbook Chapter Contents

This chapter introduces the chemistry of proteins, biologically important polyamides. It also describes the compounds that are the building blocks for proteins, the α-amino acids.

II. Learning Objectives

- Know the general structure, including stereochemistry, of α-amino acids and recognize their common names. Understand the use of three-letter abbreviations.

- Understand the amphoteric character of α-amino acids and the existence of zwitterions.

- Be able to draw the structures of α-amino acids in solutions of differing pH, and be able to show how the structure changes as the pH of a solution is changed.

- Write equations for the synthesis of α-amino acids from α-bromocarboxylic acids and from aldehydes.

- Write equations for conversion of an α-amino acid to its ester and to an *N*-acyl derivative (amide).

- Describe a peptide and a peptide bond.

- Describe what is meant by the primary structure of a protein.

- Write an equation for the complete hydrolysis of a small peptide into its constituent α-amino acids.

- Understand the concept of end-group analysis of proteins.

- Understand the concept of fragment analysis of proteins.

- From hydrolysis information and end-group analysis information be able to deduce the structure of a peptide or small protein.

- Understand the classification of proteins by composition, by shape, and by function.

- Be able to describe the secondary, tertiary, and quaternary structures of proteins. Be able to show the role of hydrogen bonding in protein structure.

- Be able to distinguish between the fibrous and globular structure of proteins, and the implications of these structures for biological function.

- Write equations for the protection of an α-amino acid prior to its use in peptide synthesis.

- Be able to show the synthesis of di- and tri-peptides using the appropriately protected α-amino acids.

- Understand the role of enzymes in biological systems and the concept of an "active site" in the enzyme.

- Understand the role of co-enzymes in biological systems.

III. Glossary

α-amino acid an alkanoic acid with an amino group attached to carbon 2 (the α-carbon)

α-helix one of two secondary structures of proteins in which the polypeptide chain coils into a right-handed spiral

amphoteric a compound that contains both acidic and basic groups. α-Amino acids are amphoteric because of the presence of the acidic carboxyl group and the basic amino group

C-terminus the α-amino acid at the end of a peptide chain which has the free carboxyl group

coenzyme the non-protein portion of an enzyme which usually is the chemically active portion of the enzyme

competitive inhibitor a compound that competes with a normal substrate for complexation at the active site of an enzyme

conjugated protein a protein which also contains a non-protein group attached to it

convergent synthesis the synthesis of larger peptides by the coupling together of two or more small peptides

DCC dicyclohexylcarbodiimide, a reagent used to form a peptide bond between two protected α-amino acids

denaturation the process by which a protein is unfolded from its tertiary structure, thereby losing its biological activity

deprotection removal of a protecting group that prevented reaction at a functional group

dipeptide a compound comprised of two α-amino acids connected through an amide (peptide) bond

Edman degradation a means of determining which α-amino acid is at the N-terminus of a protein or peptide by reaction with phenyl isocyanate to form a phenylthiohydantoin derivative of that α-amino acid

end-group analysis determination of which α-amino acids are at the two ends of a protein or peptide chain

enzyme a chemical in a biological system which serves as a catalyst to accomplish a chemical reaction under conditions present in the living organism. Enzymes are totally or partially protein in composition

essential α-amino acid an α-amino acid which can only be supplied to the body through diet—it cannot be synthesized in the body

fibrous protein a protein which contains chains of polypeptides aligned parallel to each other, resembling a multi-wound fiber bundle, and which is insoluble in water

fragment analysis analysis of protein or peptide structure by hydrolyzing peptide bonds to produce smaller fragments of peptide

globular protein a protein which is coiled into a compact approximately spherical shape and is soluble in water

hydrogenolysis the cleavage of a bond by the addition of a hydrogen atom to each fragment at the point of cleavage

isoelectric point pI, a pH value which is the average of the pK_a values for the carboxyl group and the ammonium group in an α-amino acid. At the pI value the concentration of the zwitterion form of the α-amino acid will be at its maximum

linear synthesis the synthesis of peptides by sequentially adding one α-amino acid to the growing peptide chain, forming one peptide bond at a time

macromolecule a very large molecule, some of which are polymers of one-to-three different monomers (such as starch or ABS plastic), but others involve the connection between a large number of different, structurally-related, simple compounds (such as a protein)

N-terminus the α-amino acid at the end of a peptide chain which has a free amino group

peptide a compound in which two or more α-amino acids are connected through an amide (peptide) bond(s)

peptide bond an amide bond connecting two α-amino acids

pleated sheet one of two secondary structures of proteins in which two chains of polypeptide are aligned parallel to each other with the N-terminus adjacent to the C-terminus

polyamide a compound which contains a large number of amide groups

polypeptide a compound containing a large number of α-amino acids connected by peptide (amide) bonds

primary structure of a protein the sequence in which the a-amino acids are connected to each other

protection the reaction of a functional group with another entity which forms a new compound in which the original functional group is precluded from undergoing its normal reactions. A temporary masking of a functional group

protein a polypeptide which normally has a specific biological function

quaternary structure of a protein the organization of globular proteins into aggregates or assemblies of protein

secondary structure of a protein how an individual protein chain is arranged in space, usually in either an α-helix or in a pleated sheet structure

sequence analysis determination of the sequence in which α-amino acids are connected in peptides and proteins

simple protein a protein consisting only of α-amino acids

solid phase synthesis the synthesis of peptides from α-amino acids by growing the chain from a solid polymer support

solution synthesis the synthesis of peptides from α-amino acids by forming peptide bonds in solution

Strecker synthesis a synthesis of α-amino acids from aldehydes through addition of ammonia and HCN to form an α-aminonitrile which is then hydrolyzed to the α-amino acid

tertiary structure of a protein the overall shape of a protein molecule, specifically how helices or pleated sheets are folded. The tertiary structure is either elongated (fibrous) or folded (globular)

zwitterion a form of α-amino acid containing a carboxylate anion and an ammonium cation. The acidic and basic groups have undergone a proton transfer

IV. Summary of Reactions of α-Amino Acids

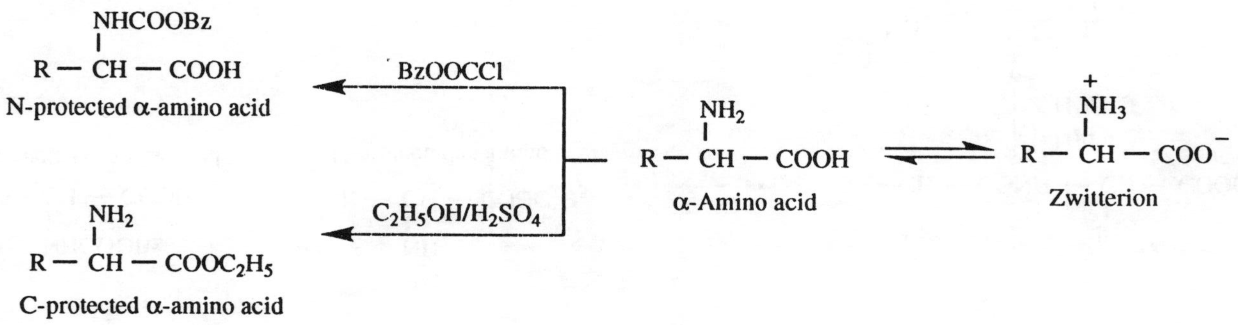
NHCOOBz
R — CH — COOH
N-protected α-amino acid
BzOOCCl
NH2
R — CH — COOC2H5
C-protected α-amino acid
C2H5OH/H2SO4
NH2
R — CH — COOH
α-Amino acid
+
NH3
R — CH — COO−
Zwitterion

Summary of Reactions of Peptides

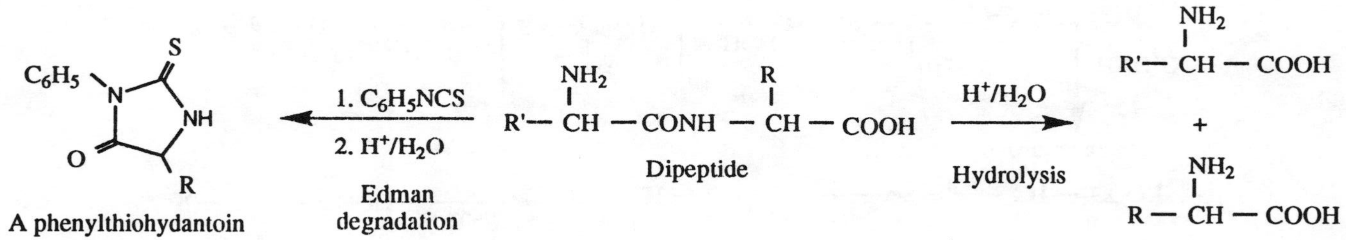
C6H5
S
N
NH
O
R
A phenylthiohydantoin
1. C6H5NCS
2. H+/H2O
Edman degradation
NH2
R
R'— CH — CONH — CH — COOH
Dipeptide
H+/H2O
Hydrolysis
NH2
R'— CH — COOH
+
NH2
R — CH — COOH

V. Summary of Preparation of α-Amino Acids

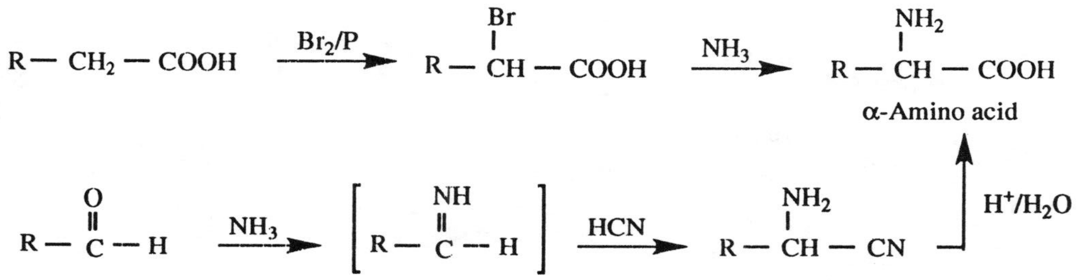
Br₂/P
NH₃
α-Amino acid
HCN
H⁺/H₂O

Summary of Preparation of Peptides

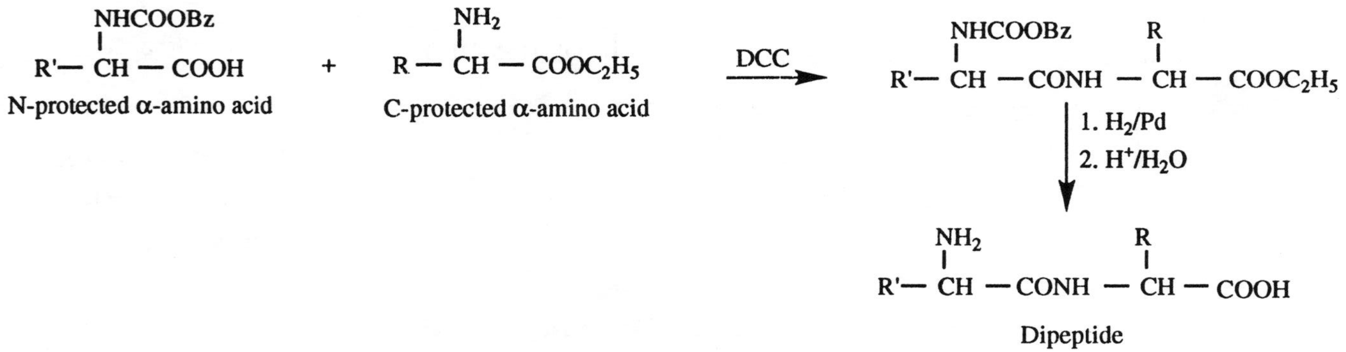
N-protected α-amino acid
C-protected α-amino acid
DCC
1. H₂/Pd
2. H⁺/H₂O
Dipeptide

VI. Solutions to Problems

For "**How to Solve a Problem,**" review page 589.

16.1 The priorities of the substituent groups about the stereocenter of alanine are **a** = amino, **b** = carboxyl, **c** = methyl, **d** = hydrogen. D-alanine requires the *R*-configuration with the substituents arranged in a clockwise manner about the stereocenter.

D-alanine
(*R*-configuration)

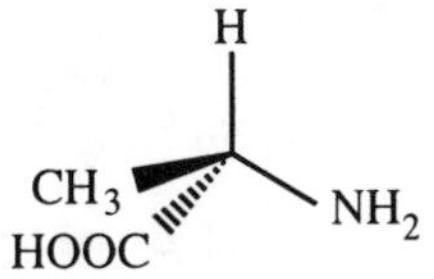

16.2

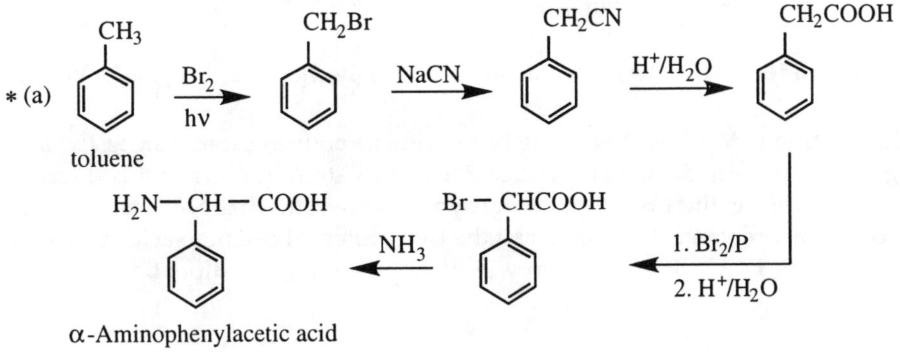

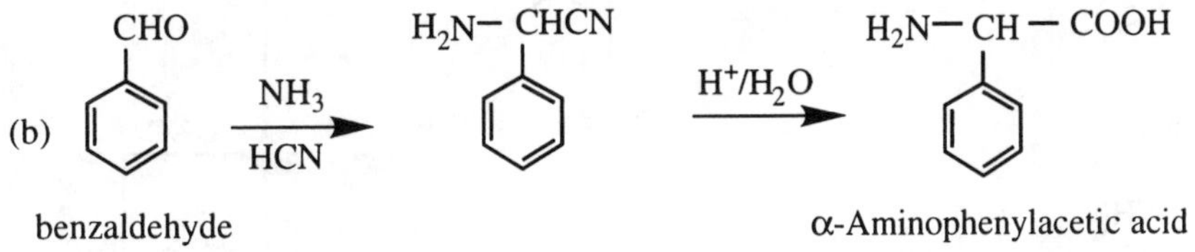

16.3 Since the molecular weight of the peptide (323) is equal to the sum of the molecular weights of its three α-amino acid constituents (89 + 115 + 155 = 359) less two molecules of water (36), the peptide contains only one of each α-amino acid. Since each α-amino acid can be either C-terminal or N-terminal there are six peptides that must be considered as possible structures. They are in three sets of two depending on which is at the N-terminus and which is at the C-terminus. The possible peptides are

Ala-His-Pro	Pro-His-Ala	His-Pro-Ala
Ala-Pro-His	Pro-Ala-His	His-Ala-Pro

16.4 For the tetrapeptide His-Lys-Phe-Leu:

(a) the Edman cleavage removes the N-terminus α-amino acid which in this case is His.
(b) trypsin cleaves a peptide at a lysine carboxyl group. In this case the two fragments from trypsin cleavage are His-Lys and Phe-Leu.

16.5 AAAA analysis indicated the presence of seven α-amino acids. Thus, the peptide is a heptapeptide. The sequence is determined by lining up the fragments such that the components overlap.

Arg — Gly — Pro

Pro — Pro

Pro — Phe — Ile — Val

Arg — Gly — Pro — Pro — Phe — Ile — Val

This heptapeptide fits the AAAA analysis of Arg, Gly, Ile, Phe, Pro_2, and Val.

***16.6** Since the peptide is Val-Phe, Val is the N-terminus, requiring that during the synthesis its amino group be protected. Similarly, since Phe is the C-terminus, its carboxyl group must be protected. Therefore, the first steps of the synthesis require that N-protected Val and C-protected Phe be prepared. Only then can the two protected α-amino acids be condensed to a dipeptide using DCC. The final step will be deprotecting the dipeptide.

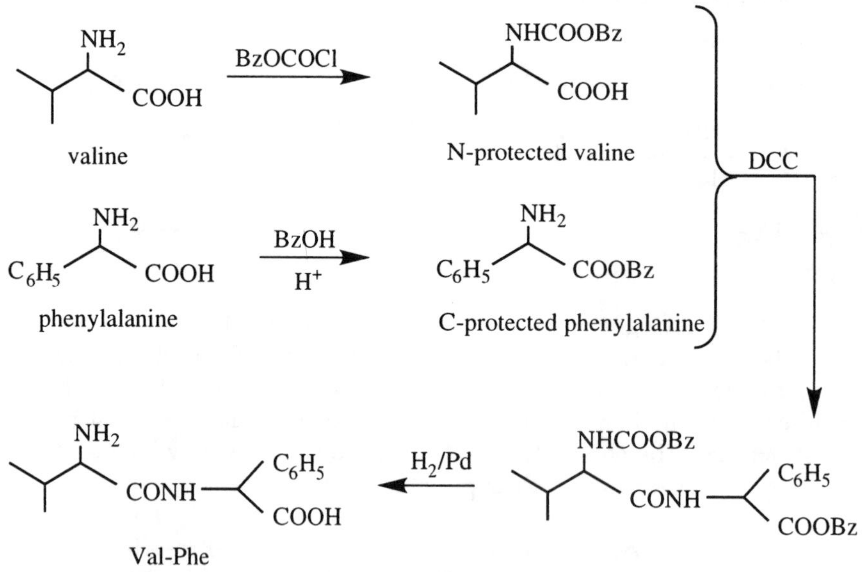
NH2
COOH
valine
BzOCOCl
NHCOOBz
COOH
N-protected valine
DCC
NH2
C6H5
COOH
phenylalanine
BzOH
H+
NH2
C6H5
COOBz
C-protected phenylalanine
NH2
CONH
C6H5
COOH
Val-Phe
H2/Pd
NHCOOBz
CONH
C6H5
COOBz

16.7 To absorb in the UV compounds must have conjugation such as in a polyene or in an aromatic group (see Section 11.4). Only four α-amino acids, all of which have aromatic components in their structures, should absorb in the UV: phenylalanine, tyrosine, tryptophan, and histidine.

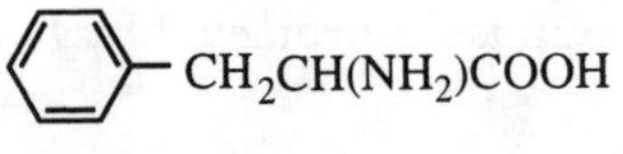
CH2CH(NH2)COOH

phenylalanine

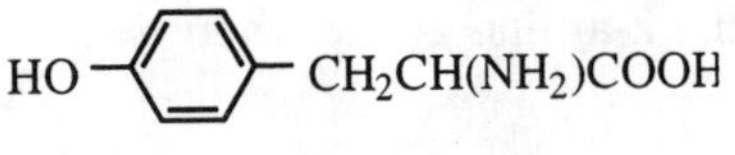
HO
CH2CH(NH2)COOH

tyrosine

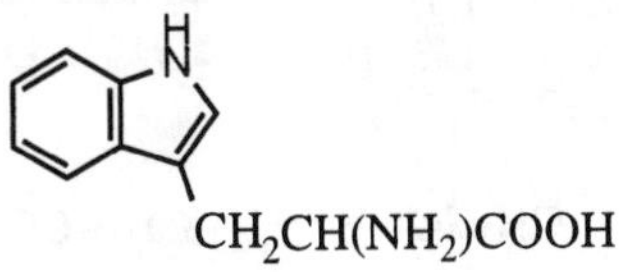
H
N
CH2CH(NH2)COOH

tryptophan

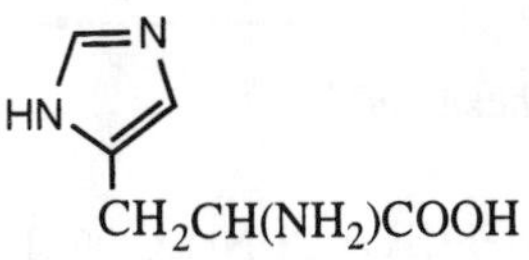
N
HN
CH2CH(NH2)COOH

histidine

16.8

(a) $C_6H_5CH_2CHNH_2COOH \xrightarrow{NaOH} C_6H_5CH_2CHNH_2COO^- \; Na^+$

(b) $C_6H_5CH_2CHNH_2COOH \xrightarrow{HCl} C_6H_5CH_2CH\overset{+}{N}H_3COOH \; Cl^-$

(c) $C_6H_5CH_2CHNH_2COOH \xrightarrow[\text{pyridine}]{C_6H_5COCl} C_6H_5CH_2CH(NHCOC_6H_5)COOH$

(d) $C_6H_5CH_2CHNH_2COOH \xrightarrow{(CH_3CO)_2O} C_6H_5CH_2CH(NHCOCH_3)COOH$

(e) $C_6H_5CH_2CH(NHCOCH_3)COOH \xrightarrow[2.\ C_2H_5OH]{1.\ SOCl_2} C_6H_5CH_2CH(NHCOCH_3)COOC_2H_5$

16.9 In designing these syntheses it is essential to determine whether a homologation is required. If so, the Strecker synthesis must be used, as for the synthesis of alanine. If not, the α-bromination of the carboxylic acid, followed by amination with ammonia, is the appropriate route. Phenylalanine and aspartic acid can be synthesized by this route.

(a) $\underset{\text{acetaldehyde}}{CH_3CHO} \xrightarrow[NH_3]{HCN} CH_3CHNH_2CN \xrightarrow{H^+/H_2O} \underset{\text{alanine}}{CH_3CHNH_2COOH}$

(b) $\underset{\text{3-phenylpropanoic acid}}{C_6H_5CH_2CH_2COOH} \xrightarrow[2.\ H^+/H_2O]{1.\ Br_2/P} C_6H_5CH_2CHBrCOOH \xrightarrow{NH_3} \underset{\text{phenylalanine}}{C_6H_5CH_2CHNH_2COOH}$

(c) $\underset{\text{succinic acid}}{HOOCCH_2CH_2COOH} \xrightarrow[2.\ H^+/H_2O]{1.\ Br_2/P} HOOCCH_2CHBrCOOH \xrightarrow{NH_3} \underset{\text{aspartic acid}}{HOOCCH_2CHNH_2COOH}$

***16.10** It is essential to protect the amino group of 6-aminohexanoic acid before brominating, and this is accomplished by converting it to an amide. After the bromination, S_N2 amination attaches the 2-amine group, then the 6-amine group is de-protected by hydrolysis to the 6-amine.

$$H_2N(CH_2)_5COOH \xrightarrow{CH_3COCl} CH_3CONH(CH_2)_5COOH$$

6-aminohexanoic acid

$$CH_3CONH(CH_2)_5COOH \xrightarrow[2.\ H^+/H_2O]{1.\ Br_2/P} CH_3CONH(CH_2)_4CHBrCOOH$$

$$CH_3CONH(CH_2)_4CHBrCOOH \xrightarrow{NH_3} CH_3CONH(CH_2)_4CHNH_2COOH$$

$$CH_3CONH(CH_2)_4CHNH_2COOH \xrightarrow{H^+/H_2O} H_2N(CH_2)_4CHNH_2COOH$$

lysine

16.11 Only three α-amino acids have more than one stereocenter (a carbon with four different groups attached) and they are isoleucine (Ile), threonine (Thr), and hydroxyproline (Hyp).

$CH_3CH_2CH(CH_3)CH(NH_2)COOH$ — isoleucine

$CH_3CH(OH)CH(NH_2)COOH$ — threonine

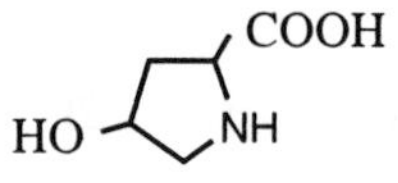

COOH
HO
NH

hydroxyproline

16.12 At pH 2 (strongly acidic) all of the basic groups will be protonated. At pH 13 (strongly basic) all of the acidic groups will be deprotonated.

(a) $H_3\overset{+}{N}CH_2COOH$ — glycine at pH 2 $\qquad$ $H_2NCH_2COO^-$ — glycine at pH 13

(b) $H_3\overset{+}{N}CH(COOH)CH_2COOH$ — aspartic acid at pH 2 $\qquad$ $^-OOCCH(NH_2)CH_2COO^-$ — aspartic acid at pH 13

(c) $H_3\overset{+}{N}CH(COOH)(CH_2)_4\overset{+}{N}H_3$ — lysine at pH 2 $\qquad$ $H_2NCH(COO^-)(CH_2)_4NH_2$ — lysine at pH 13

16.13

(a) $H_2NCH(CH_3)COOH \rightleftharpoons H_3\overset{+}{N}CH(CH_3)COO^-$

alanine

(b) 

COOH
NH
COO⁻
NH₂⁺

proline

16.14 As the pH is gradually increased (the solution is made more basic) the most acidic proton is removed first, and the least acidic is removed last. The order of *decreasing* acidity is carboxyl group (2.2), ammonium group (9.1), and phenolic group(10.1).

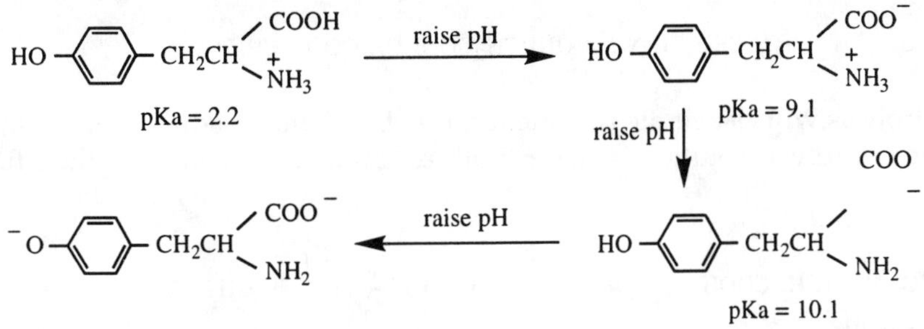

raise pH
raise pH
raise pH
pKa = 2.2
pKa = 9.1
pKa = 10.1

16.15 The pK_a of the carboxyl group is lower (that is, the group is more acidic) in the protonated form of alanine ($^+H_3NCH(CH_3)COOH$, pK_a 2.3) than in propanoic acid (CH_3CH_2COOH, pK_a 4.9) because the positively-charged ammonium group is electron withdrawing, providing stability for the negatively charged carboxylate anion. In propanoic acid there is no such stabilization for the carboxylate anion. The pK_a of 9.4 in alanine is from loss of the proton from the ammonium group.

16.16 Acetic anhydride is an effective acetylating agent and it can acetylate amino and hydroxyl groups (ammonolysis and alcoholysis, respectively, of an anhydride, see Section 15.2.2). In the case of serine the amino group is acetylated to an amide and the hydroxyl group is acetylated to an ester.

$$H_2NCH(COOH)CH_2OH \xrightarrow{(CH_3CO)_2O} CH_3CONHCH(COOH)CH_2OOCCH_3$$

16.17 By "stacking the fragments" the nonapeptide bradykinin is determined to be ArgProProGlyPheSerProPheArg.

Phe — Ser

Phe — Arg

Ser — Pro — Phe

Pro — Gly — Phe

Pro — Pro

Arg — Pro

Arg — Pro — Pro — Gly — Phe — Ser — Pro — Phe — Arg

16.18

(a) Gly-Ser $H_2NCH_2CONHCH(COOH)CH_2OH$

(b) Ala-Phe-Val $H_2NCH(CH_3)CONHCH(CH_2C_6H_5)CONHCH(COOH)CH(CH_3)_2$

(c) Lys-Gly-Cys $H_2N(CH_2)_4CH(NH_2)CONHCH_2CONHCH(COOH)CH_2SH$

16.19 The hydrolysis will cleave the peptide (amide) bond and produce glycine and alanine. Since the hydrolysis solution is acidic, both α-amino acids will be in their fully protonated form.

$$\underset{\text{Gly-Ala}}{H_2NCH_2CONHCH(CH_3)COOH} \xrightarrow[H_2O]{HCl} \underset{\text{Gly}}{H_3\overset{+}{N}CH_2COOH} + \underset{\text{Ala}}{H_3\overset{+}{N}CH(CH_3)COOH}$$

16.20 A total of six different tri-peptides can be envisioned. There are two with each peptide at the N-terminus and two with each peptide at the C-terminus. The peptides are as follows:

GlyAlaPhe	AlaGlyPhe	PheAlaGly
GlyPheAla	AlaPheGly	PheGlyAla

***16.21** The secret to solving a peptide synthesis involves four actual or conceptual steps: (1) write the dipeptide structure with the two α-amino acids connected in their proper relative positions, the N-terminal α-amino acid on the left:

$$\underset{\text{AlaPhe}}{H_2NCH(CH_3)CONHCH(CH_2C_6H_5)COOH}$$

(2) recognize that the α-amino group and carboxyl group to be involved in the formation of the peptide bond (that is, connected by the condensation step) can be connected using DCC in a **condensation** step, (3) recognize that all other amino and carboxyl groups must be **protected** before the condensation reaction is conducted, and (4) after the condensation all of the protected groups must be **deprotected**.

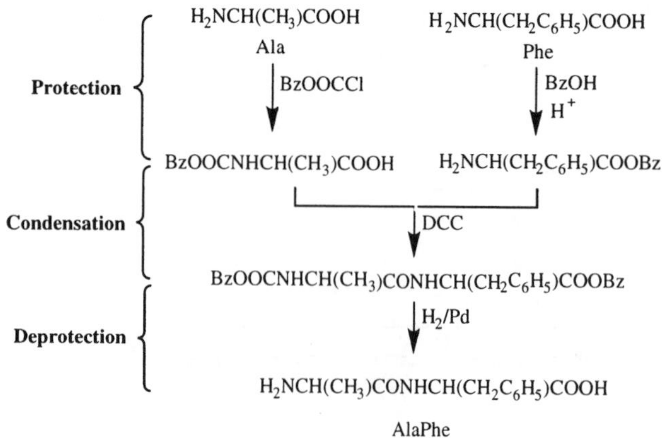
Protection
H2NCH(CH3)COOH
Ala
BzOOCCl
H2NCH(CH2C6H5)COOH
Phe
BzOH
H+
BzOOCNHCH(CH3)COOH
H2NCH(CH2C6H5)COOBz
Condensation
DCC
BzOOCNHCH(CH3)CONHCH(CH2C6H5)COOBz
Deprotection
H2/Pd
H2NCH(CH3)CONHCH(CH2C6H5)COOH
AlaPhe

16.22 The free amino group of protected phenylalanine will carry out a nucleophilic acyl substitution (ammonolysis) on the ester group of alanine. The benzyloxy protecting groups are then removed by hydrogenolysis.

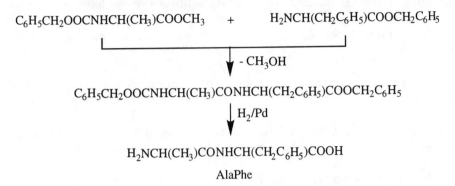

$$C_6H_5CH_2OOCNHCH(CH_3)COOCH_3 \quad + \quad H_2NCH(CH_2C_6H_5)COOCH_2C_6H_5$$

$$\downarrow \text{- } CH_3OH$$

$$C_6H_5CH_2OOCNHCH(CH_3)CONHCH(CH_2C_6H_5)COOCH_2C_6H_5$$

$$\downarrow H_2/Pd$$

$$H_2NCH(CH_3)CONHCH(CH_2C_6H_5)COOH$$

AlaPhe

16.23 (a) A peptide bond is the amide bond (CO-NH) resulting from a dehydration between two α-amino acids, such as in Gly-Ala and shown as a dash in bold type H_2NCH_2**CO-NH**CH(CH3)COOH.

(b) An essential α-amino acid is one which the body cannot synthesize. Therefore it must be supplied in the diet. There are eight such α-amino acids, an example being lysine.

(c) A zwitterion is the form in which an α-amino acid exists at the isoelectric point, half way between the pK_as of the ammonium group and the carboxyl group. It carries a positive charge on the amino group (ammonium) and a negative charge on the carboxyl group. An example is the zwitterion of glycine, $^+H_3NCH_2COO^-$.

(d) An amphoteric compound is one which can function as an acid and as a base. α-Amino acids are ampotheric because they contain the basic amino group and the acidic carboxyl group. Another example is p-aminobenzoic acid ($H_2NC_6H_4COOH$).

(e) A tripeptide is a di-amide formed from three α-amino acids. An example is Gly-Ala-Ser.

(f) The L-configuration of α-amino acids is the older description of their configuration relative to the configuration of the carbohydrates which were D. The L-configuration is a *S*-configuration in modern terms (except for cysteine). An example of an L-amino acid is L-alanine:

L-alanine
(*S*-configuration)

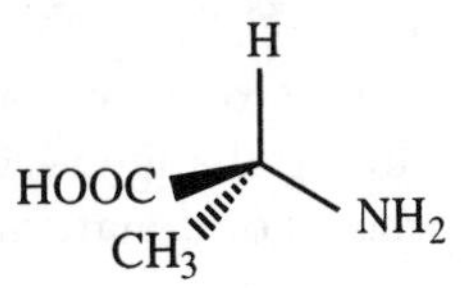
H
HOOC
CH3
NH2

16.24 (a) Proteins differ in composition depending on whether they consist entirely of α-amino acids (simple proteins) or whether they also include a non-α-amino acid compound (conjugated protein), such as a glycoprotein, a lipoprotein, or a nucleoprotein.

(b) Proteins differ in their shape and are classified as fibrous or as globular

(c) Proteins differ in their functions which include roles such as enzymes, structural, and hormonal proteins.

16.25 The primary structure of a protein is the sequence of α-amino acids which are connected via peptide linkages.

16.26 The secondary structure of proteins is determined by hydrogen bonding, mainly between amide groups. The two usual structures are the α-helix and the pleated sheet structures.

16.27 In hydrogen bonding between peptide chains the electron donor group is the carbonyl group in the amide function and the electron acceptor is the hydrogen located on the amide nitrogen.

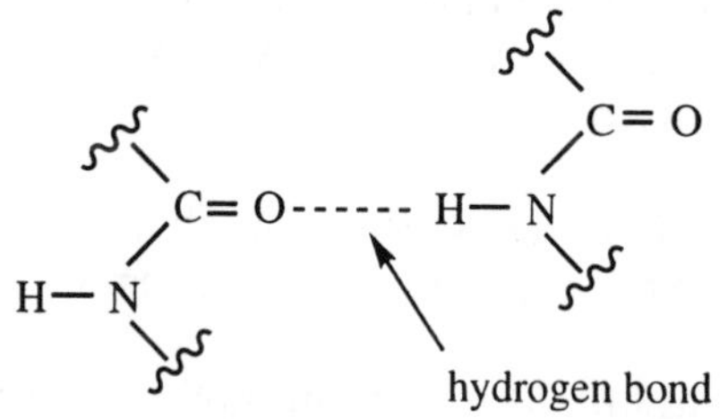
C= O
C= O------ H— N
H— N
hydrogen bond

16.28 (a) Fibrous proteins are water-insoluble (hydrophobic) so the chemical groups on the outer surface of the protein are hydrophobic groups. In α-amino acids ($RCHNH_2COOH$) non-polar R groups such as methyl (alanine), isopropyl (valine), isobutyl (leucine), *sec*-butyl (isoleucine), and benzyl (phenylalanine) are hydrophobic.

(b) Globular proteins are water-soluble (hydrophilic) so the chemical groups on the outer surface of the protein are polar hydrophilic groups, those which can hydrogen bond with water and thereby promote solubility. Exemplary groups are hydroxyl (serine, threonine and tyrosine), sulfhydryl (cysteine), carboxyl (aspartic acid and glutamic acid), and amino (lysine, arginine, and histidine).

16.29 Enzymes are globular proteins because they carry out their catalysis of reactions in an aqueous solution, whether in the cell, the intestines, or in the mouth. Thus, they must be hydrophilic.

16.30 Denaturation of a protein means the destruction of its ability to perform its biological function even though its primary and even secondary structure may be unchanged. Denaturation occurs by the shape of the protein being changed—the protein unfolds and loses its characteristic tertiary structure. The process of denaturation normally is not reversible.

16.31 Hemoglobin contains the protein globin that has a tertiary structure which is globular. The quaternary structure of hemoglobin refers to the fact that hemoglobin exists normally as an aggregate of four separate globular proteins, each with its attached heme group.

16.32 An enzyme is a biological catalyst, most of which are proteins. The role of enzymes is to catalyze the many reactions required in a living system under modest conditions (about 37°C and in aqueous solution).

16.33 A co-enzyme is a non-protein portion of a conjugate protein enzyme. It is an essential part of the enzyme and usually the chemical change undergone by the enzyme occurs in the co-enzyme portion and not in the protein portion. The role of the co-enzyme is to participate in the actual chemical reaction undergone during the catalytic process.

16.34 The active site of an enzyme is that region of the protein molecule to which the substrate becomes attached. The protein literally "holds" the substrate in the proper position for it to undergo the catalyzed reaction. The active sites and the substrates are very specific.

16.35 Enzyme-catalyzed reactions usually are stereospecific because the protein is chiral and holds the substrate in a specific spatial orientation. This permits the chemical reaction to occur from a single and specific orientation of the substrate. For example, the α-carbonyl group of pyruvic acid ($CH_3COCOOH$) is reduced enzymatically to lactic acid ($CH_3CH(OH)COOH$) to produce only a single enantiomer of the latter.

VII. Conceptual Problem

A Question of Identity

You are a chemical technician, newly employed by a biotechnology start-up company. You are asked to start a synthesis of a tripeptide, Gly-Lys-Tyr, which is needed for one of the company's hot new research programs. The individual amino acids (Gly, Lys, and Tyr) are delivered to your lab in three bottles. However, much to your dismay, the labels are lying at the bottom of the tray! Not knowing which label belongs to which bottle, and not wishing to appear incapable the first day on the job, you decide to see if you can figure out which bottle contains which amino acid.

■ What are some of ways that could uniquely identify at least one of the amino acids?

- Ans: Three methods are readily available:

  1. Determine the optical rotations in a polarimeter. Glycine is optically inactive because it is achiral. Tyr and Lys are optically active and would have different optical rotations which are reported in the literature.
  2. The ^{1}H-NMR spectra of the compounds are different. Gly is H_2NCH_2COOH, Lys is $H_2N(CH_2)_4CH(NH_2)COOH$, and Tyr is $HOC_6H_4CH_2CH(NH_2)COOH$. The most obvious a dn simple differences are that Tyr has aromatic protons and the others do not, and Lys has a lot of methylene protons while the others do not. FInally, Gly has the simplest NMR with only three kinds of protons.
  3. The three amino acids will have different isoelectric points which can be determined.

Another task that falls to you is to supervise two premedical students studying a protein in your lab during the summer. The protein they are studying has been found to catalyze part of the process of oxidizing fatty acid molecules. In preliminary experiments the students found that their protein was soluble in water and consisted only of amino acids.

■ Classify this protein by (a) composition, (b) shape, and (c) function.

- Ans: (a)-Because it contains only amino acids, it is a simple protein rather than a conjugated protein. (b)-Because it is water-soluble it is most likely a globular protein rather than a fibrous protein. (c) Because it catalyzes a reaction it must be an enzyme.

■ The protein is soluble in water. You ask them to name three amino acids that might be more than usually abundant on the outer surface of this protein.

- Ans: Any three amino acids that have oxygen or nitrogen in their side chains. These will be capable of hydrogen bonding with water, and will aid in making the protein water-soluble. Examples are serine, theonine, cycteine, aspartic acid, glutamic acid, lysine, histidine, proline, and tyrosine.

CHAPTER 17

Optical Activity

I. Textbook Chapter Contents

This chapter presents a review of the various types of isomerism encountered in earlier chapters. It then concentrates on a unique property of enantiomers, that of optical activity. It introduces compounds with multiple stereocenters. Finally it illustrates the reactions and synthesis of enantiomers.

II. Learning Objectives

- Know the different types of isomers previously discussed: constitutional isomers (skeletal, functional group, positional), stereoisomers, conformational isomers, configurational isomers, enantiomers, *cis-trans* isomers.

- Given a structural formula, be able to determine which, if any, kinds of isomerism exist for that compound.

- Know the principles of optical activity as exhibited by an enantiomer.

- Know the principle of the functioning of a polarimeter. Be able to convert an observed rotation into a specific rotation.

- Explain what is meant by the term diastereoisomer.

- Know the principles and show the equations involved in the resolution of a racemate into its two enantiomers using a resolving agent.

- For a given structure, be able to determine the number of stereocenters present, calculate the maximum possible number of configurational isomers, define the kind of stereoisomers present, and describe the relationship of enantiomers and diastereoisomers.

- Explain what is meant by the terms meso isomer and plane of symmetry.

- Be able to use Fischer projections to represent the structures of configurational isomers containing more than one stereocenter.

- Be able to write a three-dimensional structure for a chiral compound shown in its Fischer projection.

- Be able to predict the stereochemistry of S_N1 and S_N2 reactions occurring at a stereocenter.

- Understand the difficulty in producing enantiomers in chemical synthesis.

- Understand the principles of the reactions of chiral reagents with achiral compounds and of achiral reagents with chiral compounds.

- Understand the role of chiral auxiliaries in producing enantiomeric excesses of enantiomers in chemical reactions.

III. Glossary

absolute configuration the actual arrangement of four substituents about a stereocenter and represented by the symbols *R* or *S*

achiral compound a compound not having the characteristic of handedness—its structure is superimposable on its mirror image and it usually has a plane of symmetry

anomers stereoisomeric carbohydrates that differ only in the configuration at an anomeric carbon

anomeric carbon the hemiacetal carbon in a carbohydrate, about which two configurations may exist in equilibrium

chiral compound a compound having the property of handedness—its structure is non-superimposable on its mirror image

chiral auxiliary an enantiomer that can be temporarily attached to a substrate to make it chiral while a reaction is conducted with an achiral reagent. The purpose is to produce a diastereoisomeric excess

chiral drug a drug (medicinal agent or pharmaceutical) which is sold as a single enantiomer rather than as a racemate

chiral reagent a reagent which is chiral

chirality the property of handedness

cis-trans **isomers** configurational isomers that have their substituents attached to the same or opposite sides, respectively, of a fixed plane of reference (a ring or a double bond)

configurational isomers stereoisomers that cannot be interconverted other than by bond-breaking

conformational isomers stereoisomers that can be interconverted by rotation about one or more sigma bonds

constitutional isomers compounds that share the same molecular formula but have different bond connectivities

dextrorotatory an enantiomer which rotates a beam of plane polarized light to the right (clockwise)

diastereoisomers configurational isomers which do not have an object-mirror image relationship

diastereoisomeric excess the percentage by which a reaction produces an excess of one of two possible diastereoisomers

d- and l- abbreviations for dextrorotatory and levorotatory

dl-pair a 50:50 mixture of two enantiomers

enantiomeric excess the percentage by which a reaction produces an excess of one enantiomer over the other

enantiomers two configurational isomers that are chiral and that have an object-mirror image relationship. They each have the property of rotating a beam of plane polarized light

Fischer projection a line drawing of the structure of a compound in two dimensions which implies the three-dimensional structure of the compound (horizontal lines represent bonds projecting above the paper and vertical lines represent bonds projecting below the paper)

functional group isomers constitutional isomers in which the difference is the structure of the functional groups

isomers compounds that share the same molecular formula but have a different structural formula

levorotatory an enantiomer which rotates a beam of plane polarized light to the left (counterclockwise)

meso isomer an isomer with two or more stereocenters in which a plane of symmetry exists; it is therefore optically inactive

mirror image the reflection seen in a mirror when an object (including the model of a compound) is held in front of the mirror

mutarotation the gradual change of the optical rotation of a compound to an equilibrium rotation

observed rotation the magnitude and direction in which a solution of a compound rotates plane polarized light

optical activity the property of a compound by which it rotates plane polarized light

optical purity a percentage indicating the extent to which a sample of an optically active compound is a single enantiomer (the remainder is a dl- mixture)

optically active a compound which rotates a beam of plane polarized light

plane of symmetry an imaginary plane through a compound in which one half is the mirror image of the other half. Such compounds are not enantiomers (that is, they are superimposable on their mirror images)

plane polarized light light in which all the waves vibrate in the same plane

polarimeter an instrument for passing plane polarized light through a solution of a compound and measuring the extent and direction of rotation of that light

positional isomers constitutional isomers in which the difference is in the position to which substituents are attached to the carbon skeleton

racemate a 50:50 mixture of two enantiomers

racemic mixture a 50:50 mixture of two enantiomers

relative configuration the relationship of the configuration about a stereocenter in one compound to that about a stereocenter in another compound

resolution the process by which a dl- (racemic) mixture is separated into the two enantiomers

resolving agent an enantiomer used to effect a resolution by reacting with a racemate to form a mixture of two diastereoisomers which can be separated

skeletal isomers constitutional isomers in which the difference is in the carbon skeleton connectivities

specific rotation a physical property of a pure optically active compound indicating the magnitude and direction of rotation of plane polarized light under standardized conditions

stereocenter a carbon atom with four different groups attached

stereoisomers compounds that share the same molecular formula and the same bond connectivities but have different spatial arrangements of atoms or groups

stereospecific synthesis a synthesis whose reactions produce only a single enantiomer. A resolution is not needed to obtain the desired product

IV. Solutions to Problems

For "**How to Solve a Problem,**" review page 627.

17.1 The following compounds have a stereocenter which is marked with an asterisk:

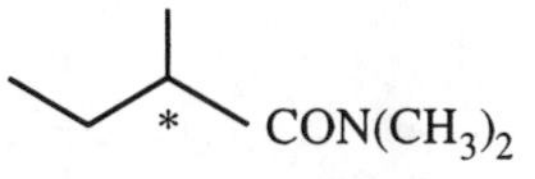

N,N-dimethyl-2-methylbutanamide

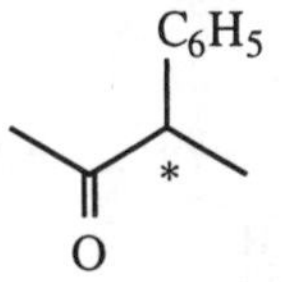

3-phenyl-2-butanone

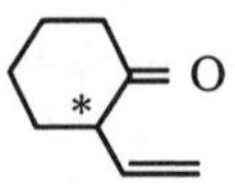

2-vinylcyclohexanone

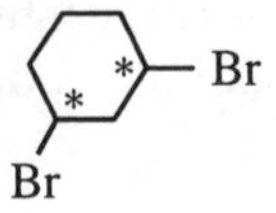

1,3-dibromocyclohexane

17.2 Stereocenters are marked with an asterisk: (a) 2-aminopropanoic acid has one stereocenter; (b) 2,5-dimethyl-3-hexanone has no stereocenters; (c) 2,3-diphenylbutane has two stereocenters; (d) sorbitol (1,2,3,4,5,6-hexahydroxyhexane) has four stereocenters.

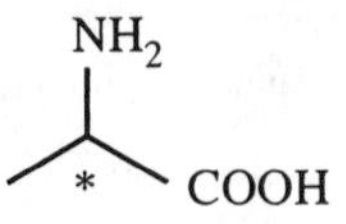

2-aminopropanoic acid

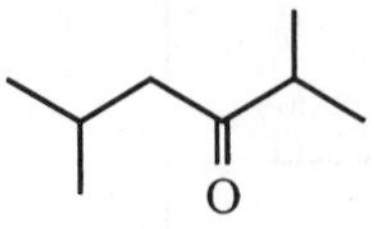

2,5-dimethyl-3-hexanone

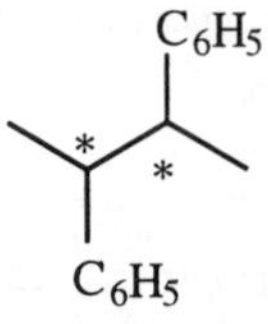

2,3-diphenylbutane

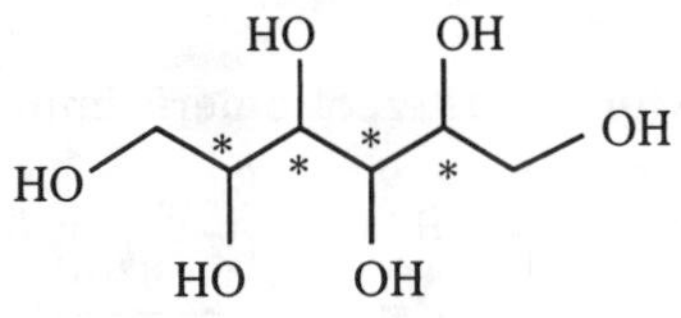

sorbitol

17.3 The specific rotation of nicotine is as follows:

$[\alpha]_D^{20} = -8.45° \div [1 \times 5\ g/100\ ml]$

$= -8.45° \div [1 \times .05\ g/ml]$

$= -169°$

17.4 The optically active compounds are (*R*)-2-phenyl-3-hexanone and (*S*)-2-methylcyclohexanone. The optically inactive compounds are *dl*-2-chloropentane (it is a racemic mixture), methyl (±)2-(*N*-methylamino)propanoate (it is a racemic mixture), and potassium 4-nitrobenzoate (it does not have a stereocenter).

17.5   An appropriate resolving agent is one which will (1) react with the compound to be resolved to form a new compound (diastereoisomers) which can be separated by normal chemical means, and (2) the diastereoisomers can be re-converted to the original compound by a simple process. Appropriate resolving agents are as follows (R* represents a group with a stereocenter):

(a) a carboxylic acid to form diastereoisomeric esters:

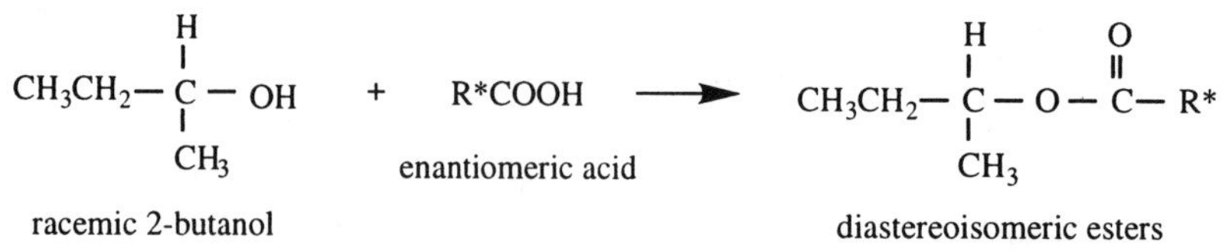

$$CH_3CH_2 - \underset{\underset{CH_3}{|}}{\overset{\overset{H}{|}}{C}} - OH \quad + \quad R*COOH \quad \longrightarrow \quad CH_3CH_2 - \underset{\underset{CH_3}{|}}{\overset{\overset{H}{|}}{C}} - O - \overset{\overset{O}{\|}}{C} - R*$$

racemic 2-butanol   enantiomeric acid   diastereoisomeric esters

(b) an alcohol to form diastereoisomeric esters, an amine to form diastereoisomeric ammonium salts, or a carboxylic acid to form different diastereoisomeric ammonium salts:

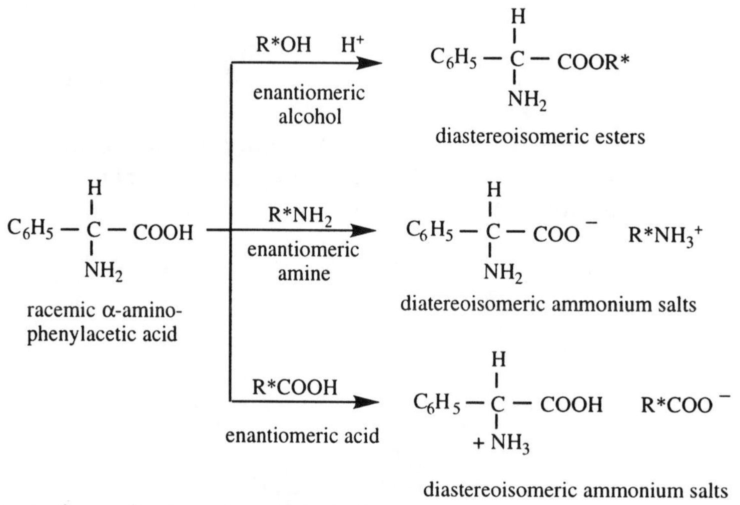

$$C_6H_5 - \underset{\underset{NH_2}{|}}{\overset{\overset{H}{|}}{C}} - COOH$$

racemic α-amino-phenylacetic acid

$$\xrightarrow[\substack{\text{enantiomeric} \\ \text{alcohol}}]{R*OH \quad H^+} \quad C_6H_5 - \underset{\underset{NH_2}{|}}{\overset{\overset{H}{|}}{C}} - COOR*$$

diastereoisomeric esters

$$\xrightarrow[\substack{\text{enantiomeric} \\ \text{amine}}]{R*NH_2} \quad C_6H_5 - \underset{\underset{NH_2}{|}}{\overset{\overset{H}{|}}{C}} - COO^- \quad R*NH_3^+$$

diatereoisomeric ammonium salts

$$\xrightarrow[\substack{\text{enantiomeric acid}}]{R*COOH} \quad C_6H_5 - \underset{\underset{+NH_3}{|}}{\overset{\overset{H}{|}}{C}} - COOH \quad R*COO^-$$

diastereoisomeric ammonium salts

(c) an amine to form diastereoisomeric imines:

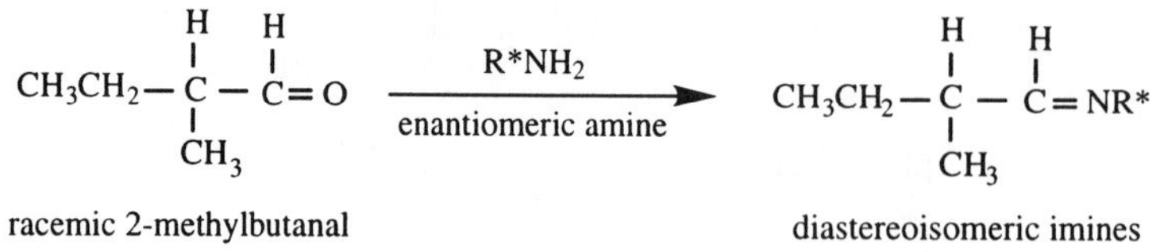

$$CH_3CH_2 - \underset{\underset{CH_3}{|}}{\overset{\overset{H}{|}}{C}} - \overset{\overset{H}{|}}{C} = O \quad \xrightarrow[\text{enantiomeric amine}]{R*NH_2} \quad CH_3CH_2 - \underset{\underset{CH_3}{|}}{\overset{\overset{H}{|}}{C}} - \overset{\overset{H}{|}}{C} = NR*$$

racemic 2-methylbutanal   diastereoisomeric imines

(d) a carboxylic acid to form diastereoisomeric ammonium salts:

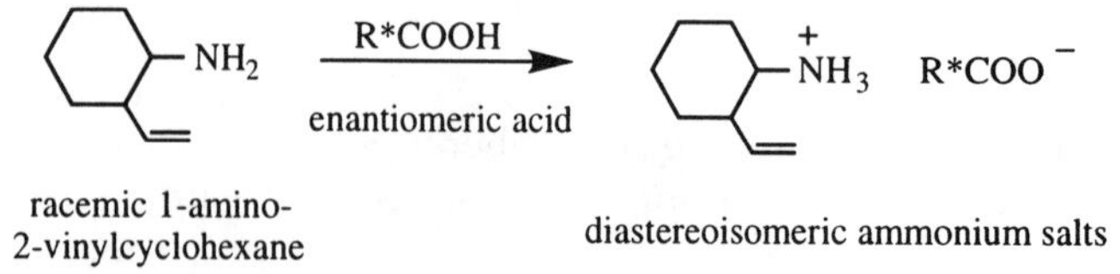

racemic 1-amino-2-vinylcyclohexane   diastereoisomeric ammonium salts

17.6 The open-chain form of fructose has three stereocenters (marked with an asterisk) so there should exist a total of $2^3 = 8$ configurational isomers. The furanose form of fructose has four stereocenters so there should exist $2^4 = 16$ configurational isomers.

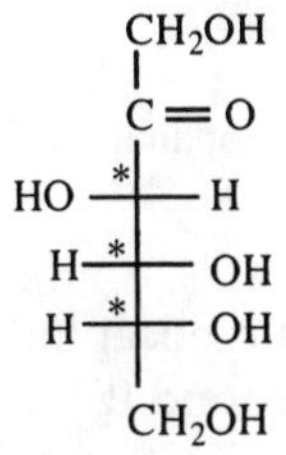

open-chain form of D-fructose

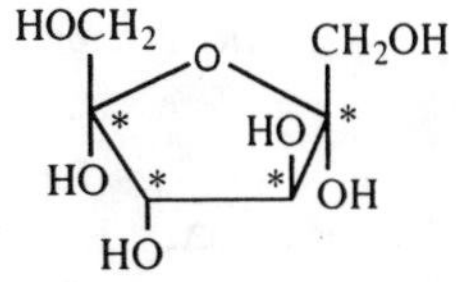

α-D-fructose

17.7 The following compounds have a meso form as shown below: 2,3-butanediamine, 2,4-dibromopentane, and 1,2-cyclopropanediol.

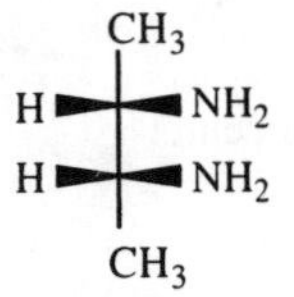

2,3-butanediamine

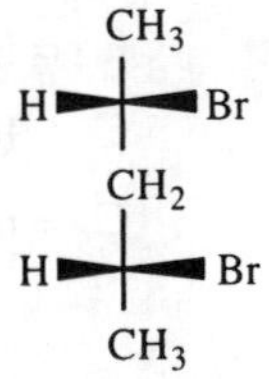

2,4-dibromoopentane

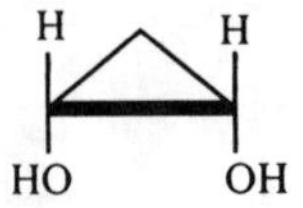

1,2-cyclopropanediol

17.8 To translate a three dimensional drawing as in (a) to a Fischer projection simply rotate it about the C-C_3H_7 axis until two substituents are oriented above the plane of the paper and two groups are oriented below the plane of the paper. The groups above the plane are those located on the horizontal axis of the Fischer projection.

(a)

(*S*)-3-hexanol

(b)

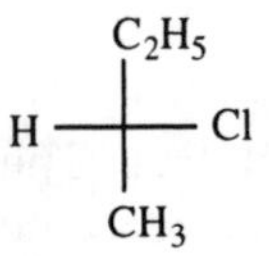

(*R*)-2-chloropentane

(c)

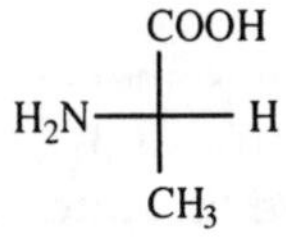

(*S*)-alanine

17.9

(a) 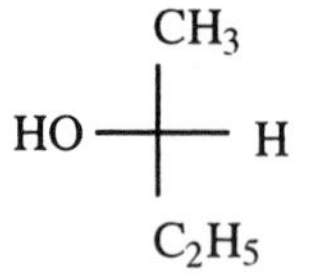
CH3
HO
H
C2H5

(*R*)-2-butanol

(b) 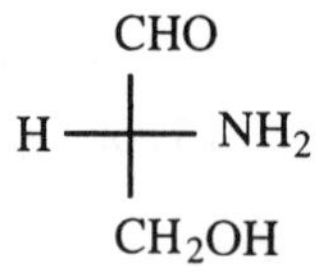
CHO
H
NH2
CH2OH

(*R*)-2-amino-3-hydroxypropanal

17.10 In analyzing glucose it is necessary to treat each stereocenter totally independently. Imagine the molecule is huge and you can "walk around it" until you can look along each C-H bond from carbon to hydrogen. Then assign priorities to each of the other three substituents. Finally, determine whether the a-to-b-to-c direction is clockwise (R) or counter-clockwise (S).

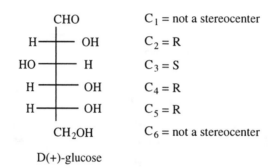

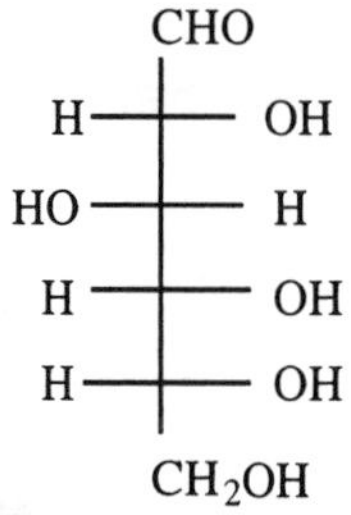
CHO
H
OH
HO
H
H
OH
H
OH
CH2OH

D(+)-glucose

C_1 = not a stereocenter
C_2 = R
C_3 = S
C_4 = R
C_5 = R
C_6 = not a stereocenter

17.11 (a) There are four isomers of 2,3,4-trihydroxybutanal. Their names are 2*R*,3*R*,4-trihydroxybutanal, followed by the 2*S*,3*S* isomer, the 2*R*,3*S* isomer, and the 2*S*,3*R* isomer. All are enantiomers and each is optically active. The 2*R*,3*R* and 2*S*,3*S* isomers comprise a racemic pair and the 2*R*,3*S* and 2*S*,3*R* are a second racemic pair. The 2*R*,3*R* and the 2*S*,3*S* isomers are diastereoisomers of the 2*R*,3*S* and 2*S*,3*R* isomers. The 2*R*,3*S* and 2*S*,3*R* isomers are diastereoisomers of the 2*R*,3*R* and 2*S*,3*S* isomers.

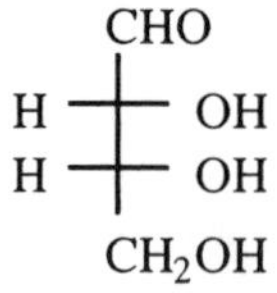
CHO
H
OH
H
OH
CH2OH

2*R*,3*R*

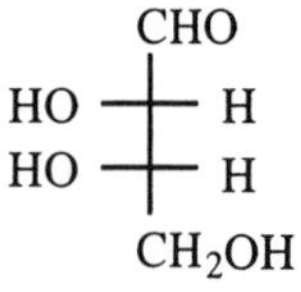
CHO
HO
H
HO
H
CH2OH

2*S*,3*S*

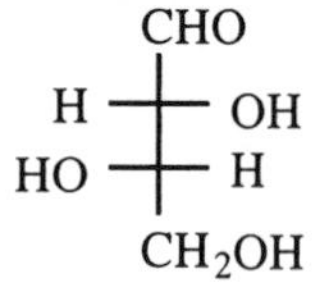
CHO
H
OH
HO
H
CH2OH

2*R*,3*S*

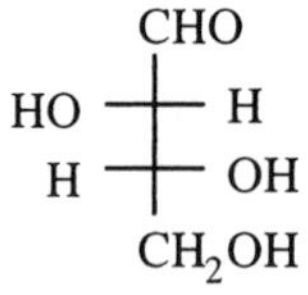
CHO
HO
H
H
OH
CH2OH

2*S*,3*R*

(b) There are three isomers of 1,2,3,4-butanetetrol. Their names are 1,2*R*,3*S*,4-butanetetrol, 1,2*S*,3*S*,4-butanetetrol, and 1,2*R*,3*R*,4-butanetetrol. The 2*R*,3*S* isomer is a meso form which is optically inactive (in spite of having two stereocenters it has an internal plane of symmetry between C_2 and C_3). The 2*S*,3*S* and 2*R*,3*R* isomers are enantiomers which are optically active and comprise a racemic pair. The 2*R*,3*S* isomer is a diastereoisomer of the other two isomers and vice-versa.

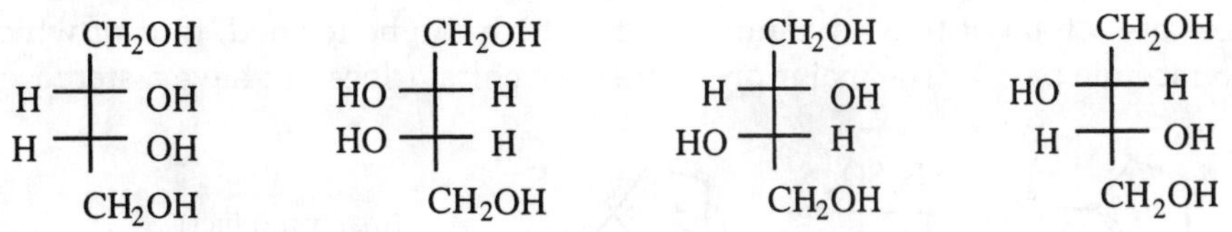
CH₂OH
H OH
H OH
CH₂OH
CH₂OH
HO H
HO H
CH₂OH
CH₂OH
H OH
HO H
CH₂OH
CH₂OH
HO H
H OH
CH₂OH

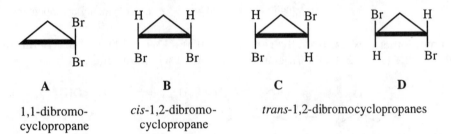

2*S*,3*R* | 2*R*,3*S* | 2*S*,3*S* | 2*R*,3*R*

identical structures

17.12 **A** is a constitutional (positional) isomer of the other three compounds. **B** is a *cis-trans* isomer (a kind of diastereoisomer) of **C** and **D**. **B** also is a meso form. **B** is a diastereoisomer of **C** and **D**, and vice-versa. **C** and **D** are enantiomers and together form a racemic mixture.

Br
Br
H H
Br Br
H Br
Br H
Br H
H Br

A — 1,1-dibromocyclopropane

B — *cis*-1,2-dibromocyclopropane

C, **D** — *trans*-1,2-dibromocyclopropanes

17.13

(a)

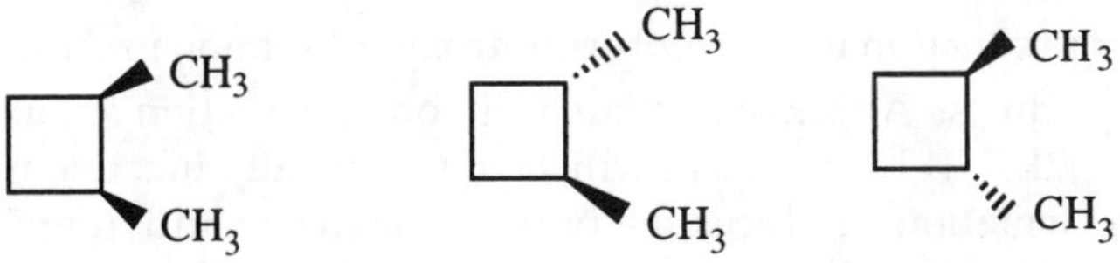
CH3
CH3
CH3
CH3
CH3
CH3

cis (meso) | trans (pair of enantiomers)

(b)

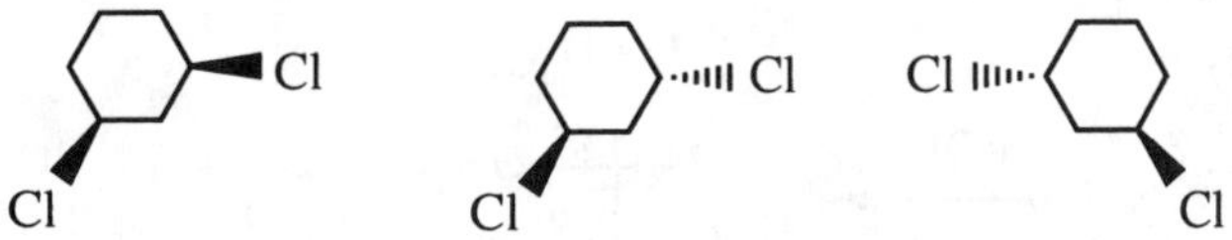
Cl
Cl
Cl
Cl
Cl
Cl

cis (meso) | trans (pair of enantiomers)

(c)

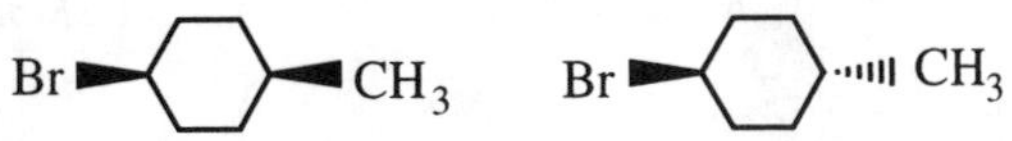
Br
CH3
Br
CH3

cis (achiral) | trans (achiral)

17.14 There are a total of five separate isomers which can be formed, four of which are chiral (as two racemic pairs). The major product is not chiral (does not have a stereocenter).

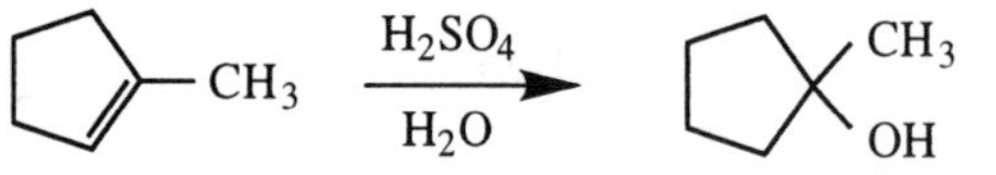
CH3
H2SO4
H2O
CH3
OH

(major product)

1-methylcyclopentanol (not chiral)

(chiral minor products)

CH3
+
CH3
OH
OH

dl-cis-2-methylcyclopentanol *dl-trans*-2-methylcyclopentanol

17.15 The enantiomeric excess from the reaction is (10.0 ÷ 13.9) x 100 = 72%. Therefore the mixture contains 72 + (1/2 x 28) = 86% *d*-enantiomer and 14% *l*-enantiomer.

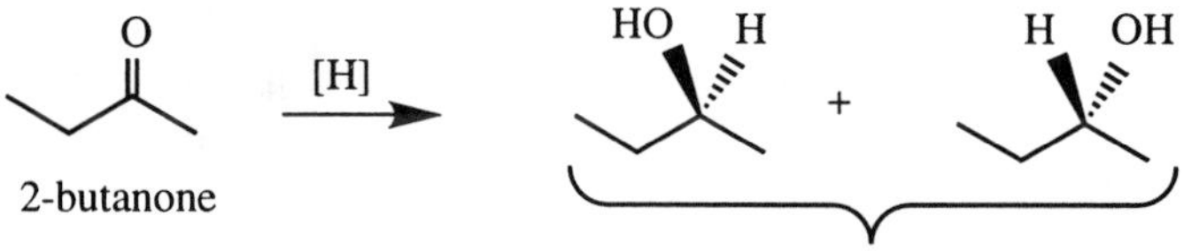
O
[H]
HO H
+
H OH

2-butanone

dl-2-butanol

17.16 The $NaBH_4$ reduction of (*R*)-1,3,4-trihydroxy-2-butanone results in a mixture of two isomeric products. Attack of hydride from one orientation about the carbonyl group produces 1,2*R*,3*S*,4-butanetetrol which is an optically inactive meso form. Attack from the opposite orientation produces the optically active enantiomer 1,2*R*,3*R*,4-butanetetrol. These two isomers are diastereoisomers and have different physical properties - therefore, they are separable by normal experimental means.

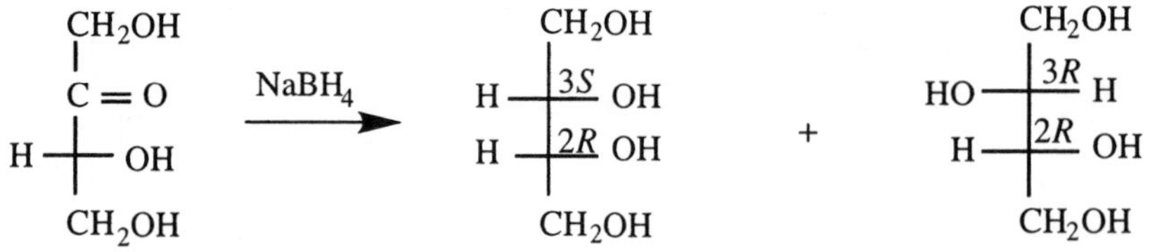
CH2OH
C = O
H OH
CH2OH
NaBH4
CH2OH
H 3S OH
H 2R OH
CH2OH
+
CH2OH
HO 3R H
H 2R OH
CH2OH

R-1,3,4-trihydroxy-2-butanone 1,2*R*,3*S*,4-butanetetrol 1,2*R*,3*R*,4-butanetetrol

17.17 The radical allylic bromination occurs to produce substitution only at C5 because the other allylic position (C2) has no hydrogen available for replacement. Since the product has a stereocenter, and substitution occurs to produce both possible products, the result of the reaction is an optically inactive mixture of two enantiomers (i.e., a racemate).

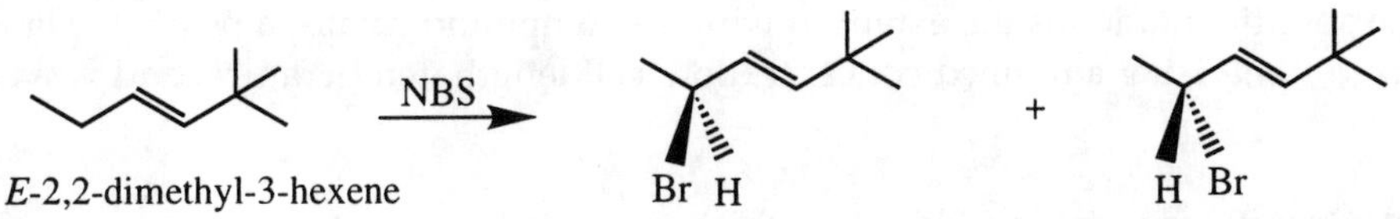

E-2,2-dimethyl-3-hexene

(*S*)-5-bromo-2,2-dimethyl-3*E*-hexene

(*R*)-5-bromo-2,2-dimethyl-3*E*-hexene

17.18 (a) isomers are two or more compounds which have the same molecular formula but different chemical structures.

(b) a stereocenter is a carbon (or similar atom such as silicon, phosphorus, nitrogen) which has four different substituents attached.

(c) a chiral molecule is one which has the property of handedness, that is in which the molecule has a mirror image which is non-superimposable.

(d) enantiomers are two non-superimposable compounds which have an object-mirror image relationship to each other.

(e) a racemic mixture is a 50/50 mixture of a pair of enantiomers.

(f) configurational isomers have the same connectivities but their atoms are oriented differently in space, and they cannot be converted into one another by rotation about sigma bonds.

(g) conformational isomers have the same connectivities but their atoms are oriented differently in space, and they can be converted into one another by rotation about sigma bonds.

(h) resolution is the process by which a pair of enantiomers (a racemate) is separated.

(i) a levorotatory compound is one which is optically active and which rotates a beam of plane polarized light to the left (counter-clockwise).

(j) diastereoisomers are configurational isomers which do not have an object-mirror image relationship to each other.

(k) plane polarized light is that which has been passed through a device such that the beam that is emitted is vibrating only in one plane.

(l) constitutional isomers are those which have different bond connectivities. The difference may be in the carbon skeleton (skeletal isomers), in the position of attachment of substituents (positional isomers), or in the nature of the functional group (functional group isomers).

(m) the specific rotation is the extent to which a compound rotates a beam of plane polarized light using a defined concentration, cell length, temperature, and wavelength of light.

(n) a dextrorotatory compound is one which is optically active and which rotates a beam of plane polarized light to the right (clockwise).

(o) a racemate is a 50/50 mixture of the pair of enantiomers.

(p) a meso isomer is one which is optically inactive because, although it has more than one stereocenter, the presence of an element of symmetry causes the object structure to be superimposable on the mirror image structure.

(q) observed rotation is the extent to which a particular sample and concentration of a compound rotates a beam of plane polarized light.

(r) *cis-trans* isomers are configurational isomers in which substituent groups are attached to opposite sides of a fixed plane of reference, such as a double bond or a cycloalkane ring.

17.19

(a) 

(b) 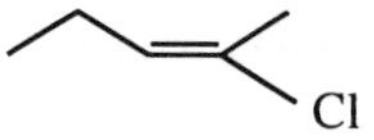
Cl

(c) 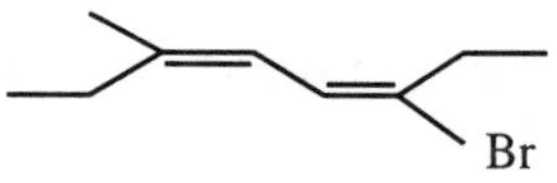
Br

17.20

(a) 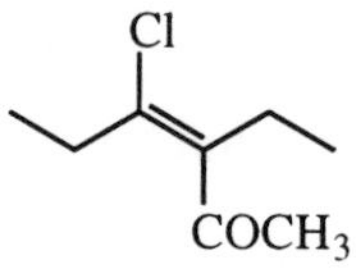
Cl
COCH$_3$

(b) 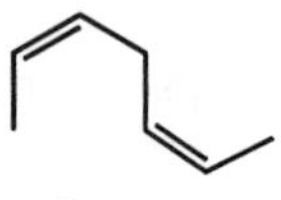

(c) 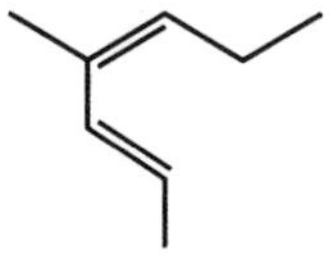

E ***Z,Z*** ***E,Z***

17.21

(a) 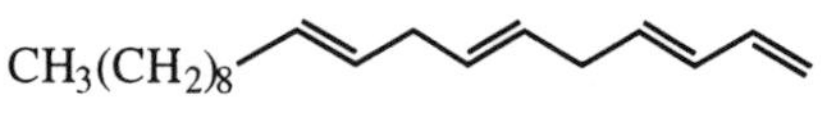
CH$_3$(CH$_2$)$_8$

(b) 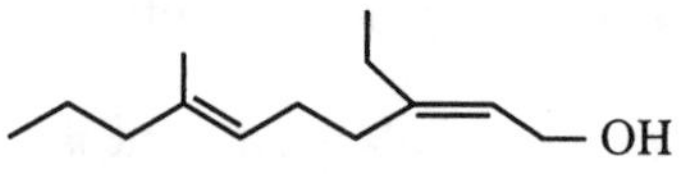
OH

(c) 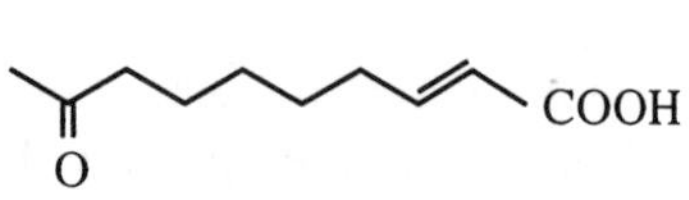
O
COOH

(d) 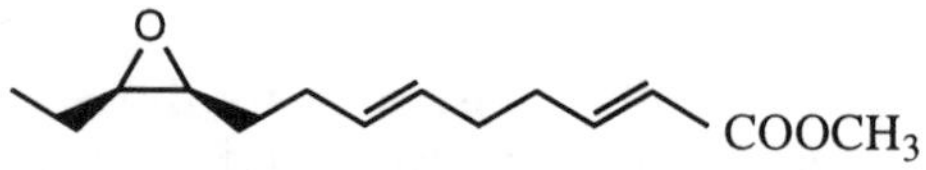
O
COOCH$_3$

17.22

(a) 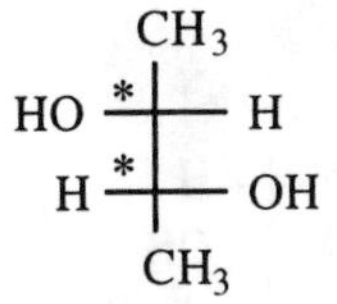

2,3-butanediol

(b) 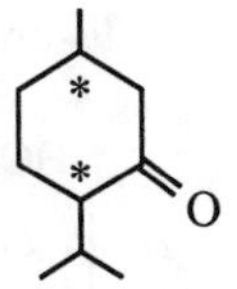

Menthone

(c) $CH_3\overset{*}{C}HOHCH_2CH_2\overset{*}{C}HBrCH(CH_3)_2$

5-bromo-6-methyl-2-heptanol

(d) $CH_3\overset{*}{C}HOH\overset{*}{C}HNH_2COOH$

Threonine

(e) 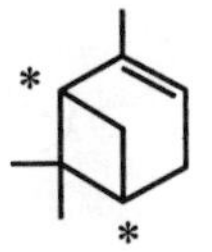

α-Pinene

(f) 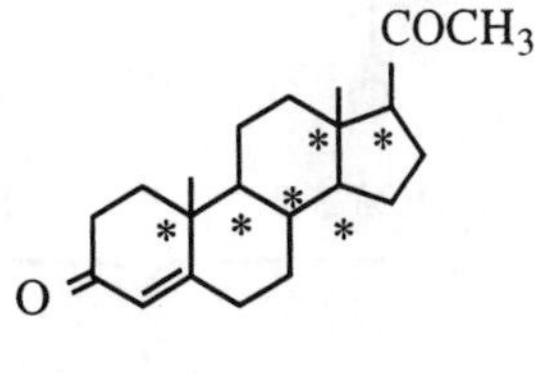

Progesterone

17.23

(a) 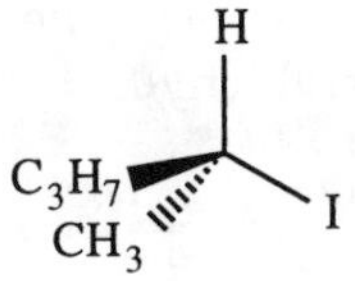

(*S*)-2-iodopentane

(b) 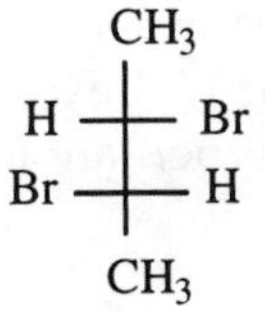

2*S*,3*S*-dibromobutane

(c) 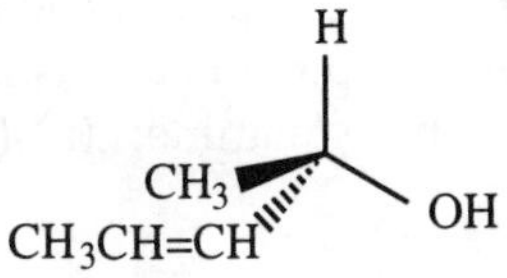

(*R*)-3-penten-2-ol

17.24 The determination of whether the named compounds exist as racemates is made by determining whether each (i) has one stereocenter, enabling the existence of a pair of enantiomers as a racemic mixture, or (ii) has two or more stereocenters and is **not** a meso form.

The following compounds exist as racemates:
(b) 2-methylpiperidine
(e) 1-phenyl-1-bromo-2-pentanone
(f) methyl cyclohex-2-en-4-onecarboxylate
(g) 2-butyl benzoate
(h) 3-methylcyclohexyl acetate
(i) 4-(*N*,*N*-dimethylamino)-2-pentyne

The following compounds do not exist as racemates for the indicated reason:
(a) *cis*-1,2-dichlorocyclohexane (meso form)
(c) *trans*-1,4-dimethylcyclohexane (no stereocenter)
(d) *cis*-1,3-divinylcyclohexane (meso form)

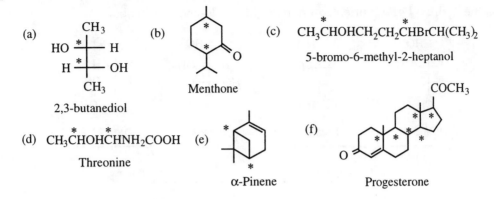

17.25 The D configuration is that in which the highest numbered stereocenter (in these cases C3) has the hydroxyl group oriented on the right in a Fischer projection.

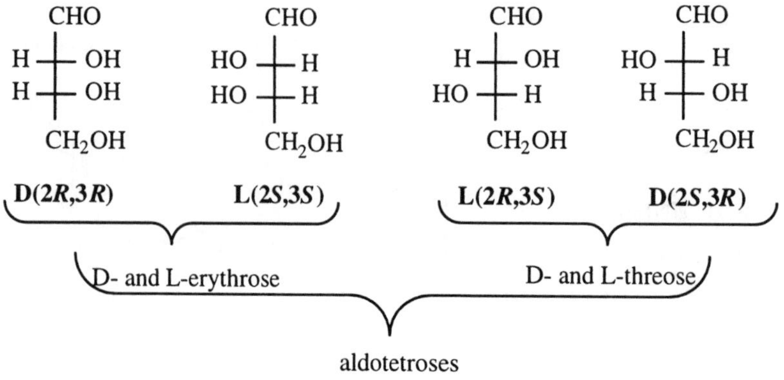

D(2R,3R)
L(2S,3S)
L(2R,3S)
D(2S,3R)
D- and L-erythrose
D- and L-threose
aldotetroses

17.26 In order to be optically active the compound must be a single enantiomer. The optically active compounds are as follows: (b) (*S*)-2-hexanol; (f) D-glyceraldehyde; (g) L-phenylalanine; (h) (*R*)-3-hydroxypentanoic acid.

17.27

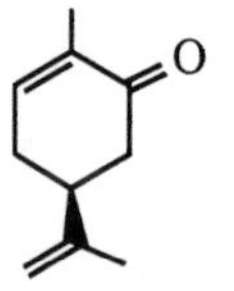

(+) Carvone
$[\alpha]_D = +62.5°$
(caraway)

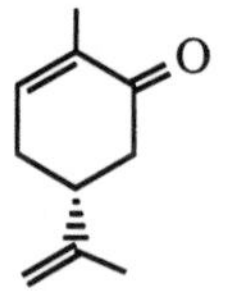

(-)Carvone
$[\alpha]_D = -62.5°$
(spearmint)

S configurations ***R***

17.28

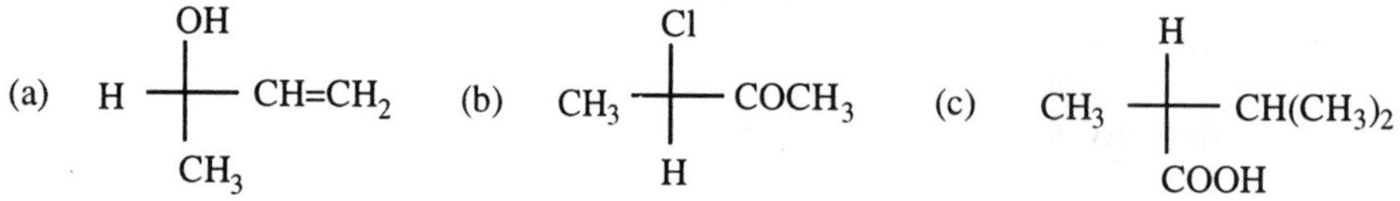

S ***R*** ***S***

17.29

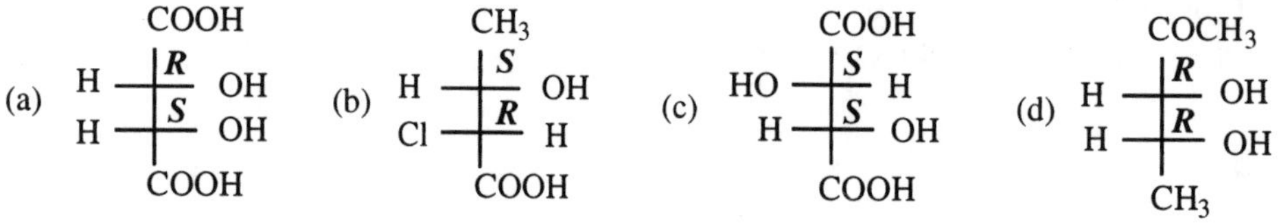

17.30 The resolving agents should be as follows: (a) carboxylic acid to form an ester; (b) carboxylic acid to form an ammonium salt; (c) amine to form an ammonium salt or an alcohol to form an ester; (d) primary amine to form an imine; (e) amine to form an ammonium salt or alcohol to form an ester; (f) amine to form an ammonium salt, an alcohol to form an ester, or a carboxylic acid to form an ester; (g) carboxylic acid to form an ammonium salt or a carbonyl compound to form an imine.

17.31 Answer this question by determining the absolute configuration of each structure drawn. Compound **A** is *R*, **B** is *S*, **C** is *R*, and **D** is *S*. Therefore, structure **C** has the same configuration as **A**. The structures **B** and **D** are enantiomers of **A** and **C**.

17.32 The maximum possible number of optical isomers for a compound with three stereocenters is $2^3 = 8$. In addition to the *RSR* and *SRS* isomers given, the other isomers are *RRR*, *SSS*, *RSS*, *SRR*, *RRS*, and *SSR* isomers.

17.33 The maximum possible number of optical isomers is $2^5 = 32$ isomers.

17.34 There is a plane of symmetry (indicated by the dotted line) for the following compounds: (a) *cis*-1,2-dibromocyclobutane; (c) *trans*-1,4-dimethylcyclohexane; (d) *cis*-1,3-dichlorocyclohexane; (e) 2*R*,3*S*-butanediol.

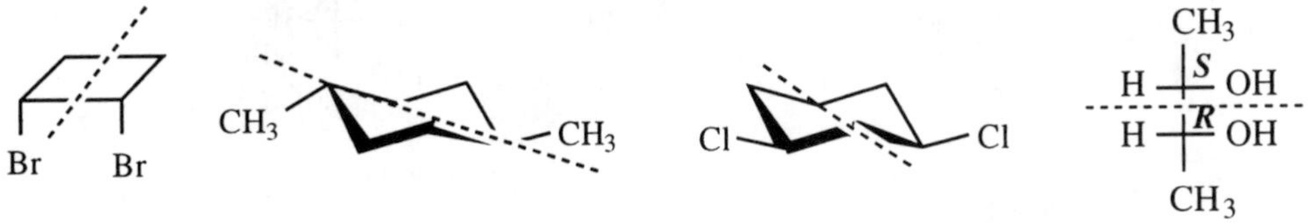
Br
Br
CH3
CH3
Cl
Cl
CH3
H
S
OH
H
R
OH
CH3

(a) (c) (d) (e)

There is not a plane of symmetry for (b) *trans*-1,2-dibromocyclopropane.

17.35 2,3-Dichloropentane exists as four configurational isomers, as two racemates each comprised of a pair of enantiomers. The relationship of any enantiomer to an enantiomer of the other racemate is that of a diastereoisomer.

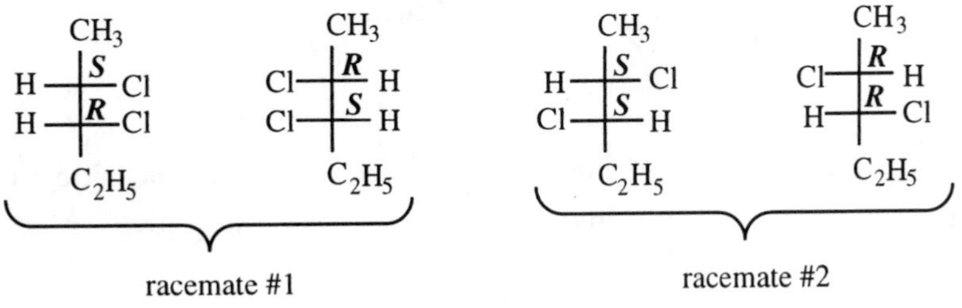
CH3
H
S
Cl
H
R
Cl
C2H5
CH3
Cl
R
H
Cl
S
H
C2H5
CH3
H
S
Cl
Cl
S
H
C2H5
CH3
Cl
R
H
H
R
Cl
C2H5
racemate #1
racemate #2

17.36 2,4-Dichloropentane exists as three configurational isomers, one meso form and a pair of enantiomers (a racemate). The relationship of the meso form to each enantiomer is that of a diastereoisomer, and vice versa.

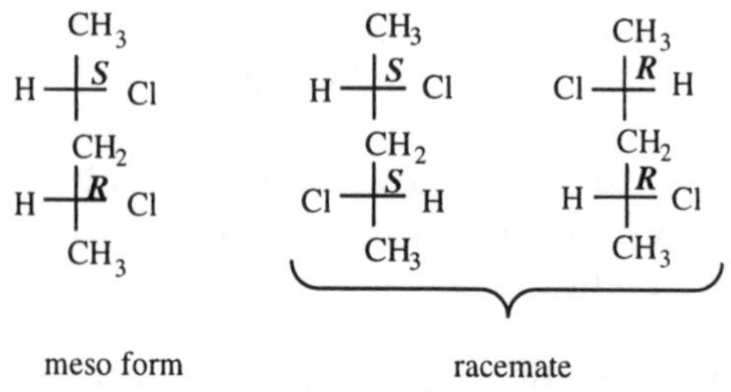

17.37 (a) Since it can be resolved the 206° isomer is a racemic mixture of two enantiomers.
(b) The 140° isomer is an optically inactive meso form.
(c) The relationship between either 170° isomers and the 140° isomer is that of diastereoisomers.
(d) The 140° isomer is 2*R*,3*S*-dihydroxybutanedioic acid.
(e) The 170° isomers are 2*R*,3*R*-dihydroxybutanedioic acid and 2*S*,3*S*-dihydroxybutanedioic acid.

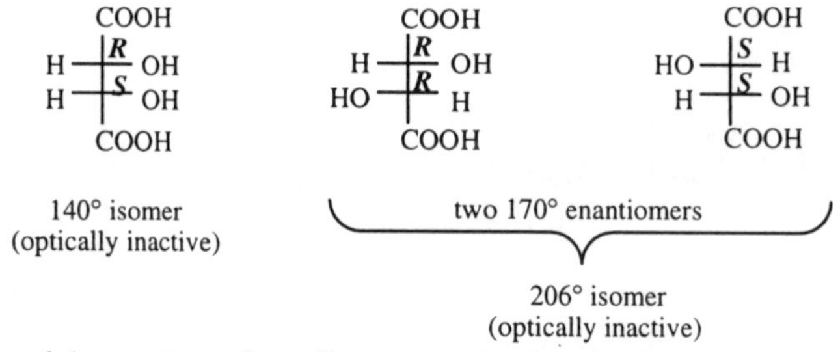

17.38 (a) (*R*)-2-butanol (retention of configuration in the alcohol because of hydroxide attack at the carbonyl group and ejection of alkoxide in a nucleophilic acyl substitution. The configuration of the stereocenter is unchanged.)

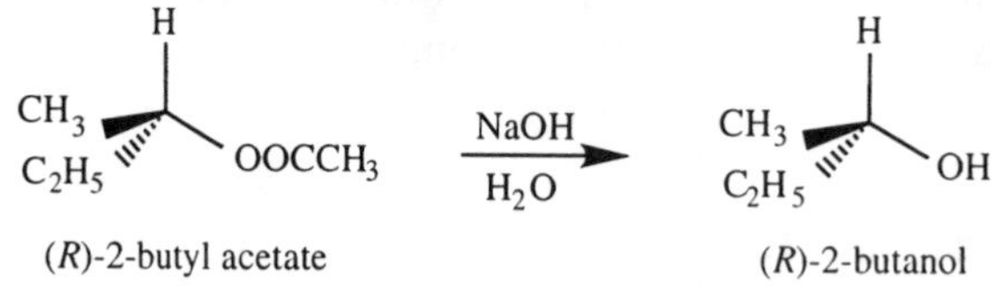

(b) (*R*)-2-pentanol (inversion of configuration because of S_N2 backside attack by hydroxide at the stereocenter, resulting in inversion and displacing tosylate)

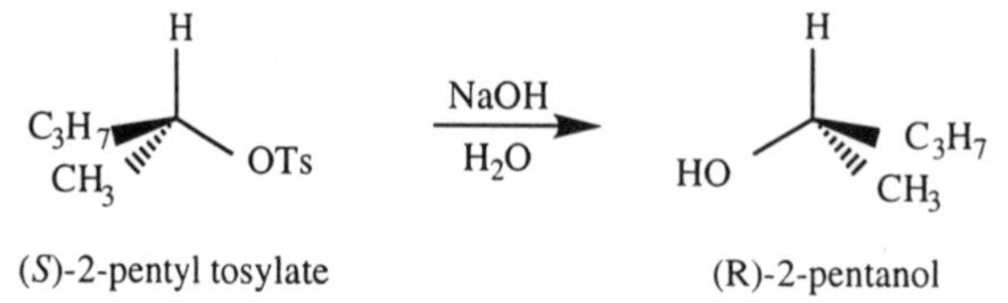

(c) racemic 1-methoxy-1-phenylethane (racemization of the stereocenter because of S_N1 solvolysis enabled by the formation of the stabilized benzylic carbocation)

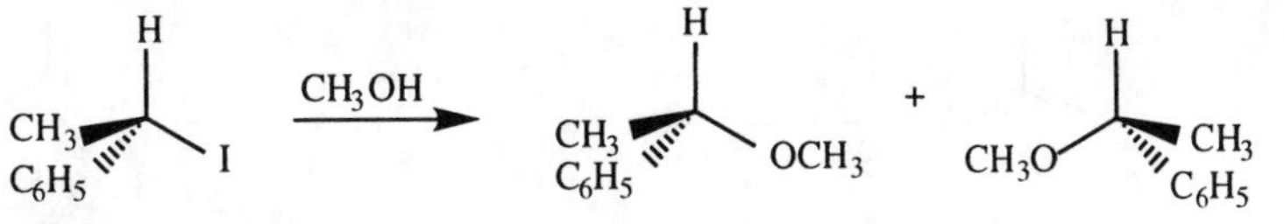

(*R*)-1-iodo-1-phenylethane   *dl*-1-methoxy-1-phenylethane

(d) (*S*)-2-methoxypentane (inversion of configuration because of S_N2 substitution by the strong base)

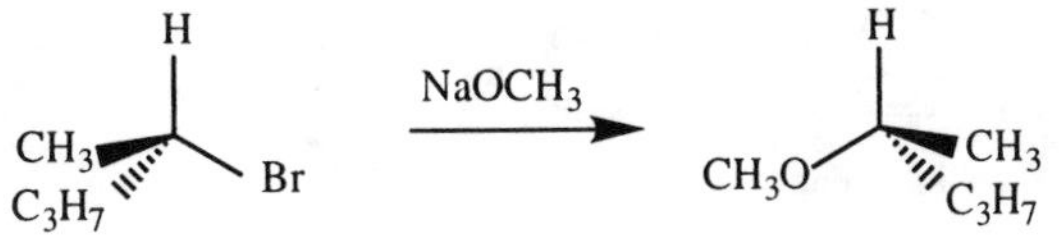

(*R*)-2-bromopentane   (*S*)-2-methoxypentane

(e) racemic 2-butanol (attack of water at the symmetric secondary carbocation forming both enantiomers)

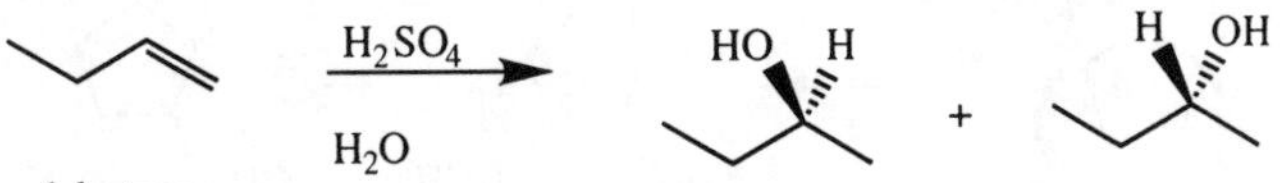

1-butene

dl-2-butanol

(f) (*S*)-2-chlorobutane (inversion of configuration because of S_N2 attack of chloride on the intermediate chlorosulfite)

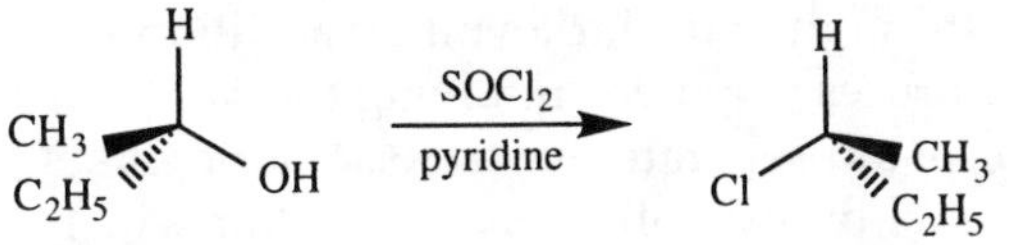

(*R*)-2-butanol   (S)-2-chlorobutane

(g) racemic 1-chloro-1-phenylethane (attack of chloride anion on either side of the planar (and therefore symmetric) benzylic carbocation formed by proton addition, thereby producing both enantiomers)

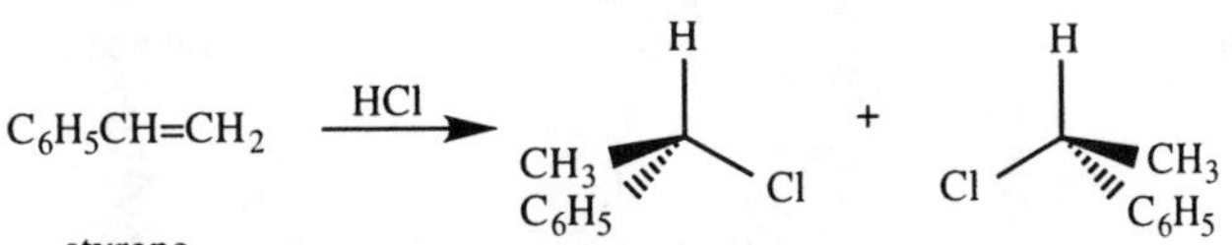

styrene

dl-1-chloro-1-phenylethane

(h) racemic 3-methyl-2-butanol (attack of diborane on both sides of the planar alkene double bond, forming both enantiomers)

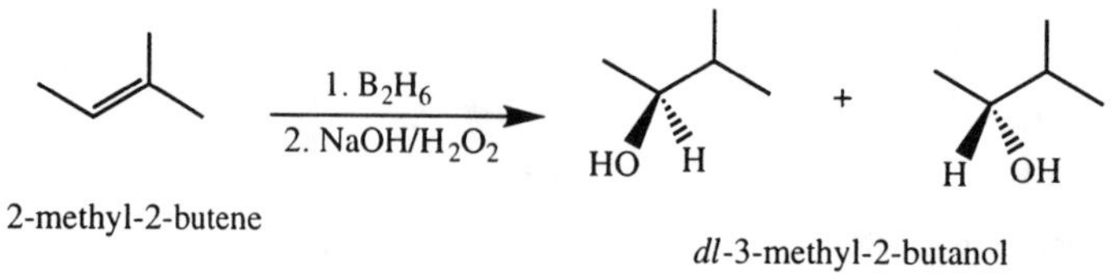
1. B_2H_6
2. $NaOH/H_2O_2$
HO H
+
H OH
2-methyl-2-butene
dl-3-methyl-2-butanol

(i) *cis*-1,2-cyclohexanediol, a meso form (*cis* addition of permanganate which is displaced by hydroxyl)

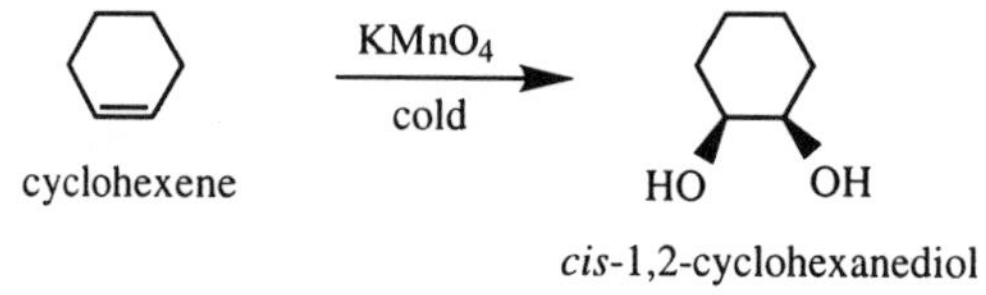
$KMnO_4$
cold
HO OH
cyclohexene
cis-1,2-cyclohexanediol

(j) racemic *trans*-2-methoxycyclopentanol (backside attack of methoxide to open the ring, attack being equally possible at C_1 or C_2)

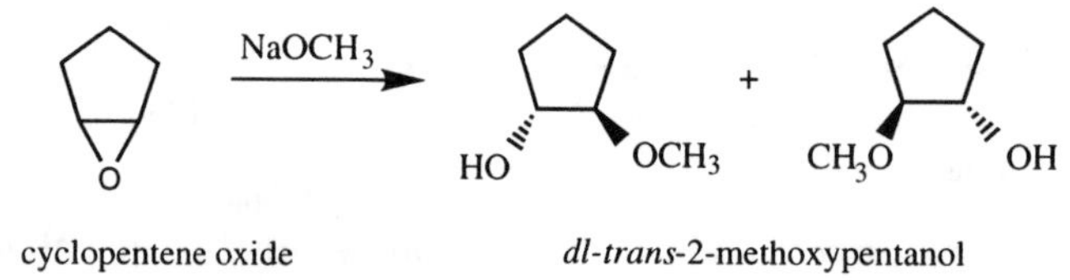
$NaOCH_3$
O
HO
OCH_3
+
CH_3O
OH
cyclopentene oxide
dl-trans-2-methoxypentanol

***17.39** The synthesis of (*R*)-3-methyl-2-butanol from 2-methyl-2-butene requires first that the alkene be converted through anti-Markovnikov addition into the alcohol which would be racemic. The second process involves resolving the racemate using an optically active carboxylic acid to form and separate diastereoisomeric esters. The final step is to recover the enantiomeric alcohol by hydrolysis of the *R*-ester which will result in retention of the configuration of the alcohol.

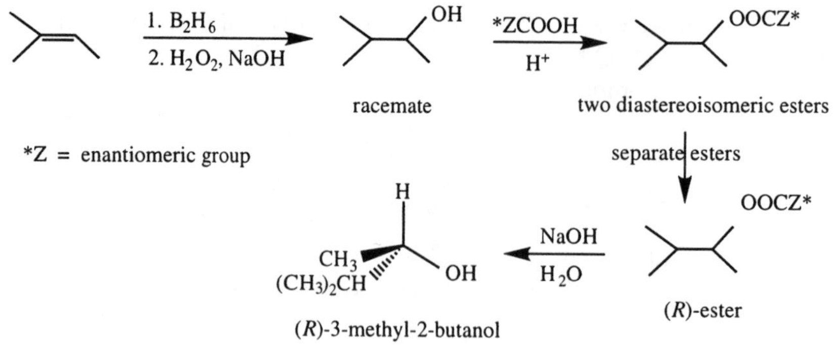
1. B_2H_6
2. H_2O_2, NaOH
OH
*ZCOOH
H^+
OOCZ*
racemate
two diastereoisomeric esters
*Z = enantiomeric group
separate esters
OOCZ*
NaOH
H_2O
H
CH_3
$(CH_3)_2CH$
OH
(R)-ester
(R)-3-methyl-2-butanol

17.40 The laboratory reduction of the C_{11} ketone group in cortisone is not stereospecific because the reagent, sodium borohydride, is not chiral. Therefore it can deliver a hydride anion from both sides of the carbonyl group. The biological reducing "agent" is an enzyme which is chiral and which therefore can recognize the chirality of cortisone. The chiral co-enzyme will deliver the reducing electrons and proton exclusively to the under side of the carbonyl group, forming hydrocortisone.

17.41 HBr is an achiral reagent and when it adds to this alkene a new stereocenter will be created. The addition reaction mechanism involves formation of a carbocation adjacent to the stereocenter, and the final step will be the approach of a bromide anion above or below the plane of the trigonal carbocation. The presence of the existing stereocenter will influence the ratio in which the two approaches occur, and therefore the ratio of the two products formed. Both products will form, and one will be 2*S*,3*R*-dibromobutane (a meso form) and the other will be 2*S*,3*S*-dibromobutane (an enantiomer). The starting material is optically active and the product mixture also will be optically active. The two products are diastereoisomers and therefore can be separated without resorting to resolution.

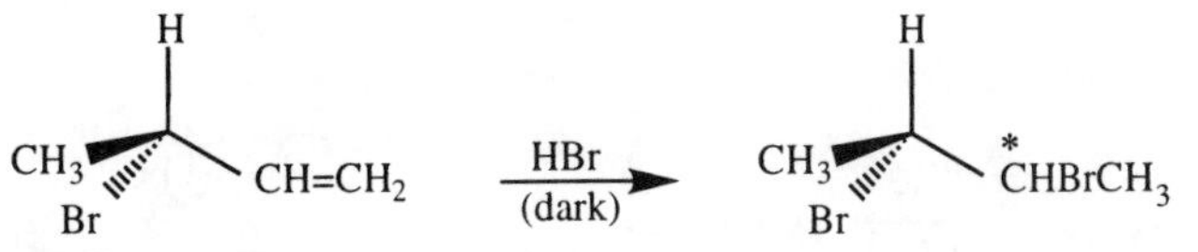
H
CH3
Br
CH=CH2
HBr
(dark)
H
CH3
Br
*
CHBrCH3

(*S*)3-bromo-1-butene 2,3-dibromobutane

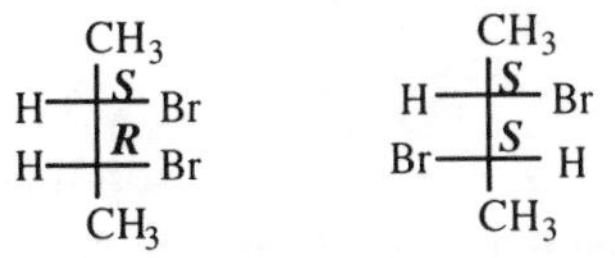
CH3
H
S
Br
H
R
Br
CH3
CH3
H
S
Br
Br
S
H
CH3

meso form enantiomer

17.42 Acid-catalyzed hydration of styrene proceeds via initial addition of a proton to form a planar carbocation, in this instance a resonance-stabilized benzylic carbocation, which is planar (trigonal). The approach of a water molecule in the second step occurs with equal probability from above or below the plane of the carbocation. Therefore, both enantiomers (a racemic mixture) will form.

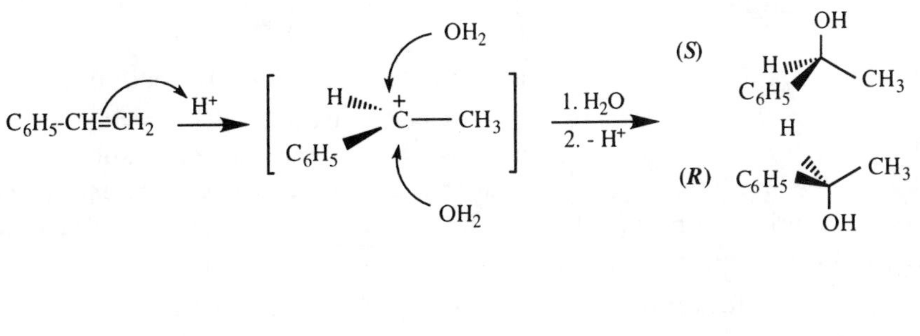
C6H5-CH=CH2
H+
H
C6H5
C
CH3
OH2
OH2
1. H2O
2. - H+
(S)
OH
H
C6H5
CH3
H
(R)
C6H5
CH3
OH

17.43

(a) 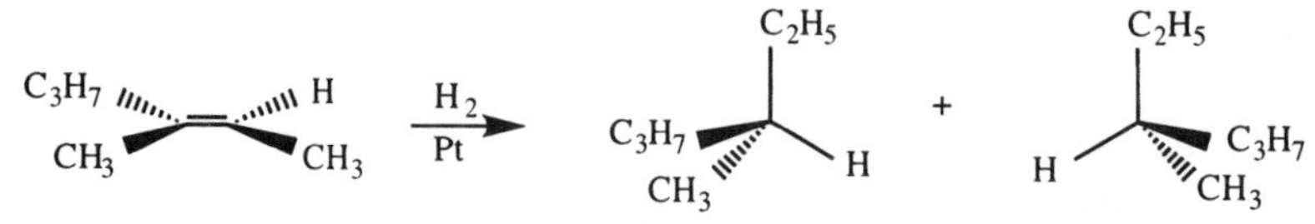

racemic mixture

(b) 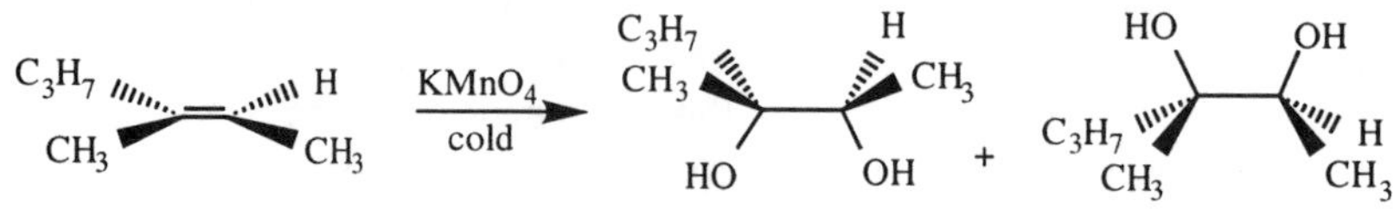

racemic mixture

(c) 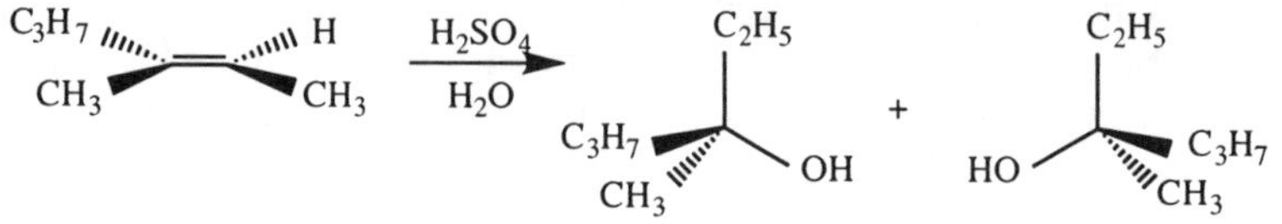

racemic mixture

(d) 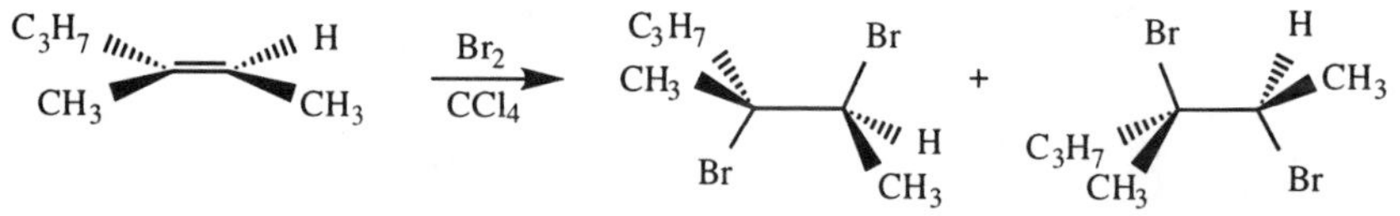

racemic mixture

17.44 (a) constitutional isomers (positional isomers); (b) the compounds are identical; (c) enantiomers; (d) *cis-trans* isomers; (e) conformational isomers; (f) enantiomers; (g) *cis-trans* isomers; (h) diastereoisomers.

17.45 The number of configurational isomers which exist are: (a) four (two *cis-trans* and two enantiomers of each); (b) none; (c) two (*cis-trans*); (d) none; (e) two (enantiomers); (f) three (two enantiomers and one meso form).

17.46

(a) $CH_3CH{=}CH\text{-}CH_2CH_2Br$ (b) $CH_2{=}CH\text{-}CHBrCH_2CH_3$

(c) $(CH_3)_2C{=}CH\text{-}CH_2Br$ (d) $CH_3CH{=}CH\text{-}CHBrCH_3$

17.47 The formula of **A** (C_8H_{14}) indicates an HDI of two and hydrogenation to C_8H_{18} (**B**) indicates the presence of a triple bond or two double bonds. The fact that only two products are obtained upon ozonolysis means there is only one multiple bond subject to ozonolysis and that **A** must be an alkyne. The fact that the carboxylic acid **C** is optically active means there is a stereocenter present. The obtaining of acetic acid (CH_3COOH) as one ozonolysis product indicates a partial structure for **A** is CH_3CC-. The fact that **A** is optically active (and therefore has four different groups attached to one carbon) while **B** is optically inactive means that hydrogenation of the triple bond produced a group which is identical to another group already attached to the stereocenter. Therefore, the C_3 alkyne unit must be attached to a carbon which also carries a propyl group and **D** represents a partial structure accounting for seven of the eight carbons in **A**. The remaining carbon can only be a methyl group. Therefore, **A** is 4-methyl-2-heptyne.

$$CH_3C \equiv CCH(CH_3)C_3H_7 \xrightarrow{\text{H}_2 \atop \text{Pt}} C_3H_7CH(CH_3)C_3H_7$$
$$\mathbf{A} \qquad\qquad\qquad \mathbf{B}$$

$$CH_3C \equiv C\!-\!\overset{|}{\underset{|}{C}}\!-\!C_3H_7 \xrightarrow{\;O_3\;} CH_3COOH \;+\; HOOCCH(CH_3)C_3H_7 \;\;(C_6H_{12}O_2)$$
$$\mathbf{D} \qquad\qquad\qquad\qquad\qquad \mathbf{C}$$

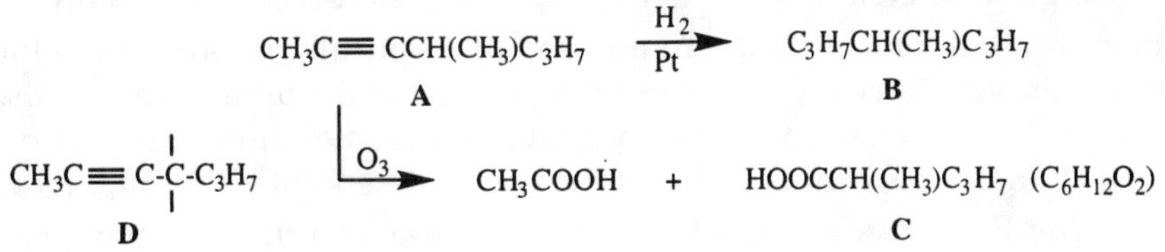

17.48

(a) 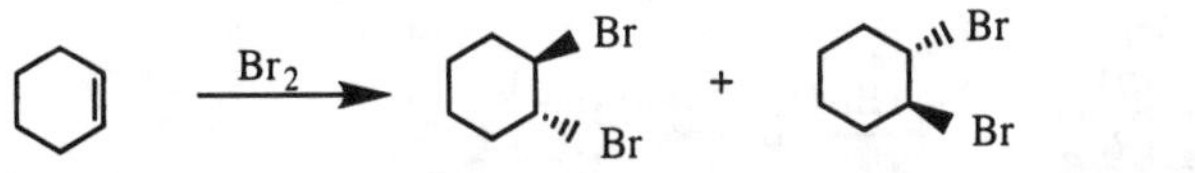

(optically inactive - mixture of two enantiomers)

(b) 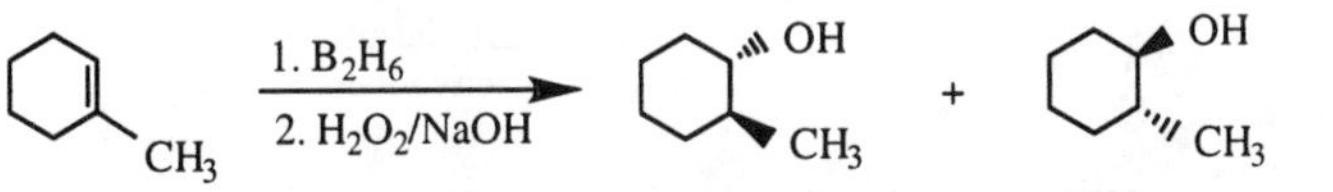

(optically inactive - mixture of two enantiomers)

(c) 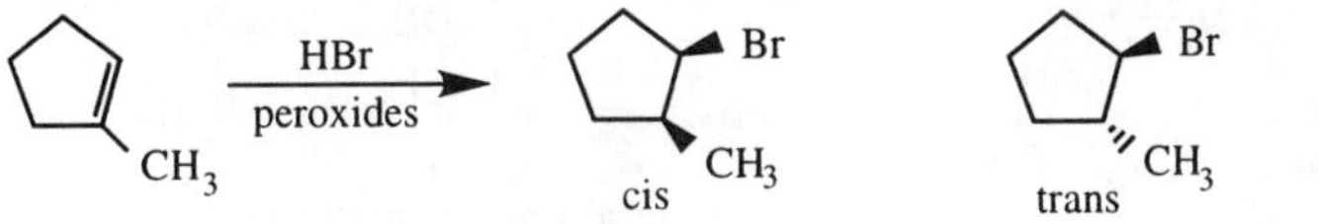

cis   trans

(optically inactive - mixture of two racemic mixtures)

(d) 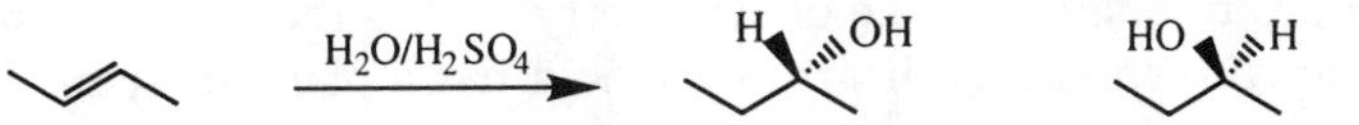

(optically inactive - mixture of two enantiomers)

(e) 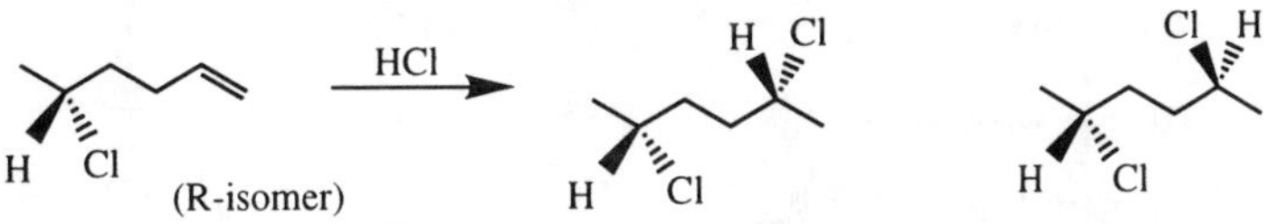

(optically active - mixture of two diastereoisomers)

(f) $CH_3CH_2CH=CHCH_2CH_3$ 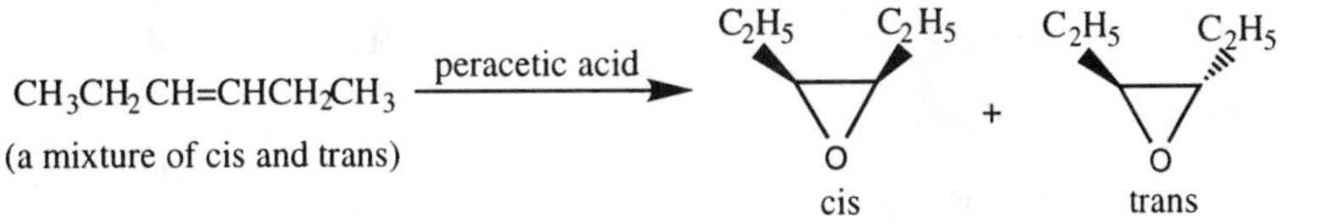

(a mixture of cis and trans)

cis   trans

(optically inactive - mixture of a cis meso form and a trans racemate)

(g) 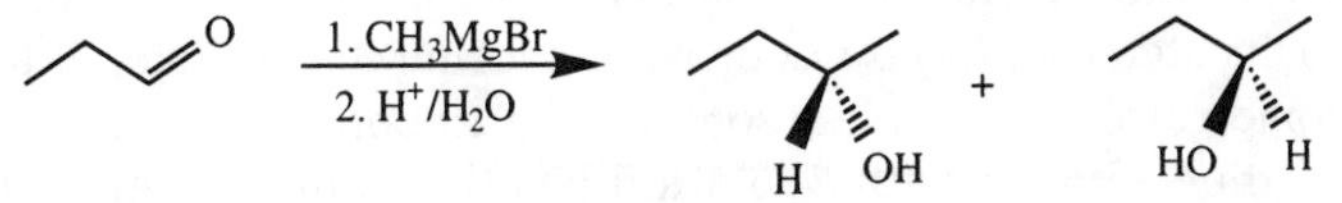

(optically inactive - mixture of two enantiomers)

17.49 Since both threose and erythrose are of the D-configuration, the stereochemistry of the lowest stereocenter (C3) is known to be *R*. Since erythrose produces a meso form of tartaric acid (in which the configuration of C3 remains unchanged but is now labelled *S* due to group priority changes), the configuration of the upper (C2) stereocenter of erythrose must be *R* in order that oxidation produce *R,S*-tartaric acid (the optically inactive meso form). Since threose (which must have the opposite configuration at the upper carbon—that is, be an epimer of erythrose) affords an optically active enantiomer of tartaric acid (which must be the *S,S*-enantiomer), the configuration of the upper stereocenter (C2) in threose is confirmed to be *S*. Therefore, the structures of erythrose, threose, and the oxidation product tartaric acids are as shown below.

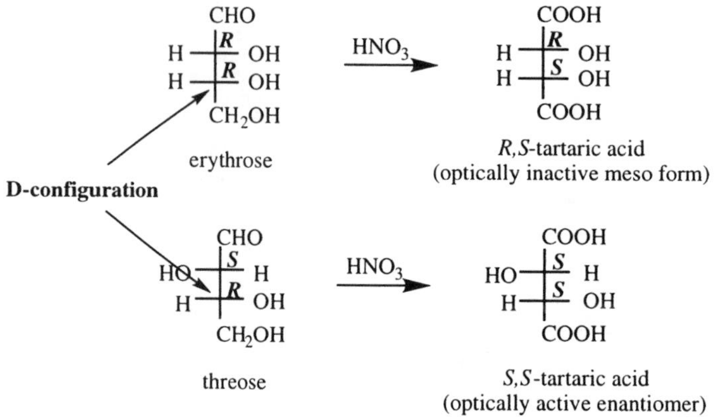
CHO
H
R
OH
H
R
OH
CH2OH
erythrose
HNO3
COOH
H
R
OH
H
S
OH
COOH
R,S-tartaric acid
(optically inactive meso form)
D-configuration
CHO
HO
S
H
H
R
OH
CH2OH
threose
HNO3
COOH
HO
S
H
H
S
OH
COOH
S,S-tartaric acid
(optically active enantiomer)

17.50 Whereas D-galactose does not have a plane of symmetry, and is therefore an enantiomer and optically active, the corresponding dicarboxylic acid has a plane of symmetry as marked with a dotted line.

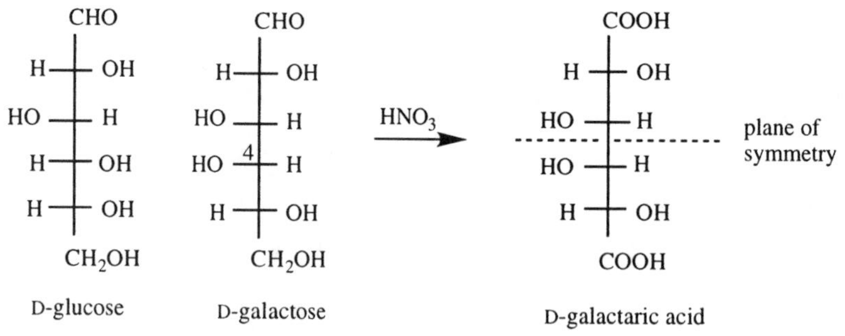
CHO
H OH
HO H
H OH
H OH
CH2OH
D-glucose
CHO
H OH
HO H
HO 4 H
H OH
CH2OH
D-galactose
HNO3
COOH
H OH
HO H
HO H
H OH
COOH
plane of
symmetry
D-galactaric acid

17.51 The configuration of the starting alcohol remains unchanged during step **A** because the carbon-oxygen bond (to the stereocenter) is not broken. During the S_N2 step **B** the carbon-oxygen bond of the alkoxide also is not broken so its configuration remains unchanged. Therefore, the product ether with a positive rotation has the same configuration as the starting alcohol. It is only coincidence that the optical rotations are in the same direction (dextrorotatory)!

The configuration of the starting alcohol also remains unchanged during the tosylation of step **C** in which the alcohol must serve as the nucleophile, the carbon-oxygen bond remaining intact. In step **D** the S_N2 displacement is effected by ethoxide anion attack at the stereocenter, inverting its configuration as the tosyl group leaves. Therefore, the product ether has the opposite configuration of the starting alcohol. Therefore, the two samples of ether formed from the two reaction sequences have the opposite configurations and, as expected, show the opposite optical rotation of approximately the same magnitude.

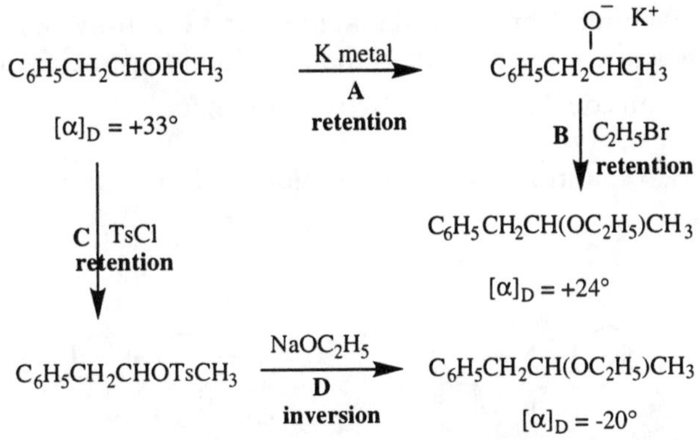

V. Conceptual Problem

Drugs

As a pharmacist, you read with interest that thalidomide has recently been approved by the Food and Drug Administration for use in the treatment of Hansen's disease (more commonly known as leprosy). This announcement comes almost 40 years after the drug was banned by that agency because it caused birth defects in babies born to women who had used the drug to combat morning sickness during early pregnancy. What's of particular interest to you are all the new regulations associated with the drug, which will be marketed as Thalomid. The manufacturer of the drug has developd a System for Thalidomide Education and Prescribing Safety (STEPS) program. Only physicians who register with the program may prescribe Thalomid. The patients, both male and female, must also register, as well as complying with mandatory contraceptive measures and filling out patient surveys. The prescriptions will be for no more than a 28-day supply, with no automatic refills.

This is quite a contrast to the drug's introduction in 1958. It was touted as non-toxic, and there was even some pressure to sell it over the counter, with no prescription needed. It was its use to control morning sickness that revealed its one terrible and tragic property. It is a powerful teratogen, a substance that causes birth defects.

■A thalidomide molecule contains one stereocenter. Where is it in the structure?

- Ans: It is the carbon to the right of the nitrogen atom on the left side of the molecule in the structure.

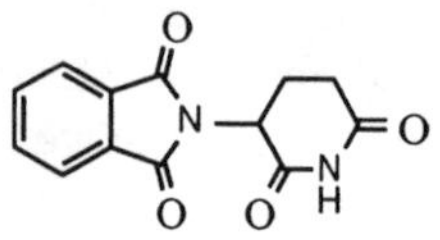

■Thalidomide was manufactured from achiral materials and carefully purified, but no resolution was performed. What was therefore present in the thalidomide prescribed for morning sickness?

- Ans: A racemic mixture, an equal mixture of two enantiomers.

■Draw structures of the two enantiomers of thalidomide, and identify the structures you have drawn as *R* and *S* isomers.

- Ans:

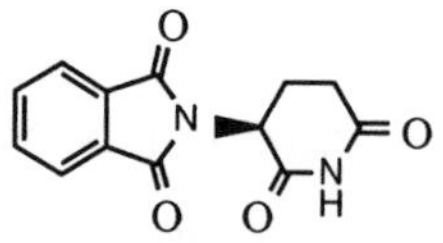

(*S*)-Thalidomide

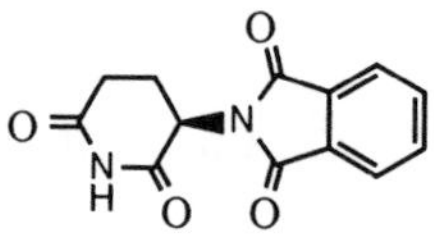

(*R*)-Thalidomide

■More recent research has shown that the *R* isomer is active against leprosy, and the *S* isomer is the teratogen. What does this tell you about the point of interaction of thalidomide with the body's biochemical systems?

- Ans: If two separated enantiomers have different effects, the biochemical molecules at the point of interaction with the thalidomide must be chiral. In fact, it is likely that the R and S isomers have their effects on completely different systems.

CHAPTER 18

Synthetic Polymers

I. Textbook Chapter Contents

This chapter describes how chemical reactions can be used to produce polymers—macromolecules in which many repeating units of one or more monomers are incorporated. It also describes the physical properties of polymers and how they relate to chemical structure.

II. Learning Objectives

- Explain the terms monomer, polymer, macromolecule, copolymer, linear polymer, branched polymer, cross-linking, elastomer, thermosetting polymer, thermoplastic polymer, addition polymerization, and condensation polymerization.

- Know the general requirements for and characteristics of crystalline and amorphous polymers.
- Be able to write a mechanism for the radical polymerization of alkenes. Be able to show the mechanism of chain transfer and how it produces branched polymers.
- Write an equation to represent the radical polymerization of a 1,3-conjugated diene.
- Be able to write mechanisms for the cationic and anionic polymerization of appropriately substituted alkenes.
- Be able to show the three-dimensional structure of an isotactic addition polymer and explain its special properties.
- Write an equation for the condensation polymerization of a diamine and a dicarboxylic acid to form a polyamide.
- Write an equation for the condensation polymerization of a diol and a dicarboxylic acid to form a polyester.
- Draw the general structure for a polycarbonate.
- Draw the general structure for a polyurethane.

III. Glossary

ABS plastic a copolymer of acrylonitrile, 1,3-butadiene, and styrene

acrilan a tradename for polyacrylonitrile

addition polymer a polymer usually formed from an alkene. All monomer units are connected end-to-end and all atoms present in the monomer are retained in the polymer. Also called a chain-growth polymer

amorphous polymer a polymer which is non-crystalline

anionic polymerization polymerization of alkenes using an anion (often a carbanion) as the initiator. It adds to the alkene producing a carbanion as the reactive intermediate which then propagates itself

aramid a polyamide in which an aromatic group connects the functional groups

atactic polymer a polymer with stereocenters in which the configurations occur randomly

block copolymer a copolymer in which there are segments of the polymer containing only one monomer. Usually produced by anionic polymerization

branched polymer a polymer in which branching occurs along the normal long continuous chain

cationic polymerization polymerization of alkenes using a Brønsted or Lewis acid as the initiator. It adds to the alkene producing a carbocation as the reactive intermediate which then propagates itself

chain reaction a polymerization reaction applied mainly to alkenes in which the propagation step (addition of a reactive intermediate to an alkene) produces a new reactive intermediate which can add to yet another monomer

chain terminator a compound added to a polymerization reaction to terminate the chain growth

chain transfer a growing radical chain abstracts a hydrogen atom from the interior of another chain, thereby creating a new radical propagation site in the interior of the chain

chain-growth polymer also called an addition polymer. The polymer grows at one end by addition to an alkene monomer

condensation polymer a polymer formed by a reaction between two different functional groups to form a new functional group. In most instances a small molecule, usually water, is ejected in the reaction

copolymer a polymer formed from two or three monomers

cross-linked polymer a polymer in which two or more chains become connected through a chemical reaction with another reagent

crystalline polymer a polymer whose structure is sufficiently ordered that it, or regions of it, crystallize

dacron a tradename for polyester fabrics

degradable plastic plastics which are especially susceptible to decomposition in the environment

elastomer an amorphous polymer with a coiled shape which gives it elastic properties

fiber a semi-crystalline polymer which is processed by drawing through a small orifice which increases the alignment of polymer molecules and its crystallinity

gutta percha *cis*-polyisoprene

HDPE high density polyethylene, a crystalline polyethylene produced using Ziegler-Natta catalysts

initiator a reagent which adds to an alkene to produce the initial reactive intermediate in the polymerization process

isocyanate a compound containing the -N=C=O group

isoprene 2-methyl-1,3-butadiene

isotactic polymer a polymer with stereocenters in which the configuration of each is identical

LDPE low density polyethylene, an amorphous polyethylene which includes considerable branching in the polymer

linear polymer a polymer in which the monomer units are connected end-to-end to form a single long chain

macromolecule a very large molecule, some of which are polymers of one-to-three different monomers (such as starch or ABS plastic), but others involve the connection between a large number of different, structurally-related, simple compounds (such as a protein)

monomer a simple compound which is capable of being joined to other molecules of itself to form a polymer

natural rubber *trans*-polyisoprene

neoprene the polymer produced from polymerization of 2-chloro-1,3-butadiene (chloroprene)

nylon a polyamide in which aliphatic groups connect the functional groups

oligomer a small polymer segment containing several monomer units already joined together

orlon a tradename for polyacrylonitrile

PET plastic crystalline poly(ethylene terephthalate)

plastic rigid materials fabricated from highly crystalline polymers

plexiglas a glass-like product fabricated from poly(methyl methacrylate)

poly(methyl methacrylate) the addition polymer produced from polymerization of methyl methacrylate (CH_2=C(CH_3)$COOCH_3$)

poly(vinyl chloride) the addition polymer (also known as PVC) produced from polymerization of vinyl chloride (CH_2=CHCl)

polyacrylonitrile the addition polymer produced from polymerization of acrylonitrile (CH_2=CHCN)

polyamide a condensation polymer in which the connecting functional group is an amide group (formed from a carboxyl group and a primary amino group)

polycarbonate a condensation polymer in which the connecting functional group is a diester of carbonic acid

polyester a condensation polymer in which the connecting functional group is an ester

polyethylene the addition polymer produced from polymerization of ethylene (CH_2=CH_2)

polymer one kind of macromolecule comprised of a large number of a repeating simple molecule

polymerization the process of converting a monomer into a polymer

polystyrene the addition polymer formed from addition polymerization of styrene (C_6H_5CH=CH_2)

polyurethane the condensation polymer containing the urethane functional group (-NH-CO-O-, the ester-amide of carbonic acid)

propagation the second step in a chain reaction in which the intermediate formed in the initiation step reacts with another molecule of monomer

PVC an abbreviation for poly(vinyl chloride)

radical polymerization polymerization using a radical initiator

recycling as applied to polymers this is the process of recapturing discarded thermoplastics and fabricating new products

resin a thermosetting polymer formed from a viscous glass polymer

rubber an elastomer polymer having properties similar to natural rubber

SBR rubber rubber that is copolymer of styrene and butadiene

step-growth polymer another term for a condensation polymer. It grows one reaction and product at a time, rather than by a chain reaction

teflon an addition polymer produced from tetrafluoroethylene (CF_2=CF_2)

termination the process by which a chain reaction is terminated, usually by conversion of a reactive intermediate into a neutral compound which is unable to continue the propagation

terylene a tradename (used mainly in Europe) for polyester fabrics

thermoplastic a polymer that can be re-melted and re-shaped

thermosetting a polymer that once cast into a shape cannot be re-melted and recycled

vulcanization a process of cross-linking synthetic or natural rubber by reaction with sulfur. This produces a harder and more heat-stable polymer

IV. Solutions to Problems

For "**How to Solve a Problem**," review page 655.

18.1   A protein is a polymer of α-amino acids, with each R- group being one of 22 possible group structures.

$$\left[HN - \overset{\overset{\displaystyle R}{|}}{CH} - CO \right]_n$$

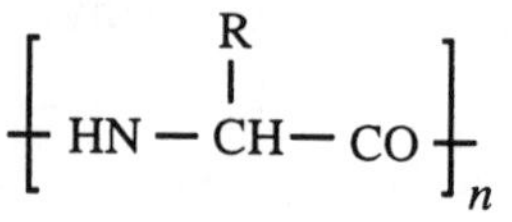

18.2   (a) The regiochemistry is determined in the initiation step by the addition of the radical initiator at the terminal alkene carbon because it forms the most stable radical intermediate, a benzylic radical.

$$C_6H_5CH{=\!=}CH_2 \xrightarrow{\ \cdot R\ } \left[C_6H_5\overset{\cdot}{C}H - CH_2R \right] \xrightarrow{styrene} \left[\underset{\overset{|}{C_6H_5}}{CH} - CH_2 \right]_n R$$

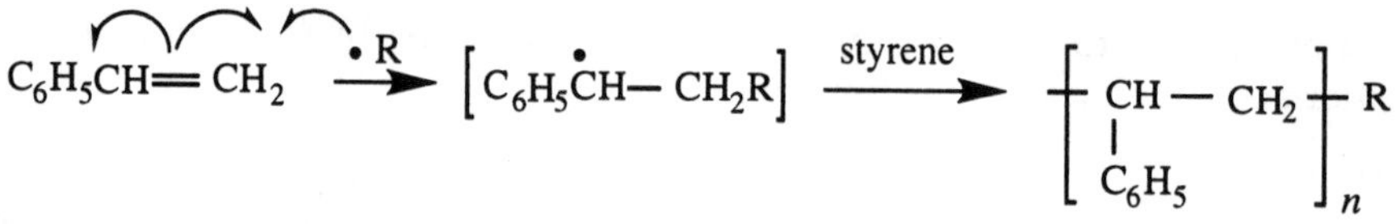

(b) The regiochemistry is determined in the initiation step by the addition of the proton to the terminal methylene group because that results in the most stable of the possible carbocations, the *t*-butyl cation.

$$(CH_3)_2C{=\!=}CH_2 \xrightarrow{\ H^+\ } \left[(CH_3)_2\overset{+}{C} - CH_3 \right] \xrightarrow{isobutylene} \left[\underset{\overset{|}{CH_3}}{\overset{\overset{\displaystyle CH_3}{|}}{C}} - CH_2 \right]_n H$$

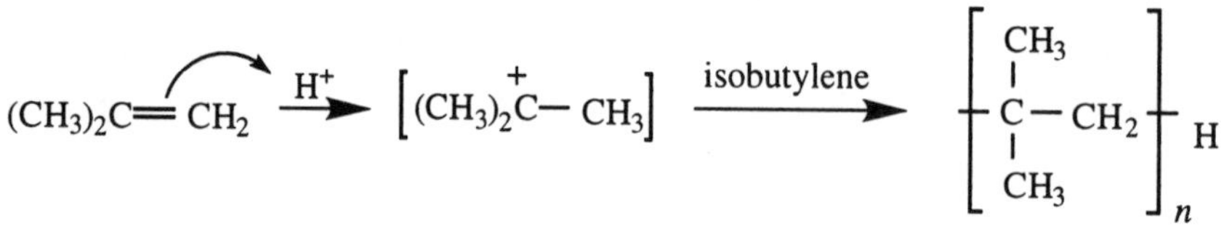

(c) The regiochemistry is determined in the initiation step by the addition of a carbanion at the methylene carbon because that results in a resonance stabilized cyanocarbanion.

$$CH_2{=\!=}CHCN \xrightarrow{\ R:^-\ } \left[RCH_2 - \overset{..}{\overset{-}{C}}HCN \right] \xrightarrow{acrylonitrile} R\left[CH_2 - \underset{\overset{|}{CN}}{CH} \right]_n$$

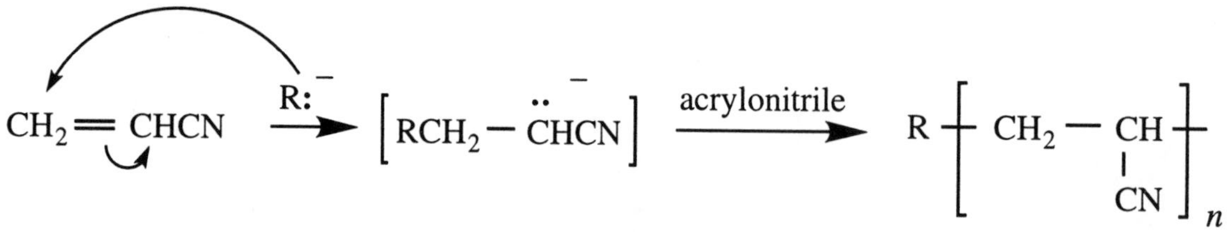

18.3   Polystyrene contains alkyl-substituted benzene rings which undergo normal aromatic substitution reactions. Therefore, sulfonation would attach sulfonic acid groups to each ring, mainly at the para position. Treatment with sodium hydroxide would effect an acid-base reaction and produce the sodium sulfonate.

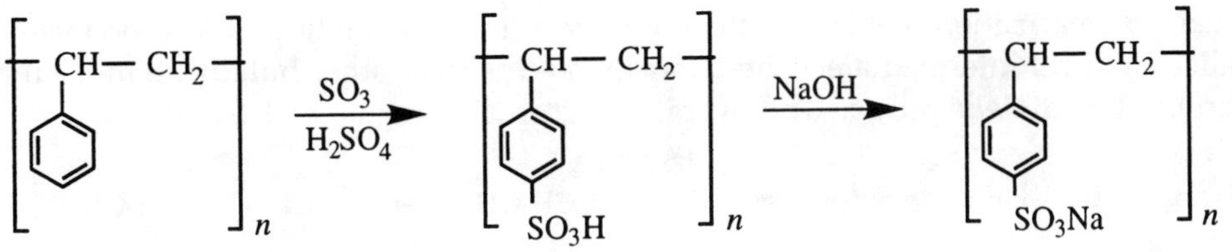

18.4 The monomers needed for these preparations are (a) $CH_2{=}C(CH_3)COOCH_3$; (b) $CH_2{=}CHC_6H_5$ and $CH_2{=}CHCN$; (c) $CH_2{=}CH{-}CH{=}CH_2$.

18.5 The regiochemistry of acid-catalyzed polymerization of styrene is determined in the initiation step which involves addition of a proton at the terminal methylene group to form a resonance-stabilized benzylic carbocation. The propagation step, in which this benzylic carbocation is attacked by another molecule of styrene, involves the same regiochemistry for the same reason, the formation of the most stabilized carbocation intermediate. Therefore, the polymer chain grows from right to left.

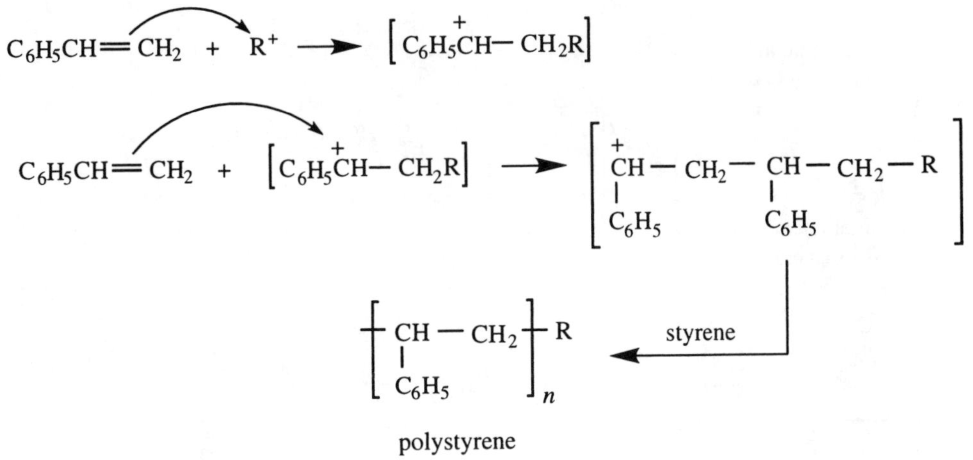

18.6 The regiochemistry for the anionic polymerization of methyl acrylate is determined in the initiation step. The carbanion initiator adds to the methylene carbon to form a carbanion intermediate which is stabilized by delocalization into the ester carbonyl group.

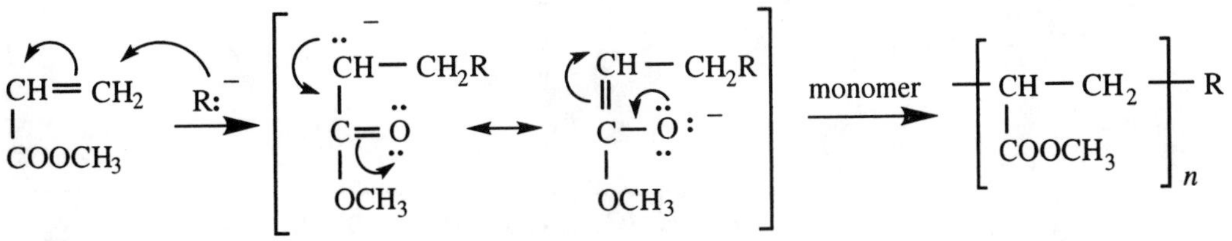

18.7 Radical polymerization of 1,3-butadiene involves initial formation of a resonance-stabilized radical intermediate. The latter then adds to another butadiene molecule using its terminal methylene group. The overall effect is a conjugate or 1,4-addition.

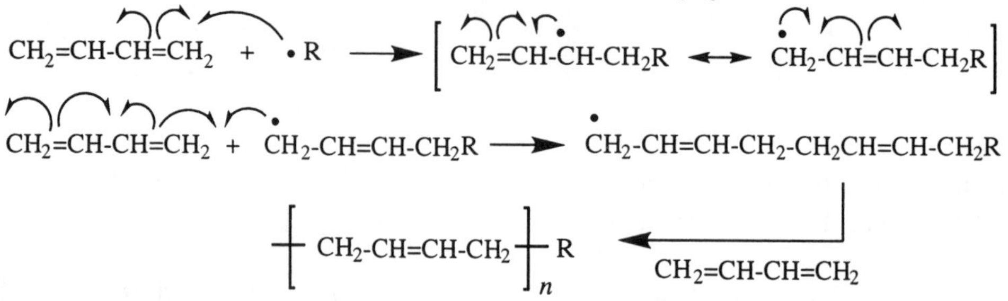
CH2=CH-CH=CH2 + •R
CH2=CH-CH-CH2R
CH2-CH=CH-CH2R
CH2=CH-CH=CH2 + CH2-CH=CH-CH2R
CH2-CH=CH-CH2-CH2CH=CH-CH2R
CH2-CH=CH-CH2 R n
CH2=CH-CH=CH2

18.8 The name of the polymers, Nylon-4,4 and Nylon-4, indicates the monomers are four-carbon units. Thus, what is needed for polymer (a) is a four-carbon diacid and a four-carbon diamine as monomers. For polymer (b) what is needed is a four-carbon lactam, γ-butyrolactam.

(a)

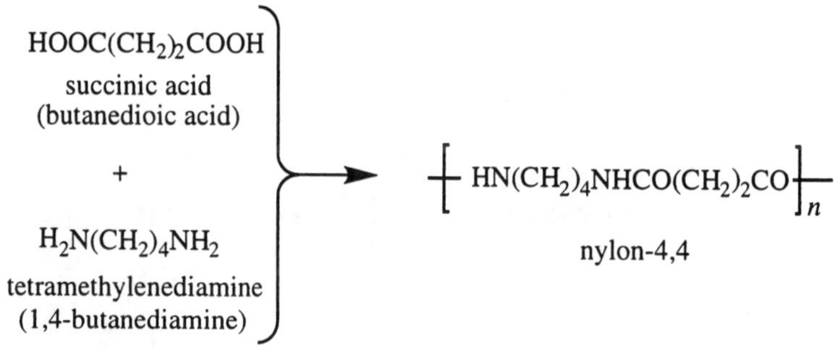
HOOC(CH2)2COOH
succinic acid
(butanedioic acid)
+
H2N(CH2)4NH2
tetramethylenediamine
(1,4-butanediamine)
HN(CH2)4NHCO(CH2)2CO
n
nylon-4,4

(b)

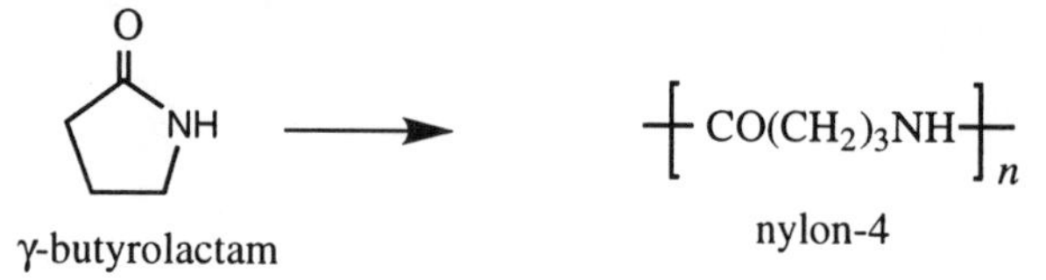
O
NH
γ-butyrolactam
CO(CH2)3NH
n
nylon-4

18.9

(a)

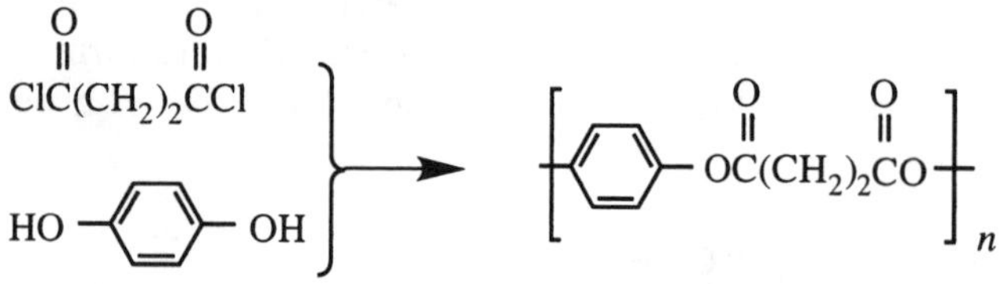
O O
ClC(CH2)2CCl
HO OH
O O
OC(CH2)2CO
n

(b)

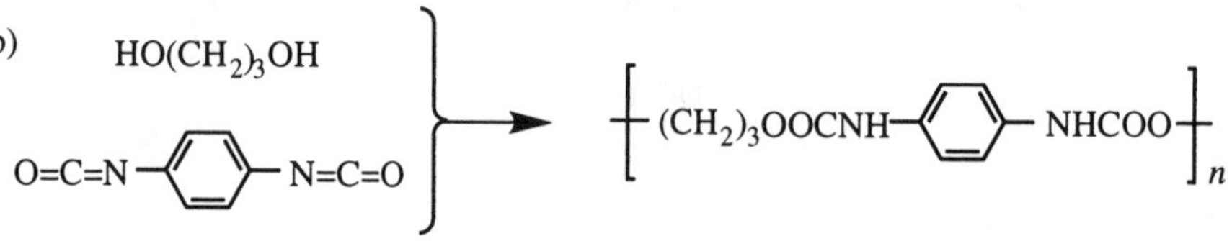
HO(CH2)3OH
O=C=N N=C=O
(CH2)3OOCNH NHCOO
n

18.10 (a) a linear polymer is one in which the "backbone" of the polymer has no branching.

(b) a cross-linked polymer is one in which linear chains have been joined by chemical bonds.

(c) an addition polymer is one which has been formed by the addition of one monomer to the multiple bond of another in a chain reaction. No atoms are lost in the process of forming an addition polymer.

(d) a condensation polymer is one formed by the reaction between two functional groups to form a new functional group, often accompanied by the elimination of the elements of a simple compound, usually water.

18.11 (a) a simple polymer of $CH_2=CHCl$.
(b) a copolymer of $CH_2=CHCl$ and $Cl_2C=CCl_2$.
(c) a simple polymer of $H_2C=O$.
(d) a copolymer of $HOCH_2CH_2OH$ and $HOOC(CH_2)_4COOH$.
(e) a copolymer of $HOCH_2CH_2OH$ and $HOOCC_6H_4COOH$ (*p*).
(f) a simple polymer of $CH_2=CCl\text{-}CH=CH_2$.

18.12 (a) a polymer is a plastic if it can be formed into rigid structures. This requires the presence of significant crystallinity and/or considerable cross-linking.

(b) a fiber is a form of a polymer which has been melted then drawn through a fine hole to produce a "thread" which has the polymer molecules aligned parallel to each other.

(c) an elastomer is a polymer which is amorphous (that is, non-crystalline) and whose natural shape is coiled. Such a polymer can be stretched but it returns to its original shape.

(d) a thermoplastic polymer is one which can be re-melted and re-shaped.

(e) a thermosetting polymer is one which cannot be re-melted and re-shaped.

(f) a crystalline polymer is one which has areas of crystallinity (that is, the atoms are highly ordered with respect to each other and the molecules are packed tightly into a crystal lattice).

(g) an amorphous polymer is one which is non-crystalline.

18.13 The *E* double bond of gutta percha means the entire polymer is relatively linear and regularly shaped, leading to its ability to pack into crystal lattices (that is, the polymer chains can be "stacked" upon each other in a regular manner). Therefore, gutta percha is a crystalline polymer and therefore not an elastomer. In contrast, the *Z* double bond of natural rubber produces a coiled shape which is less able to crystallize and so remains amorphous. The coiling presents the possibility of being stretched (uncoiled), leading to the property of elasticity.

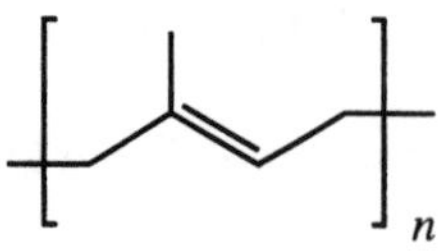

E-polyisoprene
(gutta percha)

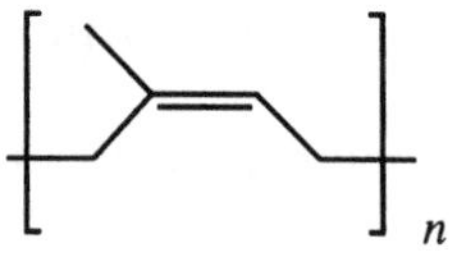

Z-polyisoprene
(natural rubber)

18.14 An isotactic polymer is one in which the configuration about the stereocenter (occurring on every second carbon in the chain) is the same. In order to produce an isotactic polymer the monomer alkene must have a single substituent, such as in propene ($CH_3CH{=}CH_2$) and styrene ($C_6H_5CH{=}CH_2$). It is the carbon carrying the single substituent which becomes a stereocenter upon polymerization.

18.15 Polyisobutylene cannot show isotacticity because the polymer does not contain a stereocenter.

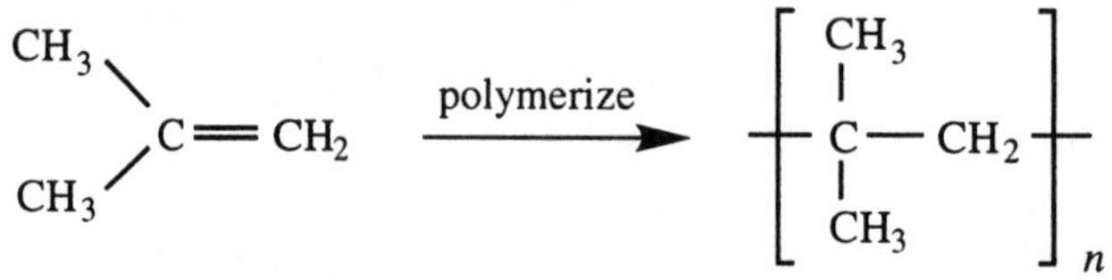
polymerize

isobutylene polyisobutylene

18.16

(a) 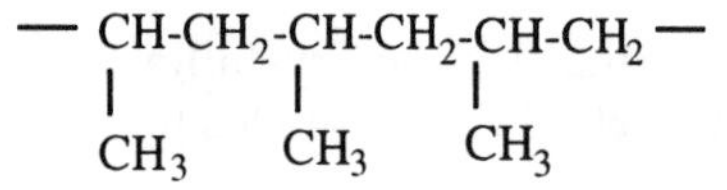

polypropylene

(b) 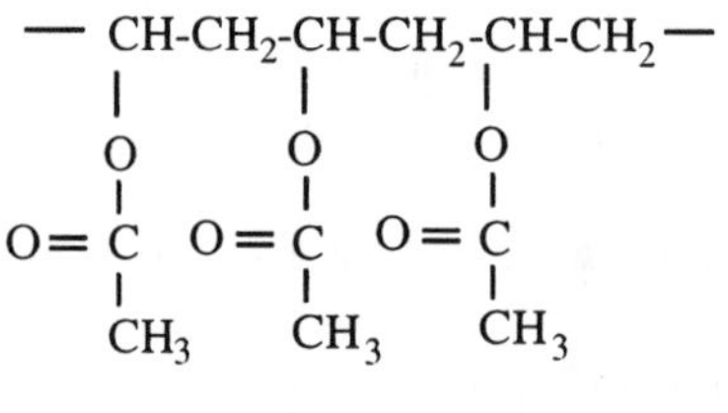

polyvinylacetate

(c) 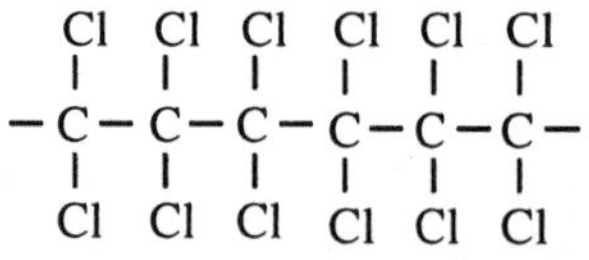

polytetrachloroethane

18.17 The initiation steps are as follows:

(a) 

(b) 

(c) 

18.18

$$ClCH=CH_2 \ + \ \cdot R \longrightarrow Cl\overset{\bullet}{C}H-CH_2-R$$

$$ClCH=CH_2 \ + \ Cl\overset{\bullet}{C}H-CH_2-R \longrightarrow \left[Cl\overset{\bullet}{C}H-CH_2-\underset{Cl}{\overset{|}{C}H}-CH_2-R \right]$$

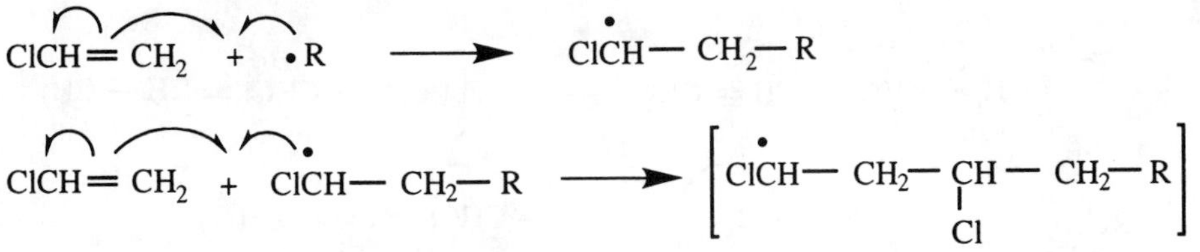

18.19   The regiochemistry of the styrene polymerization is determined in the initiation step in which the initiating electrophile (R^+) is attacked by the styrene double bond to form a benzylic carbocation (that is, the R^+ adds to the "head" of the styrene double bond). In the propagation step, which involves a carbocation adding to another styrene double bond, the same regiochemistry results for the same reason—the most stable carbocation will be formed. If the addition were tail-to-tail in the propagation step a much less stable primary carbocation would be formed and the phenyl group could not participate in stabilization of that carbocation by resonance.

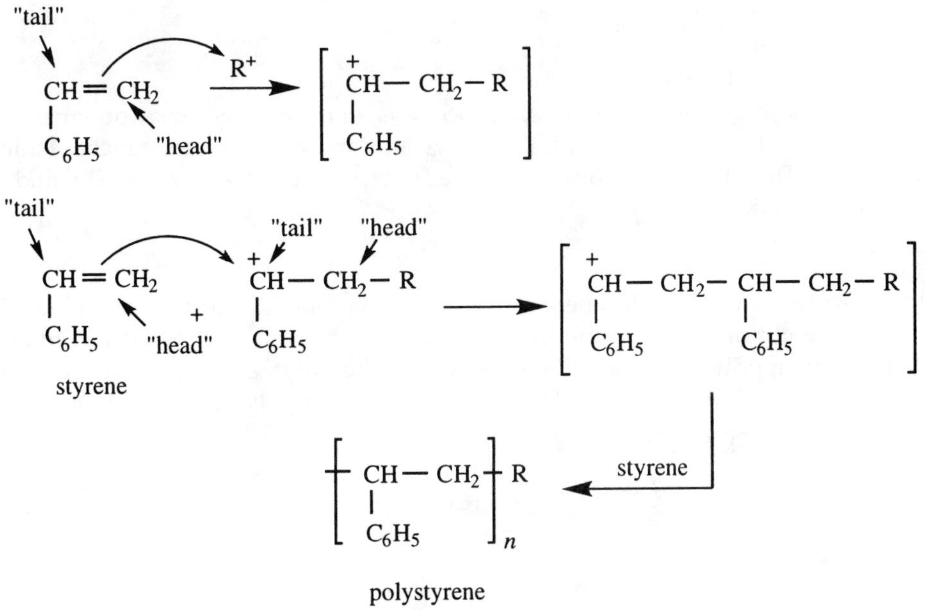

"tail"

$$\underset{C_6H_5}{\overset{|}{CH}}=CH_2 \quad \overset{R^+}{\longrightarrow} \quad \left[\overset{+}{\underset{C_6H_5}{\overset{|}{CH}}}-CH_2-R \right]$$

"head"

"tail"   "tail"   "head"

$$\underset{C_6H_5}{\overset{|}{CH}}=CH_2 \quad + \quad \overset{+}{\underset{C_6H_5}{\overset{|}{CH}}}-CH_2-R \longrightarrow \left[\overset{+}{\underset{C_6H_5}{\overset{|}{CH}}}-CH_2-\underset{C_6H_5}{\overset{|}{CH}}-CH_2-R \right]$$

"head"

styrene

$$\left[\!\!\!- \underset{C_6H_5}{\overset{|}{CH}}-CH_2 -\!\!\!\right]_{\!n} R \quad \xleftarrow{\text{styrene}}$$

polystyrene

18.20

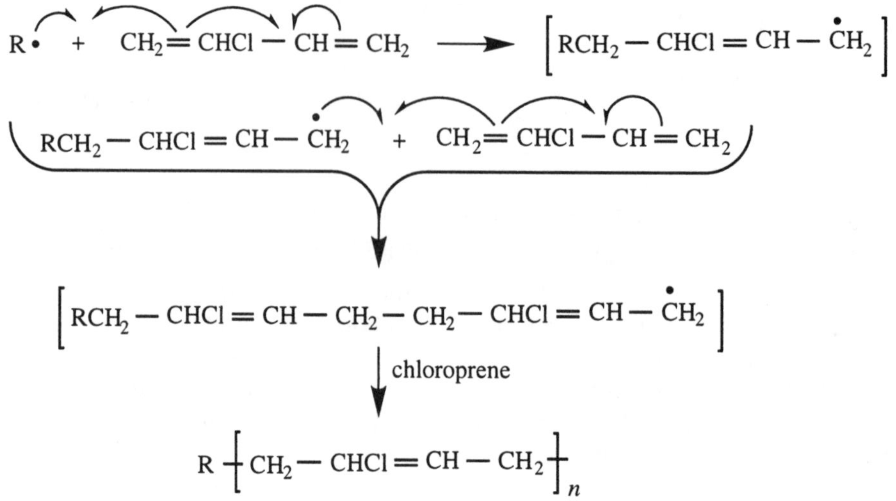
R• + CH2=CHCl—CH=CH2
[RCH2—CHCl=CH—CH2•]
RCH2—CHCl=CH—CH2• + CH2=CHCl—CH=CH2
[RCH2—CHCl=CH—CH2—CH2—CHCl=CH—CH2•]
chloroprene
R—[CH2—CHCl=CH—CH2]n

neoprene

18.21 HDPE, produced by the Zeigler-Natta process, is an absolutely linear polymer - the polymer is a continuous chain of methylene groups and there are no branches (side chains or cross links). Therefore, the molecule can be "packed" tightly and regularly, and therefore is highly crystalline.

18.22 If the polymerization of isoprene involved considerable 1,2-addition as well as the expected 1,4-addition there would result vinyl side chains, and these also could enter into radical addition polymerization. In other words, the polymer could grow in two directions, from C2 and C4. The result would be a highly branched polymer which would therefore be amorphous, not crystalline.

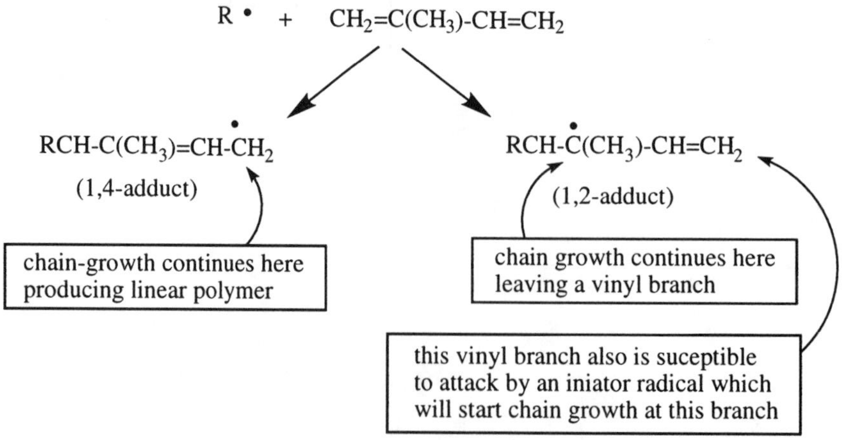
R• + CH2=C(CH3)-CH=CH2
RCH-C(CH3)=CH-CH2•
(1,4-adduct)
RCH-C•(CH3)-CH=CH2
(1,2-adduct)
chain-growth continues here
producing linear polymer
chain growth continues here
leaving a vinyl branch
this vinyl branch also is suceptible
to attack by an iniator radical which
will start chain growth at this branch

18.23 Assuming that the copolymer involves the two monomers appearing alternately in the polymer chain, which is not always a valid assumption, the repeating unit of the copolymer is as follows:

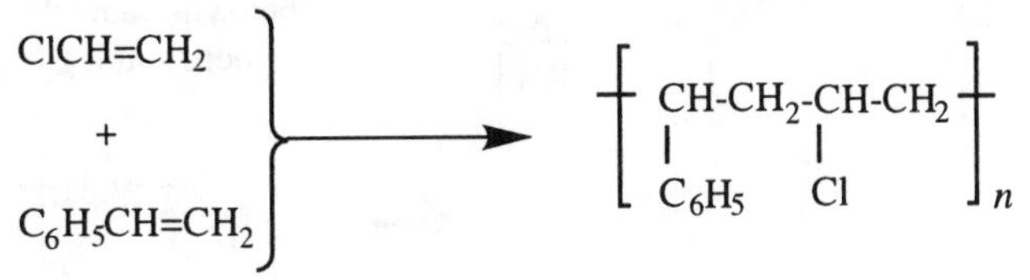
ClCH=CH2
+
C6H5CH=CH2
CH-CH2-CH-CH2
C6H5
Cl
n

18.24 (a) The mechanism of the formation of polyisobutylene is as follows:

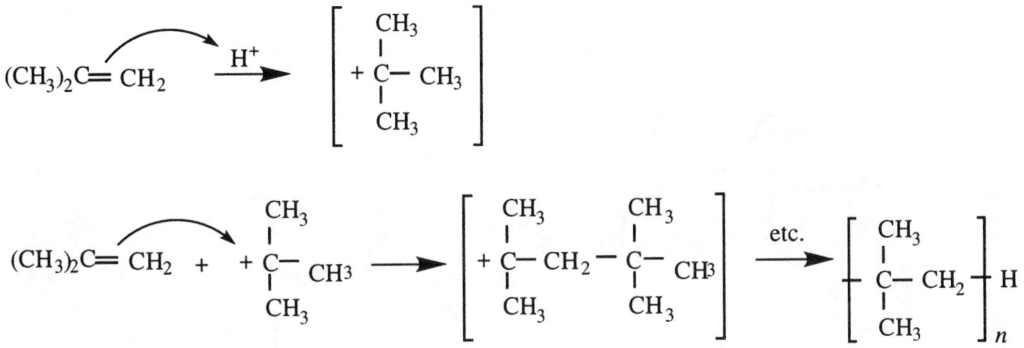
(CH3)2C= CH2
H+
CH3
+ C— CH3
CH3
etc.
CH2
H
n

(b) Polyisobutylene is an addition polymer.
(c) This is a head-to-tail polymer.
(d) The carbocation intermediate is tertiary, the most stable alkyl carbocation, which is stabilized by hyperconjugation and which therefore forms readily. If an anionic initiator were employed, the intermediate resulting from its addition would be a carbanion for which there is no delocalization in this structure.

18.25 The two hydrogens potentially removable by an attacking radical (in chain transfer) are the methinyl hydrogen (on the carbon carrying the phenyl ring) and the methylenic hydrogen. When a hydrogen is removed a new radical will be formed (either a benzylic radical or a secondary radical), and the lowest energy of activation will be for the formation of the most stable radical. Removal of a methinyl hydrogen produces a benzylic radical, which is the more stable of the two because it is stabilized by resonance. Therefore, it is the methinyl hydrogen which is removed and it is from the methinyl carbon that a new chain will grow by addition of this benzylic radical to styrene monomer.

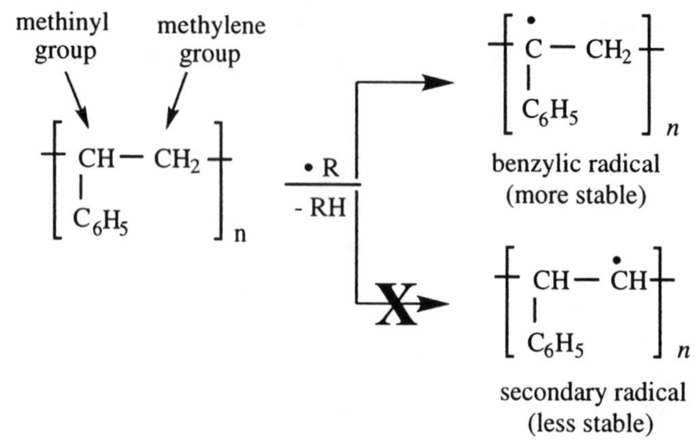
methinyl group
methylene group
• R
- RH
benzylic radical (more stable)
secondary radical (less stable)

18.26

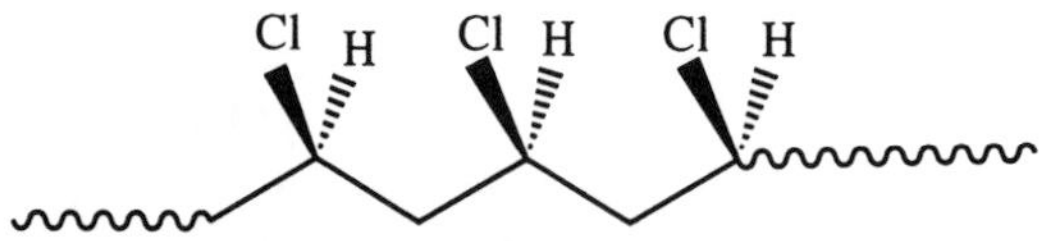

isotactic polyvinyl chloride

18.27

(a) $HOOC(CH_2)_2COOH$ (succinic acid) + $H_2N(CH_2)_3NH_2$ (1,3-propanediamine) $\longrightarrow$ $-\!\!\![\, OC(CH_2)_2CONH(CH_2)_3NH \,]\!\!\!-_n$

(b) $BrCH_2CH_2CH_2Br \xrightarrow{NaN_3} N_3CH_2CH_2CH_2N_3 \xrightarrow{LiAlH_4} H_2NCH_2CH_2CH_2NH_2$

18.28

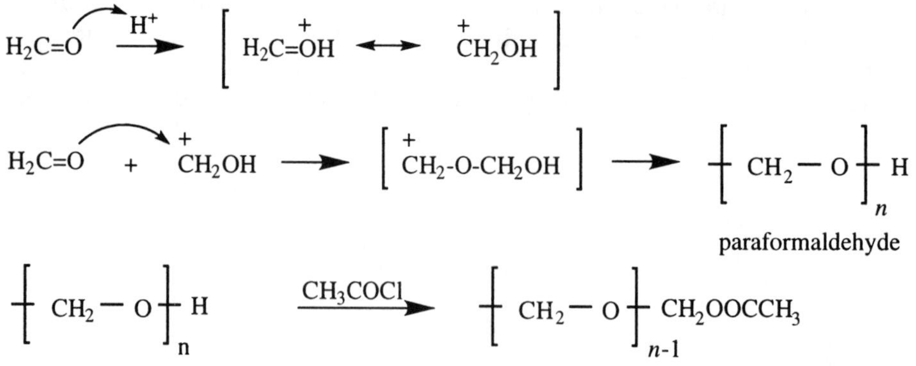
paraformaldehyde

18.29

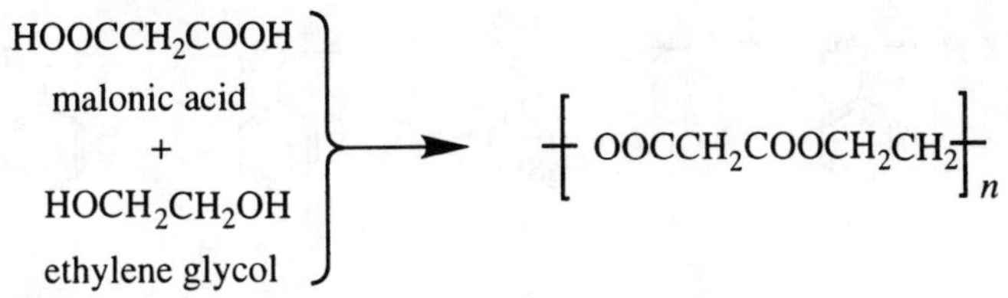
HOOCCH2COOH
malonic acid
+
HOCH2CH2OH
ethylene glycol
OOCCH2COOCH2CH2
n

18.30

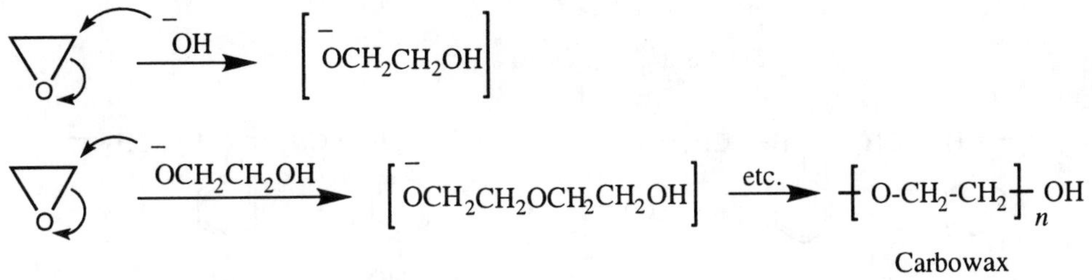
OH
OCH2CH2OH
OCH2CH2OH
OCH2CH2OCH2CH2OH
etc.
O-CH2-CH2
n
OH
Carbowax

18.31

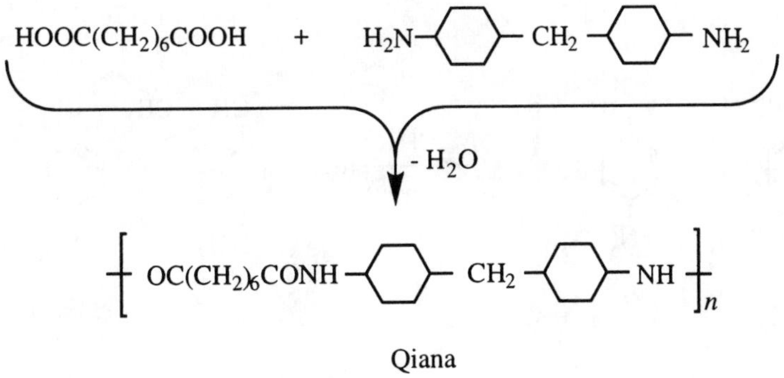
HOOC(CH2)6COOH
+
H2N
CH2
NH2
- H2O
OC(CH2)6CONH
CH2
NH
n
Qiana

18.32

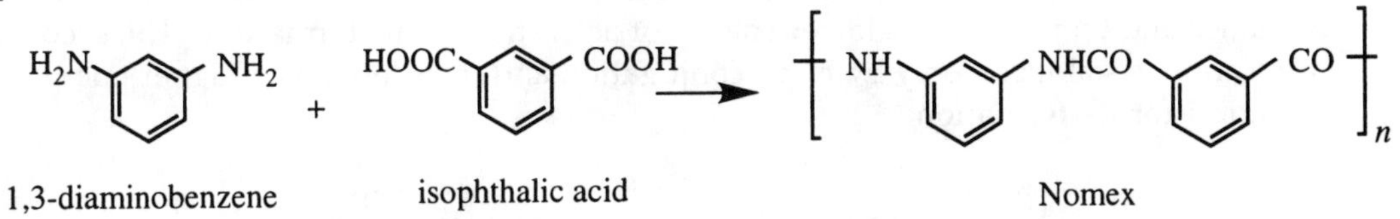
H2N
NH2
+
HOOC
COOH
NH
NHCO
CO
n
1,3-diaminobenzene
isophthalic acid
Nomex

18.33

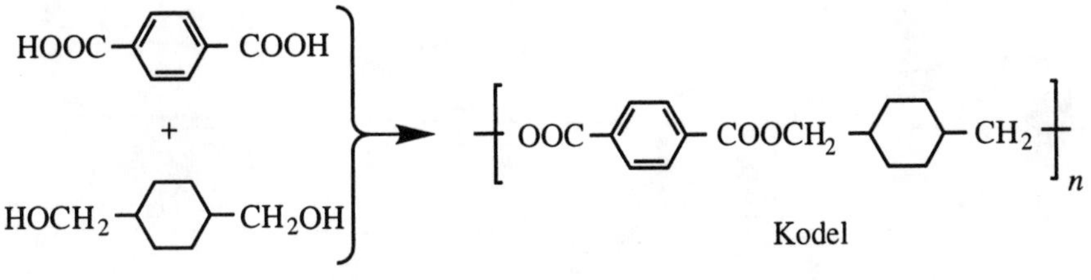
HOOC
COOH
+
HOCH2
CH2OH
OOC
COOCH2
CH2
n
Kodel

18.34

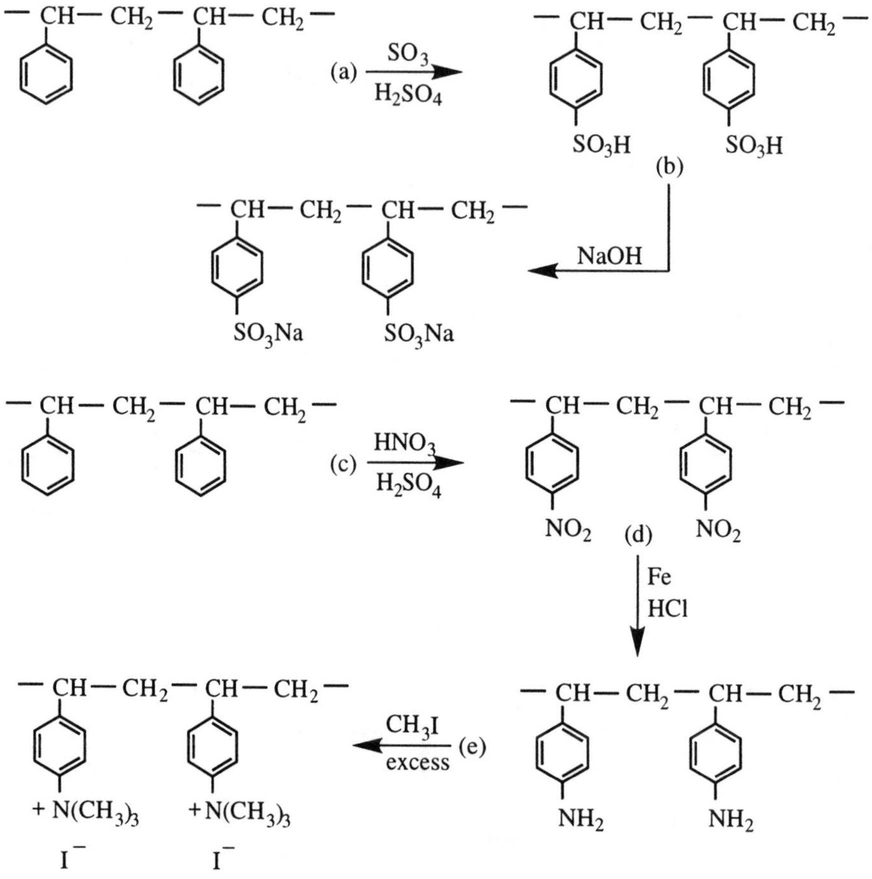
SO3
(a)
H2SO4
SO3H
SO3H
(b)
NaOH
SO3Na
SO3Na
HNO3
(c)
H2SO4
NO2
(d)
NO2
Fe
HCl
CH3I
excess
(e)
+N(CH3)3
I−
+N(CH3)3
I−
NH2
NH2

18.35 Protonation of propene in the initiation step produces a secondary isopropyl carbocation whereas protonation of styrene produces a benzylic carbocation. The latter is stabilized by resonance and therefore has a lower energy of activation for its formation. The secondary carbocation is stabilized only by hyperconjugation and therefore has a higher energy of activation for its formation.

$$\underset{\text{propene}}{CH_3CH{=}CH_2} \xrightarrow{H^+} (CH_3)_2\overset{+}{C}H \qquad \underset{\text{styrene}}{C_6H_5CH{=}CH_2} \xrightarrow{H^+} C_6H_5\overset{+}{C}HCH_3$$

18.36

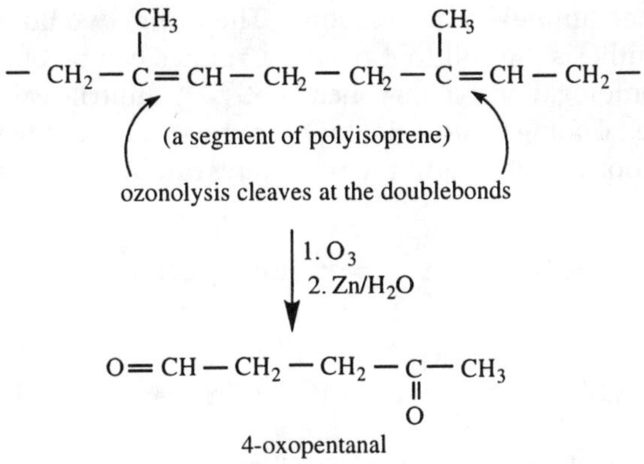

(a segment of polyisoprene)
ozonolysis cleaves at the doublebonds
1. O_3
2. Zn/H_2O
4-oxopentanal

***18.37** Apply your retrosynthetic skills to this problem. The final ester can be obtained from a precursor acid (methacrylic acid) by ordinary Fischer esterification with methanol. Then considering the structure of the starting material acetone and the needed methacrylic acid, it is clear the methylene group and the methyl group of the latter must arise from the methyl groups of acetone. Thus, a means must be found to introduce a double bond (often by an elimination reaction) and a carboxyl group (from either a bromide and carboxylation or a nitrile). The nitrile precursor can be obtained by HCN addition to acetone (to form acetone cyanohydrin), which also contains a hydroxyl group which can be used in dehydration (elimination) to form the methylene group.

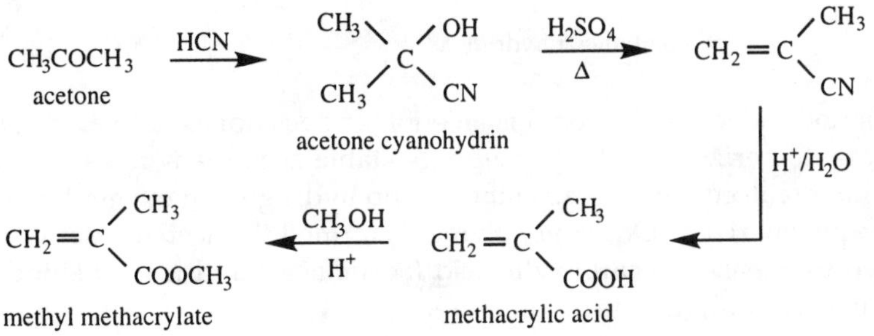

acetone
HCN
acetone cyanohydrin
H_2SO_4
Δ
H^+/H_2O
methacrylic acid
CH_3OH
H^+
methyl methacrylate

18.38

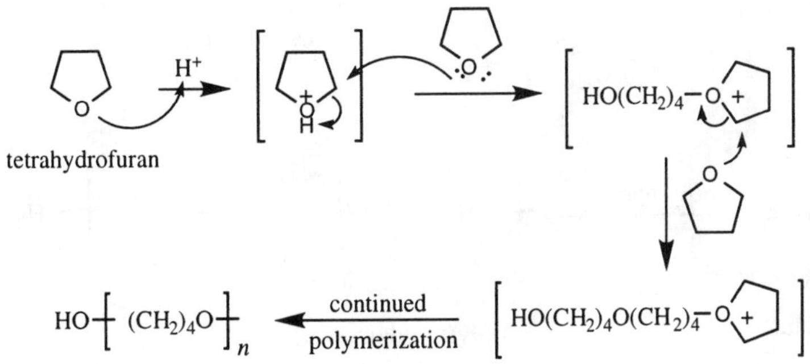

tetrahydrofuran
H^+
continued
polymerization

***18.39** First, notice that the starting compound (1,3-butadiene) has four carbons while the desired product (1,6-hexanediamine) has six carbons. Therefore, two homologations must be included in the synthesis. Recall that primary amines can be obtained from nitriles by reduction and a homologation occurs concurrently. A dinitrile can be obtained from 1,4-dibromobutane. Conjugate addition of bromine to 1,3-butadiene attaches a bromine to each end of the carbon skeleton, and the remaining double bond can be hydrogenated.

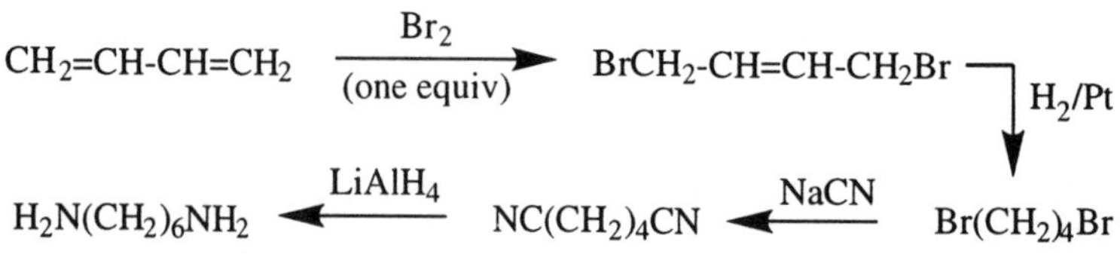
CH_2=CH-CH=CH_2
Br_2
(one equiv)
$BrCH_2$-CH=CH-CH_2Br
H_2/Pt
$Br(CH_2)_4Br$
NaCN
$NC(CH_2)_4CN$
$LiAlH_4$
$H_2N(CH_2)_6NH_2$

18.40 Glyptal, formed from the reaction of phthalic anhydride with glycerol, is a condensation polymer. An alcohol reacts with an anhydride in an alcoholysis reaction. Therefore, Glyptal is a polyester formed by reaction of a hydroxyl group of the triol with the anhydride group. The initial step is shown here. Since each hydroxyl group of the triol is capable of effecting the same reaction, a highly cross-linked polymer results. It is a thermosetting polymer.

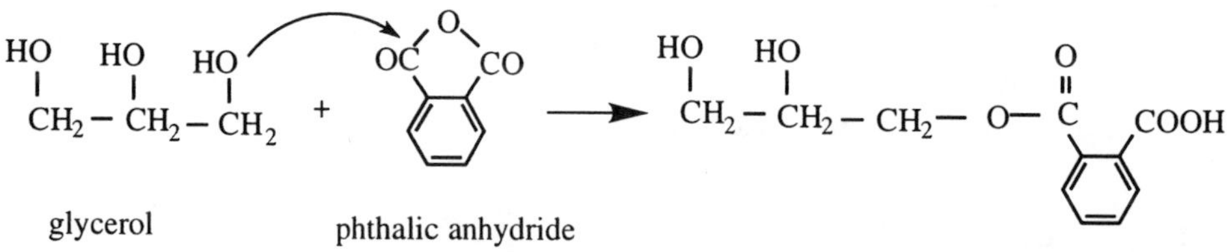
glycerol
phthalic anhydride

18.41 The compound called vinyl alcohol is an enol. It does not exist to any significant degree because it tautomerizes rapidly to the more stable acetaldehyde as shown below. Vinyl acetate cannot tautomerize (because there is no hydrogen on oxygen) and therefore is stable and can be polymerized. Once the polymer is formed the acetate ester grouping can be hydrolyzed to release the carboxylic acid (acetic acid) and leave behind the alcohol group on poly(vinyl alcohol) (no longer an enol).

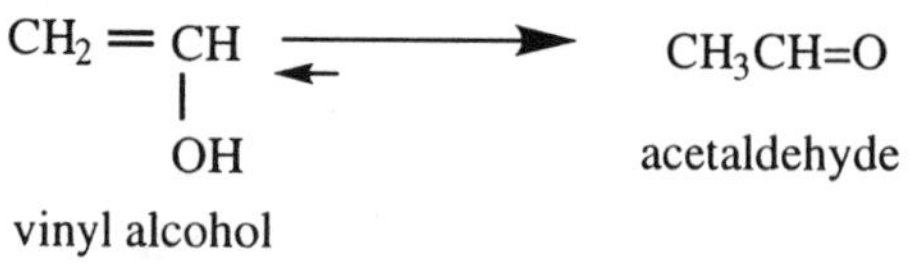
vinyl alcohol
acetaldehyde

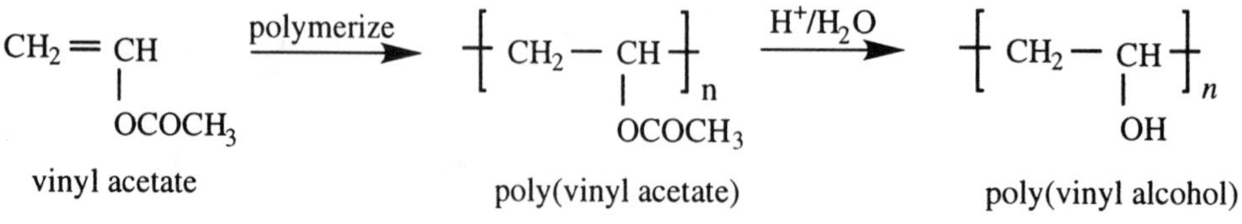
polymerize
H^+/H_2O
vinyl acetate
poly(vinyl acetate)
poly(vinyl alcohol)

18.42 This polymerization occurs so readily because the energy of activation is very low for the polymerization. It is low because the intermediate carbanion formed in the initiating step is highly stabilized, able to be delocalized through the ester group and through the cyano group. Therefore, the energy of activation for carbanion formation is very low.

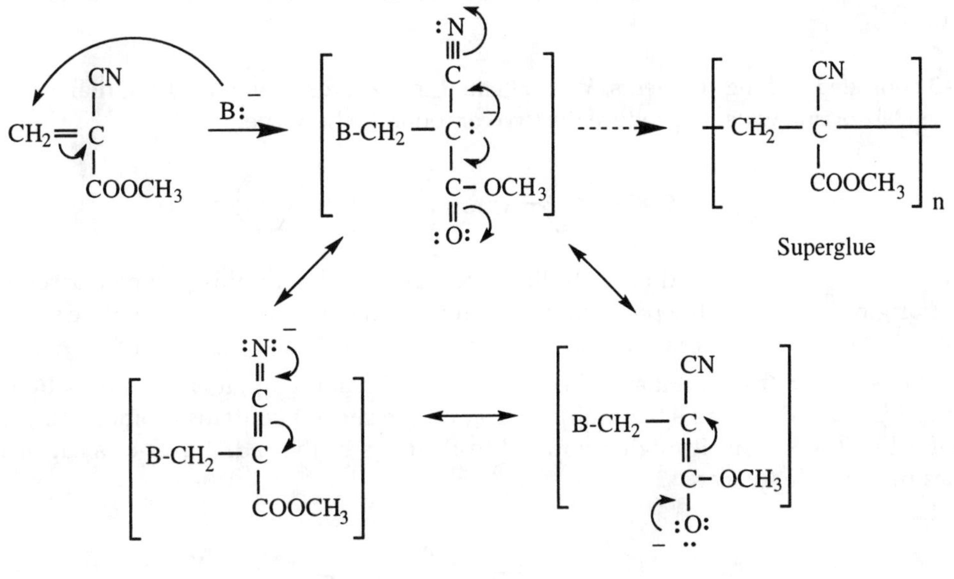
CN
CH_2=C
$COOCH_3$
B:⁻
B-CH_2 — C:
:N
C
C- OCH_3
:O:
CN
CH_2 — C
$COOCH_3$
n
Superglue
:N:
C
B-CH_2 — C
$COOCH_3$
CN
B-CH_2 — C
C- OCH_3
:O:

V. Concept Problem

Knowing Your Polymer

A materials scientist working for an auto manufacturer was considering some polymer samples for use in the new models. Unfortunately the shipment of samples had been in a warehouse in a coastal city when a hurricane hit, and the labels had come off all the samples when the warehouse flooded. Our expert decided to examine the samples anyway.

- Sample #1 was a hard solid. When it was heated strongly, even in the absence of air, it decomposed rather than melting. (a) Give two different classifications for this polymer based on its bulk properties. (b) What feature of its molecular structure is responsible for its physical properties?
  - Ans: (a) It is a plastic, a thermosetting polymer. (b) Its molecular structure would be highly cross-linked and inflexible.

■ Sample #2 was stretchable and flexible, and it returned to its original shape when released. (a) Classify this polymer based on its bulk properties. (b) What structural feature is responsible for its physical properties? (c) Where in a car is this material most likely to be used?

- Ans: (a) It is an elastomer. (b) Its molecules have a coiled structure, possibly caused by the presence of *cis* double bonds that allow it to stretch and return to its original form. (c) Probably the tires.

Sample #3 consisted of long filaments. When heated in the presence of acid the filaments decomposed, absorbing water to produce the two compounds shown below.

■ (a) Classify this polymer based on its bulk properties. (b) Classify this polymer based on its mode of origin. (c) Classify the polymer based on the functional groups present. (d) Identify the specific polymer used. Where in the car is this material most likely to be used?

- Ans: (a) It is a fiber. (b) Since it absorbed water when breaking up, it is a condensation polymer. (c) It is a polyamide, more specifically an aramid (because it contains aromatic rings). (d) Specifically, it is Kevlar. It might be found in the belts of the radial tires of a car or in the fabrics used inside the car.

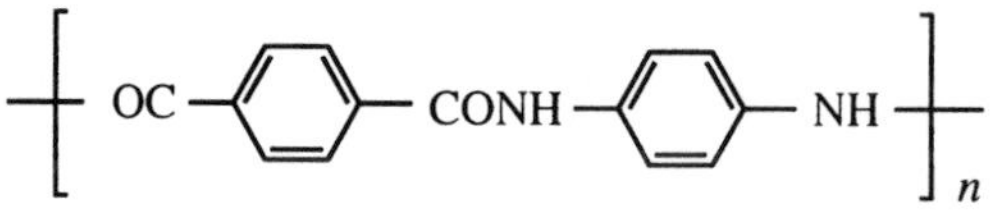

Kevlar

CHAPTER 19

Introduction to Biological Chemistry

I. Textbook Chapter Contents

Three topics from the field of biological chemistry are presented as illustrations and an introduction to the field. Included are discussions of nucleic acids, metabolism, and chemical therapies.

II. Learning Objectives

- Explain the terms nucleic acid, nucleotide, nucleoside, ribose, 2-deoxyribose.

- Distinguish between a purine base and a pyrimidine base.
- Know the abbreviations for the four DNA bases and the four RNA bases.
- Write equations for the step-wise hydrolysis of a nucleotide into its three components.
- Explain the differences between DNA and RNA. Be able to draw a schematic version of DNA and RNA. Describe the difference between the informational strand and the template strand of DNA.
- Explain the term double helix and be able to show the role of hydrogen bonding in its structure.
- Explain and schematically illustrate the terms replication, transcription, and translation.
- Explain the terms messenger RNA (mRNA) and transfer RNA (tRNA) and describe their roles in protein biosynthesis.
- Write a schematic representation of protein biosynthesis.
- Explain the terms gene, genetic code, triad, codon, and anti-codon.
- Given the base sequence of two adjacent triads on the template strand of DNA, deduce the structure of the dipeptide which would result from protein biosynthesis (using Table 19.1 for assistance).
- Explain the terms gene therapy and genetic engineering.
- Explain the terms metabolism, anabolism, catabolism, acetyl-CoA, and ATP.
- Know the overall transformation of the Embden-Meyerhoff pathway from glucose to pyruvic acid.
- Write the equation for the conversion of pyruvic acid to acetyl-CoA.
- Know the overall transformation involved in the Krebs cycle.
- Know the overall transformation of fats into acetyl-CoA.
- Know the concept behind the deamination of α-amino acids and the body's storage of nitrogen.
- Know the inter-relationships between carbohydrate, fat, and protein in their catabolism and anabolism. Be able to represent these relationships schematically.
- Know the principles behind a histamine blocker.
- Know the principles behind an anti-metabolite.
- Know the principle behind the application of chemicals to retard malignant growth.

- Explain the terms antibiotic and anti-viral agent.
- Explain the difference between the terms HIV and AIDS.
- Explain the terms reverse transcriptase inhibitor (RTI) and protease inhibitor.

III. Glossary

acetyl-CoA (CH_3CO-S-CoA) an acetyl group attached through a thiol ester linkage to coenzyme A.

anabolism equivalent to biosynthesis, the chemical processes by which the body synthesizes needed biochemicals

anti-codon a triplet of bases on tRNA which recognizes and hydrogen bonds with a codon on mRNA

anti-metabolite a compound similar enough to an essential chemical that it will be complexed by the active site of an enzyme system, thereby blocking complexation with the essential chemical and inhibiting the essential enzymatic process

anti-viral agent a chemical which kills or inhibits the functioning of a virus

antibiotic a chemical which kills bacteria responsible for infections. Examples are sulfa drugs (anti-metabolites) and lactam drugs such as penicillins and cephalosporin derivatives, both of which inhibit closure of bacterial cell walls

ATP adenosine triphosphate, a diphosphonucleotide that serves as an energy storage chemical by virtue of the so-called "high energy" phosphate-phosphate anhydride bonds

base-pair a purine base on one strand of nucleic acid and a pyrimidine base on another strand of nucleic acid. The pair of bases are strongly hydrogen bonded to each other

biosynthesis the synthesis of a compound in a biological system. An alternate term is anabolism

catabolism the chemical processes by which the body breaks down nutrients into carbon dioxide, water, and energy

chromosome a long strand of DNA that contains a number of genes

codon a sequence of three specific contiguous bases in mRNA that hydrogen bonds with an anti-codon in one of 64 tRNAs

deamination the removal of the elements of ammonia from an α-amino acid

DNA deoxynucleic acid, which exists as a double helix and contains the genes

double helix the secondary structure of DNA in which two parallel, but oppositely oriented, strands of nucleic acid are coiled about each other

Embden-Meyerhoff pathway the chemical pathway by which glucose is catabolized to two molecules of acetyl-CoA, two molecules of carbon dioxide, and during which two molecules of ATP are produced

Ene-diyne a family of compounds containing two triple bonds conjugated to one double bond and that have been found to have anti-cancer properties

gene a sequence of nucleotides in DNA carrying the information necessary for the biosynthesis of a specific protein

gene therapy replacement of a mutated section of DNA with "good" DNA

genetic code the sequence of triads that is contained in the structure of DNA and which ultimately determines the primary structure of the ~100,000 proteins biosynthesized in the cells

genetic engineering incorporation of a gene from elsewhere (natural or synthetic) into the DNA of a species, usually to facilitate biosynthesis of a protein which confers desired properties on the species

human genome the aggregate of all of the genes in *homo sapiens*

informational strand one of two strands of DNA in the double helix. When the DNA partially uncoils mRNA is synthesized along the other strand, the template strand

Krebs cycle the chemical processes by which acetyl-CoA is catabolized to carbon dioxide and during which 16 molecules of ATP are produced. Also known as the tri-carboxylic acid cycle (TCA)

malignant growth unregulated growth of cells

metabolism conversion of nutrients into other chemicals in a biological system

mRNA messenger ribonucleic acid, which receives genetic information from the template strand of DNA in the process called transcription

mutation the inclusion of a "wrong" nucleic acid base in a sequence of polynucleotides. Mutations may be caused by several different kinds of events, including accidental, biological, physical, and chemical

nucleic acid a polymer of nucleotides with a phosphate-carbohydrate backbone that contains either deoxyribose (DNA) or ribose (RNA) as the carbohydrate component

nucleoside a compound containing one of five purine or pyrimidine bases linked to ribose or deoxyribose at carbon 1′

nucleotide a compound containing a carbohydrate (ribose or deoxyribose) linked to phosphate at carbon 5′ and to one of five purine or pyrimidine bases at carbon 1′

primary structure the sequence in which the various bases are attached to the carbohydrate in the nucleic acid backbone

protease inhibitor an inhibitor which blocks the synthesis of the protein coating of a virus

replication the process by which DNA reproduces itself in the nucleus

retrovirus a viral infecting agent composed mainly of an outer core of protein surrounding an inner core of RNA. In order for it to reproduce and accomplish its infection, it must use the host cell's nucleic acid synthesis system to first produce its own DNA. This DNA then uses the cell's chemical processes to produce additional viral RNA to accomplish further infection

reverse transcriptase an enzyme system which decodes the viral RNA to enable the synthesis of viral DNA from RNA

RNA ribonucleic acid

RTI an inhibitor which blocks the reverse transcriptase enzyme system that decodes the viral RNA and synthesizes viral DNA

secondary structure the double helix arrangement of two parallel strands of nucleic acid

TCA cycle the tri-carboxylic acid cycle, better known as the Kreb's cycle

template strand one of two strands of DNA in the double helix. When the DNA partially uncoils mRNA is synthesized along the template strand

transamination the transfer of the elements of ammonia from an α-amino acid to pyridoxal or from pyridoxamine to an α-keto acid

transcription the process by which mRNA is formed along the template strand of DNA in the nucleus of the cell, after which mRNA leaves the nucleus and enters the cytoplasm

translation the process by which tRNA units (carrying α-amino acids) are attracted to specific locations on mRNA in the cytoplasm, following which protein biosynthesis occurs

triad a sequence of three nucleotides

triplet code a specific sequence of three nucleotides which comprises a codon or anti-codon

tRNA a small polynucleotide (70-100 nucleotides) that carries an anti-codon sequence of bases and which is responsible for carrying α-amino acids, in the form of an ester, to a codon site along a sequence of mRNA

virus an infecting agent composed mainly of an outer core of protein surrounding an inner core of DNA. It commandeers the host cell's DNA replication system in order to multiply and infect additional cells. Some viruses, called retroviruses, have an inner core of RNA instead of DNA

IV. Solutions to Problems

For "**How to Solve a Problem**," review page 679.

19.1 The five different nucleic acid bases (adenine, guanine, cytosine, thymine, uracil) are derived from two different parent heteroaromatic structures, pyrimidine and purine. Pyrimidines are monocyclic with two nitrogen atoms in the ring. The pyrimidine bases are "keto" forms of pyrimidine analogs of phenols - tautomeric forms. Purine bases are bicyclic with four nitrogens in the two rings. Adenine is aromatic and guanine is a "keto" form of a purine phenol - a tautomeric form. See the answer to problem 19.3 for the tautomeric forms of the pyrimidine bases.

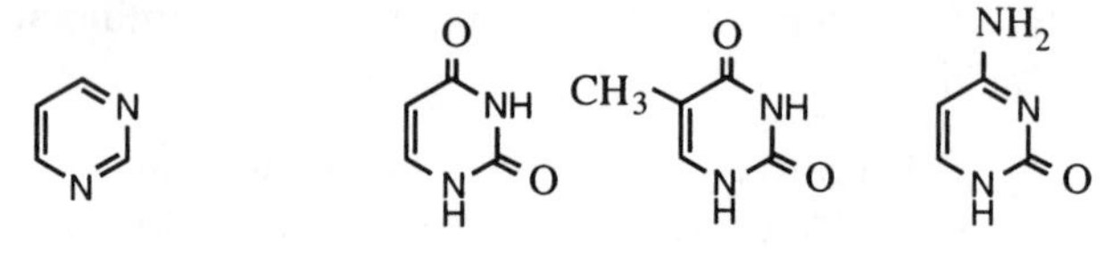

pyrimidine uracil thymine cytosine

Pyrimidine Bases

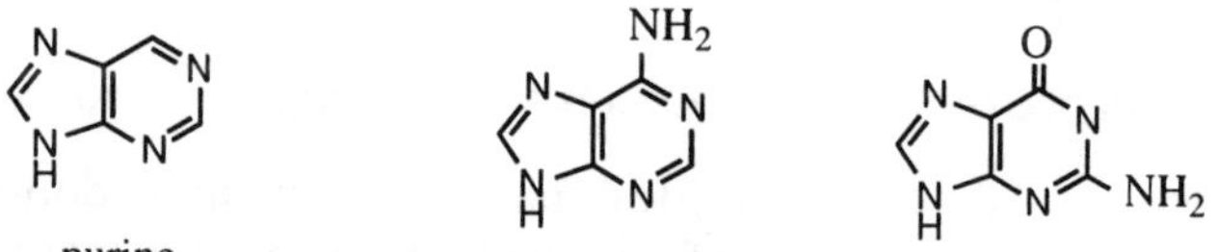

purine adenine guanine

Purine Bases

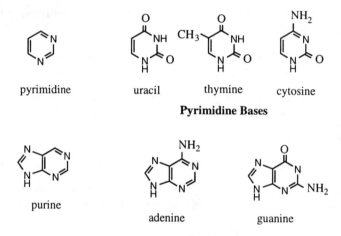

19.2 Adenine and guanine both contain NH groups on the five-membered ring whereas caffeine contains a N-CH_3 group in the comparable position and has no N-H groups. In the formation of a nucleoside the N-H hydrogen atom of the nucleic acid base is replaced by a carbohydrate (ribose or deoxyribose). This replacement cannot occur with caffeine because of the blocking effect of the N-methyl group.

19.3

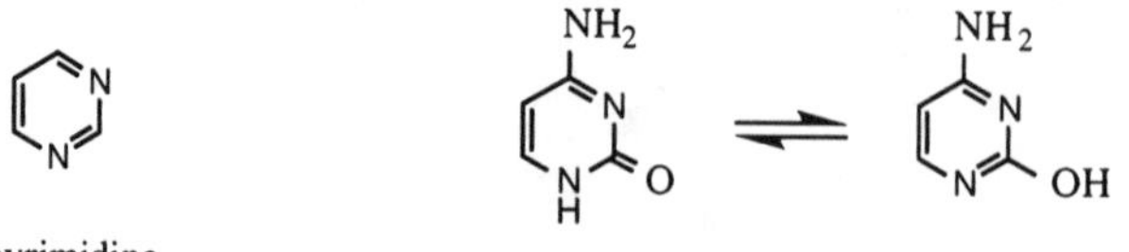

pyrimidine cytosine

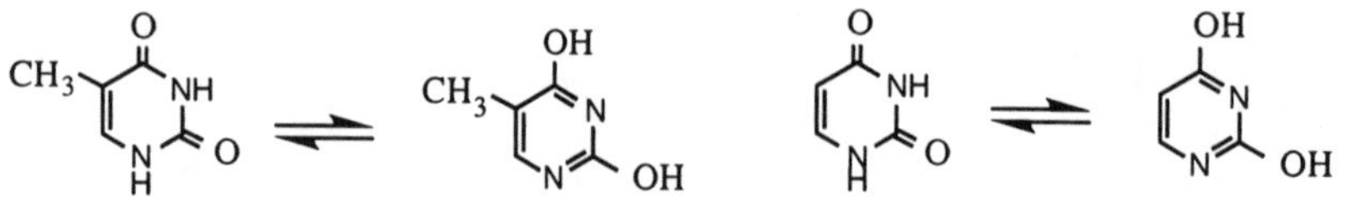

thymine uracil

19.4 A nucleotide contains a nucleic acid base bonded to carbon 1 of a C5-carbohydrate which is in turn bonded to a phosphate at carbon 5. The carbohydrate can be ribose or 2-deoxyribose. An example is adenine nucleotide.

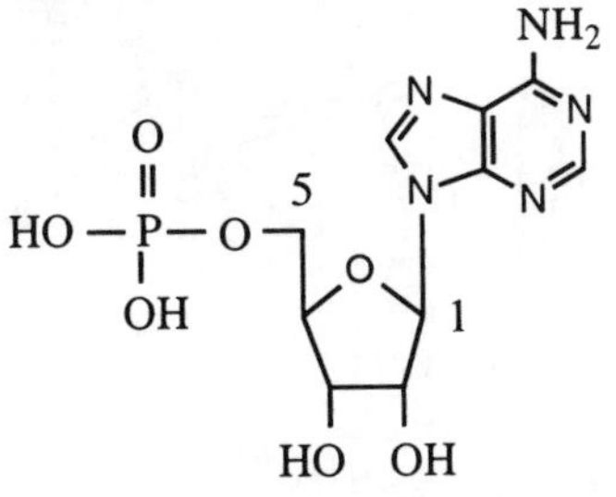

adenine nucleotide

19.5 A nucleoside contains a nucleic acid base bonded to carbon 1 of a C5-carbohydrate. The carbohydrate can be ribose or 2-deoxyribose. An example is adenosine (adenine nucleoside).

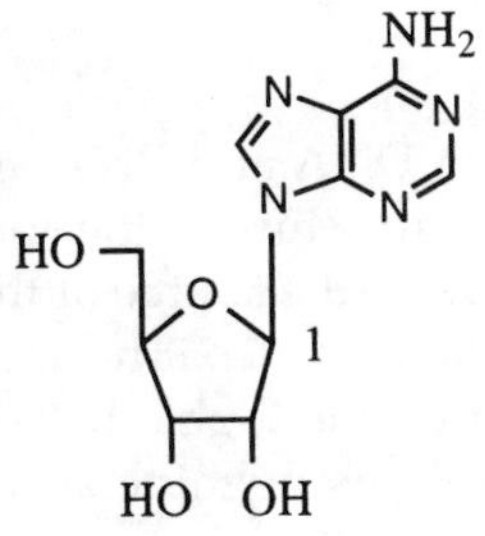

adenosine

19.6 The connection between the nucleic acid base and the carbohydrate in a nucleoside is that of an aminoacetal, analogous to the acetal linkage in a glycoside. Whereas an acetal involves a carbon single-bonded to two oxygens, in an aminoacetal one of the oxygens has been replaced by a nitrogen. Just as acetals can be formed from alcohols and hemiacetals (in turn formed from aldehydes), aminoacetals can be formed from amines and hemiacetals. In both cases they are formed and can be hydrolyzed under acid catalysis but are inert to base catalysis. Thus, adenosine is derived from the amine adenine and the hemiacetal form of ribose, and it can be hydrolyzed in acid to those starting materials.

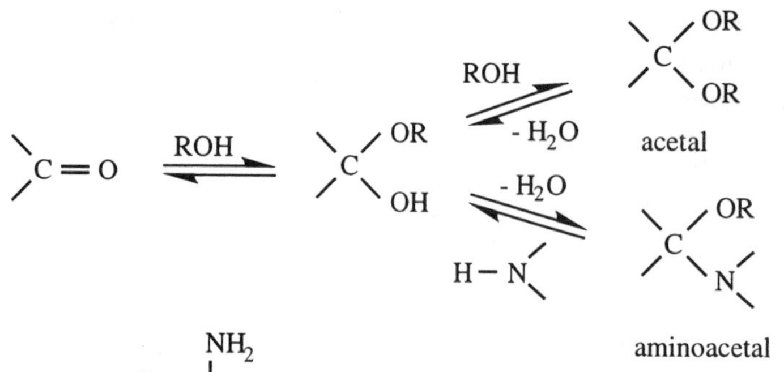
ROH
OR
OH
ROH
- H_2O
OR
OR
acetal
- H_2O
H−N
OR
N
aminoacetal

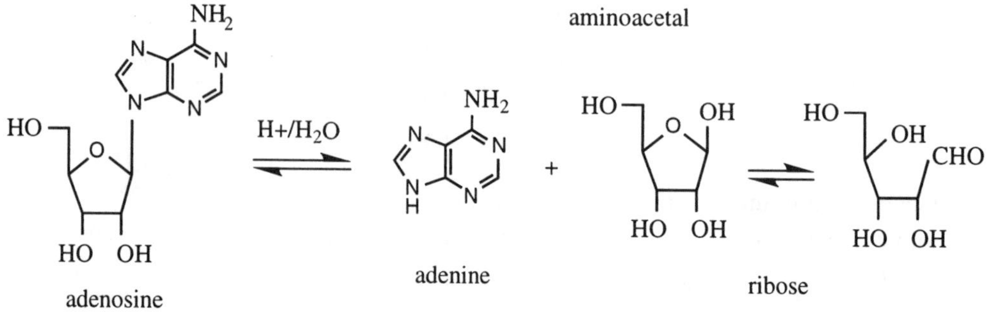
NH_2
HO
H+/H_2O
NH_2
HO
OH
HO
OH
CHO
HO OH
HO OH
HO OH
adenosine
adenine
ribose

19.7 The essential differences between DNA and RNA are three-fold. One difference is the carbohydrate incorporated in the structure of the constituent nucleotides, with **D**NA nucleotides including 2-deoxyribose (the source of the letter **D**) and **R**NA nucleotides including ribose (the source of the letter **R**). The second difference is that DNA exists in a double-stranded α-helix structure (the double helix) whereas RNA is single-stranded. The third difference is that uracil replaces thymine as a pyrimidine base in RNA.

19.8 A base-pair refers to two nucleic acid bases, one a purine base and the other a pyrimidine base, whose structures are complementary in that hydrogen bonding between the two bases effectively holds them together. Base-pairs occur in DNA with one base incorporated in each of two different strands of DNA. The aggregate of the hydrogen bonds from a large number of base-pairs results in sufficient energy to stabilize the double-stranded helical shape of DNA. In addition, the "pairing" of two specific bases accounts for the transfer of genetic information from DNA to RNA. Shown below is the hydrogen bonding between adenine (a purine base) and thymine (a pyrimidine base).

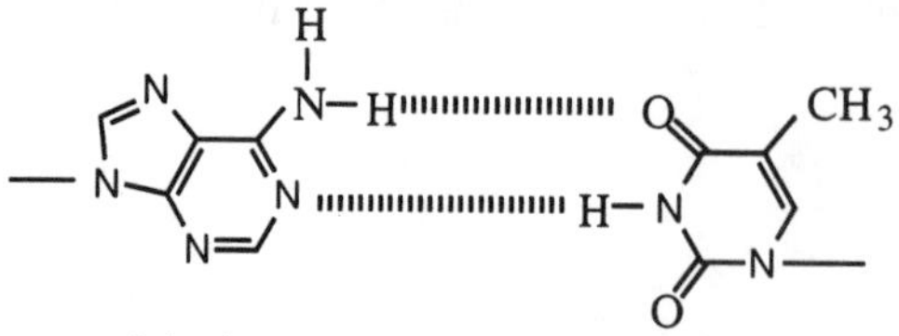
H
N−H
O
CH_3
N
N
H−N
N
N
O
Adenine
Thymine

19.9 A gene is a segment of DNA whose precise structure (that is, its sequence of bases) is responsible for the biosynthesis of a specific protein which carries out a specific biological function.

19.10 (a) transcription is the process of transfer of genetic information (that is, base sequence) from DNA to messenger RNA (mRNA).

(b) translation is the process of transfer of genetic information (that is, base sequence) from mRNA to transfer RNA (tRNA) which carries out the biosynthesis of proteins through the joining together of the α-amino acids carried by each tRNA.

(c) replication is the process by which DNA reproduces itself.

(d) a codon is a three-base sequence located on mRNA.

(e) an anti-codon is a three-base sequence on tRNA which is attracted to hydrogen bond with a complementary codon on mRNA.

19.11 The role of tRNA is to attach itself by an ester linkage (using the 3'-hydroxyl group) to a specific α-amino acid and then become hydrogen bonded at a specific complementary site on mRNA. The tRNA holds the α-amino acid in place while peptide bonds are formed with adjacent α-amino acids, thereby producing a protein. The tRNAs are located in the cytoplasm of the cell.

19.12 The genetic code is a "triplet" code because it requires a sequence of three nucleic acid bases (a "triad") to "encode" for the incorporation of a specific α-amino acid in protein biosynthesis.

19.13 Genetic engineering is the process of incorporating a synthetic polynucleotide sequence into the DNA of an organism in order that the organism will biosynthesize a necessary or desired protein which will perform specific functions or add desired properties to the organism.

19.14 The PCR (polymerase chain reaction) process involves use of the DNA enzyme polymerase to rapidly replicate a sample of DNA.

19.15 The human genome is the sum of all of the genes in *homo sapeins*. They are responsible for synthesis of the proteins essential for all of the functions of the human organism.

19.16 This reaction is the ammonolysis of an ester and involves a nucleophilic acyl substitution.

$$CH_3COOCH_3 + C_2H_5NH_2 \longrightarrow CH_3CONHC_2H_5 + CH_3OH$$

19.17 The DNA sequence of A-C-G-A-T will result in a mRNA sequence of U-G-C-U-A.

19.18 The codon U-G-C in problem 19.17 results in an anti-codon in tRNA being A-C-G.

19.19

DNA (informational strand)	TAG-CAA-GTG-TGT-TGA
DNA (template strand)	ATC-GTT-CAC-ACA-ACT
mRNA codon	UAG-CAA-GUG-UGU-UGA
peptide produced	Glu-Val-Cys

19.20 A TAT triad of the informational strand of DNA produces a ATA triad in the template strand of DNA and a triad of UAU in mRNA which encodes for the α-amino acid tyrosine. A mutated TGT triad in the informational strand of DNA produces a ACA triad in the template strand and a triad of UGU in mRNA which encodes for the α-amino acid cysteine. Therefore, the mutation would result in the replacement of tyrosine by cysteine in the protein. This change would likely result in a change in the effectiveness and/or function of the protein.

19.21 The ATG triad produces TAC in the template strand of DNA, AUG in the mRNA triad, and UAC in the tRNA anticodon.

19.22 Alanine is encoded by four different triads of mRNA, GCA, GCU, GCG, and GCC. The template strand triads of DNA which would produce these mRNAs are CGT, CGA, CGC, and CGG. The informational strand triads of DNA would be GCA, GCT, GCG, and GCC.

19.23 Several base sequences could produce the peptide Ala-Gly-Phe-Tyr-Trp, one of which is as follows:

peptide produced	Ala-Gly-Phe-Tyr-Trp
mRNA codon	GCA-GGA-UUC-UAC-UGG
DNA (template strand)	CGT-CCT-AAG-ATG-ACC
DNA (informational strand)	GCA-GGA-TTC-TAC-TGG

19.24

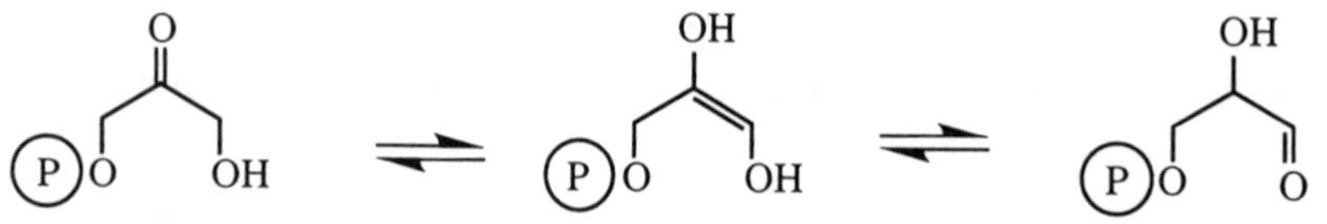

O
P
O
OH
OH
P
O
OH
OH
P
O
O

Dihydroxyacetone monophosphate

Glyceraldehyde-3-phosphate

19.25

(a)

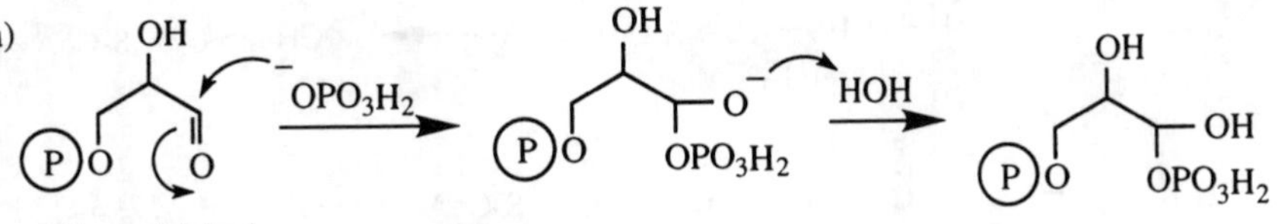

Glyceraldehyde-
3-phosphate

(b)

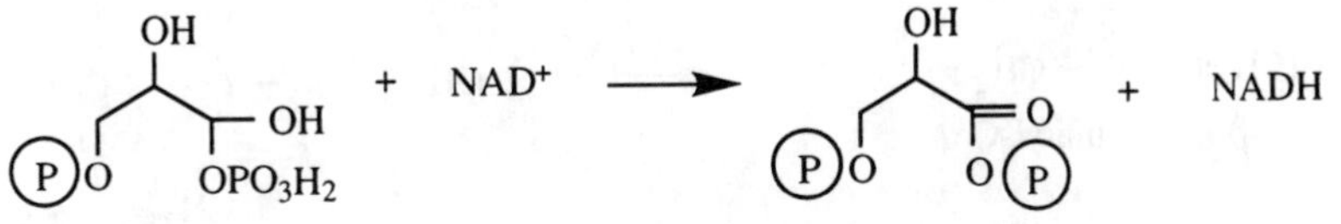

1,3-diphosphoglycerate

19.26 If pyruvic acid were to be decarboxylated the product would be acetaldehyde. In order to obtain acetic acid an oxidation also would be required. Therefore, the conversion of pyruvic acid to acetyl-CoA involves a decarboxylative oxidation effected by thiamine and NAD^+.

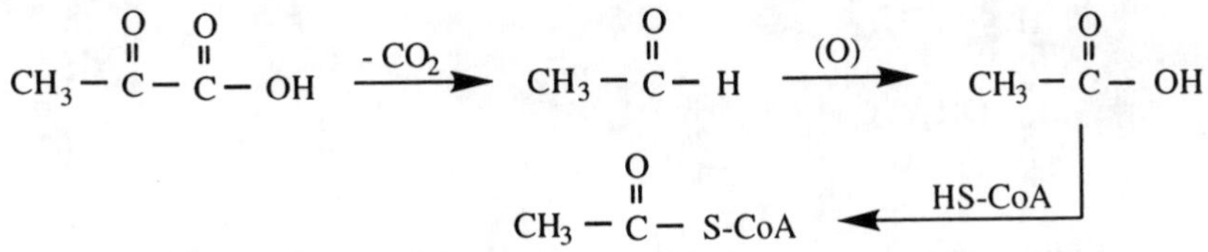

19.27

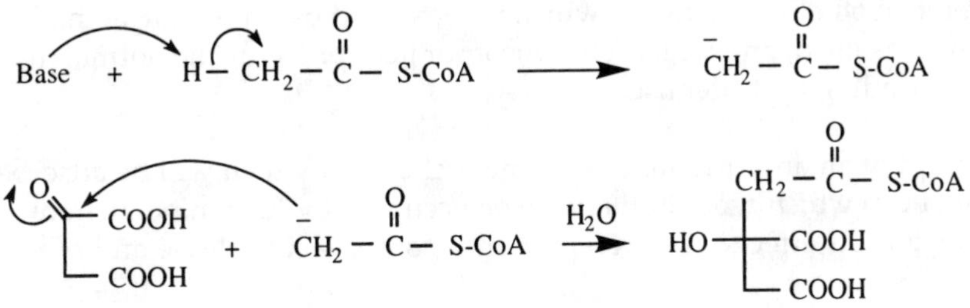

19.28

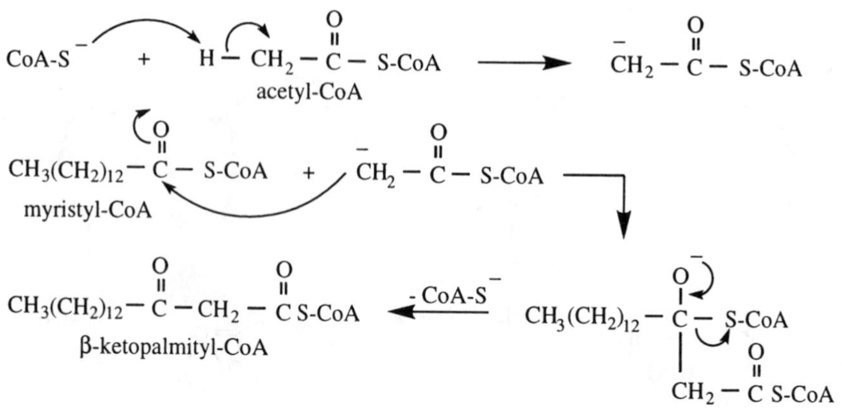
CoA-S
H
CH2
S-CoA
acetyl-CoA
CH2
S-CoA
CH3(CH2)12
S-CoA
myristyl-CoA
CH2
S-CoA
CH3(CH2)12
CH2
S-CoA
β-ketopalmityl-CoA
CoA-S
CH3(CH2)12
S-CoA
CH2
S-CoA

19.29

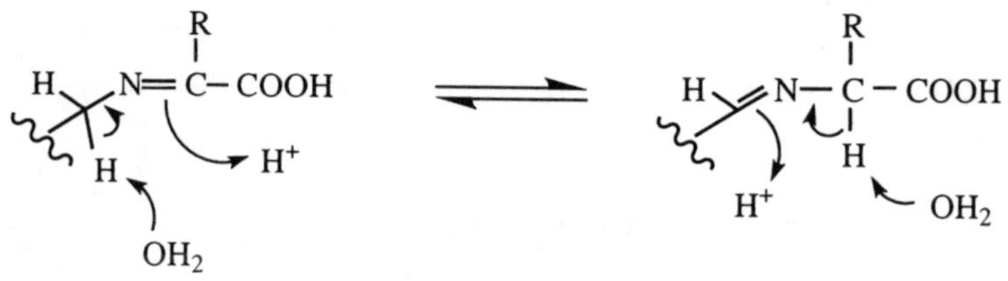
R
H
N
C
COOH
H
H+
OH2
R
H
N
C
COOH
H
H+
OH2

19.30 The term antibiotic means a medicinal which destroys bacterial infections.

19.31 An anti-metabolite is a medicinal which is consumed by an organism in place of a substance normally consumed, and which, once incorporated, prevents the normal functioning of the organism, leading to its demise.

19.32 The concept of an antihistamine is to find a chemical which will be adsorbed into the receptor site(s) which would otherwise be occupied by histamine, thereby blocking the histamine and its effects. The receptor sites control acid-release and other effects.

***19.33**

(a)

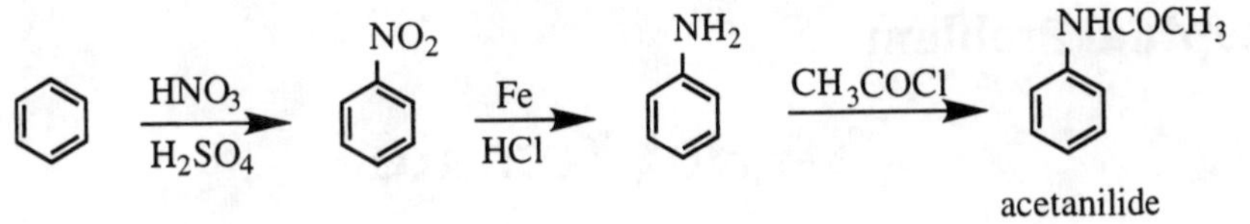

(b)

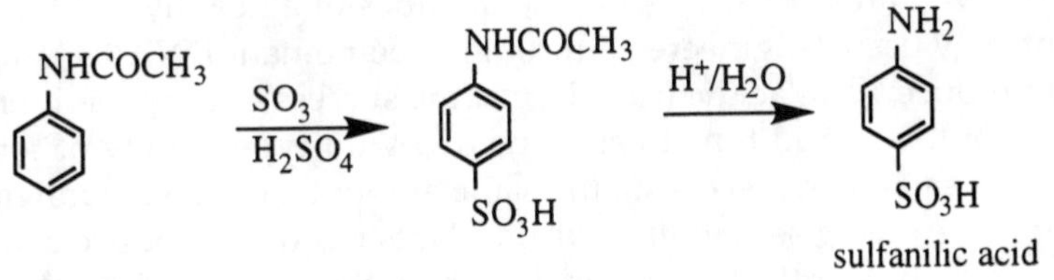

(c)

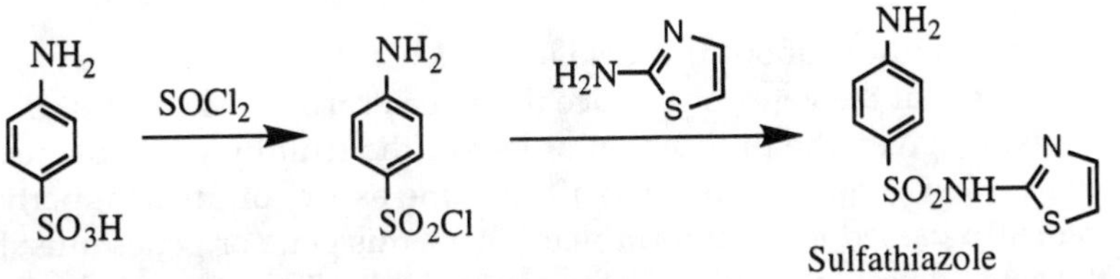

19.34 Most common viruses are comprised mainly of DNA and they undergo replication by the normal DNA unfolding process. A retrovirus is a virus which is comprised of RNA, not of DNA. In order for it to replicate it has to be able to produce DNA, which then produces more RNA. This is referred to as a retro-replication.

19.35 AIDS stands for autoimmune deficiency syndrome. HIV stands for human immunodeficiency virus. HIV is the name assigned to the virus which carries out the infection. AIDS is the combination of diseases which usually eventually results from HIV infection and destruction of the immune system.

19.36 The key concept in fighting a viral disease is to prevent the virus from reproducing (replicating). In principle this can be accomplished several ways, including preventing the polymerization of nucleotides, incorporating "wrong" bases or nucleosides or nucleotides in the retrosynthesis or replication process, providing inhibitors which block essential enzymatic sites, etc.

The key concept employed in fighting bacterial infections is to impede the bacterial metabolic processes.

V. Conceptual Problem

A Hot Tomato

As a horticulturist, you are asked to assess the qualities of a new hybrid tomato plant. The plant has reportedly been "engineered," through recombinant DNA technique, to carry a gene that will produce a less acidic fruit. To test the success of the genetic engineering, you plant a test plot of the hybrid tomato and one of a wild-type variety of tomato. Both plots are cared for in exactly the same way, receiving the same amounts of water, sunlight, and fertilizer. At the end of the growing season, the hybrid plants not only produce a sweeter fruit—as advertised—but they are significantly larger and healthier than the wild-type plants.

■ What conclusions can you draw about this case in particular?

- Ans: You can conclude that the gene to produce the sweeter fruit was successfully incorporated into the hybrid plants, given the production of less acidic fruit by those plants. In addition, it is possible that some other gene or genes that affect some aspect of growth, perhaps the ability to fix nitrogen, were also passed to the hybrid plant. If so, this gene or genes must be in close proximity to the gene governing acidity in the source DNA. This kind of observation is the sort used in a genetics technique called gene mapping.

■ What conclusions can you draw about the ramifications of recombinant DNA techniques in general?

- Ans: Generally, the experiment highlights the possibility of unintentionally transplanting into recombinant DNA other genes in addition to those intended. These "tagalong" genes could have relatively positive effects, as they did in this this experiment; this is exactly the way many useful advances are made in science—serendipitously. Or, they could have no discernible effect or even a latent effect, which only becomes evident at some time in the future. Finally, there could be negative effects. Any hybrids formed by genetic engineering need to be tested thoroughly in order to ensure that they do not contain genes that may cause harmful side effects.

Summary of Preparations of Families of Compounds

In the textbook the methods available for the preparation (synthesis) of each family of compounds are described in the chapter devoted to that family. However, other methods evolve in later chapters describing other families in the course of discussions about their reactions. This summary brings together in a single section all the major methods for the preparation of each family of compound together with a chapter reference for each reaction. The individual reactions described herein also can be placed in context on the *Key to Transformations* chart contained in the textbook *Invitation to Organic Chemistry* and included with the introductory section of this *Study Guide*.

The families of compounds are organized in alphabetical order.

1. Acid chlorides

a. From carboxylic acids (15.1.4)

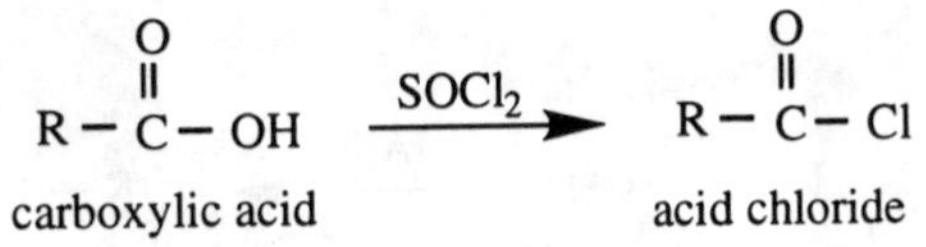
SOCl2
carboxylic acid
acid chloride

2. Alcohols

a. Substitution of alkyl halides (3.4)

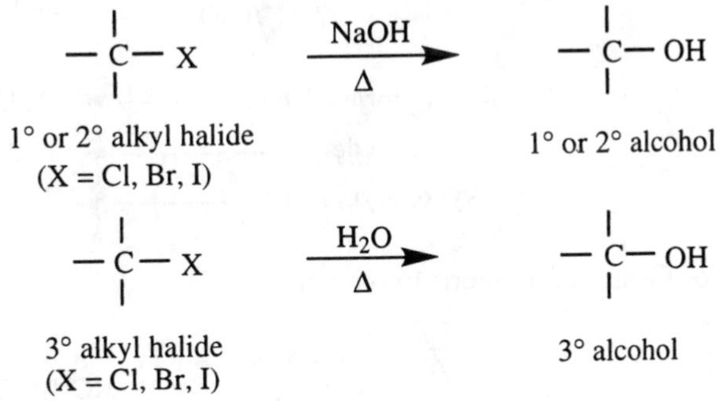
NaOH
Δ
1° or 2° alkyl halide
(X = Cl, Br, I)
1° or 2° alcohol
H2O
Δ
3° alkyl halide
(X = Cl, Br, I)
3° alcohol

b. Hydration of alkenes (6.4.2)

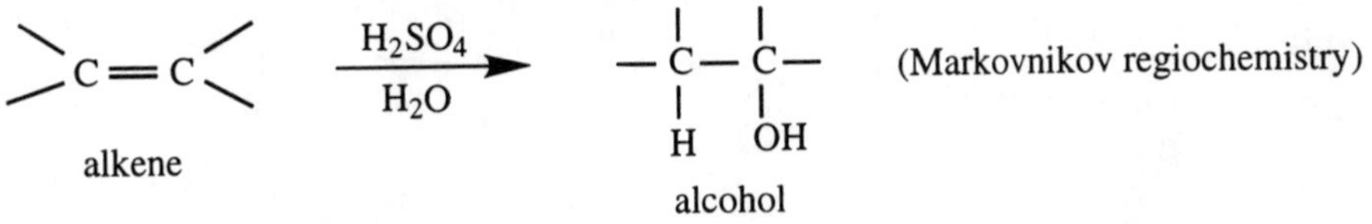
H2SO4
H2O
alkene
alcohol
(Markovnikov regiochemistry)

c. Hydroboration/oxidation of alkenes (6.4.2)

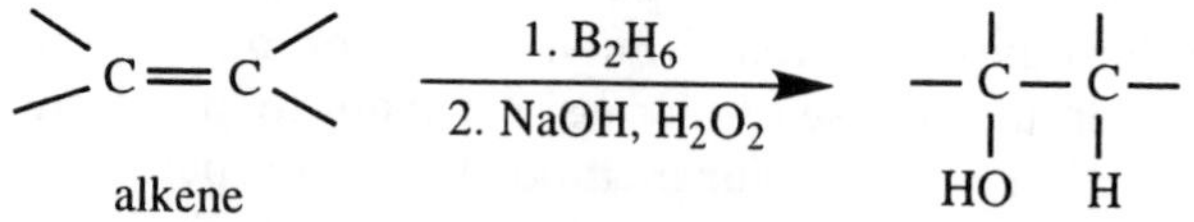

$$
\text{alkene} \quad \xrightarrow[\text{2. NaOH, H}_2\text{O}_2]{\text{1. B}_2\text{H}_6} \quad \underset{\text{HO} \quad \text{H}}{\overset{|\quad\;|}{-\text{C}-\text{C}-}} \qquad \text{(Anti-Markovnikov regiochemistry)}
$$

alcohol

d. Reduction of carbonyl compounds (13.3.1)

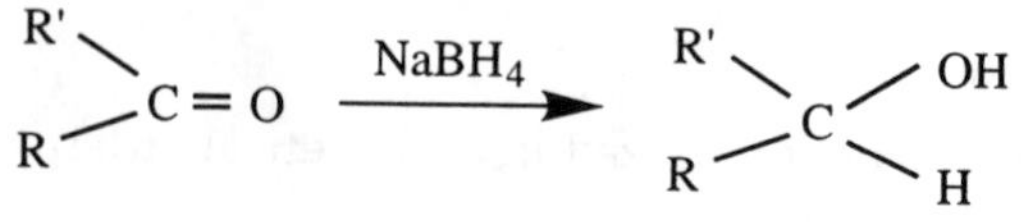

$$
\underset{R}{\overset{R'}{>}}\!\!C=O \quad \xrightarrow{\text{NaBH}_4} \quad \underset{R}{\overset{R'}{>}}\!\!C\underset{H}{\overset{OH}{<}}
$$

R' = H: aldehyde $\longrightarrow$ 1° alcohol

R' = alkyl or aryl: ketone $\longrightarrow$ 2° alcohol

e. Reduction of carboxylic acids (14.3.1)

$$
\overset{\overset{\displaystyle O}{\displaystyle \|}}{R-C}-OH \quad \xrightarrow{\text{LiAlH}_4} \quad R-CH_2-OH
$$

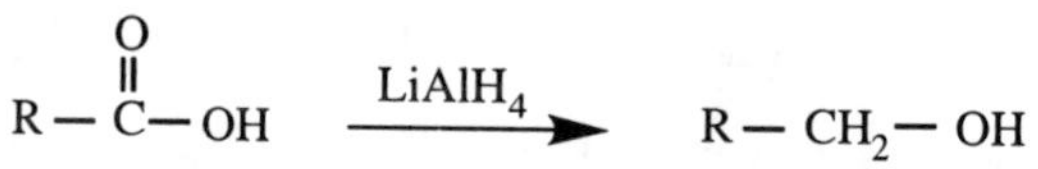

carboxylic acid   1° alcohol

f. Addition of Grignard reagent to carbonyl compounds (13.5.1)

$$
\underset{R}{\overset{R'}{>}}\!\!C=O \quad \xrightarrow[\text{2. H}^+/\text{H}_2\text{O}]{\text{1. R''MgBr}} \quad \underset{R}{\overset{R'}{>}}\!\!C\underset{R''}{\overset{OH}{<}}
$$

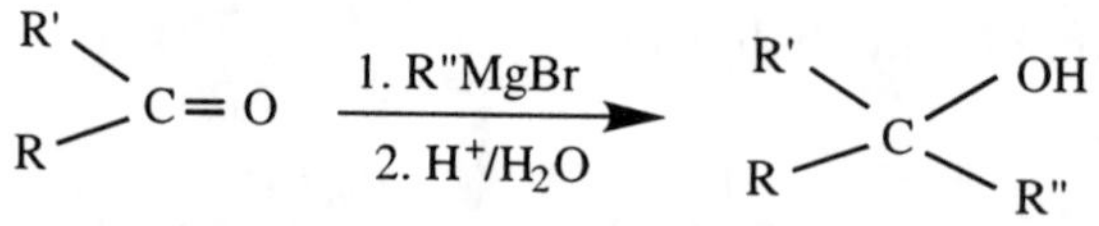

R' = R = H; formaldehyde $\longrightarrow$ 1° alcohol

R' = H: aldehyde $\longrightarrow$ 2° alcohol

R' = alkyl or aryl: ketone $\longrightarrow$ 3° alcohol

g. Addition of Grignard reagent to oxirane (5.4.2)

$$
\overset{\triangledown}{\underset{\text{O}}{}} \quad \xrightarrow[\text{2. H}^+/\text{H}_2\text{O}]{\text{1. RMgBr}} \quad RCH_2CH_2OH
$$

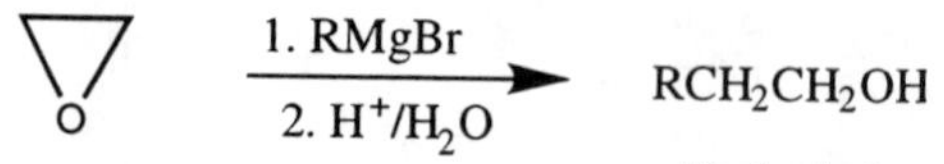

oxirane   1° alcohol

h. Diols from oxidation of alkenes (6.5.2)

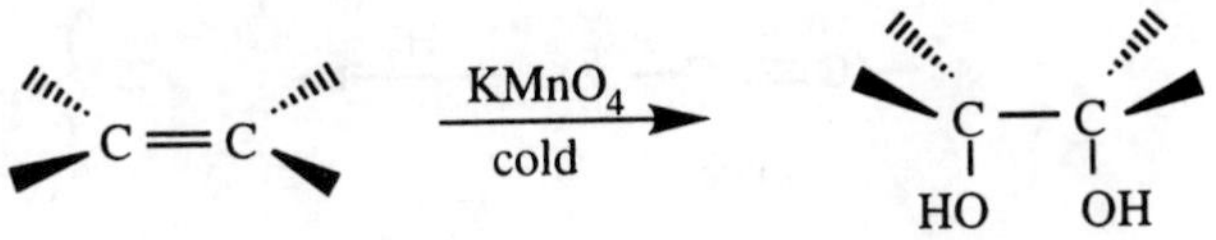
KMnO4
cold
HO
OH

alkene

vicinal diol

i. Diols from ring-opening of oxiranes (5.2.3 and 4)

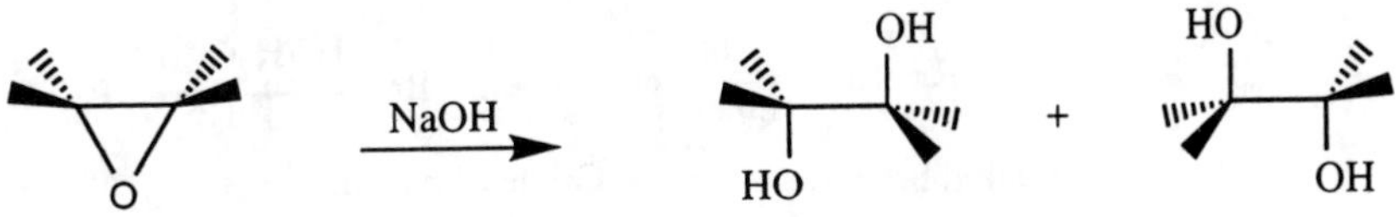
O
NaOH
OH
HO
+
HO
OH

vicinal diol

oxirane

3. Aldehydes

a. Oxidation of 1° alcohols (4.4 and 13.6.1)

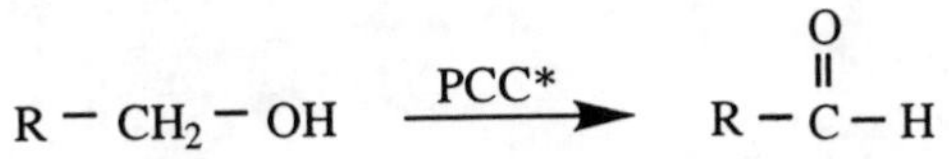
R − CH2 − OH
PCC*
O
R − C − H

1° alcohol

aldehyde

(PCC = pyridinium chlorochromate)

b. Reduction of acid chlorides (13.6.2)

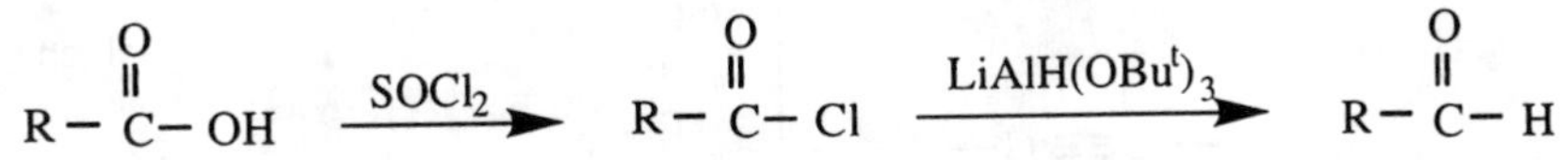
O
R − C − OH
SOCl2
O
R − C − Cl
LiAlH(OBu^t)3
O
R − C − H

carboxylic acid

acid chloride

aldehyde

4. Alkanes (including cycloalkanes)

a. Hydrogenation of alkenes (6.3)

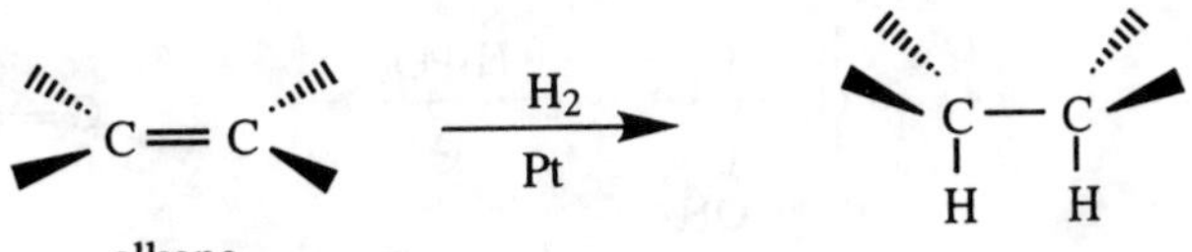
H2
Pt
H
H

alkene

alkane

b. Hydrogenation of alkynes (7.3.1)

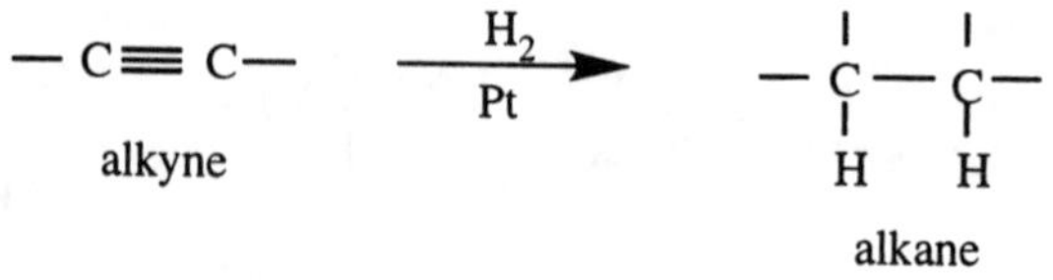
H_2
Pt
alkyne
alkane

c. Acidification of a Grignard reagent formed from an alkyl bromide (3.5.1)

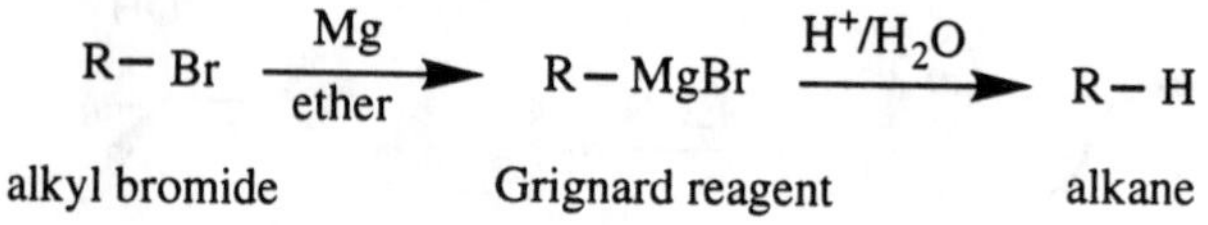
R– Br
Mg
ether
R– MgBr
H^+/H_2O
R– H
alkyl bromide
Grignard reagent
alkane

d. Cuprate reagent reacting with an alkyl halide (3.5.2)

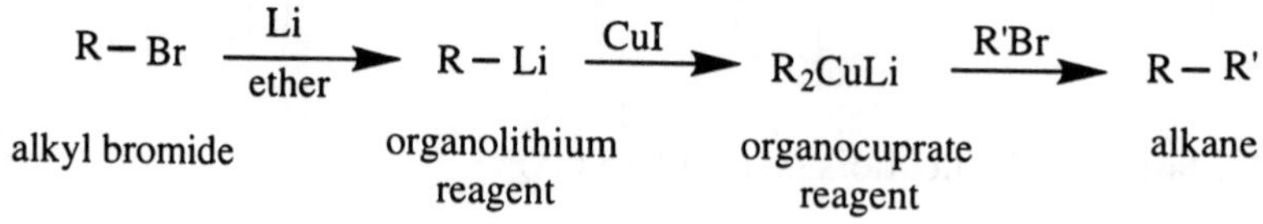
R– Br
Li
ether
R– Li
CuI
R_2CuLi
R'Br
R– R'
alkyl bromide
organolithium reagent
organocuprate reagent
alkane

5. Alkenes

a. Hydrogenation of alkynes (7.3.1)

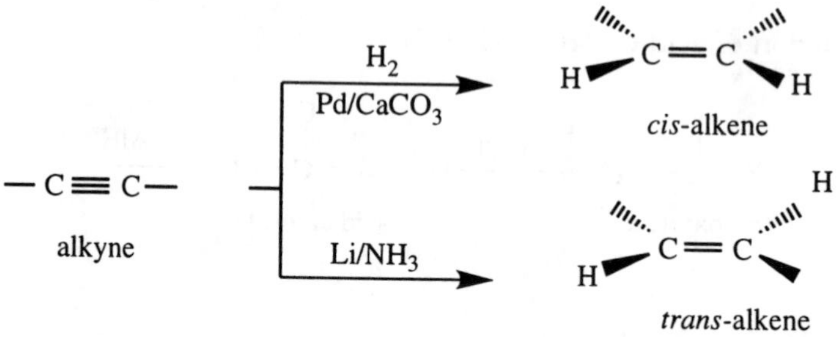
H_2
$Pd/CaCO_3$
cis-alkene
alkyne
Li/NH_3
trans-alkene

b. Dehydration of alcohols (6.6.1)

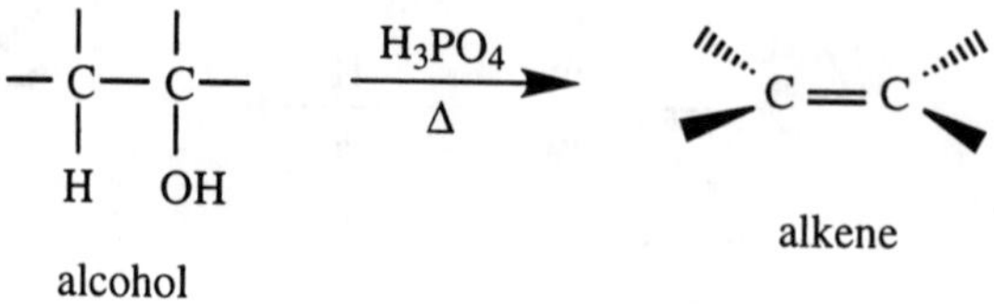
H_3PO_4
Δ
alcohol
alkene

c. Dehydrohalogenation of alkyl halides (6.6.2)

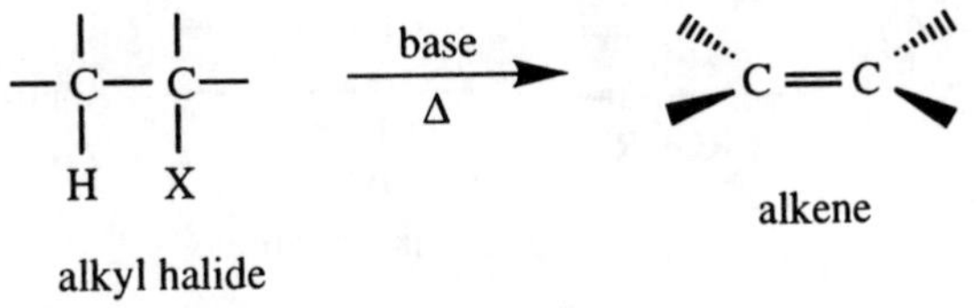
base
Δ
H
X
alkene
alkyl halide

(bases varying in strength from NaOH, to $NaOC_2H_5$, and $KOBu^t$)

d. Wittig reaction (6.6.4)

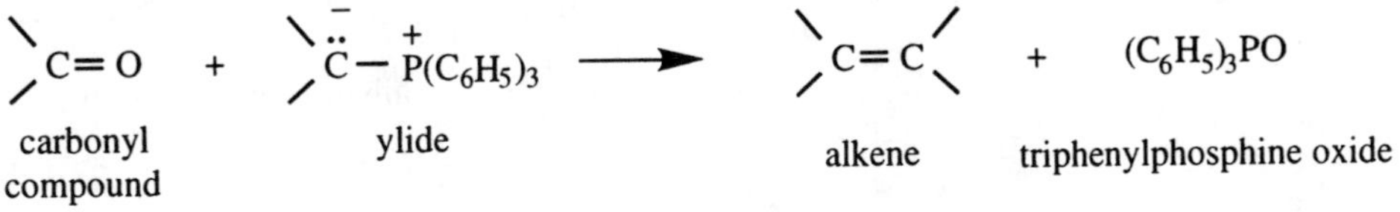
$P(C_6H_5)_3$
$(C_6H_5)_3PO$
carbonyl compound
ylide
alkene
triphenylphosphine oxide

6. Alkyl Halides

a. Radical halogenation of alkanes (10.2.2)

$$\underset{\text{alkane}}{R-H} \xrightarrow[h\nu]{Br_2} \underset{\text{alkyl bromide}}{R-Br}$$

b. From alcohols with hydrogen halides (4.3.1)

$$\underset{\text{alcohol}}{R-OH} \xrightarrow{HX} \underset{\text{alkyl halide}}{R-X} \qquad (X = Cl, Br, I)$$

c. From alcohols with $SOCl_2$ or PBr_3 (4.3.2)

$$\underset{\text{alkyl chloride}}{R-Cl} \xleftarrow{SOCl_2} \underset{\text{alcohol}}{R-OH} \xrightarrow{PBr_3} \underset{\text{alkyl bromide}}{R-Br}$$

d. Addition of HX to alkenes in the dark (6.4.1)

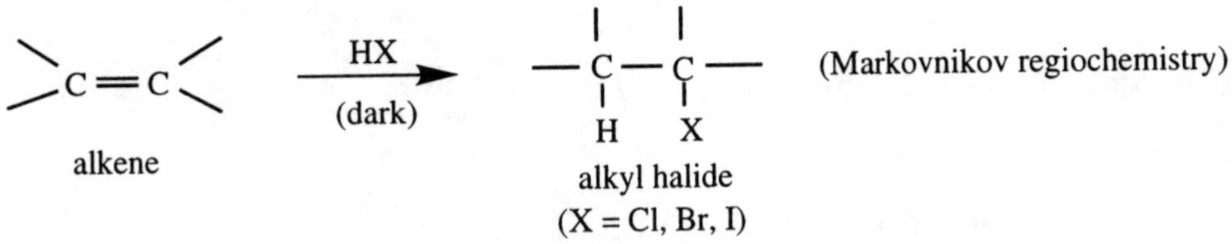
HX
(dark)
H
X
(Markovnikov regiochemistry)
alkene
alkyl halide
(X = Cl, Br, I)

e. Addition of HBr to alkenes under radical conditions (10.3)

HBr
ROOR
alkene
Br
H
alkyl bromide

(anti-Markovnikov regiochemistry)

f. Halogenation of allylic or benzylic compounds (10.2.3)

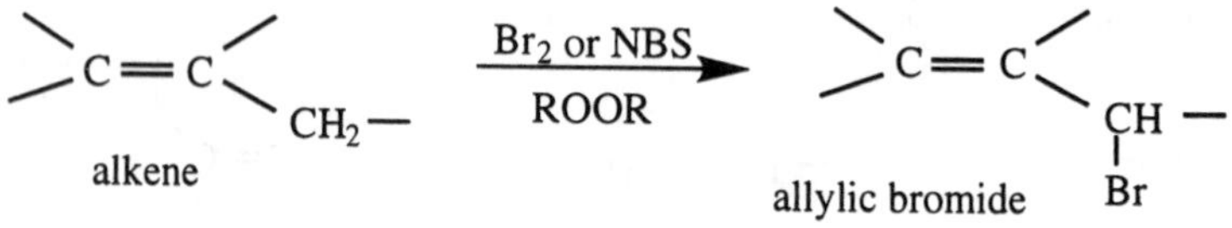
alkene
Br2 or NBS
ROOR
allylic bromide
Br

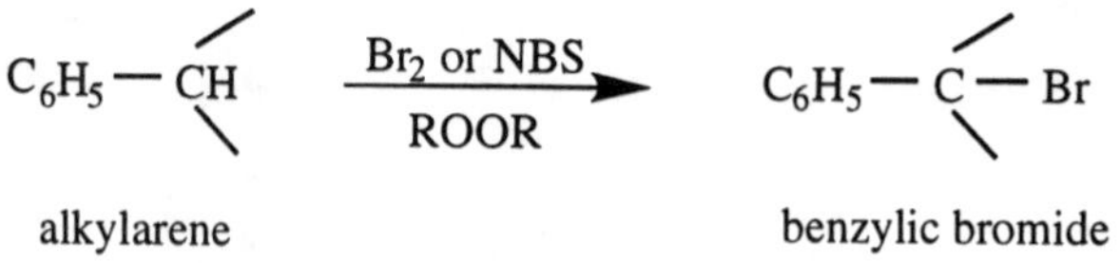
alkylarene
Br2 or NBS
ROOR
benzylic bromide

7. Alkynes

a. Alkylation of acetylene (7.4)

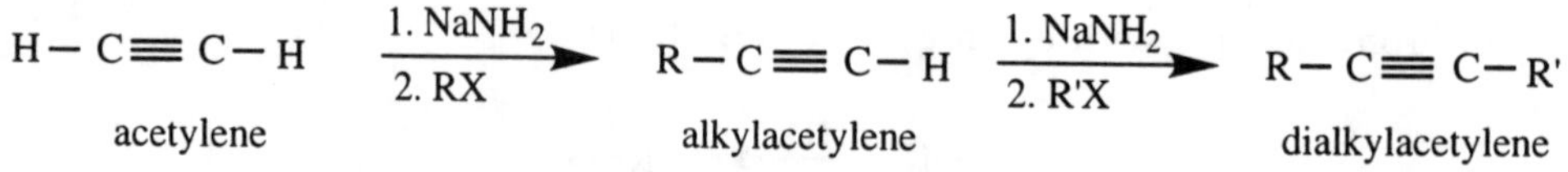
acetylene
1. NaNH2
2. RX
alkylacetylene
1. NaNH2
2. R'X
dialkylacetylene

(R and R' = 1° or 2° alkyl halides)

8. Amides

a. Ammonolysis of acid chlorides (15.1.2 and 15.4.3)

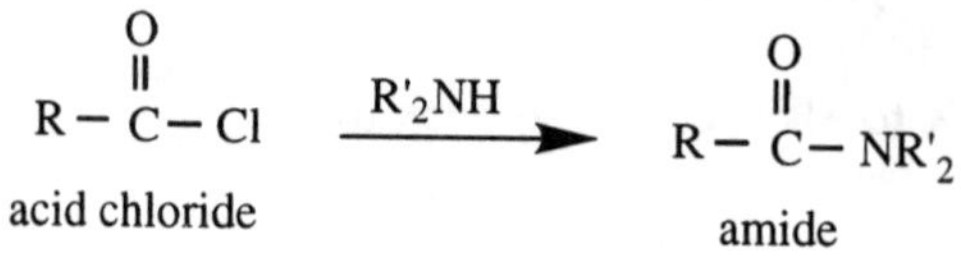
acid chloride
R'2NH
amide

b. Ammonolysis of anhydrides (15.2.2 and 15.4.3)

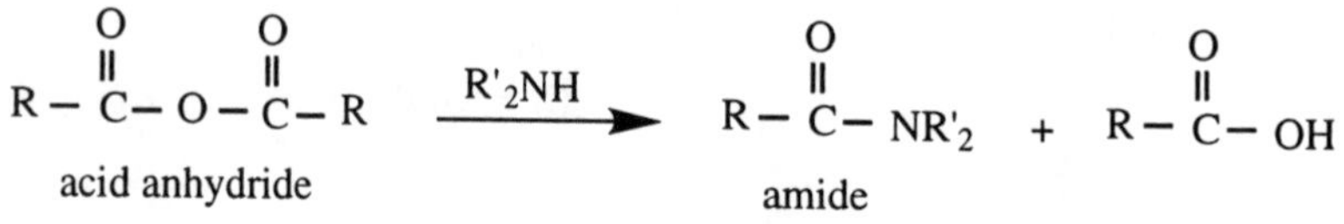
acid anhydride
R'2NH
amide

c. Ammonolysis of esters (15.3.2 and 15.4.3)

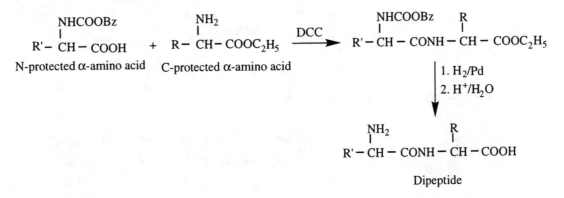

$$\underset{\text{ester}}{R-\overset{O}{\overset{\|}{C}}-OR'(Ar)} \xrightarrow{R'_2NH} \underset{\text{amide}}{R-\overset{O}{\overset{\|}{C}}-NR'_2}$$

d. Peptides using dicyclohexylcarbodiimide (DCC) (16.4)

$$\underset{\text{N-protected }\alpha\text{-amino acid}}{R'-\overset{NHCOOBz}{\overset{|}{CH}}-COOH} + \underset{\text{C-protected }\alpha\text{-amino acid}}{R-\overset{NH_2}{\overset{|}{CH}}-COOC_2H_5} \xrightarrow{DCC} R'-\overset{NHCOOBz}{\overset{|}{CH}}-CONH-\overset{R}{\overset{|}{CH}}-COOC_2H_5$$

$$\xrightarrow{1.\ H_2/Pd;\ 2.\ H^+/H_2O} \underset{\text{Dipeptide}}{R'-\overset{NH_2}{\overset{|}{CH}}-CONH-\overset{R}{\overset{|}{CH}}-COOH}$$

9. Amines

a. Alkylation of ammonia (12.6.1)

$$\underset{\text{alkyl halide}}{R-Br} \xrightarrow[\text{excess}]{NH_3} \underset{1^\circ\text{ amine}}{R-NH_2}$$

b. Reduction of azides (from alkyl halides) (12.6.2)

$$\underset{\text{alkyl halide}}{R-Br} \xrightarrow{NaN_3} \underset{\text{alkyl azide}}{R-N_3} \xrightarrow{LiAlH_4} \underset{1^\circ\text{ amine}}{R-NH_2}$$

c. Reduction of nitriles (from alkyl halides) (12.6.2)

$$\underset{\text{alkyl halide}}{R-Br} \xrightarrow{NaCN} \underset{\text{nitrile}}{R-CN} \xrightarrow{LiAlH_4} \underset{1^\circ\text{ amine}}{R-CH_2-NH_2}$$

d. Reduction of amides (12.6.2)

$$R - \overset{\overset{\displaystyle O}{\|}}{C} - NH_2 \quad \xrightarrow{\text{LiAlH}_4} \quad R - CH_2 - NH_2$$

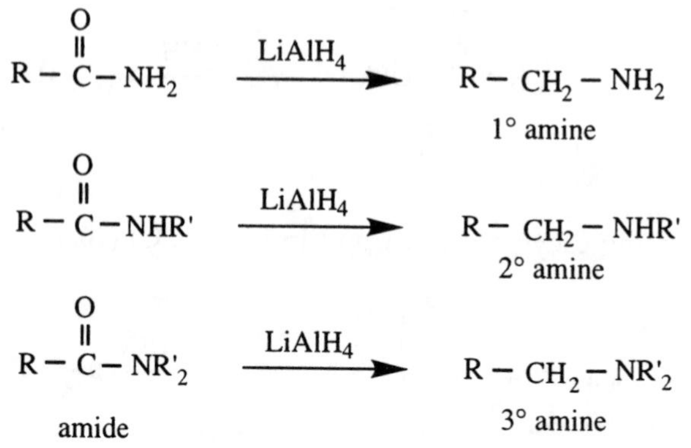

1° amine

$$R - \overset{\overset{\displaystyle O}{\|}}{C} - NHR' \quad \xrightarrow{\text{LiAlH}_4} \quad R - CH_2 - NHR'$$

2° amine

$$R - \overset{\overset{\displaystyle O}{\|}}{C} - NR'_2 \quad \xrightarrow{\text{LiAlH}_4} \quad R - CH_2 - NR'_2$$

amide   3° amine

e. Reduction of nitroaromatics (12.6.3)

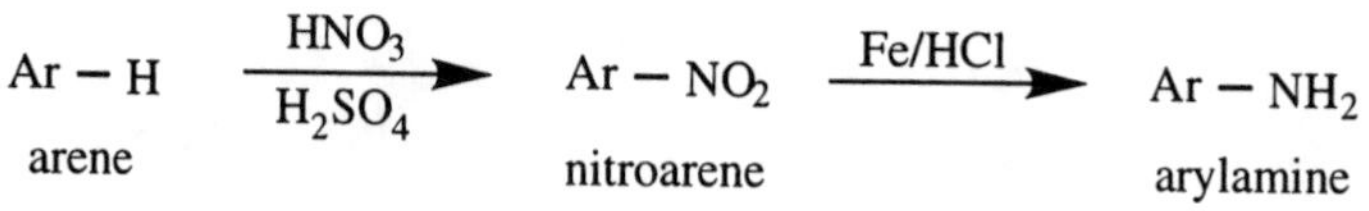

$$Ar - H \quad \xrightarrow[\text{H}_2\text{SO}_4]{\text{HNO}_3} \quad Ar - NO_2 \quad \xrightarrow{\text{Fe/HCl}} \quad Ar - NH_2$$

arene   nitroarene   arylamine

10. α -Amino acids

a. From α-bromo carboxylic acids (16.4)

$$R - CH_2 - COOH \quad \xrightarrow{\text{Br}_2/\text{P}} \quad R - \overset{\overset{\displaystyle Br}{|}}{CH} - COOH \quad \xrightarrow{\text{NH}_3} \quad R - \overset{\overset{\displaystyle NH_2}{|}}{CH} - COOH$$

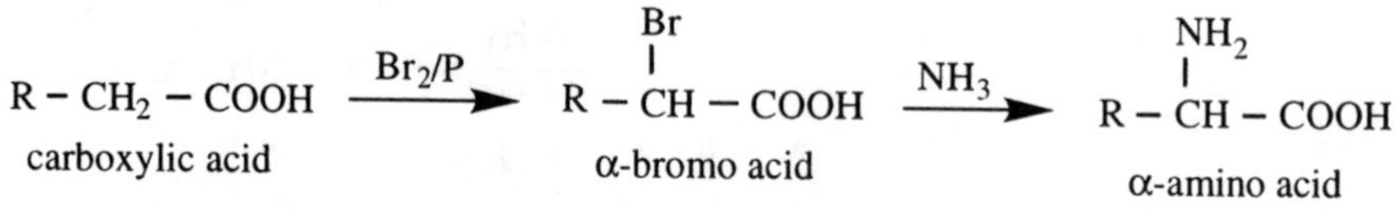

carboxylic acid   α-bromo acid   α-amino acid

b. From aldehydes (Strecker synthesis) (16.4)

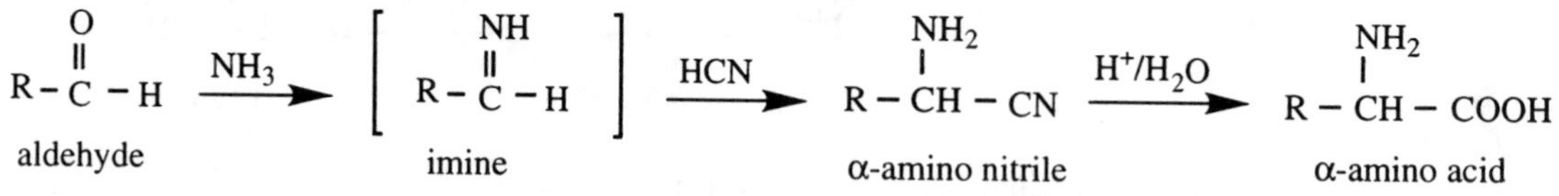

$$R - \overset{\overset{\displaystyle O}{\|}}{C} - H \quad \xrightarrow{\text{NH}_3} \quad \left[R - \overset{\overset{\displaystyle NH}{\|}}{C} - H \right] \quad \xrightarrow{\text{HCN}} \quad R - \overset{\overset{\displaystyle NH_2}{|}}{CH} - CN \quad \xrightarrow{\text{H}^+/\text{H}_2\text{O}} \quad R - \overset{\overset{\displaystyle NH_2}{|}}{CH} - COOH$$

aldehyde   imine   α-amino nitrile   α-amino acid

11. Aromatic compounds

a. Halogenation of arenes (9.3.2)

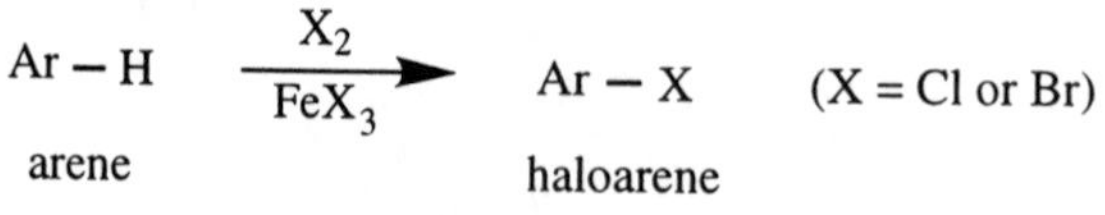

$$Ar - H \quad \xrightarrow[\text{FeX}_3]{\text{X}_2} \quad Ar - X \qquad (X = Cl \text{ or } Br)$$

arene   haloarene

b. Haloarenes from diazonium salts (12.5.2)

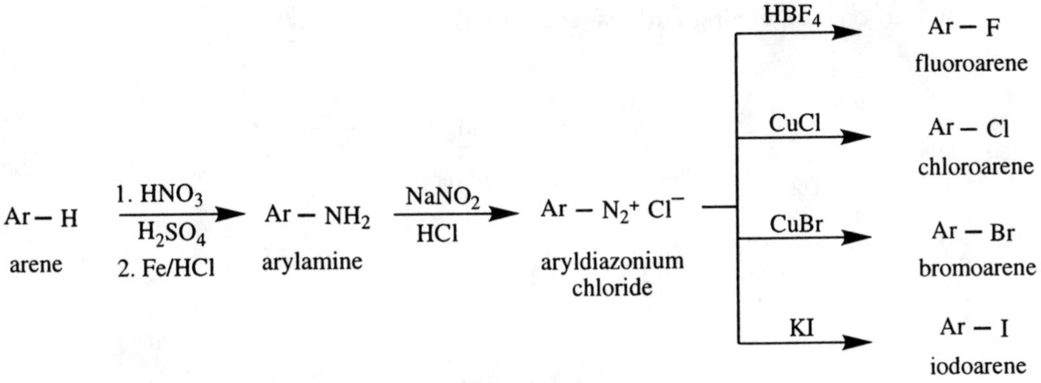
Ar – H
arene
1. HNO3
H2SO4
2. Fe/HCl
Ar – NH2
arylamine
NaNO2
HCl
Ar – N2+ Cl−
aryldiazonium chloride
HBF4
Ar – F
fluoroarene
CuCl
Ar – Cl
chloroarene
CuBr
Ar – Br
bromoarene
KI
Ar – I
iodoarene

c. Nitration of arenes (9.3.3)

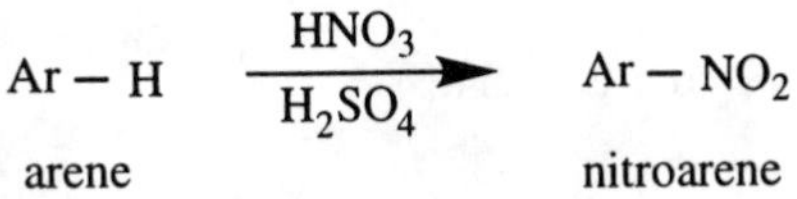
Ar – H
arene
HNO3
H2SO4
Ar – NO2
nitroarene

d. Sulfonation of arenes (9.3.4)

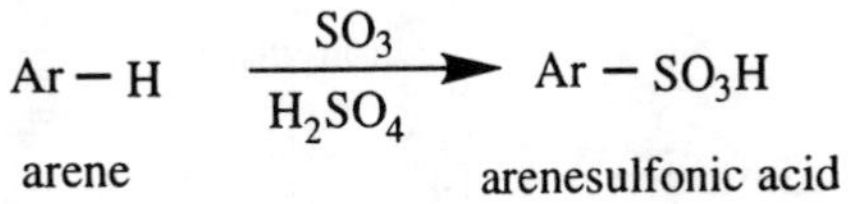
Ar – H
arene
SO3
H2SO4
Ar – SO3H
arenesulfonic acid

e. Alkylation of arenes (9.3.5)

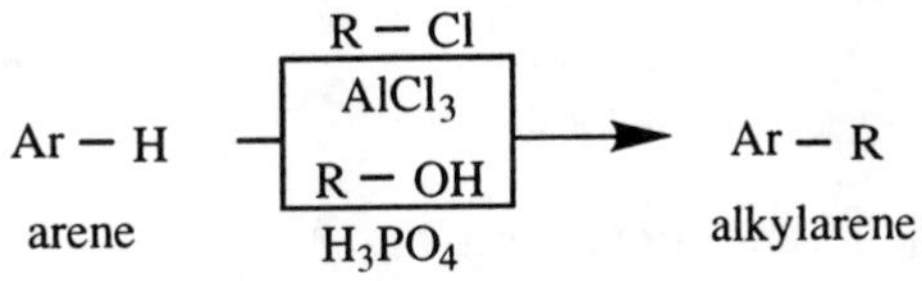
Ar – H
arene
R – Cl
AlCl3
R – OH
H3PO4
Ar – R
alkylarene

f. Acylation of arenes (9.3.6)

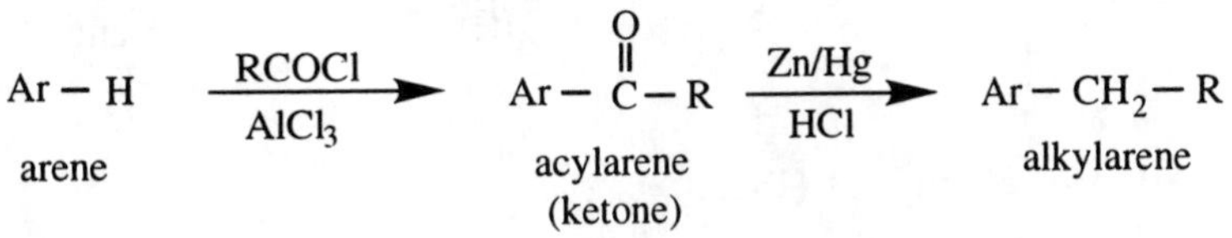
Ar – H
arene
RCOCl
AlCl3
Ar – C(=O) – R
acylarene
(ketone)
Zn/Hg
HCl
Ar – CH2 – R
alkylarene

12. Carboxylic acids

a. Carbonation of Grignard reagent (14.4.1)

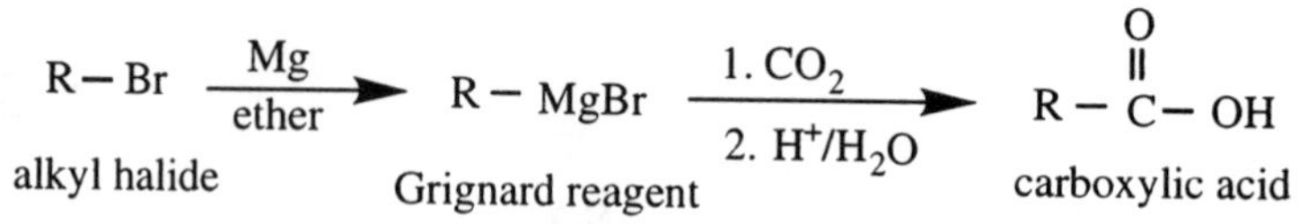

R– Br
Mg
ether
R– MgBr
1. CO_2
2. H^+/H_2O
R– C(=O)– OH
alkyl halide
Grignard reagent
carboxylic acid

b. Hydrolysis of nitriles:

i. from alkyl halides (14.4.2)

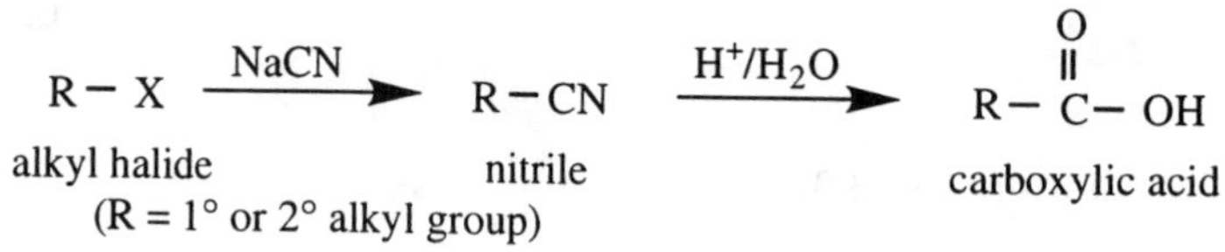

R– X
NaCN
R–CN
H^+/H_2O
R– C(=O)– OH
alkyl halide
nitrile
carboxylic acid
(R = 1° or 2° alkyl group)

ii. from cyanohydrins (14.4.2)

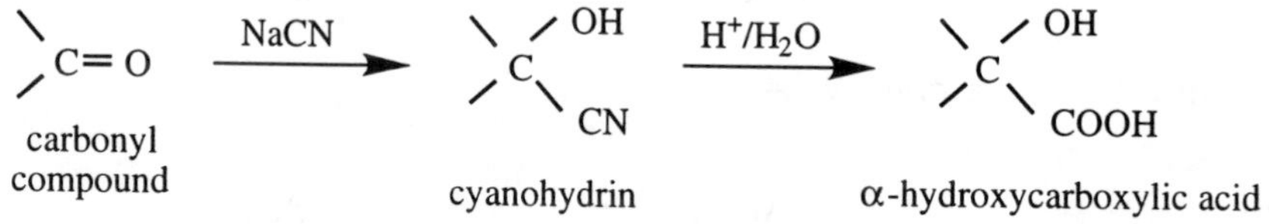

C= O
NaCN
OH
C
CN
H^+/H_2O
OH
C
COOH
carbonyl compound
cyanohydrin
α-hydroxycarboxylic acid

iii. from aromatic amines (14.4.2)

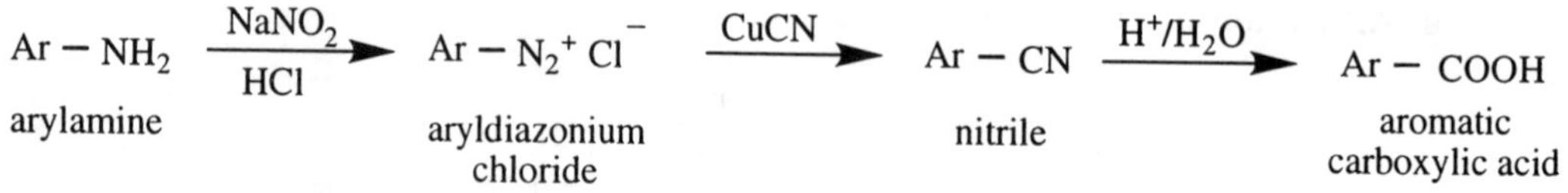

Ar – NH_2
$NaNO_2$
HCl
Ar – N_2^+ Cl^-
CuCN
Ar – CN
H^+/H_2O
Ar – COOH
arylamine
aryldiazonium chloride
nitrile
aromatic carboxylic acid

c. Oxidation of alkylarenes (9.6.3 and 14.4.3)

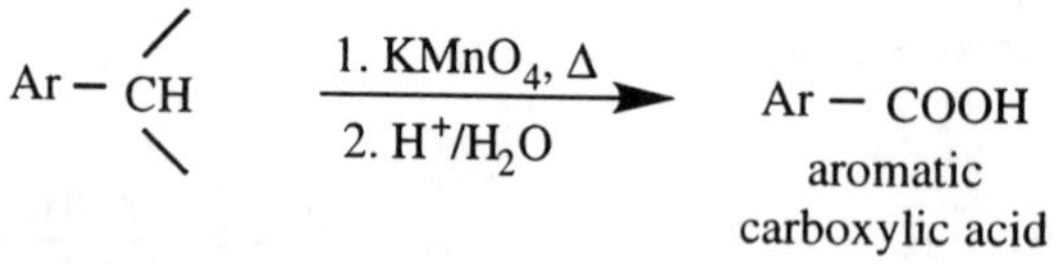

Ar – CH
1. $KMnO_4$, Δ
2. H^+/H_2O
Ar – COOH
aromatic carboxylic acid

d. Oxidation of aldehydes (13.2.2)

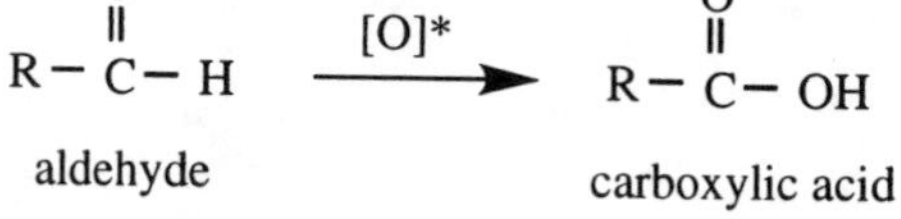

R– C(=O)– H
[O]*
R– C(=O)– OH
aldehyde
carboxylic acid

* a wide range of oxidizing reagents can be employed, including O_2, HNO_3, $KMnO_4$, $Na_2Cr_2O_7$, etc.

e. Oxidation of 1° alcohols (4.4)

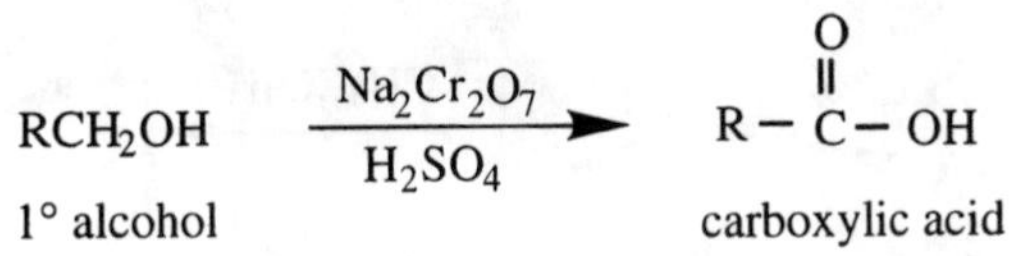
RCH2OH
Na2Cr2O7
H2SO4
R − C − OH
1° alcohol
carboxylic acid

13. Esters

a. Alcoholysis of acid chlorides (15.1.2 and 15.3.4)

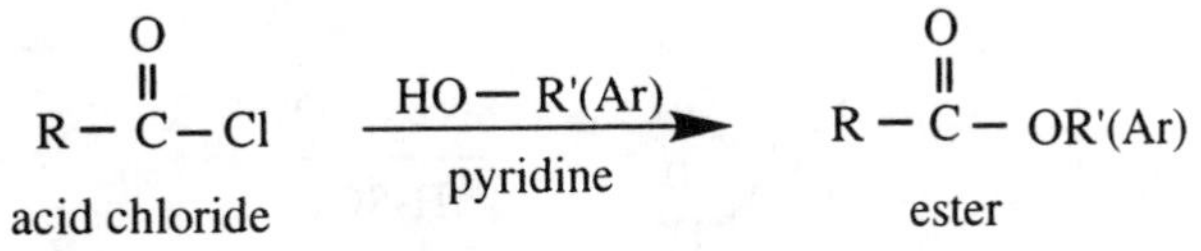
R − C − Cl
HO − R'(Ar)
pyridine
R − C − OR'(Ar)
acid chloride
ester

b. Alcoholysis of anhydrides (15.2.2 and 15.3.4)

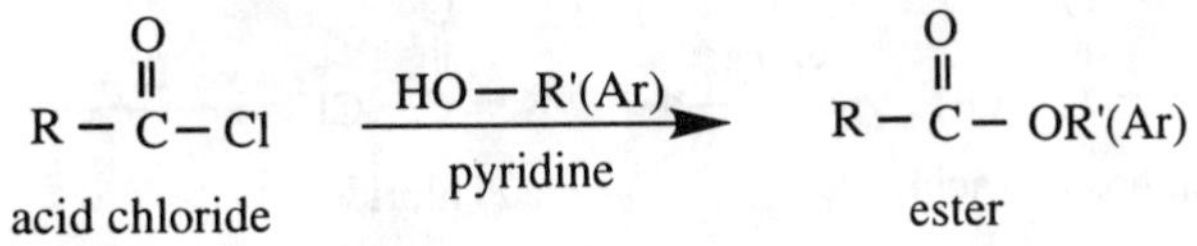
R − C − Cl
HO − R'(Ar)
pyridine
R − C − OR'(Ar)
acid chloride
ester

c. Fischer esterification (15.3.4)

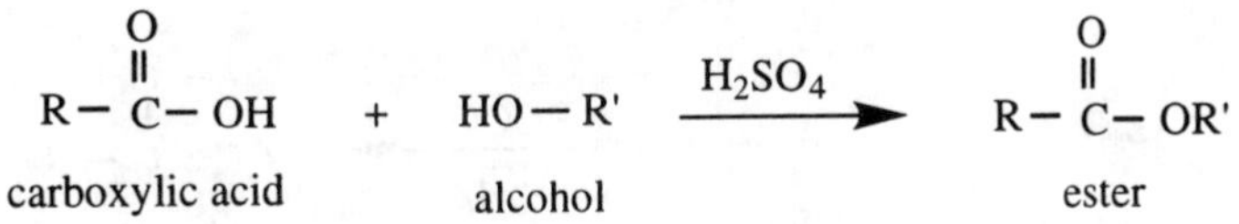
R − C − OH
+
HO − R'
H2SO4
R − C − OR'
carboxylic acid
alcohol
ester

14. Ethers

a. Williamson synthesis (5.1.2)

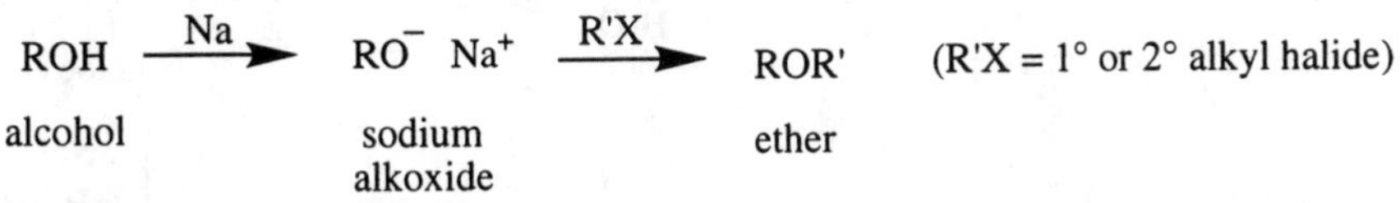
ROH
Na
RO⁻ Na⁺
R'X
ROR'
(R'X = 1° or 2° alkyl halide)
alcohol
sodium alkoxide
ether

b. Epoxidation of alkenes (6.5.1)

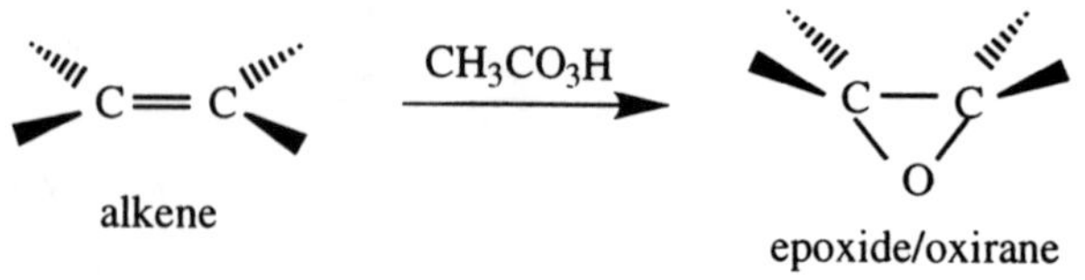
C=C
CH_3CO_3H
C—C
O
alkene
epoxide/oxirane

15. Ketones

a. Oxidation of 2° alcohols (4.4 and 13.6.1)

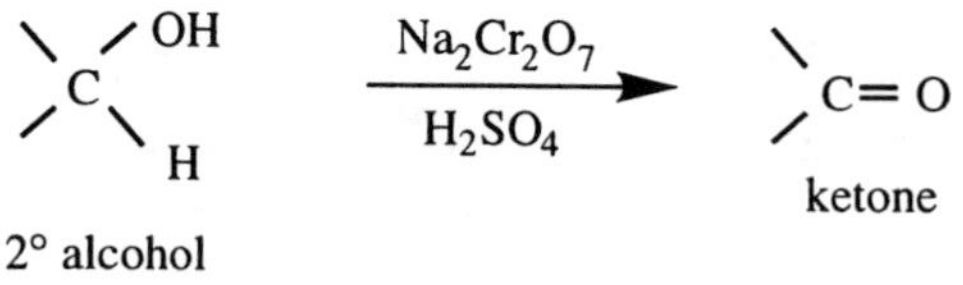
OH
C
H
$Na_2Cr_2O_7$
H_2SO_4
C= O
2° alcohol
ketone

b. Cuprate reagent with acid chlorides (13.6.3)

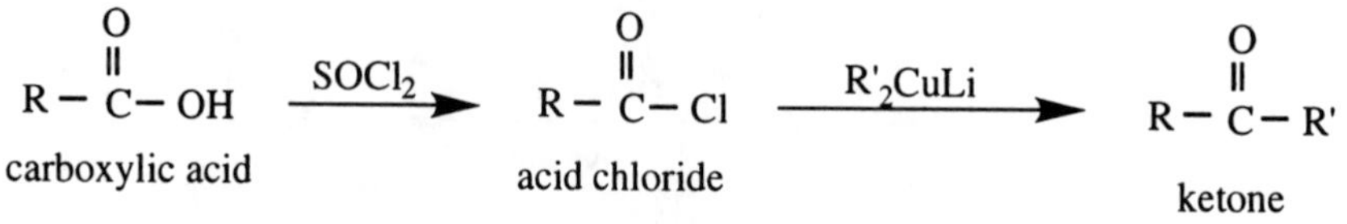
R − C − OH
$SOCl_2$
R − C − Cl
R'_2CuLi
R − C − R'
carboxylic acid
acid chloride
ketone

c. Friedel-Crafts acylation of arenes (9.3.6)

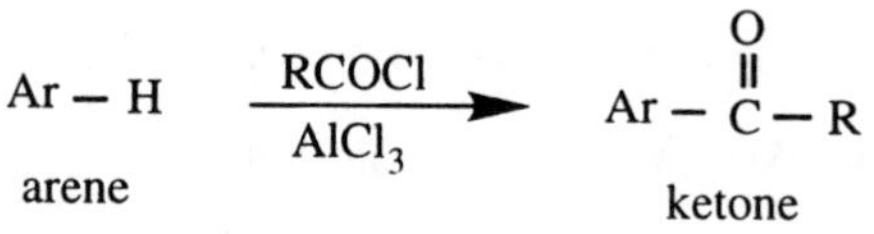
Ar − H
RCOCl
$AlCl_3$
Ar − C − R
arene
ketone

d. Claisen condensation of esters (15.3.3)

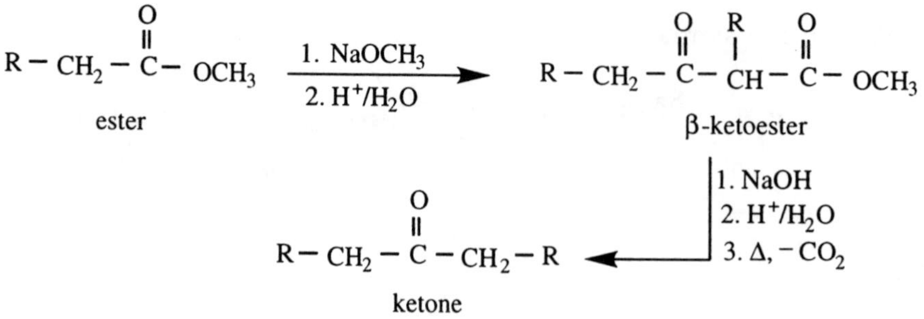
$R - CH_2 - C - OCH_3$
1. $NaOCH_3$
2. H^+/H_2O
$R - CH_2 - C - CH - C - OCH_3$
ester
β-ketoester
1. NaOH
2. H^+/H_2O
3. Δ, $-CO_2$
$R - CH_2 - C - CH_2 - R$
ketone

16. Nitriles

a. Substitution of alkyl halides (3.4.1)

$$\underset{\text{alkyl halide}}{R-X} \xrightarrow{\text{NaCN}} \underset{\text{nitrile}}{R-CN} \qquad (R = 1° \text{ or } 2° \text{ alkyl group})$$

b. Cyanohydrin formation (13.3.2)

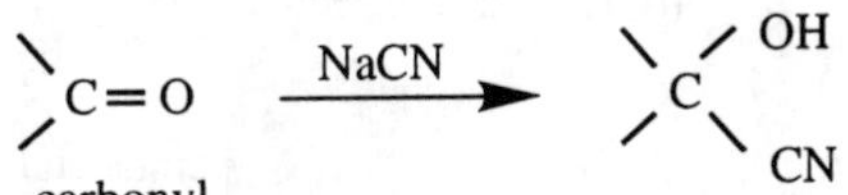

carbonyl compound → cyanohydrin

c. From diazonium salts (12.5.2)

$$\underset{\text{arylamine}}{Ar-NH_2} \xrightarrow[\text{HCl}]{\text{NaNO}_2} \underset{\text{aryldiazonium chloride}}{Ar-N_2^+\,Cl^-} \xrightarrow{\text{CuCN}} \underset{\text{nitrile}}{Ar-CN}$$

17. Phenols

a. Hydrolysis of diazonium salts (9.5.4 and 12.5.2)

$$\underset{\text{arylamine}}{Ar-NH_2} \xrightarrow[\text{HCl}]{\text{NaNO}_2} \underset{\text{aryldiazonium chloride}}{Ar-N_2^+\,Cl^-} \xrightarrow[\Delta]{H_2O} \underset{\text{phenol}}{Ar-OH}$$

18. Miscellaneous compounds

a. Grignard reagents (3.5.1)

$$\underset{\text{alkyl bromide}}{R-Br} \xrightarrow[\text{ether}]{\text{Mg}} \underset{\text{Grignard reagent}}{R-MgBr}$$

b. Organothium reagents (3.5.1)

$$\underset{\text{alkyl bromide}}{R-Br} \xrightarrow[\text{ether}]{\text{Li}} \underset{\text{organolithium}}{R-Li}$$

c. Cuprate reagents (3.5.1)

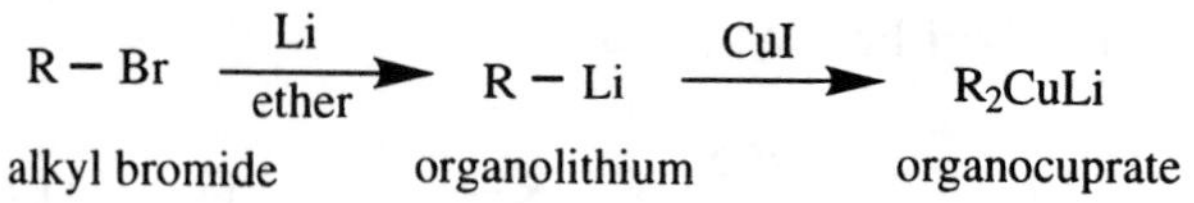
R − Br
Li
ether
R − Li
CuI
R2CuLi
alkyl bromide
organolithium
organocuprate

d. Acetals (13.4.2)

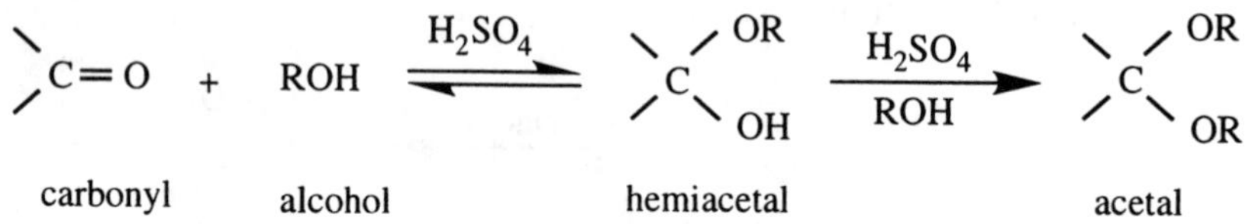
C=O
+
ROH
H2SO4
OR
OH
H2SO4
ROH
OR
OR
carbonyl
alcohol
hemiacetal
acetal

e. Thioacetals (13.4.2)

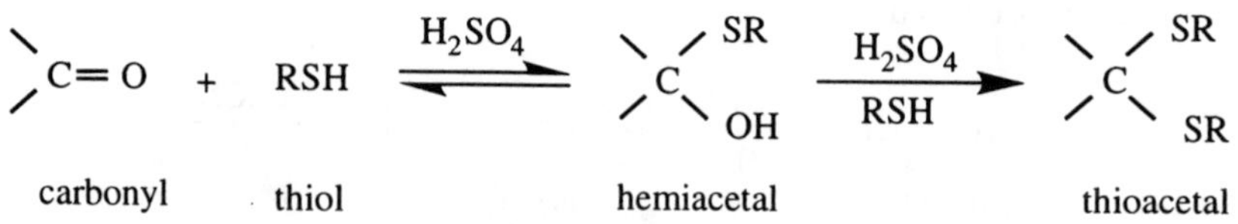
C=O
+
RSH
H2SO4
SR
OH
H2SO4
RSH
SR
SR
carbonyl
thiol
hemiacetal
thioacetal

f. Imines (13.4.1)

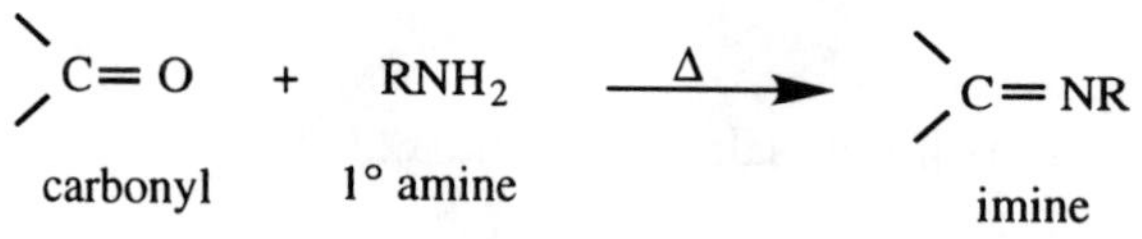
C=O
+
RNH2
Δ
C=NR
carbonyl
1° amine
imine